Evaluation Guide for *Algebra 1*

Algebra 1 presents a balance of new and traditional mathematics in an informal setting. With an emphasis on skill-building and applications, the approach of the text ensures success for students of average ability. To strengthen the presentation of the text material with the intent of increasing the student's understanding and interest in mathematics, many special features have been included in the text.

To examine selected examples of the features of *Algebra 1,* please turn to the following pages.

(pp. 7-39)   **The Metric System** (SI Units) is presented in Chapter 1 and used extensively throughout the text.

(pp. 42-43)   **Flow charts** are used where they aid students' visualization of procedures.

(p. 127)   **Concepts** are developed intuitively to enhance student understanding.

(p. 200)   Each section of the Teacher's Annotated Edition contains **Performance Objectives** which are keyed to the Evaluation Program. Other helpful features are **answers** and **annotations** placed as close to the problems as possible, and **teaching suggestions.**

(pp. 254-288)   Special emphasis is given throughout the text to **problems relat-, ing algebra to the real world.**

(pp. 324-325)   **New terms** appear in boldface type when in a defining situation and **important concepts** are set off between color bars.

(p. 365)   **Special interest pages** featuring applications, recreation, and history are interspersed throughout the text.

(pp. 402-404)   All of the **key concepts** of the chapter are summarized in the Chapter Summary. In addition, **review exercises** are keyed by section so that students may return to sections for further review.

(pp. 446-448)   **Fully worked example problems** are provided before a student is asked to work the exercises. Problem solving skills are emphasized through the 5500+ exercises and chapter review exercises in *Algebra 1.*

(pp. 519-534)   **Tables** of Trigonometric ratios, squares, square roots, and an **index** are provided for student use.

Teacher's Guide
Algebra 1

Merrill Secondary Mathematics Series

MERRILL MATH

Nibbelink
Graening

ISBN 0-675-05899-6

Published by
CHARLES E. MERRILL PUBLISHING CO.
A Bell & Howell Company
Columbus, Ohio 43216

Contents of The Teacher's Guide

Chapter Overview

Each Chapter Overview contains information about such things as the relative importance of the various sections, teaching strategies for the chapter, and how a particular chapter relates to the text as a whole. Some Chapter Overviews present alternative sequencing of chapters and the prerequisites necessary for those alternatives.

Teaching Notes

The teaching notes on each section contain specific information on how to present material. Common student errors are identified to help the teacher recognize student difficulties. Suggestions for alternative methods are made where one method of presentation may not satisfy all students. Material and exercises critical to the development of the course are identified.

Time Schedules

There are two types of time schedules. The first applies to homogeneously grouped classes. The chart contains a maximum, an average, and a minimum course with suggested assignments of exercises. The second type of schedule applies to classes that contain students with widely varying abilities. The chart shows how the text may be used even in these heterogeneously grouped classes. By using this schedule, *all* students can be challenged throughout the year.

Answers

Whenever possible, answers to exercises and to any questions in the text appear on the annotated page of the student edition. However, because of space limitations some answers have been placed at the end of the related teaching notes in the Teacher's Guide.

Performance Objectives

Performance Objectives appear as annotations on the text pages near the beginning of each section. Phrases such as "The student should be able..." or "The student will be able..." are omitted from the beginning of each Performance Objective. It is left to the teacher to determine the percent of correct responses on exercises or tests that will indicate that an objective has been met.

Evaluation Program

A complete separate evaluation program is available in spirit duplicating form. Each question on Pretests and Posttests is keyed to a Performance Objective by the section number. The section numbers and answers are printed in nonreproducing form near the question.

Coding Exercises

In this Teacher's Annotated Edition certain exercises are coded either with a color dot (•) or a color ring (○) around the numeral that identifies the exercise. This coding does not appear in the student edition.

• Exercises marked with this symbol provide a minimal but adequate assignment for a section. For slow students, especially those with reading handicaps, it may be appropriate to treat some of these exercises as class discussion rather than as homework assignments.

○ Exercises marked with this symbol are provided to challenge able students. These exercises may be assigned in addition to those needed to teach or reinforce the material in a section.

Exercises not marked with either symbol may be assigned at the teacher's discretion to some or all students for additional practice and reinforcement.

Ideal pacing and an accommodation of a

variety of student abilities may be accomplished by using the exercises to the best advantage.

Italics, Boldface, and Color Bars

Many words appear in the text in either **boldface** or *italic* type. The use of boldface type indicates an important concept that will be used throughout the text. The words are in boldface type when they appear in a "defining situation." (Some words, such as **set,** are undefined terms and students are usually given examples to clarify the use of the term as much as possible.) The use of italic type indicates words that are important in developing a concept but that are not a basic part of the course.

Students need not know these distinctions. For review purposes, a study of the words in boldface type is sufficient. Students need not be concerned about words in italic type for tests or quizzes.

Often, statements are set off between two color bars. These statements present either a summary of a discussion or a concept the students will use again. They are not necessarily definitions or theorems, but rather, important concepts students should learn.

Suggested Activities, Excursions in Mathematics, and Special Interest Pages

These optional materials appear throughout the book. They are designed primarily as motivational aids and as a ready source of supplemental material for the teacher.

Excursions in Mathematics range in difficulty from very easy to very difficult. Some Excursions in Mathematics are merely interesting problems. Others contain material required by certain curriculums but which are not essential to the flow of this text. Some Excursions in Mathematics raise questions that extend concepts beyond what is presented in the text. Others clarify or reinforce material already presented in the text. Excursions in Mathematics should be assigned with care according to the needs and abilities of students. Some slow students may become discouraged by the open-ended questions designed to challenge able students to further inquiry. On the other hand, some able students may view the easy Excursions in Mathematics as unnecessary drill. All Excursions in Mathematics may be used for class discussion or assigned for independent work.

Suggested Activities are primarily student-centered research or experiments to be completed outside of class. Reports may be made in class concerning student experiences with these activities.

Special Interest Pages occur throughout the text. These motivating pages stress careers, recreations, history, or applications of mathematics. They may be used as starting points for class discussions or for further independent investigation by students.

Daily Lesson Chart

The following table presents suggested daily lessons for homogeneous classes. Minimum, average, and maximum courses are presented. This table may also be used to construct individualized programs. In this case, the teacher should match assignment length and difficulty with student ability. Initial individualization can be accomplished by matching each student with one of the three courses. Further individualization can be obtained by speeding or slowing the course relative to the suggested pacing.

Teachers responsible for heterogeneous classes should refer to the table on page 12 for further assistance.

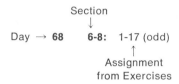

Day	Minimum Course	Average Course	Maximum Course
1	**1-1:** 1-9 (odd), 11-14, 21-26	**1-1:** 1-9 (odd), 11-15, 21-26	**1-1:** 1, 3, 12, 13, 15-20, 21, 23, 27-30
2	**1-2:** 2-5, 8, 18, 19, 21-31 (odd)	**1-2:** 1-8, 9-15 (odd), 18, 19, 21-31 (odd)	**1-2:** 2-5, 8, 9-15 (odd), 18, 19, 21-33 (odd), 34
3	**1-3:** 1-10	**1-3:** 1-10, 11-19 (odd)	**1-3:** 1-20 **1-4:** 1-21, Excursions in Mathematics
4	**1-4:** 1-10, 18, 19	**1-4:** 1-14, 16-19	**1-5:** 1-7 (odd), 9-13, 16, 17, 19-30
5	**1-5:** 1-7 (odd), 9-13, 16, 17	**1-5:** 1-7 (odd), 9-13, 16, 17, 19-25 (odd)	**1-6:** 1, 7, 8, 12, 13, 15-20
6	**1-6:** 1-4, 8, 12, 13	**1-6:** 1, 4, 6, 8, 12, 13, 15, 20	Review and/or test
7	Review and/or make-up	Review and/or make-up	**2-1:** 1-4, 7-9, 5-31
8	Review and/or test	Review and/or test	**2-2:** 1-8, 11-14, 17-30, Excursions in Mathematics
9	**2-1:** 1-14, 15, 16, 23, 25, 31	**2-1:** 1-14, 15-31 (odd)	**2-3:** 1-19, Excursions in Mathematics
10	**2-2:** 1-18	**2-2:** 1-8, 9-10, 13, 14, 17-22, 25-27, 30	**2-4:** 1-37 (odd)
11	**2-3:** 1-8, 16-19	**2-3:** 1-19	**2-5:** 11-37 (odd), 39-44, 45-51 (odd)
12	**2-4:** 1-7, 11-21 (odd)	**2-4:** 1-27 (odd), 34, 36	**2-6:** 1(e,f,g,h), 2, 3(e,f,g,h), 4, 5(d,e,f), 6
13	**2-5:** 1-25 (odd), 39-47 (odd)	**2-5:** 5-31 (odd), 39-47 (odd)	**2-7:** 1-35 (odd), Excursions in Mathematics

Day	Minimum Course	Average Course	Maximum Course
14	**2-6:** Discuss 1 (b,d,f), 2, 3(b,d,f), 4, 6. Devote any time remaining to Section **2-5**.	**2-6:** 1(b,d,f), 2, 3(b,d,f), 4, 5(a,b), 6	**2-8:** 3, 7, 11, 13-23, 25-59 (odd), 60-67, Excursions in Mathematics
15	**2-7:** 1-29 (odd)	**2-7:** 1-35 (odd)	**2-9:** 1-21 (odd), 22-25, Excursions in Mathematics
16	**2-8:** 1-11 (odd), 13-18, 20-23	**2-8:** 3, 7, 11, 13-18, 20-23, 25-59 (odd), 60-65	Review and/or test
17	**2-8:** Discuss 60-67, assign 25-51 (odd), 54-56	**2-9:** 1-21 (odd), 22-24	**3-1:** 1-30
18	**2-9:** 1-17 (odd), 22, 23	Review and/or make-up	**3-2:** 1-29 (odd), 30
19	Review and/or make-up	Review and/or test	**3-3:** 1-49 (odd)
20	Review and/or test	**3-1:** 1-14, 16-29	**3-4:** 1-15 (odd), 16-19, 21-33 (odd)
21	**3-1:** 1-7, 16-20, 25-27	**3-2:** 1-9 (odd), 13-29 (odd)	**3-5:** Read Exploratory Exercises, assign 3, 4, 6, 7, 9, 11, 12, 17-25 (odd), 27-31
22	**3-2:** 1-9 (odd), 13-25 (odd)	**3-3:** 1-49 (odd)	**3-6:** 1-4, 7-16, 18-22 (even)
23	**3-3:** 1-9 (odd), 17, 19, 25-29 (odd), 35-39 (odd)	**3-4:** 1-15 (odd), 16-19, 21-27 (odd)	**3-7:** 1-19 (odd), 20, 21-45 (odd), 46-50
24	**3-4:** 1-11 (odd), 16-19, 21-27 (odd)	**3-5:** 3, 4, 6, 7, 9, 11, 12, 17, 21	**3-8:** 7-24 **3-9:** 1-15 (odd), 16, 19, 21, 24, 27, 28, 30
25	**3-5:** Discuss Exploratory Exercises, assign 1, 2, 5	**3-6:** 1-4, 7-14, 17, 18	**3-10:** 15-36
26	**3-5:** 3, 4, 6, 7, 9, 11, 12, 17, 21	**3-7:** 1-19 (odd), 20, 21-45 (odd)	**3-11:** 1-12
27	**3-6:** 1-4, 7, 11, 13, 18	**3-8:** 7-24	**3-11:** 13-18
28	**3-7:** 1-17 (odd), 19 (a,b,c), 20 (a,b,c), 21, 25, 29, 35	**3-9:** 1-15 (odd), 16, 19, 21, 23-30	Review and/or test
29	**3-8:** 7-23	**3-10:** 1-13 (odd), 15-22, 29, 30, 33, 34	**4-1:** 1-37 (odd), 38-43
30	**3-9:** 1-15 (odd), 16, 19, 21, 24, 25	**3-11:** 2, 8, 9, 11, 12, 14, 17	**4-2:** 10-15, 25-33, 35-55 (odd)
31	**3-10:** 1-13 (odd), 15-20, 27-29	Review and/or make-up	**4-2:** Excursions in Mathematics **4-3:** 1-10
32	**3-11:** 1, 2, 8, 11	Review and/or test	**4-4:** 5-24, 29-30, 37-40

Day	Minimum Course	Average Course	Maximum Course
33	Review and/or make-up	**4-1:** 1-37 (odd), 38-40	**4-5:** 11-45 (odd), **4-6:** 19-31 (odd), 32-36
34	Review and/or test	**4-2:** 1, 4, 7, 10, 13, 16, 19, 22, 25, 28, 31, 35-43 (odd)	**4-7:** 1-3, 5-25 (odd) **4-8:** 16-21, 42-49, Excursions in Mathematics
35	**4-1:** 1-17 (odd), 21, 25, 29, 31, 38-40	**4-2:** 44-50 **4-3:** 1-8	**4-9:** 15-18, 25-27, 37-41, 44, 48-55
36	**4-2:** 1, 4, 7, 10, 13, 16, 19, 22, 25, 28, 31	**4-4:** 5-24, 29	Review and/or test
37	**4-2:** 39-43 (odd), 44-50 **4-3:** 2, 4, 6	**4-5:** 1-45 (odd)	**5-1:** 1, 3, 5-19 **5-2:** 1-3, 5, 7, 9, 11-14
38	**4-4:** 5-10, 18, 19, 21-28	**4-6:** 13-35 (odd)	**5-3:** 1-4, 10-12, 16-21, 29-43 (odd) **5-4:** 1-25 (odd), 27-39 (odd), 41-46
39	**4-5:** 1-45 (odd)	**4-7:** 1-3, 5-25 (odd)	**5-5:** 5-31 (odd), 32-34, 35-55 (odd)
40	**4-6:** 1-31 (odd)	**4-8:** 1-47 (odd)	**5-6:** 1-13 (odd), 14-17, 19-37 (odd), 38
41	**4-7:** 1-3, 5-15 (odd)	**4-9:** 11-41 (odd), 42-44, 48-50	**5-7:** 5-12, 13-63 (odd)
42	**4-8:** 1-21 (odd), 22-33, 45, 47	Review and/or make-up	**5-8:** 1-9 (odd), 11-19, 21-27 (odd), 32-37
43	**4-9:** 1-29 (odd), 31-34, 39-44	Review and/or test	**5-9:** 18-26, 27-39 (odd), 40-53
44	Review and/or make-up	**5-1:** 1, 3, 5-17	**5-9:** 54-58 **5-10:** 1-3 (odd), 7-49 (odd)
45	Review and/or test	**5-2:** 1-3, 6-9, 11, 13	**5-11:** 11-57 (odd)
46	**5-1:** 1, 3, 5-13, 15, 17	**5-3:** 1-4, 10-12, 16-21, 29-37, 39, 41	**5-11:** 59, 60 **5-12:** 4-18
47	**5-2:** 1, 2, 6-9, 13	**5-4:** 1-25 (odd), 26, 27-39 (odd), 41-46	Review and/or test
48	**5-3:** 1-31	**5-5:** 5-55 (odd)	**6-1:** 1-27 (odd), 28-30
49	**5-4:** 1-39 (odd), 41-46	**5-6:** 1-13 (odd), 14-17, 19-37 (odd), 38	**6-2:** 1-45 (odd)
50	**5-5:** 1-39 (odd)	**5-7:** 5-12, 13-63 (odd)	**6-3:** 1-10, 11-21 (odd)
51	**5-5:** 41-55 (odd) **5-6:** 1-13 (odd), 14-20	**5-8:** 1-9 (odd), 11-19, 21-33 (odd)	**6-4:** 1-10, 22-36
52	**5-7:** 5-12, 13-39 (odd)	**5-9:** 8-26, 27-39 (odd), 40-43, 53-56	**6-5:** 1-31 (odd), 32
53	**5-8:** 1-9 (odd), 11-19, 21-27 (odd), 29, 33	**5-10:** 1-3 (odd), 7-49 (odd)	**6-6:** 1-9 (odd), 10-12, 13-39 (odd)

Day	Minimum Course	Average Course	Maximum Course
54	**5-9:** Discuss 8-11, assign 12-26, 27-39 (odd), 40-43, 53, 54	**5-11:** 1-59 (odd)	**6-7:** 1-10
55	**5-10:** 1-3 (odd), 7-37 (odd)	**5-12:** 4-18	**6-8:** 1-25 (odd)
56	**5-11:** 1-49 (odd)	Review and/or make-up	**6-9:** 1-3, Excursions in Mathematics
57	**5-11:** 20-58 (even)	Review and/or test	Review and/or test
58	**5-12:** 1-12	**6-1:** 1-27 (odd), 28, 30	**7-1:** 1-13, 15-21 (odd) **7-2:** 1-4, 5-35 (odd)
59	Review and/or make-up	**6-2:** 1-45 (odd)	**7-3:** 1-31 (odd) **7-4:** 1-4, 5-21 (odd)
60	Review and/or test	**6-3:** 1-6, 7 (as discussion), 9, 11-21 (odd)	**7-5:** 1-21 (odd) **7-6:** 1-15 (odd), 17, 18, 31-49 (odd)
61	**6-1:** 1-27 (odd)	**6-4:** 1-8, 9-31 (odd), 33, 34	**7-7:** 1-33 (odd)
62	**6-2:** 1-37 (odd), 38-41	**6-5:** 1-31 (odd)	**7-8:** 1-29 (odd)
63	**6-3:** 1-6, 11-21 (odd)	**6-6:** 1-9 (odd), 13-39 (odd)	**7-9:** 1-4, 5-19 (odd)
64	**6-4:** 1-8, 9-31 (odd)	**6-7:** 1-3, 6-9	**7-10:** 3-15 (odd), 16-18
65	**6-5:** 1-31 (odd)	**6-8:** 1-17 (odd), 18	**7-10:** 19-27
66	**6-6:** 1-9 (odd), 13-21 (odd)	**6-9:** 1-3	Review and/or test
67	**6-6:** 22-34 (even) **6-7:** Discuss 1-3, 6, 9	Review and/or make-up	**8-1:** 5-17
68	**6-8:** 1-17 (odd)	Review and/or test	**8-2:** 1-5, 9-11
69	**6-9:** Discuss 1-3, begin review and/or make-up	**7-1:** 1-13, 15-21 (odd)	**8-3:** 1-3, 5, 7, 8, 10, 12, 13
70	Review and/or test	**7-2:** 1-4, 5-35 (odd)	**8-4:** 3-8, 13-16, 17-27 (odd), 29, 33, 37, 39-44
71	**7-1:** 1-13, 15-21 (odd)	**7-3:** 1-37 (odd)	**8-5:** 2-8 (even), 10-13, 15-22 (even)
72	**7-2:** Discuss 1 and 4, assign 5-35 (odd)	**7-4:** 1-4, 5-21 (odd)	**8-5:** 23-35
73	**7-3:** 1-31 (odd)	**7-5:** 1-21 (odd)	**8-6:** 1-13, 22-26, Excursions in Mathematics
74	**7-4:** Discuss 1 and 4, assign 5-21 (odd)	**7-6:** 1-15 (odd), 17-20, 21-45 (odd)	**8-7:** 1-7, 9-23 (odd), 30-37
75	**7-5:** 1-21 (odd)	**7-7:** 1-33 (odd)	**8-8:** 1, 4, 5-14, 15, 18, 21, 24, 25-30, 34-42
76	**7-6:** Discuss 17-20, assign 1-15 (odd), 21-45 (odd)	**7-8:** 1-29 (odd)	**8-9:** 1, 4, 5-8, 11-15 (odd), 16-35
77	**7-7:** 1-29 (odd)	**7-9:** 1-12	Review and/or test
78	**7-7:** 31-34 **7-8:** 1-17 (odd)	**7-10:** 1-5 (odd), 11-15 (odd), 18, 19, 22, 25, 26	**9-1:** 1-9 (odd), 11-14, Excursions in Mathematics

Day	Minimum Course	Average Course	Maximum Course
79	**7-8:** 19-30	Review and/or make-up	**9-2:** 1-15 (odd), 16-20
80	**7-9:** Discuss 1-4, assign 5-12	Review and/or test	**9-3:** 1-7 (odd), 12-18
81	**7-10:** 3, 5, 11, 15, 18, 25	**8-1:** 1-10, 11, 13, 15, 16	**9-4:** 10-15, 22-36
82	Review and/or make-up	**8-2:** 1-8	**9-5:** 1-7, 10-13
83	Review and/or test	**8-3:** 1-3, 5, 7, 8, 10	**9-6:** 1-7 (odd), 10-13
84	**8-1:** 1, 2, 5, 6, 11, 13, 15, 16	**8-4:** 1, 3, 5, 11-14, 17-27 (odd), 29-41 (odd)	**9-7:** 1-5 (odd), 7-16
85	**8-2:** 1-5	**8-5:** 1-13 (odd), 15-19 (odd), 27, 29, 33	**9-8:** 1, 2, 4-7
86	**8-3:** 1-3, 5, 7, 8	**8-6:** 1-13, 15-23 (odd)	**9-9:** 5-14, Excursions in Mathematics
87	**8-4:** 1, 3, 5, 11-14, 17-29 (odd)	**8-7:** 1-6, 9-37 (odd)	Semester review
88	**8-4:** 8, 16, 33-37 (odd) **8-5:** 1-5 (odd)	**8-8:** 1, 4, 5-14, 15, 18, 21, 24, 25-30, 31-41 (odd)	Semester exam
89	**8-5:** 7-19 (odd), 33	**8-9:** 1, 5-8, 11-15 (odd), 16-21, 25, 35	**10-1:** 1-15 (odd) **10-2:** 1-11 (odd)
90	**8-6:** 1-13, 17, 19	Review and/or make-up	**10-2:** 15-23 (odd), Excursions in Mathematics
91	**8-7:** 1-6, 9-31 (odd)	Semester review	**10-3:** 3-15 (odd) **10-4:** 1-15 (odd), 16, 21-25 (odd)
92	**8-8:** 1, 4, 5-14, 15, 18, 21, 24, 25-28, 31, 33, 37, 39	Semester exam	**10-5:** 1, 3, 5, 9, 13, 17, 21, 25, 33-36, Excursions in Mathematics
93	**8-9:** 1, 5-8, 11-15 (odd), 16-21	**9-1:** 1-9 (odd), 11-14	**10-6:** 1, 3, 5, 9, 13, 17, 21, 25
94	Review and/or make-up	**9-2:** 1-15 (odd), 16, 19, 20	**10-7:** 1-13 (odd), Excursions in Mathematics
95	Semester review	**9-3:** 1-17 (odd)	**10-8:** 4, 5, 9-18
96	Semester exam	**9-4:** 1, 5, 9, 13, 17, 21, 25-35 (odd)	**10-8:** 19-30
97	**9-1:** 1-11 (odd)	**9-5:** 1-7, 11, 12	Review and/or test
98	**9-2:** 1-7 (odd), 13-16, 19	**9-6:** 1-13 (odd)	**11-1:** 1, 5, 9, 13, 17, 21, 25, 29 **11-2:** 1, 5, 9, 13-19 (odd), 21, 25, 29, 33, 37-41 (odd)
99	**9-3:** 1-7 (odd) 15, 17	Review and/or test	**11-3:** 1-29 (odd), 33-36
100	**10-1:** 1-15 (odd)	**10-1:** 1-15 (odd)	**11-4:** 5-11 (odd), 12-20
101	**10-2:** 1-11 (odd), 15-25 (odd)	**10-2:** 1-25 (odd)	**11-5:** 1-9 (odd), 13, 17, 21, 25, 29, 33, 37, 39, Excursions in Mathematics

Day	Minimum Course	Average Course	Maximum Course
102	**10-3:** 1-13 (odd)	**10-3:** 1-17 (odd)	**11-6:** 1, 5, 9, 13, 17, 21, 25, 31, 35
103	**10-4:** 1-15 (odd), 16	**10-4:** 1-15 (odd), 16, 23, 25	**11-7:** 1-25 (odd)
104	**10-5:** 1-17 (odd)	**10-5:** 1, 3, 5, 7, 13, 17, 21, 25, 33-34 (as discussion), 35, 36	**1-8:** 1-17 (odd), Excursions in Mathematics
105	**10-5:** Discuss 33 and 34, assign 21-29 (odd), 35, 36	**10-6:** 1, 3, 5, 9, 13, 17, 21, 25	**11-9:** 1-3, 5, 6, 13-19 (odd), 20
106	**10-6:** 1-17 (odd)	**10-7:** 1-13 (odd)	Review and/or test
107	**10-6:** 2, 19-25 (odd) **10-7:** 1-5 (odd)	**10-8:** 4, 5, 7, 12-16, 20, 25, 28	**12-1:** 1-39 (odd)
108	**10-8:** 4, 5, 15, 16, 20, 28	Review and/or make-up	**12-2:** 1-25 (odd), 30-32
109	Review and/or make-up	Review and/or test	**12-3:** 9, 13, 17, 21, 25, 29-32
110	Review and/or test	**11-1:** 1, 5, 9, 13, 17, 21, 25, 29 **11-2:** 1, 5, 9, 13-19 (odd), 21, 25, 29, 33, 37-41 (odd)	**12-4:** 1-7 (odd), 9-11, 13, 17, 21, 25, 29, 33, 37, 41
111	**11-1:** 1, 5, 9, 13, 17, 21, 25, 29	**11-3:** 1-29 (odd)	**12-5:** 1-9, 21-27, 31-63 (odd)
112	**11-2:** 1, 5, 9, 13-19 (odd), 21, 25, 29, 33, 37-41 (odd)	**1-4:** 1-11 (odd), 12-15	**12-6:** 1-25 (odd), 26
113	**11-3:** 1-13 (odd), 27	**11-5:** 1-9 (odd), 13, 17, 21, 25, 29, 33, 37, 39	**12-7:** 7-14
114	**11-4:** 1-11 (odd)	**11-6:** 1, 5, 9, 13, 17, 21, 25, previous Excursions in Mathematics if time permits	Review and/or test
115	**11-5:** 1-9 (odd), 13, 17, 21, 25, 29, 33, 37, 39	**11-7:** 1-25 (odd)	**13-1:** 1-11
116	**11-6:** 1, 5, 9, 13, 17, 21, 25	**11-8:** 1-17 (odd)	**13-2:** 1, 3, 6, 7, 9, 11, 13-19 (odd)
117	**11-7:** 1-25 (odd)	**11-9:** 1-3, 5, 6, 13-19 (odd)	**13-3:** 1-17 (odd), 21-23
118	**11-8:** 1, 3, 5, 9, 11-17 (odd)	Review and/or make-up	**13-4:** 1-12, 13-17 (odd)
119	**11-9:** 1-3, 5, 6, 19	Review and/or test	**13-5:** 1-13 (odd), 14-20
120	Review and/or make-up	**12-1:** 1-39 (odd)	**13-6:** 1-17 (odd), 18
121	Review and/or test	**12-2:** 1-25 (odd)	**13-7:** 1-13 (odd), 15-18
122	**12-1:** 1-33 (odd)	**12-3:** 1-6, 9, 13, 17, 21, 25, 29	**13-8:** 1-4, 5, 7, 9, 10-12, 21-29 (odd)
123	**12-1:** 30, 32, 34-40	**12-4:** 1-7 (odd), 9-11, 13, 17, 21, 25, 29, 33, 37, 41	**13-8:** Excursions in Mathematics
124	**12-2:** 1-15 (odd)	**12-5:** 1-9, 21-27, 31-63 (odd)	**13-9:** 1-11 (odd), 13-16, 17-31 (odd)

Day	Minimum Course	Average Course	Maximum Course
125	**12-3:** 1-6, 9, 13, 17, 21, 25, 29	**12-6:** 1-25 (odd)	**13-9:** 33-39 (odd), 41-44
126	**12-4:** 1-9 (odd), 13, 17, 21, 25, 29, 33, 37, 41	**12-7:** 1-13 (odd)	Review and/or test
127	**12-5:** 1-9, 21-27, 31-35 (odd)	Review and/or make-up	**14-1:** 1-47 (odd)
128	**12-5:** 32-36 (even), 37-61 (odd)	Review and/or test	**14-2:** 1-19 (odd)
129	**12-6:** 1-23 (odd)	**13-1:** 1-9	**14-3:** 1-31 (odd)
130	Review and/or make-up	**13-2:** 1, 3, 6, 7, 9, 11, 13-19 (odd)	**14-4:** 1-33 (odd), 34-40
131	Review and/or test	**13-3:** 1-17 (odd), 21, 22	**14-5:** 1-13 (odd), 15-30
132	**13-1:** 1, 3-6, 8, 9	**13-4:** 1-12, 13-17 (odd)	**14-6:** 1-20
133	**13-2:** 1, 3, 6, 7, 9, 11, 17, 19	**13-5:** 1-13 (odd), 14-20	**14-7:** 9-20
134	**13-3:** 1-17 (odd), 21	**13-6:** 1-17 (odd), 18	**14-8:** 1-25 (odd), 27, 28, 29-39 (odd)
135	**13-4:** 1-12	**13-7:** 1-13 (odd), 15-18	**14-8:** 41-44, Excursions in Mathematics
136	**13-4:** 13-19 (odd) **13-5:** 1-9 (odd)	**13-8:** 1-4, 5, 7, 9, 10-12, 21-29 (odd)	Review and/or test
137	**13-5:** 11-20	**13-9:** 1-11 (odd), 13, 14, 17-29 (odd), 35-39 (odd)	**15-1:** 1-13, 18-29
138	**13-6:** 1-11 (odd), 12, 13	Review and/or make-up	**15-2:** 3-6, 11-16 **15-3:** 1-6
139	**13-7:** 1-15 (odd)	Review and/or test	**15-3:** 7-21 (odd)
140	**13-8:** 1-4, 5, 7, 9, 10-12, 13, 15, 17	**14-1:** 1-47 (odd)	**15-4:** 1-15 (odd), 17-19
141	**13-9:** 1-11 (odd), 17-29 (odd)	**14-2:** 1-19 (odd)	**15-5:** 7-19 (odd), 20-24
142	Review and/or make-up	**14-3:** 1-31 (odd)	Review and/or test
143	Review and/or test	**14-4:** 1-33 (odd), 34-40	**16-1:** 1, 5, 9, 13, 17 **16-2:** 1-19 (odd), 21, 25, 29, 35
144	**14-1:** 1-29 (odd), 32-36 (even)	**14-5:** 1-13 (odd), 15-30	**16-3:** 1-25 (odd)
145	**14-1:** 31-35 (odd), 37-48	**14-6:** 1-10, 11-19 (odd)	**16-4:** 1-11 (odd), 13-17, 19-25 (odd)
146	**14-2:** 1-19 (odd)	**14-7:** 1, 5, 11-19 (odd)	**16-4:** 26-32, Excursions in Mathematics
147	**14-3:** 1-25 (odd), 27, 28	**14-8:** 1-25 (odd), 29-39 (odd)	Review and/or test
148	**14-4:** 1-33 (odd)	Review and/or make-up	**17-1:** 1-19 (odd), 20, 21-25 (odd), 26-29

Day	Minimum Course	Average Course	Maximum Course
149	**14-4:** 34-40 **14-5:** 1-13 (odd), 15-17	Review and/or test	**17-2:** 5, 9, 13, 17-20
150	**14-5:** 18-30	**15-1:** 1-5, 6-13, 18-29	**17-3:** 1-21 (odd)
151	**14-6:** 1-10, 11-19 (odd)	**15-2:** 3-6, 11-16	**17-4:** 1-3, 11-23
152	**14-7:** 1-17 (odd)	**15-3:** 1-21 (odd)	**17-5:** 9-12, 16-22
153	**14-8:** 1-15 (odd), 17-19	**15-4:** 1-17 (odd)	**17-6:** 1-13 (odd)
154	**14-8:** 12-16 (even), 20-26, 37, 39	**15-5:** 7-19 (odd), 20	Review and/or test
155	Review and/or make-up	Review and/or make-up	**18-1:** 1-5, 15-19
156	Review and/or test	Review and/or test	**18-2:** 1-6 **18-3:** 1-9 (odd)
157	**15-1:** 1-5, 6-9, 18-29	**16-1:** 1, 5, 9, 13, 17	**18-3:** 11-26
158	**15-2:** 3-6, 11-16	**16-2:** 1-19 (odd), 21, 25, 29, 35	**18-4:** 1-14
159	**15-4:** 1-15 (odd)	**16-3:** 1-15 (odd)	**18-5:** 1-21 (odd), 23-42
160	**16-1:** 1, 5, 9, 13, 17	**16-3:** 17-23 (odd) **16-4:** 1-9 (odd)	**18-6:** 1-9, 11-17 (odd)
161	**16-2:** 1-19 (odd), 21, 25, 29	**17-1:** 1-19 (odd), 20, 21-25 (odd), 26-29	**18-6:** 12-16 (even), 18-21
162	**16-3:** 1-13 (odd)	**17-2:** 5, 9, 13, 17, 19	**18-7:** 1-39 (odd)
163	Review and/or make-up	Review and/or make-up	**18-7:** 18, 24, 30, 38, 40, 41-43
164	Semester or final review	Semester or final review	Semester or final review
165	Semester or final exam	Semester or final exam	Semester or final exam

Lesson Chart For Heterogeneous Classes

This chart contains suggested lesson plans for pacing heterogeneous classes as a group. It is constructed in such a way as to provide a basic first-year algebra program for every student while able students complete additional work individually or in groups.

Daily assignments for slow students should closely follow those listed under Minimum Course in the preceding chart (page 4). However, these daily assignments should *at least* include all exercises marked with a color dot (•) to assure adequate coverage of the material. Daily assignments for average students may range from those listed under Minimum Course to those listed under Average Course. Daily assignments for able students may range from those listed under Minimum Course to those listed under Maximum Course. Individualization within tracks may be obtained by varying assignment length and difficulty.

The terms slow, average, and able are used merely as convenient descriptors. It is not intended that a student be classified as slow, average, or able at the beginning of the year and kept in one classification throughout the program. It is likely, in fact, that students will be moved from one category to another from time to time.

This chart should be used in conjunction with the Chapter Overviews. The overviews contain more detail on the implementation of an independent study program for average and able students.

Days
76-84   **8** ← Chapter

Days	Slow Students	Average Students	Able Students
1-6	1	1	1
7	Review and/or test	Review and/or test	Review and/or test
8-16	2	2	2
17	Review and/or test	Review and/or test	Review and/or test
18-28	3	3	3
29-30	Review and/or test	Review and/or test	Review and/or test
31-39	4	4	4
40	Review and/or test	Review and/or test	Review and/or test
41-52	5	5	5
53	Review and/or test	Review and/or test	Review and/or test
54-62	6	6	6
63-64	Review and/or test	Review and/or test	Review and/or test

Days	Slow Students	Average Students	Able Students
65-74	7	7	7
75	Review and/or test	Review and/or test	Review and/or test
76-84	8	8	8
85-95	**1-8:** Intensive review **9:** As time permits	**1-8:** Review as required **9:** As time permits, independent study	**1-8:** Review as required **9:** Independent study
96	Semester exam	Semester exam	Semester exam
97-104	10	10	10
105	Review and/or test	Review and/or test	Review and/or test
106-113	11	11	11
114	Review and/or test	Review and/or test	Review and/or test
115-124	**12:** Section 7 may be omitted for a review	**12** **18:** Sections 1-3, independent study	**12** **18:** Sections 1-4, independent study
125-126	Review and/or test	Review and/or test	Review and/or test
127-138	13	**13** **18:** Sections 4-5, independent study	**13** **18:** Sections 5-7, independent study
139	Review and/or test	Review and/or test	Review and/or test
140-150	14	**14** **16:** Sections 1-3, independent study	**14** **16:** Independent study
151	Review and/or test	Review and/or test	Review and/or test
152-157	**15:** Sections 3 and 5 may be omitted for review	**15** **17:** Sections 1-3, independent study	**15** **17:** Sections 1-3, independent study
158-164	**16:** Sections 1-3 **10-15:** Intensive review	**17:** Sections 4-5, independent study **10-17:** Review as required	**17:** Sections 4-6, independent study **10-17:** Review as required
165	Semester or final exam	Semester or final exam	Semester or final exam

Section Notes

Chapter 1   Sets of Numbers
Overview

This chapter is devoted mainly to the presentation of definitions and concepts which will be used in subsequent chapters. The material may be covered in various ways. For example, the chapter may be used to establish quickly a minimal list of key definitions. In this case emphasis may be given only to those exercises marked with a color dot. On the other hand, the chapter may be used to study set ideas and sets of numbers in more detail. In this case, exercises with no marking or those with color rings should be used. In either case, able students may view the entire chapter as review and be able to move ahead quickly with little direction.

The main purpose of Chapter 1 is to establish key concepts and not to burden students with vocabulary and symbolism. Therefore, in evaluating student work emphasis should be placed on the students' ability to use the concepts. This is much more important than their ability to verbalize about the concepts at this time.

1-1
Pages 1-3

Set-builder notation is intentionally avoided in this section and will not be introduced until it is useful to course content. By avoiding set-builder notation during concept development, students may convert easily from listing elements to describing them verbally and vice-versa. For example, students will write $\{2, 3, 5, 7, 11, \dots \}$ = {prime numbers} instead of $\{2, 3, 5, 7, 11 \dots\}$ = $\{x \mid x$ is a prime number$\}$. Thus, the load of new symbols is kept minimal and plural nouns are used to describe sets with many elements. This approach also avoids the requirement that students worry about a "dummy variable" in describing sets at this time.

Note that the concept *well-defined* is treated in terms of clarity of communication. This is both mathematically acceptable and convenient in allowing for a range of alternative definitions. Poor definitions may be labeled *unclear, subjective*, etc. An attempt to treat the concept of *well-defined* as a property of sets themselves is mathematically unsound and usually leads to confusion for ninth graders.

1-2
Pages 4-7

The concepts in this section will be used often in subsequent chapters to discuss sets of allowable values for a variable and to describe solution (truth) sets. To avoid the usual confusion involving 0, {}, and {0}, discourage students from using the word *nothing* for the word *zero*. The distinction between {} and {0} will be important later when finding the solution sets of $x^2 + 1 = 0$ and $x + 1 = 1$.

Some able students may wonder why *proper subsets* and the symbol $\subset$ are not treated. These students may be informed that only those concepts needed in later work are presented here. This chapter is not meant to be a complete treatment of set theory. Of course, if desirable supplementary work on these and other topics may be given.

1-3
Pages 10-12

It is assumed that students are already familiar with the number line for whole numbers and perhaps for negative integers. However, if any students are not familiar with the number line, time should be spent now developing an acquaintance. Urge students to learn and use the conventional symbols N, W, and Z for the set of natural numbers, whole numbers, and integers, respectively. These symbols will be used frequenty and it will be assumed that students know them from this point on.

A statement about how to read the symbol $^-2$ ("minus two" or "negative two") is purposely avoided in the student edition for two reasons. First, some teachers feel very strongly about the matter and there is no universal agreement. Second, students from different backgrounds may have already agreed on how to read it. In any event, it is left to the teacher to inform students which reading(s) will be permitted or preferred.

1-4
Pages 12-14

This section completes the introduction of the real numbers in terms of a correspondence with points on the number line. The existence of irrational numbers is merely announced in this section. There are two reasons for this introduction at this time. First, it prevents students from concluding that the points of the number line named by elements of Q exhaust the points in the number line. Second, students are prevented from believing that the words *real* and *rational* mean the same thing. The purpose of this section is to define Q and R intuitively, not to treat the subject in detail.

Various strategies may be adopted to deal with possible reactions from students to irrational numbers. Which of the following will be done, of course, depends on the particular reaction and the mathematical ability of the students.

A. Provide the explanations for rational and irrational numbers presented on page 179 and the examples on pages 179 and 180. Note that this method does not prove the existence of irrational numbers.

B. Present the *Excursions in Mathematics* found on page 181 which shows the existence of an irrational number. This method probably should be reserved for very able students.

C. Explain to students that when arithmetic computation is done, rational numbers are almost always used in place of irrational numbers. Suggest that in the case of π, the rational number approximations 3, 3.14, $\frac{22}{7}$, 3.14159265, and so on, may be used depending on the degree of accuracy required. The actual value for π is rarely used because it cannot be given using our decimal numeration system.

1-5
Pages 15-18

If Chapter 1 is being treated minimally as a review or preparation for later work, then the study of Venn diagrams may be omitted. However, the concept of *universal set* should be covered. The necessary material in the section is the first thirteen lines of the text and Exercises 1 and 2. The primary reason for treating universal sets is to allow students to be more comfortable later when restrictions are placed on variables in open sentences. For example, $x^2 - 4 = 0$ will have different solution sets depending on whether Z or W is the set of allowable replacements.

It often helps slow students to think of Venn diagrams as fences surrounding elements that have been grouped or herded together into a pasture. This allows students to be comfortable with the fact that a fenced-in area may contain no elements (the empty set). Also, students readily accept that the size of the fenced-in area has no relation to the number of elements contained in the area. Lastly, treating Venn diagrams as fences allows students to use overlapping circles to represent sets which may be disjoint without causing confusion. Many students assume that drawing overlapping circles implies a nonempty intersection. This assumption, of course, should not be made.

1-6
Pages 20-23

The concept of set intersection is basic to solving systems of open sentences, and therefore is included here. See the examples on page 296. The study of Venn diagrams may be omitted again as in Section 1-5 if the chapter is being treated minimally.

The concept of set union is perhaps less critical (less used) in *Algebra 1* than the concept of set intersection. However, it will be used in solving certain inequations as seen on page 441.

Chapter 2   Properties of Operations

Overview

In Chapter 2 statements about real numbers are made to and by students whose computational skills may cover only non-negative rational numbers. This is no accident, but rather the first step in the following instructional strategy.

First, on the basis of limited evidence and experience, students agree to a set of general statements such as $a(b + c) = ab + ac$.

Then, upon looking later at unexplored areas, definitions are made in a way that preserves statements which have been agreed to. For example, on page 139 a value is assigned to $(+5)(-3)$ by insisting that $a(b + c) = ab + ac$ must remain true for integers.

Using this instructional strategy offers several advantages in treating the traditional content of *Algebra 1*.

1. Students have an active part in developing the real number system. Because of this, the mystery is removed from statements such as $(-a)(-b) = ab$.

2. Developing the real number system as an axiomatic system and asking for largely deductive thinking is postponed until *Algebra 2*. At that time students will know the system well enough to appreciate the power of the axioms. Very few students beginning *Algebra 1* are capable of this.

3. By developing the real number system intuitively over several chapters, the new concept and symbol load are held to a minimum.

4. This intuitive, build-the-system approach is both more true to the historical development of the real number system and more natural to the way students think at this age.

2-1
Pages 27-30

The purpose of this section is to put students at ease when using letters to represent numbers. Words such as variable, replacement set, solution set, etc., are intentionally avoided at this stage of development. Once students are comfortable with general statements about numbers, the presentation of some of the field properties of real numbers in the next section should be easier.

Slow students may have trouble grasping the idea that statements using letters may be true for many different number replacements. Have them discuss statements such as $2a = 4$, $a = a + 3$, $2a = a + a$, $3x - 2x = x$, $xy = 24$, and $xy = yx$ deciding if each is true for no numbers, some numbers, or all numbers. The discussion may be limited to whole number replacements. Then define as "true in general" a statement which seems always to be true no matter which of the allowable numbers is substituted for the letter.

2-2
Pages 30-32

The axioms about numbers are stated as being true for real numbers. However, all

examples and exercises are selected so that students need to use whole number replacements only, since it is assumed that most students do not know how to perform computations with negative numbers. Able students may be encouraged to investigate the statements with other sets of numbers.

If students seem to be concerned that the axioms are about all real numbers, stress that it is more important now that they appreciate what the statements say for numbers familiar to them. Point out that these statements will be investigated for more inclusive sets of numbers at a later time.

2-3
Pages 33-34

This section continues the study of variables, replacements, and general statements. The statements in this section, however, are probably less familiar to the students than the ones in previous sections. Again, students may complete the exercises using only their knowledge about the set of whole numbers.

2-4
Pages 35-38

Parentheses are introduced as punctuation in mathematics. At first students are asked to imagine that parentheses are the only means of indicating which operations are to be performed in what order. For students not acquainted with the order of operations this, of course, demands no imagination. For students already acquainted with the order of operations agreements, the exercises should remind them of the importance of these agreements.

Time-worn statements like, "Start at the inside and work out," are still useful in helping slow students. At first students may be encouraged to show a step each time punctuation is removed.

2-5
Pages 39-42

The emphasis in this section is on the application of the order of operations agreements. Many students who apply these correctly do so from good habits. Often, they have no deep appreciation of the confusion that would result without the agreement. A good understanding of punctuation and the order of operations agreements will aid students later when they work with more complicated expressions containing variables.

Some of the exercises contain variables. Help slow students by encouraging them to think of arbitrarily chosen numerals in place of the variables whenever in doubt. If this is suggested, also suggest a different numeral for each different variable.

2-6
Pages 42-45

Although flow-charting is introduced, this section offers a summary and further practice on Sections 2-4 and 2-5 as its primary goal.

If flow-charting is held to be important, then this section may be used as an introduction to that skill. If not held to be important to the course, flow-charting may be presented merely as a "follow-the-arrows" way of giving directions. In this case Exercise 5 may be omitted. Also, place little emphasis on learning the conventions given on page 43. The remainder of the text is written in such a way that flow-charting is not necessary. However, it is used occasionally to summarize procedures.

Section 2-6 may be assigned to able students as independent work while slow students spend further time with Sections 2-4 and 2-5.

2-7
Pages 46-49

The generalization for commutativity and associativity is presented in a unique way.

The presentation allows the generalization to depend in part on the order of operations agreement. By doing this, the generalization is established for students who would not yet appreciate the proposition, $a - b = a + (-b)$. Also the presentation allows slow students "to move numerals with pre-fixed operation signs." This is very important for students who persist in seeing addition and subtraction as distinct operations. Thus, presenting the Rearrangement Property allows these students to keep up with their fellow students. Eventually all students will see subtraction as addition of additive inverses, but only after sufficient exposure to negative real numbers.

It is assumed at this point that students are not acquainted with the multiplication of negative factors. The examples and exercises for the Generalized Distributive Property are therefore limited to multiplication of whole numbers.

2-8
Pages 49-52

In this section x^n is defined for $n \in N$ and $n \geq 2$. This material may be a review for many students. Watch closely for students who may be careless in applying the definitions where there are parentheses. Upon spotting an error, have the student check the work by using whole number replacements for the variables.

Exercises 60-67 contain some of the basic laws involving exponents. Able students may be encouraged to investigate these further.

2-9
Pages 54-55

This section is a brief introduction to $\sqrt[n]{m}$ where $n \in N$, $n \geq 2$ and $m \geq 0$. The concept *principal nth root* is not presented at this time because computations with negative numbers have not been studied. The exercises require working only with whole numbers so that computational demands are minimal.

For $x \geq 0$ and $n \in N$, some students may be ready for the statement $\sqrt[n]{x^n} = x$. However, slow students may be somewhat confused by such a statement.

Chapter 3   The Language of Algebra
Overview

This chapter establishes many of the primary concepts of algebra. However, it is designed to make minimal demands on students' computational abilities.

Sections 3-1 through 3-9 are critical for subsequent chapters. The concepts established here will be applied to increasingly larger subsets of the real numbers. If the material is learned now, students should enjoy a relatively low new-concept load in later chapters.

Sections 3-10 and 3-11 are labeled as optional. They are important for everyday applications of mathematics but not critical for continuing in this book. Hopefully all students can go beyond Section 3-9. However, students who continue to have trouble with Section 3-9 should study that section until it is learned. These students may have to omit Sections 3-10 and 3-11.

3-1
Pages 59-61

This section defines the terms *open sentence* and *statement*. Use is made of blanks (_?_) and pronouns in several of the examples. These examples provide security for those students who tend to think of open sentences as "fill-in-the-blank" exercises. Also, these examples can be used as models for students who have higher verbal skills but have concluded that mathematics has nothing to do with language.

It may be helpful to have slow students think of the variable as a blank to be filled in. This way of thinking is not ideal from a mathematical point of view. However, making this suggestion is preferable to leaving students bewildered.

3-2
Pages 63-64

The terms solution and solution set are defined. Stress the fact that to find the solution set, it is important to know the allowable values (replacements) for the variable.

It may be helpful to use nonmathematical examples. In the following example *it* is the variable.

> *It* has a lion's body, wings, and a woman's head.

If *it* is a variable on the set of living earth creatures, the solution set is ϕ. But if *it* is a variable on the set of fictitious monsters, "sphinx" is a solution.

Stress the fact that to solve an open sentence, one must have the following.
1. An open sentence
2. A specified set of replacements allowable for the variable

3-3
Pages 64-66

The emphasis is on solving very simple linear equations and establishing what it means to solve an equation. Students are still permitted to think of the variable as a blank to be filled with a number that makes a true statement. The usual techniques for solution will be developed later. By using the approach of this section, students should have a goal (finding the solution set) clearly in mind when eventually they deal with "adding the same number to both sides," etc. In brief, the more formal approaches to solving equations are being delayed until there is a need for more mathematical sophistication. This relieves the teacher from forcing students to use procedures which they may see as unnecessary and cumbersome at this stage. Also, more formal procedures are not necessary, given the degree of difficulty found in most exercises of this section.

3-4
Pages 66-68

The students are told that there are basically two ways to derive mathematical sentences from data presented verbally.
1. By translation
2. By fitting data to a familiar formula (known, but not given)

If some students fail to see this from the examples, it may help to use the following or similar examples. Each example yields the same mathematical statement.
1. Seven multiplied by x gives 21.
   Translation: $7 \cdot x = 21$
2. The sides of a rectangle measure 7 inches and x inches. The area of the rectangle is 21 square inches.
   Implied (provided the student knows $l \, w = A$): $7 \cdot x = 21$

The writing of sentences is basic to being able to apply mathematics to physical situations. This skill will be practiced throughout the book. However, the basics for developing the skill are presented here.

3-5
Pages 68-74

For most students, this section should be a review. The section reviews the assignment of ordered pairs to points in the plane. By beginning with a familiar model from social studies students who have never quite understood this concept are provided a temporary perceptual crutch.

For slow students, it may be necessary to treat the Exploratory Exercises as class discussion questions. The concepts involved in naming points in the plane by ordered pairs are critical to work in *Algebra 1*. Enough substantial exercises are provided to challenge able students if the classroom pace must be slowed to accommodate slow students.

1.

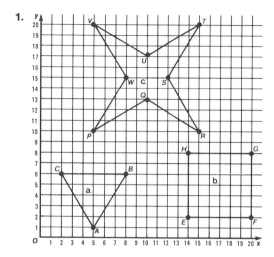

2.

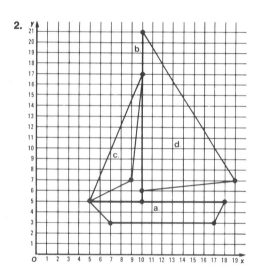

12.

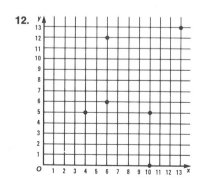

13.

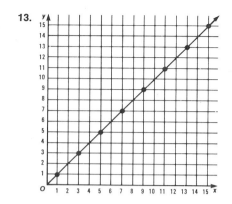

14.

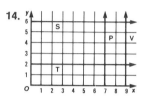

15.

3-6
Pages 74-76

This section essentially continues Section 3-5. However, an added important concept is included: Sets of ordered pairs may be generated by finding solution sets of equations in two variables.

The word *graph* is defined here to be the picture itself. In fact, a graph is not really a picture at all, but a set of ordered pairs. However, insisting on the distinction at this time may not be worth the resulting confusion for many students.

Some students may be helped by using the vertical format instead of the horizontal format, when listing ordered pairs.

Exercises 3-6

16.

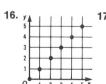

17.

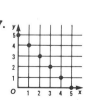

18.

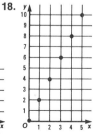

19.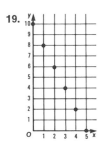

20.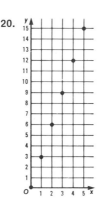

21.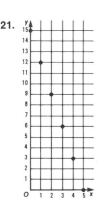

22.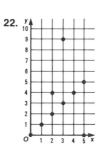

3-7
Pages 77-80

This section introduces the words *term* and *coefficient*. A careful definition of *polynomial* will be given later. It is not needed at this time.

Some students may not grasp completely from the narrative the concept *term*. Allow these students to think of a term as "one of the things to be added or subtracted along with the preceding operation sign." This will allow those students to keep pace without difficulty. Later in the course the fact that $a - b = a + (-b)$ will be emphasized.

Stress the following: $x = 1x$ (not $0x$); $xy^2 = 1 \cdot xy^2$ (not $0xy^2$); etc. That is, when no coefficient is written, the coefficient is 1.

3-8
Pages 80-81

Students already have what was called the Rearrangement Property for the operations of addition and subtraction. This section presents this property for multiplication.

Learning to write monomials in simplest form is prerequisite to the next section. In Section 3-9 these skills will be applied in simplifying polynomials by focusing on like terms.

3-9
Pages 82-84

This section ties together in a single concept (simplifying an expression) the properties of real numbers and the definitions of previous sections. Exercises are kept simple. Therefore any student who appears to be in trouble deserves immediate attention. The content of this section is basic to any Algebra 1 course. Students should be able to do all of Exercises 1-21 as a demonstration of minimum competency.

Sections 3-10 and 3-11 do not contain material necessary to course development. For some classes, it may be appropriate to allow most of the students to go on with Sections 3-10 and 3-11 while slow students continue to study exercises like those of this section.

3-10
Pages 84-87

In this section the emphasis is on the *use* of formulas. A formula is simply described as an often-used equation. There are, of course, formulas which are not equations. However, to raise this issue now may yield more confusion than understanding. Also, many students are frightened by the word formula, since it means to them, "A statement handed from above with stiff penalties implied for forgetting it during a test." Therefore, treating formulas as run-of-the-mill equations will raise the confidence of these students.

3-11
Pages 87-91

In this section the emphasis is on *creating* formulas. Stress that this work is the same as was done for word problems. The main difference from previous exercises is that more quantities may be expressed with variables.

In the discussion for Section 3-9 it was stated that Sections 3-10 and 3-11 were not critical to a student's successful completion of 'Algebra 1. This in no way implies that Sections 3-10 and 3-11 are not important. For most students, mathematics will be important in later life only if they can apply it. Sections 3-10 and 3-11 stress precisely that skill.

Review Exercises

37.

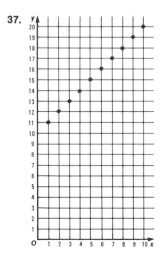

Chapter 4   Using Whole Number Expressions
Overview

This is the last chapter which affords students the luxury of using whole numbers only. Sections 4-1 through 4-4 are devoted to examining the order relation. Sections 4-5 and 4-6 provide a very basic review of previous work and may be used according to teacher discretion. Section 4-7 provides a checkpoint on how willing students are to work with letters as representing numbers. Sections 4-8 and 4-9 are again basic review.

The goal for this chapter is a simple one: Students are to master manipulative skills before being asked to use these skills with more inclusive subsets of real numbers. Therefore, Sections 4-8 and 4-9 should be viewed as a critical point in the course. If students find any one of Sections 4-5, 4-6, 4-8, or 4-9 difficult, slow the pace of presentation. Do not risk forging ahead on the assumption that these students will catch up later.

4-1
Pages 95-98

For many students, Section 4-1 may be review of prior work. Watch for students who have trouble assigning truth values to statements of the form $a \le b$ ($a < b$ or $a = b$) or to statements of the form $a < b < c$ ($a < b$ and $b < c$).

Truth tables are not included since the students who have trouble with statements such as $a \le b$ or $a < b < c$ often find that truth tables do no more than increase the load of symbols to be learned.

However, it may be helpful to examine the words *or* and *and* with a few examples like the following.

1. They went to Chicago *or* they went to Detroit.
   Will this be true if
   a. they went only to Omaha?
   b. they went to Chicago but not Detroit?
   c. they went to both Chicago and Detroit?
2. They went to Chicago *and* they went to Detroit.
   Will this be true if **a, b, c** above?

A summary such as the following may be in order. When statements are connected by *or,* the resulting complex (bigger, longer) statement will be true if and only if *just one* of the original statements is true. When statements are connected by *and,* the resulting complex statement will be true if and only if *all* of the original statements are true.

However, at this stage in algebra, it is sufficient if students are able to assign truth values without being able to present precise verbal explanations or definitions.

4-2
Pages 98-101

The term *inequation* is defined. To capitalize on earlier learning (to facilitate transfer), stress the fact that equations and inequations are just two different types of open sentences. The concept *open sentence* has already been covered in detail, and using that term should arouse in the students a readiness to think "solution," "solution set," etc.

Exercises 4-2

1. {0, 1, 2, 3}

2. {0}

3. {0, 1, 2, 3}

4. {0, 1}

5. {0, 1, 2, 3, 4}

6. {2, 3, 4}

7. {3, 4, 5}

8. {4, 5}

9. {1, 2, 3, 4, 5}

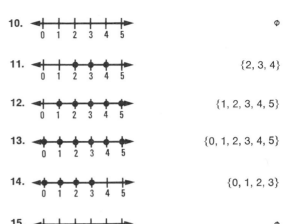

10. φ

11. {2, 3, 4}

12. {1, 2, 3, 4, 5}

13. {0, 1, 2, 3, 4, 5}

14. {0, 1, 2, 3}

15. φ

4-3
Page 102

This section has two purposes. It provides more practice in deriving mathematical statements from statements presented verbally. The section also establishes relevance for inequations by demonstrating that inequations are common in everyday life. As with some other application sections, this section is not critical to course development. Its main benefits are found in raising student interest levels and facilitating transfer of mathematical learning.

4-4
Pages 103-105

In this section *greater than* ($>$) and *less than* ($<$) are defined without appealing to the number line. Section 4-4 is not critical to later material if students can already use the symbols $>$ and $<$ accurately. Students who have trouble with Section 4-2 may be given more practice and help while other students may move ahead and investigate the concepts more formally. Then all students may be brought together for Section 4-5.

Possibly withholding Section 4-4 from some slower students is based on the proposition that these students may be confused by a second approach. Often such students treat two approaches as unrelated when neither is learned well.

Excursions in Mathematics: Modular Arithmetic

Page 108

2.

a	b	c	b⊕c	a⊗(b⊕c)	a⊗b	a⊗c	(a⊗b) ⊕ (a⊗c)
2	1	3	4	3	2	1	3
4	2	1	3	2	3	4	2
1	4	3	2	2	4	3	2
3	3	3	1	3	4	4	3
4	2	3	0	0	3	2	0

4-5
Pages 105-107

4-6
Pages 108-110

Sections 4-5 and 4-6 are review sections. Many classes will be able to omit them.

It may be the case that only some students in a class should complete these two sections. In this event, slow students may go through these sections while able students work with the Excursion on pages 107-108. If the able students run out of activities, the following challenges may be offered as an extension of the Excursion.

Let $S = \{0, 1, 2, 3, 4, 5\}$ where $a \oplus b =$ the remainder of $6\overline{)a + b}$ and $a \otimes b =$ the remainder of $6\overline{)a \cdot b}$

1. Can you find $a \in S$ such that $a \otimes 5 = 1$?
2. Can you find $a \in S$ such that $a \otimes 3 = 1$?
   defined as on page 107, can you find
3. If $S = \{0, 1, 2, 3, 4\}$ and, $\oplus$ and $\otimes$ are $a \in S$ such $a \otimes 3 = 1$?
4. Why was the answer No for 2 and Yes for 3?
5. Why was the answer Yes for 1 and No for 2?

4-7
Pages 110-111

This section establishes the following statement at an intuitive level. $\dfrac{a + b}{c} =$

$\dfrac{1}{c}(a + b) = \dfrac{a}{c} + \dfrac{b}{c}$ (even when a, b, and/or c contain variables).

This section may be used to spot potential problems that will become handicaps in future work. For example, a student who is comfortable with Exercise 16 but not with 15 is probably not yet comfortable with the idea of letting letters represent numbers. In brief, this section may be used as a diagnostic tool.

4-8
Pages 112-113

4-9
Pages 113-116

Sections 4-8 and 4-9 are review sections. However, omitting these sections completely is advised only for advanced classes. Average classes may be assigned about half of the exercises for drill. Much of this work may be done in class. For classes of slow students, these sections should be viewed as a last chance to work with algebraic manipulation while still enjoying the luxury of whole number replacements only. In heterogeneous classes, assign the Excursion on page 113 to able students while slow students spend more time on the exercises. Able students may extend the Excursion by investigating other operations of their own invention.

Chapter 5

Exploring Integers

Overview

The concepts of order and the four operations are extended to the integers in this chapter. The approach used in the presentation is that *what is true for whole numbers is to remain true for integers.* Thus, students may feel that by their investigations they have a part in defining order and the four operations on the integers.

In this chapter the axioms of Chapter 2

are sometimes used as starting points. However, they do not serve as first premises for deductive proofs. Rather the axioms are presented as statements to be upheld by any new definitions. The reasoning required of students in the chapter is thus largely inductive. That is, students look first at a few particular examples to see how definitions must be made. Then they declare these definitions to be applicable to all integers.

5-1
Pages 121-123

This section is a review of the definition of Z first presented in Chapter 1. The number line is used to present an intuitive definition of Z. In the exercises, the thermometer is used as a model. This model is chosen because it is familiar and also may be used when presenting the extended *y*-axis in Section 5-2. In preparation for the next section, it might be helpful to remind slow students that the thermometer is, in a way, a vertical number line (*up* positive and *down* negative).

5-2
Pages 123-125

This section is devoted to plotting and naming points in the plane corresponding to points in Z × Z. Some students may be a bit slow in acquiring this skill and will need additional practice. The other students may spend time on the Suggested Activity on page 125. Beside the examples in Section 5-1, students may refer back to Chapter 1 as an additional source for the activity.

5-3
Pages 125-127

In this section, *is less than (is greater than)* is defined as *is left of (is right of)* using the number line model. Using this rather intuitive definition offers two advantages to the beginning algebra student.

1. It permits defining *less than,* $<$, prior to work with the operations on integers.
2. It offers an acceptable means of viewing *less than,* $<$, for the student who is prone to say, "-8 is greater than -4 because $-8°$ is colder than $-4°$," or, "-200 is greater than -50 because -200 is a greater debt than -50."

For students who are still tempted to say $-200 > -50$ by such reasoning, suggest using the sea-level model. Let students translate "less than" as "lower than" for the time being. If this fails, insist on the translation *is left of* a bit more loudly.

5-4
Pages 127-128

Addition in Z is defined intuitively in terms of moving along a number line. The reason for this introduction is to offer students a set of expectations as to how addition in Z should behave. By so doing, students will be more receptive to examining the properties of addition presented later. Without first establishing these expectations, some students would see addition of integers as an investigation of absurdities. In support of the strategy used in this text, money, temperature, and altitude are still offered as models for students who need them to supply meaning for this topic.

5-5
Pages 129-132

Beyond stating that the Commutative and Associative Properties hold for addition in Z, this section is devoted to giving students sufficient practice in what they should already know about the topic. In the next section the concept of additive inverse will be introduced. If the prerequisite skills (those of this section) are learned to the point of habit, students will be able then to devote attention exclusively to the new concept of Section 5-6. If this section is covered lightly and sufficient skill is not learned, slow students may be confused later when confronted with too large a concept load. In summary, this section should be studied thoroughly, even if it appears to be relatively easy for many students.

Exercises 5-5

4.

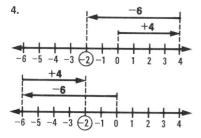

5-6
Pages 132-133

In this section the additive inverse of a is also called the negative of a. Some students may insist that the word negative implies that the referent is always less than zero. In this situation use the term additive inverse frequently.

Students should have learned by the end of this section that the symbol $-a$ may refer to a nonnegative number. Any student who continues to say that "$-a$" means "a is less than zero" is sure to have further trouble if not corrected.

An ability to work with absolute value is desirable but not critical to future material. Therefore assign Exercises 18-38 only after students demonstrate facility with Exercises 1-17.

Notice that in Sections 5-5 and 5-6 integers are no longer discussed in terms of everyday situations. Student dependence on everyday models should decrease from this point on. The reason is that almost no everyday model serves generally. For example, $7-(-3)$ could be troublesome to students who think primarily in terms of checking accounts. Therefore, the number line is being treated more and more as the primary model for aiding work with integers.

5-7
Pages 134-136

Subtraction with integers is first defined intuitively by using the number line. From this definition, the statement $a - b = a + (-b)$ evolves as a summary covering all cases. Some students may need to be reminded with examples that $-b$ may be nonnegative. For example if $a = 6$ and $b = -2$, then $a - b = 6 - (-2) = 6 + 2 = 8$. Here $-b = 2$. Stress the fact that $-b$ refers to "the additive inverse of b."

5-8
Pages 136-138

This section continues Section 5-7, with polynomials allowed as minuends, subtrahends, and differences. As pointed out on page 137 in the note to the teacher, give a cook-book rule only as a last-ditch effort to avoid losing a student.

5-9
Pages 139-142

The product $x \cdot y$ is defined here for any $x, y \in Z$. By this time in the course, using the Commutative, Associative, and Distributive Properties should be very natural to students. The strategy for defining $x \cdot y$, where $x, y \in Z$, is to ask the following question: How must $x \cdot y$ be defined for any $x, y \in Z$ if these properties must still hold?

On pages 139 and 140, specific products are determined and general rules are drawn from these examples. Students are almost sure to accept that for $a, b \in W$, the following statements are true: $a \cdot b = ab$; $a \cdot (-b) = -ab$; $(-a) \cdot b = -ab$; $(-a) \cdot (-b) = ab$.

However, stress that these statements are true for any two *integers* a and b. Many students will readily see that if this set of statements is true for whole numbers, it is true for integers. For others, especially those who still think of $-a$ as always negative, it may be necessary to check some or all of the 16 cases involving $a \neq 0$ and $b \neq 0$. This should be done using numerical examples.

Even then, some students may still fail to see the full impact of these statements because they persist in thinking of $-a$ as less than zero. This is, of course, a bit sad, but it is not fatal. Later, there will be enough "shocking" solutions to equations and inequations to rid students gradually of this misconception. ("Shocking" here means going through algebraic manipulations thinking $-x < 0$ and finding that the last step renders a result such as $-x = +3$.)

5-10
Pages 142-145

Practice in using the Commutative, Associative, and Distributive Properties with integers is provided in this section. Remind students occasionally that variables are now on Z because multiplication of integers has been defined. Remind students that multiplication was defined so as to preserve the number properties, and that these properties were the only ones previously used. Therefore, they cannot go wrong so long as they keep their previous good habits. The only additional concern is the set of definitions (rules) stated on page 140.

5-11
Pages 145-146

This section provides practice with simplifying expressions. Difficult expressions such as $5[x + (-2)y] = (-3)(-x - y)$ have been omitted for two reasons.
1. Such expressions are not common in an Algebra 1 course.
2. There are likely to be enough other rough spots to iron out as it is.

Most difficulties students encounter in this section may have to do with the several uses of the minus sign (indicating either subtraction or additive inverse). Consider the first example given on page 145: $-2a - 6a$.

Some students will immediately write $(-2 - 6)a$ or simply $-8a$, hardly being concerned with the precise meaning of each sign. This sort of spontaneous response is highly desirable, but students should know why it is permissible.

Other students will need patient coaching to reach this level of spontaneity. They will need to be shown what it is that may be done mentally. Examples like the following should be discussed.

$$3x - 5(x - 3y) + 2y \qquad \text{Written}$$
$$= 3x - [5(x - 3y)] + 2y$$
$$\qquad \text{Usually not written}$$
$$= 3x - (5x - 15y) + 2y$$
$$\qquad \text{Written}$$
$$= 3x - 5x + 15y + 2y$$

$$\text{or}$$

$$3x - 5(x - 3y) + 2y \qquad \text{Written}$$
$$= 3x + [(-5)(x + 3y)] + 2y$$
$$\qquad \text{Usually not written}$$
$$= 3x + [(-5)x + (-5)(3y)] + 2y$$
$$= 3x + (-5x + 15y) + 2y$$
$$\qquad \text{Written}$$
$$= 3x - 5x + 15y + 2y$$

In the end, students should develop confidence in using the following brief form.

$$3x - 5(x - 3y) + 2y \qquad \text{Written}$$
$$\qquad \text{Usually not written}$$
$$= 3x + (-5)x + (-5)(-3y) + 2y$$
$$\qquad \text{Written}$$
$$= 3x - 5x + 15y + 2y$$

In a sense, this streamlines the previous step-by-step procedure.

Exercises 6, 12, 32, and 36 may be used for demonstration prior to making an assignment. To foster spontaneous responses by students, follow each detailed explanation with a streamlined procedure as presented above.

In the end, students should be using the streamlined procedures. They should however, be able to demonstrate a more detailed step-by-step procedure upon request.

5-12
Pages 146-148

This section presents a first way to think of $a \div b$ where a, b, $\frac{a}{b} \in Z$, $b \neq 0$. From arithmetic there will be a general agreement to the proposition $c \div b = a$ if $a \cdot b = c$. Division in Z is defined by holding as a goal the continued validity of this statement.

This section may *seem* optional because the topic is presented again later. However, for some students accepting $c \div b = a \iff a \cdot b = c$ may be the key which yields tolerance for and facility with fractions of integers (the rationals).

Chapter 6   Exploring
Rational Numbers
Overview

The rational numbers are presented and treated almost exclusively as quotients of integers. Variables sometimes appear in numerators and denominators with no domain specified. Students are almost sure to think of these variables as representing integers. This is completely acceptable. However, some students may show concern that expressions become difficult to think about when such variables may be rational numbers. Give these students the following guideline for working in this chapter: Unless otherwise specified, you may think of all variables as representing integers. Able students who show no apprehension at letting variables represent rational numbers may be encouraged to explore the topic independently.

The chapter ends with an introduction to density and irrational numbers. The stage is thus set for talking about real numbers in subsequent chapters.

6-1
Pages 151-155

In Section 5-12, care was taken to include only work with integers a, b, where $a \div b \in Z$. In Section 6-1 a, $b \in Z$ with $a \div b \in Q - Z$ is permitted. (For example, $\frac{-5}{3} \in Q - Z$.) Students may not notice the distinction. The best strategy is to spend time plotting rationals (quotients of integers) on the number line. Instead of belaboring this distinction, allow students to think of $\frac{-a}{b} = \frac{a}{-b} = -\frac{a}{b}$ and $\frac{-a}{-b} = \frac{a}{b}$ as already agreed to in Section 5-12.

With the definition for equivalent fractions, some students may be pleasantly surprised that each of $\frac{a}{b}$, $\frac{ac}{bc}$, and $\frac{a \div c}{b \div c}$ name the same point on the number line. Again, plotting points on the number line is in order.

The emphasis should be on *agreeing to the definitions as ones which make rational numbers behave as we want them to.* Do not burden the students with the complexities of viewing a single element in Q as an equivalence class, a subset of $Z \times Z$. Rather, allow beginning algebra students to write $\frac{-3}{2} = \frac{9}{-6}$ while thinking, " $\frac{-3}{2}$ names the same rational number as $\frac{9}{-6}$." This does not require them to think, " $\frac{-3}{2}$ and $\frac{9}{-6}$ name the same equivalence class in a partition of $Z \times Z$."

6-2
Pages 156-158

A fraction is in simplest form when the numerator and denominator have no common factors except 1 and -1. This definition is not strange to Algebra 1 students. It fits their grade school experiences.

However, for some students it is confusing to say that a fraction such as $\frac{2x}{y}$ is in simplest form. What if $x = 6$ and $y = 9$? The response such students would like to make is, "You don't know if $\frac{2x}{y}$ is in simplest form, unless you know the values for x and y." This problem results from a failure to think of x and y as variables. For such students, define a *common factor* as a factor which is common to both numerator and denominator *for all allowable replacements* for the variables. The fraction $\frac{2x}{y}$ is thus in simplest form because if $x = 3$ and $y = 5$, then $2x$ and y have only 1 and -1 as common factors.

On the other hand, $\frac{xy}{3x^2}$ $(x \neq 0)$ is not in simplest form, because x is a factor common to numerator and denominator *for all possible replacements* for the variable.

Watch very closely for students who write such things as $\frac{-8xy - 4x}{-16x} = \frac{8xy - 4x}{16x}$. It will help to ask them to identify the number used as a multiplier or divisor of the numerator *and* denominator.

6-3
Pages 159-161

The statement on page 159 is as follows:
If a, b, $c \in Z$, $b \neq 0$, then $\frac{a}{b} + \frac{c}{b} = \frac{a + c}{b}$.
On the basis of grade school experiences, students should be committed to this statement for a, b, $c \in W$, $b \neq 0$. Extending this to the quotient of integers may be done in one of two ways.

1. Call the statement on page 159 the *definition* and proceed to use it.
2. Perform several additions using the number line. Let these experiences lead to the *discovery* that the statement on page 159 describes how to find sums.

Stress that in adding fractions the denominators must be equal. One cannot be the additive inverse of the other. For example, $\frac{5}{4} + \frac{2}{-4} \neq \frac{7}{4}$ and $\frac{5}{4} + \frac{2}{-4} \neq \frac{7}{-4}$.

6-4
Pages 161-166

The new concept in this section is *Least Common Denominator*. The term *prime* is defined rather loosely here without first defining polynomial and degree of a polynomial. Students are allowed to think of prime as meaning, "the expression cannot be factored any further." Since factoring at this point is restricted to removal of a common monomial, this is adequate. In later chapters, the definition of the word *prime* will be extended to account for other factorizations.

Continually stress that the task which precedes finding sums and differences for fractions is that of replacing fractions by equivalent fractions.

6-5
Pages 167-170

It is assumed here that students agree that $\frac{a}{b} \cdot \frac{c}{d} = \frac{ac}{bd}$ for a, $c \in W$ and b, $d \in N$. After a reminder of this, it is simply declared on page 168 that this also defines multiplication for a, b, c, $d \in Z$ with $b \neq 0$ and $d \neq 0$.

An optional approach is to obtain this definition for a, b, c, $d \in Z$ with $b \neq 0$ and $d \neq 0$, by appealing to the properties proclaimed for real numbers. Letting a, $c \in W$ and b, $d \in N$, these steps could be followed.

A. $\frac{a}{b} \left(\frac{c}{d} + \frac{-c}{d} \right) = \frac{a}{b} \cdot \frac{c}{d} + \frac{a}{b} \cdot \frac{-c}{d} = \frac{ac}{bd} + \frac{a}{b} \cdot \frac{-c}{d}$ (Highlighted material has not been defined.) Also, $\frac{a}{b} \left(\frac{c}{d} + \frac{-c}{d} \right) = \frac{a}{b} \cdot 0 = 0$. It follows that $\frac{ac}{bd} + \frac{a}{b} \cdot \frac{-c}{d} = 0$. So, $\frac{a}{b} \cdot \frac{-c}{d} = -\left(\frac{ac}{bd} \right) = \frac{-ac}{bd} = \frac{a(-c)}{bd}$.

B. $\left(\dfrac{a}{b} + \dfrac{-a}{b}\right) \cdot \dfrac{-c}{d} = \dfrac{a}{b} \cdot \dfrac{-c}{d} + \dfrac{-a}{b} \cdot \dfrac{-c}{d} =$

$-\dfrac{ac}{bd} + \dfrac{-a}{b} \cdot \dfrac{-c}{d}$ From step A.

Also, $\left(\dfrac{a}{b} + \dfrac{-a}{b}\right) \cdot \dfrac{-c}{d} = 0 \cdot \dfrac{-c}{d} = \dfrac{0}{1} \cdot \dfrac{-c}{d} =$

0, from step A. It follows that

$-\dfrac{ac}{bd} + \dfrac{-a}{d} \cdot \dfrac{-c}{d} = 0.$ So, $\dfrac{-a}{b} \cdot \dfrac{-c}{d} =$

$-\left(-\dfrac{ac}{bd}\right) = \dfrac{ac}{bd} = \dfrac{(-a)(-c)}{bd}$.

The remainder of the cases follow fairly directly. After exhausting the possibilities, it should be concluded that the statement on page 168 is the one desired for multiplication of rational numbers.

Obtaining the definition as above may prove too difficult for slow students.

6-6
Pages 170-173

The procedure for dividing with fractions of integers is stated after a reminder on how dividing with fractions of natural numbers was done. The definition could be obtained by first insisting that $x \div y = z$ if and only if $y \cdot z = x, y \neq 0$. That is, let $\dfrac{a}{b} \div \dfrac{c}{d} = \dfrac{x}{y}$. Then $\dfrac{x}{y} \cdot \dfrac{c}{d} = \dfrac{a}{b}$. The solution is $\dfrac{x}{y} = \dfrac{ad}{bc}$ since $\dfrac{ad}{bc} \cdot \dfrac{c}{d} = \dfrac{a}{b}$. Therefore, insisting that $x \div y = z$ if and only if $y \cdot z = x$, $y \neq 0$, is true for real numbers yields no choice for $\dfrac{a}{b} \div \dfrac{c}{d}$ except $\dfrac{ad}{bc}$.

6-7
Pages 174-176

This is a summary section. The exercises are concerned more with abstract concepts than those of previous sections. Slow students may need to review previous sections while more able students proceed with this section. In that case, merely introduce slow

students to the notation a^{-1}. If time permits also treat selected exercises as discussion exercises for slow students.

The exercises for this section may give able students an appreciation of which properties of numbers are gained as the set under consideration is expanded from N to W to Z to Q.

6-8
Pages 176-178

The principal concept in this section is the *density* of points named by rational numbers on the number line. The purpose is not to present a complete analysis of the relation "less than" on Q.

If necessary, a step-by-step procedure may be outlined for finding the smaller of a, $b \in$ Q. The method is presented briefly at the bottom of page 176.

Section 6-8 may be treated as a discussion section. There are no skills presented which are critical to work in future chapters.

6-9
Pages 178-180

In this section, no attempt is made to prove that a is a rational number if and only if a has a repeating or terminating decimal expansion. Nor is any attempt made to prove that each nonterminating decimal expansion names a unique real number. This section may be treated as a discussion section.

The students should leave Chapter 6 believing (or at least having heard) the following.

1. For each point on the number line there is a corresponding real number.
2. Each segment of the number line which has any length at all contains infinitely many rational number points and infinitely many irrational number points.
3. In real life, the rational numbers are

used almost exclusively. In computations, an irrational number is almost always approximated by a suitably close rational number.

Chapter 7   Solving Open Sentences

Overview

Chapter 7 is devoted to solving linear open sentences (equations and inequations) by finding more manageable equivalent open sentences. The major concept in this chapter is that of "equivalent open sentences." The development of this concept is often a gradual process for students.

The symbol $\Longleftrightarrow$ is used to mean *is equivalent to.* By the end of the chapter, most of the students should be willing to think of the symbol $\Longleftrightarrow$ as meaning *has the same solution set as.* Able students may reach the point of being comfortable in thinking of the symbol $\Longleftrightarrow$ as meaning *if and only if.* The section notes show in more detail how to foster development of these meanings for the symbol.

7-1   7-2
Pages 185-187   Pages 187-190

In Sections 7-1 and 7-2 the usual procedures for finding equivalent equations are presented. Most students will readily memorize and apply the procedures, grinding out solutions to equations. However, not all students will appreciate fully the fact that the intermediate and final equations are equivalent to the original equation and to each other. In the minds of these students the name of the game is likely to be "isolate the variable." They will view the variable as a mystery number. They are not likely to be thinking, "A replacement for the variable makes the original equation true if and only if it makes this equation true."

Exercises 1 and 2 in Section 7-1 and Exercises 1-4 in Section 7-2 are intended to

invite these students to appreciate more fully the meaning of the word *equivalent.* It might be unrealistic to demand a full appreciation of this concept. It is, on the other hand, realistic to require competence in applying the rules for finding solution sets at this time.

7-3
Pages 190-192

Section 7-3 is a practice section. A major distinction is that the exercises here require that both procedures of Sections 7-1 and 7-2 be used in the solution of an open sentence. Adequate time should be provided for examining the examples.

On page 191 the first example is shown a second time labeled, "As you gain experience." Assure students that there is no correct number of steps. Stress that everyone should use whatever number of steps they require to be certain about each step.

7-4
Pages 192-194

Working with inequations has a way of forcing students closer to an appreciation of the meaning of equivalence. In other words it is difficult to approach an inequation thinking, "I must find out what x is." The reason is that a final sentence such as $x < 4$ does not describe x as a specific real number.

Exercises 1-4 offer a further invitation to students to appreciate more fully the meaning of equivalent open sentences. An appreciation of equivalence can be helped along by reading aloud the symbol $\Longleftrightarrow$ as *has the same solution set as.*

Even with this second set of invitations, some students will still miss the point by viewing a final sentence such as $x < 4$ as, ". . . about as far as I can go with this one in finding x." The only serious consequence these students will encounter is a modest jolt in Section 7-9. There is no harm in waiting until Section 7-9 for that jolt.

7-5
Pages 194-195

Set-builder notation is introduced in this section. Set-builder notation is now useful to students because it facilitates naming solution sets for inequations with variables on Q or R.

Some students may be enlightened regarding the concept *equivalent* by being instructed that $\{x \mid x + 3 < 8, x \in Q\} = \{x \mid x < 5, x \in Q\}$. In response to this, some students may ask why $\{x \mid x + 3 < 8, x \in Q\}$ is not acceptable as the solution set for $x + 3 < 8$. Technically it is correct. Therefore, simply inform students that when using set-builder notation the most manageable form of the open sentence should be given to aid the reader. As further incentive, announce even more plainly that only such descriptions will be accepted.

7-6
Pages 197-200

This section introduces the procedures for multiplying (dividing) both sides of an inequation by a nonzero real number. A limited number of examples are presented in the text for generating the rules. Some students may need more examples to be convinced of these statements. If more examples are needed, choose numbers a and b to cover the cases $0 < a < b$, $a < 0 < b$, and $a < b < 0$.

Exercise pairs 17-18 and 19-20 provide further opportunity to understand the concept *equivalent.* These may be treated as discussion exercises.

7-7
Pages 200-201

This is a practice section. As in the previous practice section, exercises require that several of the procedures of Sections 7-4 and 7-6 be used in solving an inequation. The comments made for Section 7-3 also apply here.

23. $\{x \mid x < -4, x \in Q\}$
24. $\{y \mid y \le 4, y \in Q\}$ 25. $\{z \mid z \le -\frac{13}{2}, z \in Q\}$ 26. $\{p \mid p < -8, p \in Q\}$ 27. $\{x \mid x < 1, x \in Q\}$ 28. $\{x \mid x \ge -\frac{1}{2}, x \in Q\}$
29. $\{x \mid x \le \frac{4}{3}, x \in Q\}$ 30. $\{x \mid x < 1, x \in Q\}$ 31. $\{x \mid x < 5, x \in Q\}$ 32. $\{x \mid x \ge \frac{9}{2}, x \in Q\}$
33. $\{x \mid x \ge \frac{14}{5}, x \in Q\}$
34. $\{x \mid x < -\frac{3}{2}, x \in Q\}$

7-8
Pages 202-204

It is suggested that as a first step in solving open sentences any denominators should be eliminated. This is accomplished by multiplying both sides of the open sentence by the LCD of the denominators. For slow students especially, it may be necessary to emphasize that the "entire expression" on both sides of the relation symbol must be multiplied by the LCD. The emphasis may be achieved by placing parentheses around these "entire expressions" before multiplying by the LCD. Then, after students demonstrate a mastery of the skills needed to remove denominators, the use of parentheses may be dropped.

7-9
Pages 204-206

Open sentences with special solution sets, R and ϕ, are examined in this section. The quest for a manageable equivalent open sentence ends with a statement void of variables.

Able students who will agree to read the symbol $\Leftrightarrow$ as *if and only if* should have no trouble with this. Their reasoning should be as follows for Example 1 on page 204 and Example 1 on page 205. If the original open sentence is true if and only if $0 = 6$, then the original open sentence is *never* true. Therefore its solution set is ϕ. If the original open sentence is true if and only if

0 = 0, then the original open sentence is true *in general*. Therefore its solution set is all allowable replacements for the variable.

Students who read the symbol $\Leftrightarrow$ as *has the same solution set as* may be a bit shocked by the loss of the variable in the last step. For these students, point out that 0 may be replaced by $0 \cdot x$ at any time. Thus $0 = 6$ is equivalent to $0x = 6$ and $0 = 0$ is equivalent to $0x = 0$.

In spite of all previous efforts in this chapter, there may be students who still see solving open sentences *exclusively* as "use the approved procedures to isolate the variable." For these students, the sentences studied in Section 7-9 provide a jolt. Remind them once again that the symbol $\Leftrightarrow$ means *has the same solution set as.* If all else fails, simply ask these students to remember that if the last step gives a *false* statement about specific real numbers, there are *no* solutions. If the last step gives a *true* statement about specific real numbers, *all* replacements are solutions.

Exercises 7-9

1.

Sentence: $2(x + 3) = 4(x + 3) - 2x$

Replacement	Statement
2	$2(2 + 3) = 4(2 + 3) - 2 \cdot 2$
3	$2(3 + 3) = 4(3 + 3) - 2 \cdot 3$
4	$2(4 + 3) = 4(4 + 3) - 2 \cdot 4$
5	$2(5 + 3) = 4(5 + 3) - 2 \cdot 5$
0	$2(0 + 3) = 4(0 + 3) - 2 \cdot 0$
−1	$2(-1 + 3) = 4(-1 + 3) - 2 \cdot (-1)$
−2	$2(-2 + 3) = 4(-2 + 3) - 2 \cdot (-2)$
−3	$2(-3 + 3) = 4(-3 + 3) - 2 \cdot (-3)$

Simplified Statement	True or False
10 = 16	F
12 = 18	F
14 = 20	F
16 = 22	F
6 = 12	F
4 = 10	F
2 = 8	F
0 = 6	F

3.

Sentence: $3(x + 3) + 2x > 5x + 6$

Replacement	Statement
2	$3(2 + 3) + 2 \cdot 2 > 5 \cdot 2 + 6$
3	$3(3 + 3) + 2 \cdot 3 > 5 \cdot 3 + 6$
4	$3(4 + 3) + 2 \cdot 4 > 5 \cdot 4 + 6$
5	$3(5 + 3) + 2 \cdot 5 > 5 \cdot 5 + 6$
0	$3(0 + 3) + 2 \cdot 0 > 5 \cdot 0 + 6$
−1	$3(-1 + 3) + 2 \cdot (-1) > 5 \cdot (-1) + 6$
−2	$3(-2 + 3) + 2 \cdot (-2) > 5 \cdot (-2) + 6$
−3	$3(-3 + 3) + 2 \cdot (-3) > 5 \cdot (-3) + 6$

Simplified Statement	True or False
19 > 16	T
24 > 21	T
29 > 26	T
34 > 31	T
9 > 6	T
4 > 1	T
−1 > −4	T
−6 > −9	T

7-10
Pages 207-211

Section 7-10 asks students to apply material learned earlier in the chapter. There are enough exercises so that able students may be kept at productive work while special attention may be given to any difficulties slow students are still having with Sections 7-1 through 7-9.

Exercises 7-10

24.

	Rate	Time	Distance
On the Road	54 km/hr	$2 - t$	$54(2 - t)$
In the City	22 km/hr	t	$22 \cdot t$
Total		2 hr	$54(2 - t) + 22t = 92$

$t = \dfrac{1}{2}$ hr

25.

	Volume in cm³	Amount of Antifreeze
Original Solution	16	.40(16)
100% Antifreeze	x	1.00(x)
Final Solution	$16 + x$	.50($16 + x$)

$x = 3.2$ qt

Chapter 8   Mappings and Their Graphs

Overview

Sections 8-1 through 8-5 present the basic concepts needed to work with functions. For slow students, this may be a difficult part of *Algebra 1* because slightly more abstract thinking is required than in previous chapters. Sections 8-6 through 8-9 present linear open sentences exclusively. In these sections, the work is intentionally limited to linear equations and inequations to allow discouraged slow students to regain confidence. Slow students experiencing difficulty with Sections 8-6 through 8-9 may need more time on this material while others in the class begin Chapter 9. The notes for Section 8-9 and the overview for Chapter 9 present more detailed information on how this may be managed.

8-1
Pages 215-219

In this section, four ways are presented for describing a mapping (relation) from set A to set B. Many of the examples are intentionally nonalgebraic.

On page 216 the mathematically preferred definition for mapping is presented. Demanding an immediate, full appreciation for this definition by slow students may be unrealistic. For some slow students, the reasonable requirement may be that they work successfully a few of the less difficult exercises.

Exercises 8-1

3. P is less than Q   **5.** S is one less than T

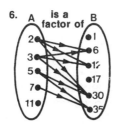

6. A is a factor of B

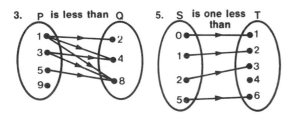

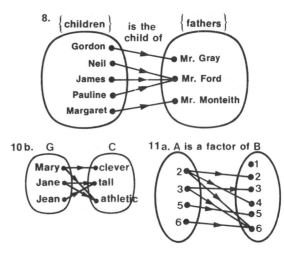

8. {children} is the child of {fathers}

10 b. G   C   **11 a.** A is a factor of B

8-2
Pages 219-222

This section presents the definition of *function.* For many students it may be in order to define function intuitively. This can be done using each of the following methods used in Section 8-1 to describe mappings.

1. Present ordered pairs given by the listing method or set-builder notation. Explain that each element of the first set is a first coordinate *exactly once.*
2. Present arrow diagrams. Explain that each element of the first set has *exactly one* arrow directed from it into the second set.
3. Present graphs where the first set of each function or nonfunction is represented by the horizontal axis. Explain that each point on the horizontal axis has *exactly one* point in the graph directly above (on, or below) it.

Additional examples of functions and nonfunctions should be presented with each method.

Exercises 8-2

5a. S   T

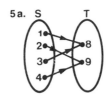

5c.

8-3
Pages 222-226

As with functions, 1-1 correspondences may be defined intuitively using the methods of Section 8-1.

1. Present examples using ordered pairs. Explain that each element of the first set is a first coordinate *exactly once*. Also, each element of the second set is a second coordinate *exactly once*.
2. Present examples using arrow diagrams. Explain that each element in the first set has *exactly one* arrow coming from it. Also, each element in the second set has *exactly one* arrow coming toward it.
3. Present examples using graphs. Explain that each element of the first set graphed on the horizontal axis has *exactly one* element in the graph above (on, or below) it. Also, each element of the second set graphed on the vertical axis has *exactly one* element in the graph to the right (on, or to the left) of it.

Exercises 8-3

12.

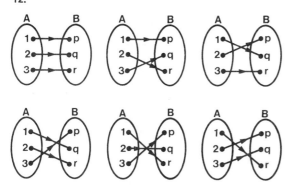

8-4
Pages 226-229

In this section functions are described by formulas (rules) using the following forms.

1. An arrow: $x \rightarrow 4 - x^2$
2. An equation: $y = 4 - x^2$
3. Functional notation: $f(x) = 4 - x^2$

The arrow form may be related to arrow diagrams. Stress that x names an arbitrary element in the first set.

For the equation form, stress that the solution set for the equation is the function.

Students in Algebra 1 often find security in thinking of a function as "doing something." They may be encouraged to think of a machine for which "x" names an "input for the machine" and for which "$f(x)$" names the corresponding "output by the machine." Thus, an (input, output) pair may be symbolized as $(x, f(x))$. This leads naturally to graphing functions.

Exercises 8-4

3.

4.

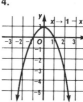

5.

6.

7.

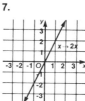

8.

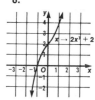

9.

10.

11.

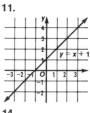

12.

13.

14.

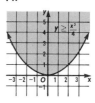

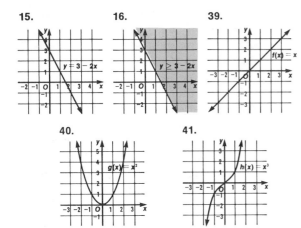

15. **16.** **39.**

40. **41.**

8-5
Pages 230-234

The definitions given for domain and range *assume* that there is a formula using one variable which describes the function. This restriction on the definition is made for two reasons.

1. It permits students who were uncomfortable thinking abstractly of subsets of $A \times B$ to feel secure and forge ahead with greater confidence.
2. The functions to be studied are covered by these restricted definitions.

For students who are comfortable thinking of functions as subsets of $A \times B$, domain and range may be defined more generally.

If $f \subseteq A \times B$ is a function, then
1. Domain of $f = \{a \mid (a, b) \in f$ for some $b \in B\}$.
2. Range of $f = \{b \mid (a, b) \in f$ for some $a \in A\}$.

This may be stated less symbolically.
1. The domain of f is the set of all first coordinates of ordered pairs in the function.
2. The range of f is the set of all second coordinates of ordered pairs in the function.

These definitions are not suggested for slow students who still have trouble thinking of functions as sets of ordered pairs.

Exercises 8-5

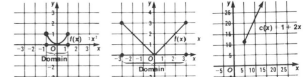

1. **2.** **11.**

8-6
Pages 234-238

Section 8-6 shifts attention from functions in general to linear open sentences and their graphs.

The student should complete this section able to graph solutions for open sentences of forms $x \circ c$ and $y \circ c$ where $\circ \in \{ =, <, >, \leq, \geq \}$.

Exercises 8-6

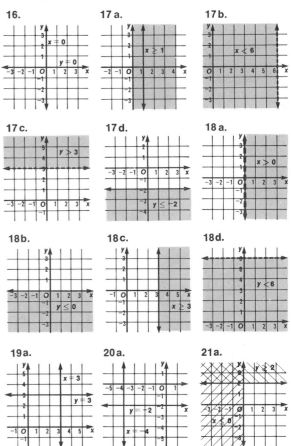

16. **17 a.** **17 b.**

17 c. **17 d.** **18 a.**

18 b. **18 c.** **18 d.**

19 a. **20 a.** **21 a.**

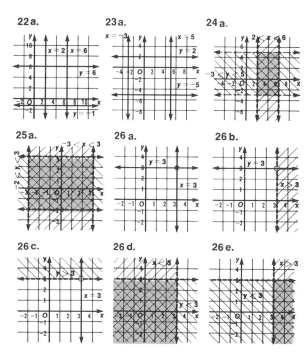

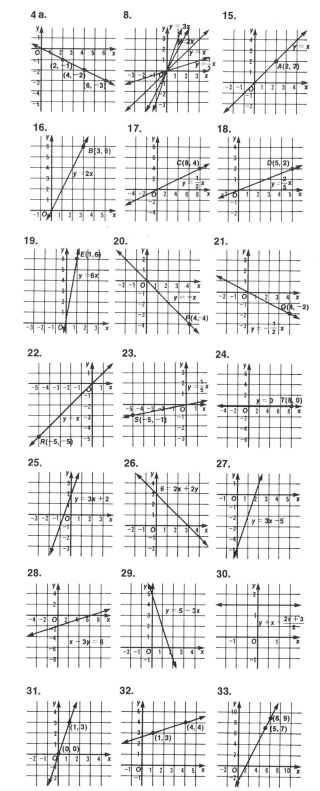

8-7
Pages 239-242

The study of straight lines is continued focusing on the forms $y = x + c$ and $y = -x + c$. In the exercises, students are required to apply the procedures for finding equivalent equations to equations containing two variables. Some students will need to be assured that these procedures apply regardless of the number of variables in the sentence.

8-8
Pages 242-245

The concept *slope* is introduced for straight lines. Section 8-8 sets the stage for the first statement of Section 8-9.

Exercises 8-8

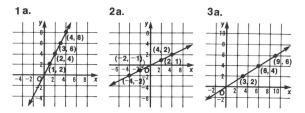

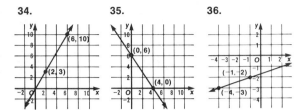

8-9
Pages 245-247

This section completes the process of placing straight lines in the plane in categories. At this point, slow students who may have had some trouble early in this chapter should have regained confidence and should be doing acceptable work. *If this is not the case,* consider sending only those students who are ready to Chapter 9, while slow students learn the content of Sections 8-6 through 8-9 thoroughly. The content of these sections is critical to success in Chapter 10.

Exercises 8-9

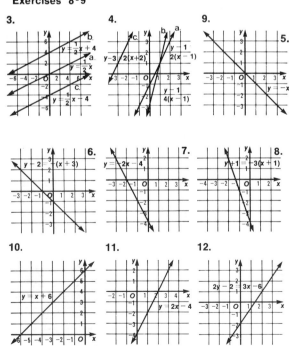

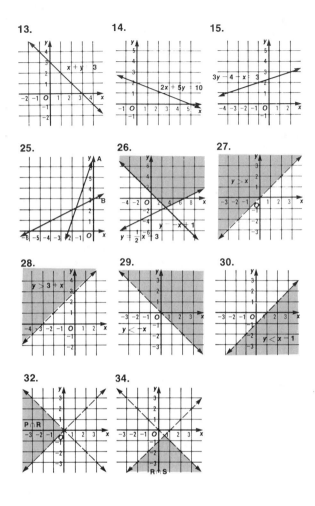

Chapter Review

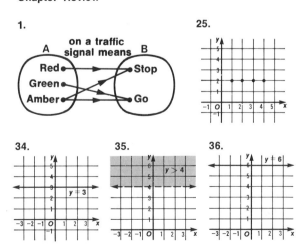

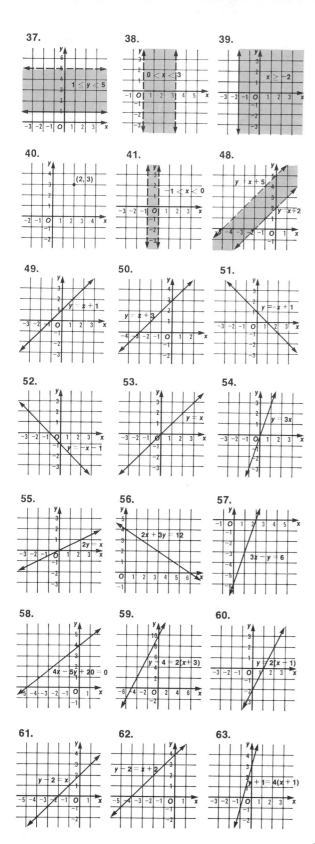

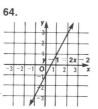

Chapter 9

Ratio and Proportion

Overview

Chapter 9 gives relevance to the content of Sections 8-6 through 8-9. It presents the kinds of settings students are likely to encounter outside of school. The emphasis is on the application of concepts.

By the nature of the material, increased reading demands are placed on students. Students with below-average reading abilities should be allowed to work with others. Students with average or above-average reading abilities who did well with Sections 8-6 through 8-9 should have little trouble in the chapter.

If some students must be held back to learn the material in previous sections, they may complete later as much of Chapter 9 as time permits. In that case, the class may be brought together again to enter Chapter 10. If no students need to be held back, Chapter 9 may be omitted and the entire class moved directly from Chapter 8 to Chapter 10.

Chapter 9 is not prerequisite to subsequent work. This does not mean, however, that the content of Chapter 9 is unimportant. On the contrary, it is rich in the types of applications which are common and important to everyday life.

9-1
Pages 253-255

The term *ratio* is defined in this section. Some students may need help seeing that $x{:}y$ and $\frac{x}{y}$ have the same meaning where ratios are concerned.

9-2
Pages 255-259

This section gives students an understanding of the word *rate* and establishes the *unitary method* of solving rate problems. The section also prepares students for understanding more easily the definition of *direct proportion* presented in the next section.

An example is given using tons per ton. This example and others like it should prevent students from forming the opinion that rate pairs always are different units of measurement. Such examples also suggest why the distinction between *rate* and *ratio* is not always a clear one. Therefore, the teacher's primary concern should be that students apply the concepts of the section and not that all students talk exactly alike about them.

For slow students, emphasize the method of Exercise 19. It permits solving rate problems without doing any computation. Also, in problems where more accuracy is required graphing may provide a check on computational work.

9-3
Pages 259-262

This section completes the work begun in Section 9-2 by presenting the *ratio method* for calculation involving ratios. Both methods, unitary and ratio, are important. This is not because both are needed in everyday life. Rather, the methods are important because they provide alternate ways of appreciating linear equations of the form $y = mx$.

9-4
Pages 262-264

Section 9-4 introduces the rule which many cooks, carpenters, etc., use in working with ratios: The product of the means equals the products of the extremes. Knowing this rule is not critical to the content of the course. However, many students may find it useful later in life.

This section may be omitted with no serious consequences. However, some students may be due for a bit of drill in solving equations. For them, the exercises are in order.

9-5
Pages 264-267

Section 9-5 may be viewed as a "sharpen-your-wits" section. The material requires students to make the decision whether or not a given situation may be modeled by a direct proportion. The material in this section is based on the premise that for concept learning knowing what something *is not* strengthens knowing what it *is*.

9-6
Pages 267-270

Section 9-6 investigates scale drawings as representations of concrete realities. The content of this section is not mathematically new, but it is certainly valuable to almost everyone's experiences out of school.

9-7
Pages 270-273

The concept *inverse proportion* is introduced here. As an additional assignment, students may be encouraged to draw graphs for the situation suggested in the exercises. Then they may try to reach a conclusion about the shape of such graphs generally.

9-8
Pages 275-279

Section 9-8 looks at the assignment of different unit lengths on the x-axis and y-axis to make graphs more readable. Exercises 6 and 7 should be reserved for able students or treated in class discussion. These exercises require applying the concepts associated with rate and ratio to using different unit lengths for axes.

2 a.

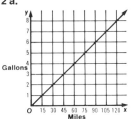

Gallons / Miles

3 a.

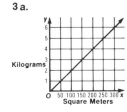

Kilograms / Square Meters

4.

Speed in km/hr	9600	12,800	16,000
Time in hr	40	30	24
	19,200	25,600	32,000
	20	15	12

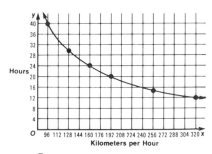

Hours / Kilometers per Hour

5.

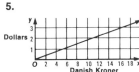

Dollars / Danish Kroner

9-9
Pages 279-282

Section 9-9 presents the formula $d = rt$ in a way that emphasizes its use in cases which do not fit the form $y = mx$. This section should give the student an appreciation of the relationship between actual rate and average rate. For able students the *Excursions in Mathematics* may be used to suggest how relationships between d, r, and t may be treated without making the assumption of a straight line function. In essence, the two Excursions provide just a taste of two major ideas in the calculus.

Exercise 9-9

1-4

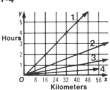

Hours / Kilometers

Chapter 10   Systems of Open Sentences

Overview

Chapter 10 treats the solution of systems of linear open sentences. It should be viewed as an introduction to this subject. As an introduction, the material is limited both in the type of reasoning required of the students and in the types of open sentences treated. The notes for Sections 10-5 and 10-6 explain these limitations in more detail.

Heterogeneous classes are often split into two groups by material in Sections 10-5 and 10-6. If this happens, able students may proceed independently into Sections 10-7 and 10-8. As implied by the option, Sections 10-7 and 10-8 are not prerequisite to subsequent chapters.

10-1   10-2
Pages 289-292   Pages 292-294

Sections 10-1 and 10-2 are largely review sections. It is important that they be mastered. This will allow students to concentrate on what will be new to them in Section 10-3. In that section the concept of solving a system of open sentences is introduced.

Exercises 10-1

3.   **4.**   **5.**

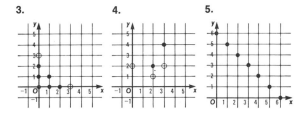

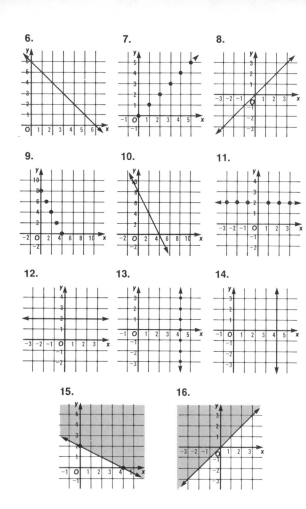

6. **7.** **8.**

9. **10.** **11.**

12. **13.** **14.**

15. **16.**

Exercises 10-2

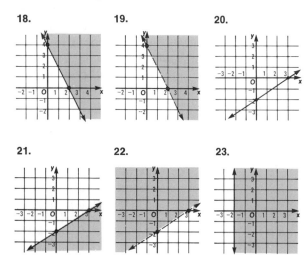

18. **19.** **20.**

21. **22.** **23.**

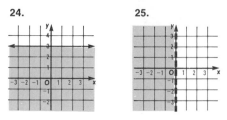

24. **25.**

10-3
Pages 295-297

10-4
Pages 297-299

Sections 10-3 and 10-4 strongly emphasize one point. If A, B, ... are solution sets for open sentence I, open sentence II, ..., then the solution set for the system is defined to be A ∩ B ∩ .... In teaching these sections, it should be stressed often that the graph of an open sentence indicates the set of solutions for that open sentence.

The intuitive method presented in Sections 10-3 and 10-4 for finding solutions is the following.

1. Graph in the same plane the *set* of solutions for each open sentence.
2. By inspection, find the *intersection* of these sets to determine the solution set of the system.

It is very important that students understand this method. Otherwise, the methods of the following sections may appear to be no more than teacher-required applications of obscure rules which yield answers.

Exercises 10-3

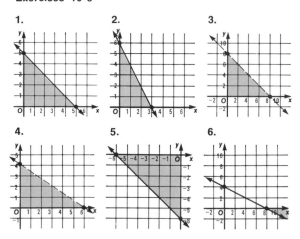

1. **2.** **3.**

4. **5.** **6.**

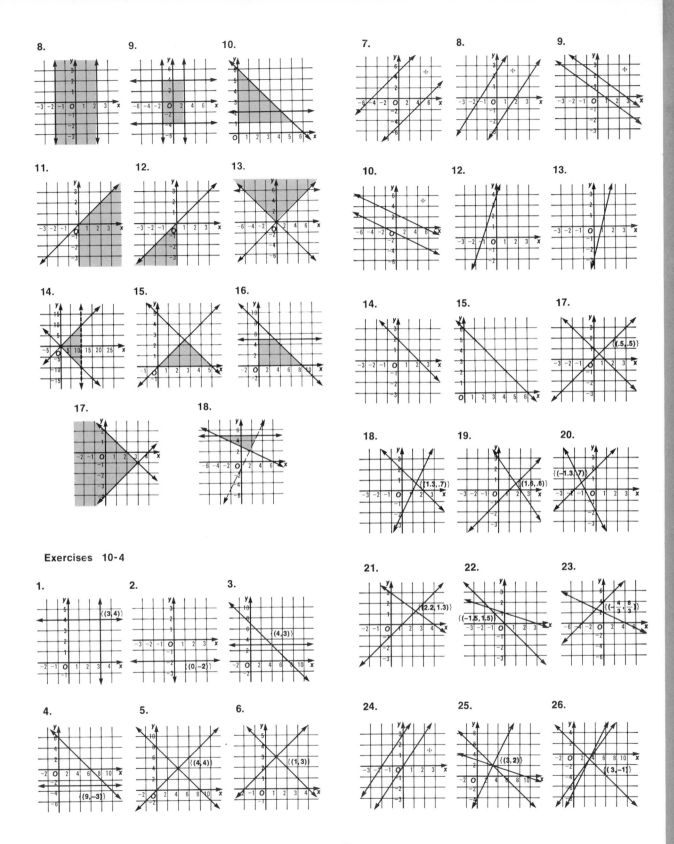

8.

9.

10.

7.

8.

9.

11.

12.

13.

10.

12.

13.

14.

15.

16.

14.

15.

17.

$\{(.5,.5)\}$

17.

18.

18.

$\{(1.3,.7)\}$

19.

$\{(1.6,.6)\}$

20.

$\{(-1.3,.7)\}$

Exercises 10-4

1.

$\{(3,4)\}$

2.

$\{(0,-2)\}$

3.

$\{(4,3)\}$

21.

$\{(2.2,1.3)\}$

22.

$\{(-1.5,1.5)\}$

23.

$\{(-\frac{4}{3},\frac{8}{3})\}$

4.

$\{(9,-3)\}$

5.

$\{(4,4)\}$

6.

$\{(1,3)\}$

24.

25.

$\{(3,2)\}$

26.

$\{(3,-1)\}$

43

10-5
Pages 299-304

10-6
Pages 306-307

In *Algebra 2*, solving a system of open sentences is treated as a matter of replacing the system by a more manageable equivalent system. The reasoning required by such an approach is more than many *Algebra 1* students can manage. Therefore, the treatment in this book is that of, "Find out what numbers the letters represent." That is, (1) treat the given open sentences as true statements about x and y. Then, (2) find out what x and y must be. This approach is logically respectable; it is just not as sophisticated mathematically as the approach to be used in *Algebra 2*.

For the elimination method of Section 10-5 the students may use the following reasoning. The system $ax + by = c$ and $px + qy = d$ is to be solved.

A. I want an (x, y) pair of values which makes *both* equations true statements.

B. For the (x, y) I want, $px + qy$ is just another way to write d.

C. I know that if $ax + by = c$, then $ax + by + d = c + d$.

D. For the (x, y) I want, this means that $ax + by + px + qy = c + d$.
This may be written as follows.
$$ax + by = c$$
$$px + qy = d$$
$$(a + p)x + (q + b)y = (c + d)$$

E. I want $a + p = 0$ or $q + b = 0$. This would make it easy to find either x or y. And once I know either x or y, the other can be found easily.

F. If the addition does not "eliminate" either x or y, I will replace one or both of the original equations by equivalent equations so one variable will be "eliminated."

For the substitution method of Section 10-6, the reasoning is much the same, involving $ax + by = c$ and $y = px + d$.

A. I want an (x, y) pair of values which is a solution to both of the equations.

B. For the (x, y) I want, $px + d$ is just another way to write y.

C. If $ax + by = c$, then it must be that $ax + b(px + d) = c$. From this expression I can find x. Once I have x, I can find y using $y = px + d$.

Notice that the reasoning required is not "if and only if" reasoning. Because of this, it may be in order to remind students that for two linear equations in two unknowns, only one of three things can occur.

1. The corresponding graphs are parallel lines. In this case the search for a solution will produce a false statement such as $0 = 1$.

2. The corresponding graphs are lines which intersect in a single point. In this case the search for a solution will produce a single value for x and a single value for y.

3. The corresponding graphs are the same line. In this case the search for a solution will produce a true statement such as $0 = 0$. The solution set for either equation is also the solution set for the system.

The reasoning outlined may need repeating several times for slow students. This would be accomplished best if repeating it were accompanied by an example each time.

Exercises 10-5

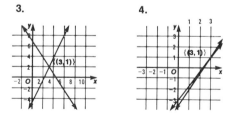

3.   4.

10-7
Pages 309-310

Section 10-7 applies the content of earlier sections. Students are to find m and c in $y = mx + c$ given two points which satisfy the equation.

It is acceptable to keep slow students on Sections 10-5 and 10-6 while other students study Section 10-7. This section is not critical to course development.

10-8
Pages 311-315

Section 10-8 may be assigned to those who are ready while slow students continue with Sections 10-5 and 10-6. However, depriving slow students completely of Section 10-8 is not advised since it establishes relevance for Sections 10-5 and 10-6. Consider treating some exercises as group work for these students or encouraging students who worked exercises to present their solutions with the class.

Review Exercises

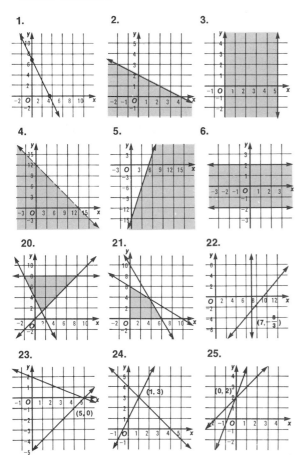

1.
2.
3.
4.
5.
6.
20.
21.
22.
23.
24.
25.

Chapter 11   Using Square Roots
Overview

Chapter 11 constitutes a first step toward the study of quadratic equations. The chapter focuses on understanding and using squares and square roots. Looking ahead to Chapter 13 and the quadratic formula, it will be important that students are very confident in using square roots. They might be overwhelmed if they lack this prerequisite knowledge.

From the student's point of view, the goal for Chapter 11 is to learn to use squares and square roots. This culminates in a presentation of the Pythagorean Theorem followed by applications. Knowing this theorem will be useful to many students outside of school.

11-1
Pages 319-321

Principal square root is defined in this section. Students should become very familiar with the symbol $\sqrt{}$ and its meaning. This is important later in this chapter for working with the distance formula, and still later in using the quadratic formula.

11-2
Pages 321-323

It is often assumed, sometimes incorrectly, that *Algebra 1* students can work with decimals and read tables. If they can, this section may be merely review. If not, it may be appropriate to present slow students with some basic rules concerning the manipulation of decimals.

1. Each time the decimal is moved one place to the left, multiply by 10 to keep the same number. For example, $379 = 37.9 \times 10 = 3.79 \times 10 \times 10$, or 3.79×100.
2. Each time the decimal is moved one place to the right, divide by 10 to keep

the same number. For example, $.0379$
$$= \frac{.379}{10} = \frac{3.79}{10 \times 10}, \text{ or } \frac{3.79}{100}.$$

11-3
Pages 323-326

11-4
Pages 326-328

Every student should complete Sections 11-3 and 11-4 convinced that both $\sqrt{mn} = \sqrt{m} \sqrt{n}$ and $\sqrt{\dfrac{m}{n}} = \dfrac{\sqrt{m}}{\sqrt{n}}$ for $m \geqq 0$ and $n > 0$.

Notice that the definition given for simplest form is really a partial definition covering only the cases to which the exercises are limited. However, it is completely adequate for the requirements of *Algebra 1*. A more comprehensive definition for simplest form is therefore reserved for *Algebra 2*.

11-5
Pages 328-330

Section 11-5 is devoted to finding square roots by using a table and the statements $\sqrt{mn} = \sqrt{m} \sqrt{n}$ and $\sqrt{\dfrac{m}{n}} = \dfrac{\sqrt{m}}{\sqrt{n}}$. These skills will be required at several points later in the course.

Able students who complete the content of this section quickly may be challenged by the following questions.

1. If $n \in W$ and $\sqrt{n} \notin W$, does it follow that $\sqrt{n}$ is an irrational number? (Yes)
2. $\sqrt{0.123}$ is given as 0.351. Does the fact that three nonzero digits are used to give $\sqrt{0.123}$ imply that it must be an irrational number? (Yes)
3. Can the square root of an irrational number be a rational number? (No)

Also, if slow students need still more time on this section, other students may be assigned the *Excursions in Mathematics*.

11-6
Pages 332-334

The primary purpose here is to establish an awareness that using approximate values

is common. The section introduces the symbol $\doteqdot$.

Notice that the definition for *significant digits* is not extended to apply to numerals like 3200, since doing so would require the use of scientific notation. For example writing 3.2×10^3 indicates two significant digits, writing 3.20×10^3 indicates three significant digits, etc. However, the treatment of significant digits in this section is adequate for purposes of this course.

If the teacher wishes or if students request it, the more inclusive definition may be given at this time. In this series, such definitions are presented in *Algebra 2* and related to common logarithms.

11-7
Pages 334-337

11-8
Pages 338-342

Section 11-7 establishes the Pythagorean Theorem with an intuitive proof. After a little practice in applying the theorem, the standard distance formula for two points in the plane is developed in Section 11-8.

It is suggested that students be required to use the tables and give decimal answers to problems at this stage. In applications, a decimal answer is more easily evaluated by students as being reasonable than a radical. For example, a student might accept $\sqrt{45}$ as an answer but reject it as unreasonable upon writing it as 6.71.

11-9
Pages 343-347

This section deals with changing the subject of a formula. Since the content of this section is not prerequisite to subsequent work, assigning exercises may be omitted. However, students should at least be introduced to the term *literal equation* as it is used later in the text.

Consider assigning exercises only to more able students if slow students need further work with earlier sections.

Chapter 12   Polynomials
Overview

Chapter 12 provides practice with multiplying and simplifying expressions. The new content of the chapter is the following.

1. The set of definitions associated with the term *polynomial*
2. The examination of products of polynomials, with emphasis on the product of the binomials

Chapter 12 may seem to be mainly review for able students and not for slow students, thus widening the gap between these two groups. If this seems to be the case, consider managing the class as follows.

1. Keep the entire class together on Chapter 12, choosing a pace agreeable to the slow students.
2. Ask more able students to enter Chapter 18 simultaneously, using any spare time to move forward on their own, working individually or in small groups.

This option is genuine in that all prerequisites for Chapter 18 are satisfied by Chapters 1-11.

12-1   12-2
Pages 351-353   Pages 353-356

Section 12-1 is largely review. In Section 12-2 the concept of *degree of a polynomial* is presented. It is suggested that degree be decided by "adding exponents." Some students may need to be reminded that $x = x^1$ and not x^0. An alternative approach to defining degree for a monomial is the following.

1. Imagine or write the monomial as a product without exponents: $4xy^3 = 4xyyy$.
2. The degree of the monomial is the number of factors which are variables: $4xyyy$ has 4 variable factors.

Exercises 12-2   **30.**   **31.**

 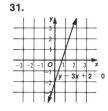

32. Its graph would be a straight line.

12-3   12-4
Pages 356-358   Pages 358-361

12-5
Pages 361-363

These sections present multiplication of two polynomials by stressing repeated applications of the Distributive Property. The emphasis is on products which yield quadratic expressions, thus helping set the stage for investigating quadratic functions and open sentences.

After completing Section 12-4, students should be able to write the product of two binomials by inspection. Section 12-5 continues to sharpen this skill by focusing on the special forms $(a + b)^2$, $(a - b)^2$, and $(a + b)(a - b)$. Notice that Exercises 55-63 of Section 12-5 stress a skill which must be used in checking certain solutions generated by applying the quadratic formula.

12-6
Pages 363-364

Under the guise of solving equations, the major purposes of Section 12-6 are the following.

1. To provide still further practice in multiplying polynomials
2. To provide review and practice in applying the procedures for finding equivalent equations

While working in this section, remind students occasionally that the equations being solved are not typical of those containing quadratic expressions. They are atypical in that each is chosen to be equivalent to a very manageable linear equation. A degree of expectation regarding this matter is desirable when entering Chapter 13.

Exercises 12-6

24.
Original Area = 16m², New Area = $(4 + t)^2$ cm², Increase in Area = $-16 + (4 + t)^2$, .81 cm²

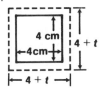

25. Outer radius $= r + w$

$$\begin{aligned}
\text{Area} &= \pi\,(r + w)^2 - \pi\,r^2 \\
&= \pi\,(r^2 + 2rw + w^2 - r^2) \\
&= \pi(2rw + w^2) \\
&= \pi w(2r + w)
\end{aligned}$$

26. a. $\overline{OD} = r - 12$ **b.** $r^2 =$
$(r - 12)^2 + (18)^2$ **c.** $r = 19\frac{1}{2}$

12-7
Pages 366-367

In Section 12-7 the term "identity" is defined for equations. Section 12-7 may be assigned to able students while slow students continue to study Sections 12-3 through 12-6.

Review Exercises

78. $y^2 - 6y + 9$; trinomial of degree 2
79. $4x^8 + 20x^4 + 25$; trinomial of degree 8
80. $9y^2 - 12y + 4$; trinomial of degree 2
81. $89 - 36\sqrt{2}$
82. $48 + 24\sqrt{3}$
83. $\frac{3}{16} + \frac{\sqrt{2}}{8}$ **84.** $\frac{7}{4} - \frac{1}{2}\sqrt{6}$
85. $\frac{49}{25} - \frac{12\sqrt{5}}{25}$ **86.** $\frac{113}{36} + \frac{2\sqrt{7}}{9}$
87.-89. Methods will vary.

Chapter 13   Quadratic Equations

Overview

The unique feature of Chapter 13 is that it *builds* the quadratic formula step-by-step. The development makes maximum use of pictures (graphs) before each mathematical statement so that each such statement will be greeted by the student with a high degree of anticipation. Thus, the quadratic formula emerges with meaning for the student, and not as a cumbersome equation which suddenly appeared as an afterthought to completing the square.

The advantages of this treatment which should be kept in mind throughout this chapter are the following.

1. Students will see clearly the relationship between $f(x) = ax^2 + bx + c$ and $ax^2 +$ $bx + c = 0$. Seeing this relationship is extremely important for applying the concepts of this chapter to solving problems and for working with quadratic inequations in Chapter 15.

2. Students will view applying the quadratic formula, not factoring, as the general method for solving quadratic equations. Too often the *Algebra 1* treatment of this topic allows students to think of factoring as the principal method, with the quadratic formula added on later to take care of the dreadful cases.

3. When the test for factorability is presented in Section 14-6, students will be working with a formula that is already familiar. Thus, they will be able at that time to concentrate exclusively on the problem at hand.

13-1
Pages 371-372

By doing the exercises, students should develop strong suspicions about the shape of the graph of a quadratic function. Many students may even conclude the following about $f(x) = ax^2 + bx + c$ from their work here.

  1. $a > 0$ implies a graph is concave upward.

  2. $a < 0$ implies a graph is concave downward.

  3. Changing the value of c raises or lowers the graph without changing its shape.

Student discovery of these facts may be promoted at this time, but it is not required.

Some students may need some help with graphing functions. Also, students with severe reading problems may need help understanding what is required by the exercises. Therefore, some or all of the exercises may be treated as discussion or group work.

13-2
Pages 372-375

The major purpose of this section is to establish further familiarity with the shape of the graph of a quadratic function. To do this, students should learn what is meant by a maximum point and a minimum point.

The exercises will establish for many students the following expectation. If f is a quadratic function with maximum (or minimum) value at $x = m$, then $f(m - w) = f(m + w)$ for any $w \in$ R. This may be made explicit at this time if students seem ready to accept it.

Exercises 13-2

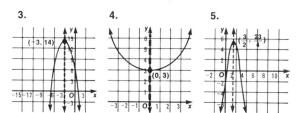

3.

4.

5.

13-3
Pages 376-380

Section 13-3 partially unveils the quadratic formula. Upon completing this section students should be convinced of the following for $f(x) = ax^2 + bx + c$.

1. The equation of the axis of symmetry is $x = \dfrac{-b}{2a}$

2. The maximum (or minimum) point is $\left(\dfrac{-b}{2a}, f\left(\dfrac{-b}{2a}\right)\right)$.

3. The function will have a maximum point if $a < 0$, and a minimum point if $a > 0$.

After completing Section 13-3, students should be able to name the maximum or minimum point for any quadratic function without drawing a graph.

13-4
Pages 380-382

13-5
Pages 382-389

These two sections are devoted to determining how many real number solutions $ax^2 + bx + c = 0$ has. Heavy emphasis is placed on the fact that $ax^2 + bx + c$ equals 0 for precisely those values of x where the graph of $f(x) = ax^2 + bx + c$ intersects the x-axis. That is, saying $ax^2 + bx + c$ equals 0 is the same as saying $f(x)$ equals 0.

In Section 13-4, decisions on the number of solutions for $ax^2 + bx + c = 0$ are made by inspecting graphs directly. In Section 13-5 students are asked to make these decisions without actually drawing a graph. Rather, these decisions should now be made by considering the location of the maximum or minimum point relative to the x-axis and whether the graph is concave upward or downward.

That students think in these terms is important here and will be important in Chapter 15 when quadratic inequations are examined.

Exercises 13-4

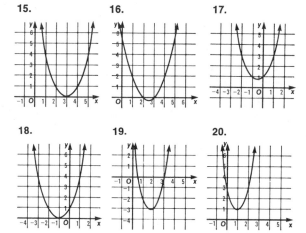

15.

16.

17.

18.

19.

20.

13-6
Pages 384-387

For many students, the expression
$$\frac{\sqrt{b^2 - 4ac}}{2a}$$
may be frightening in appearance. For that reason, this section uses the letter w in its place. In this section, the student masters the fact that if there are two solutions for a quadratic equation, they may always be given by $\dfrac{-b}{2a} + w$ and $\dfrac{-b}{2a} - w$ for some suitable value w.

Thus, upon entering Section 13-7, students will have a goal (finding w) clearly in mind, a goal which was established using minimal symbolism.

13-7
Pages 387-391

13-8
Pages 392-396

These sections unveil the quadratic formula completely as two statements $x = \dfrac{-b}{2a} + \dfrac{\sqrt{b^2 - 4ac}}{|2a|}$ and $x = \dfrac{-b}{2a} - \dfrac{\sqrt{b^2 - 4ac}}{|2a|}$ Essentially the *only* new material is a formula for w, which was first used in Section 13-6. Thus, the major task for students reduces to becoming accustomed to using the expression $\dfrac{\sqrt{b^2 - 4ac}}{|2a|}$.

This period of becoming accustomed to the expression is followed in Section 13-8 by presentation of the usual form, $x = \dfrac{-b \pm \sqrt{b^2 - 4ac}}{2a}$. Also the exercises of Section 13-8 establish intuitively the fact that the quadratic formula may *always* be used in solving $ax^2 + bx + c = 0$, regardless of the number of solutions.

Exercises 13-8

9.
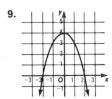

13-9
Pages 397-402

The discussion on pages 397-398 requires students to think as follows. "I know (believe) the quadratic formula *always* works. What does that force me to believe about $b^2 - 4ac$ for the different possibilities?"

This reasoning does not constitute a proof and that is not the intention here. Proofs regarding this topic are reserved for *Algebra 2*.

Notice that the statements at the top of page 399 are not presented as *if and only if* statements even though they could be. Notice, too, that for each $p \Rightarrow q$ statement of pages 397-398 there is a corresponding $q \Rightarrow p$ statement at the top of page 399. Slow students are not expected to see this. It is adequate for them to know the statements at the top of page 399. However, able students, when asked, should be able to conclude that they are now in possession of three $p \Leftrightarrow q$ statements. The most able students might be able to conclude this using only the statements on page 399 and the principle of trichotomy. Using only the statements of pages 397-398 and the fact that there can be at most two solutions will yield the same results.

Chapter 14   Factoring Quadratic Expressions
Overview

Chapter 14 presents the factoring of quadratic expressions. This chapter also completes the instructional strategy outlined by the overview of Chapter 13.

Factoring is often very difficult for slow students. For that reason, this book is designed so that Chapters 14 and 16 may be covered simultaneously, provided Section 14-6 precedes Section 16-4.

Thus, a class may be kept together on Chapter 14 at a pace agreeable to slow students. At the same time, more able students may be instructed to use any spare time progressing through Chapter 16, working individually or in groups.

14-1
Pages 407-410

In this section the concept of factoring is extended beyond removal of a common term. The section also reviews different special products, since recognizing how a product was obtained can be helpful in factoring it. To foster this idea, related expansions and factorizations are given in blocks in the exercises.

Exercises 14-1

27. $(3d + 1)(3d + 1)$
28. $(h - 13)(h - 13)$
29. $(x - 2)(x - 2)$
30. $2x(1 + a)(1 + a)$
31. $x^2 + 3x + 2$ 32. $y^2 + y - 6$
33. $x^2 + 5x - 50$
34. $x^2 - 5x - 50$
35. $d^2 + 8d + 7$
36. $x^2 + (c + d)x + cd$

14-2
Pages 410-411

The section provides a review of what is meant by reducing or simplifying algebraic fractions. It also provides practice with the material in Section 14-1.

As students work Exercises 7-20 on page 411, watch for errors such as the following. $\frac{x^2 - 4}{x^2 - 9} = \frac{-4}{-9}$; $\frac{a - 3}{3a^2 - 27} = \frac{1}{3a - 9}$; etc.

Students making such errors need reminding that equivalent fractions are found by multiplying or dividing the *entire* numerator and denominator by the same nonzero number.

14-3
Pages 411-415

Students should learn to remove the common term so that the resulting polynomial has relatively prime integers as coefficients. In the case of integral coefficients in the original polynomial, students can accomplish this simply by removing *all* common integral and variable factors. However, in the case of rational number coefficients, slow students may need to learn the following step-by-step procedure.

1. Find the LCD of all coefficients.
2. Express each coefficient as a fraction having this LCD as denominator.
3. Use the distributive property to factor out $\frac{1}{LCD}$.

4. Factor out the common term of the resulting polynomial with integral coefficients.

14-4
Pages 415-417

The terms irreducible and prime are introduced. Notice that in Exercises 34-40 students are handicapped by not yet having the discriminant test. For these exercises, *irreducible* or *prime* may mean "I give up." Students may then worry that the decision is not correct. Introducing such concerns provides motivation for the next section.

Exercises 14-4

22. $(x + 4)(x - 4)$
23. $3x(x + 3)(x - 2)$
24. $\frac{1}{3}w(w - 3)(w + 2)$

14-5
Pages 417-419

This is primarily a practice section involving expressions of the form $ax^2 + bx + c$ where $a, b, c \in Z$ and $a \neq 1$. For many students, this will appear to be an exercise in guessing. With practice, it will gradually appear less as guessing. Notice that "principles for better guessing" are not listed, but rather embodied in the exercises. How many principles should be stated explicitly will depend on the students' abilities.

14-6
Pages 419-422

In this section the relationship between $\sqrt{b^2 - 4ac}$ and the factorability of $ax^2 + bx + c$ is explored and discussed, *not proved*. Notice that the primary statement on page 420 assumes that students believe the following:
$a_1x^2 + b_1x + c_1 = a_2x^2 + b_2x + c_2$, for all $x \in R \Rightarrow a_1 = a_2, b_1 = b_2, c_1 = c_2$.

If some able students challenge this, present the following discussion.
1. $a_1x^2 + b_1x + c_1 = a_2x^2 + b_2x + c_2 \Leftrightarrow$
   $(a_1 - a_2)x^2 + (b_1 - b_2)x + (c_1 - c_2)$
   $= 0$

2. Since the equation must hold for $x = 0$, $0 + 0 + (c_1 - c_2) = 0$, which yields $c_1 = c_2$.

3. The equation thus becomes $(a_1 - a_2)x^2 + (b_1 - b_2)x = 0$.

4. Since the equation must hold for $x = 1$ and $x = 2$, it must be that $4(a_1 - a_2) + 2(b_1 - b_2) = 0$ and $(a_1 - a_2) + (b_1 - b_2) = 0$. Solving this system for $(a_1 - a_2)$ and $(b_1 - b_2)$ yields both equal to zero.

This gives the desired results of $a_1 = a_2$ and $b_1 = b_2$.

If no student demands a proof, it may be best to leave the subject alone. It could confuse slow students by forcing them to consider more problems at once than they can manage.

Notice too that the narrative for Section 14-6 shows that if $ax^2 + bx + c$ is factorable, then $\sqrt{b^2 - 4ac} \in W$. However, that $\sqrt{b^2 - 4ac} \in W$ implies $ax^2 + bx + c$ is factorable is simply stated. The reason for not showing (deriving) both statements is that the second is probably too difficult for the average *Algebra 1* student. For able students, the following steps may be used to establish the second statement.

1. Show that $ax^2 + bx + c =$
$$a \left(x + \frac{b + \sqrt{b^2 - 4ac}}{2a} \right) \left(x + \frac{b - \sqrt{b^2 - 4ac}}{2a} \right)$$

2. If $\sqrt{b^2 - 4ac} \in W$, then $b + \sqrt{b^2 - 4ac}$, $b - \sqrt{b^2 - 4ac} \in Z$. Let $p = b + \sqrt{b^2 - 4ac}$ and $q = b - \sqrt{b^2 - 4ac}$ where $p, q \in Z$.

3. Then $ax^2 + bx + c = a(x + \frac{p}{2a})(x + \frac{q}{2a}) = \frac{1}{4a}(2ax + p)(2ax + q)$

This last sentence is a factorization for $ax^2 + bx + c$.

This section provides review and practice with factoring in the context of simplifying rational expressions.

The usual method of solving a quadratic equation by first factoring the quadratic expression is presented. The section also offers a review of the quadratic formula.

After completing Section 14-8 students possess all skills required for Section 15-5, which may be assigned at this time.

Chapter 15   Quadratic Inequations

Overview

Chapter 15 presents the quadratic inequation in much the same style as for the quadratic equation. That is, the graph of the corresponding quadratic function is used as an intuitive basis for examining the inequation.

After completing Chapter 14, students possess all skills required for Chapter 17. Hence, Chapter 15 may be treated at a realistic pace for slow students while more able students simultaneously study Chapter 17.

In these sections the quadratic inequation is defined and solved by appealing to the graph of its corresponding quadratic function. The strategy is identical to that of Sections 13-4 and 13-5.

Exercises 15-2

11. $\{x \mid -\frac{5}{3} < x < \frac{1}{2}\}$

12. $\{x \mid x < -\frac{5}{3}\} \cup \{x \mid x > \frac{1}{2}\}$

13. $\{x \mid x \leq -\frac{5}{3}\} \cup \{x \mid x \geq \frac{1}{2}\}$

14. $\{x \mid -\frac{5}{3} \leq x \leq \frac{1}{2}\}$

15. $\{x \mid x \in R\}$ 16. ϕ

17.

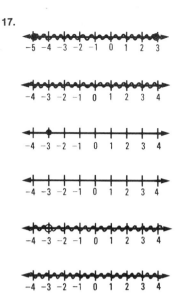

15-3
Pages 438-440

This section may be treated as optional. Students are asked to name a quadratic inequation given a suitable solution set. Slow students still having trouble with Sections 15-1 and 15-2 may continue with those sections while other students study Section 15-3.

15-4
Pages 441-442

The standard procedure for solving quadratic inequations by factoring is presented. Attention is directed to considering the relationship of a product $a \cdot b$ to zero. Students are required to deal with the logical form (P and Q) *or* (S and T) where P, Q, S, and T are open sentences.

The reasoning (logic) in this section may overwhelm slow students. Allow such students to use the methods of Sections 15-1 and 15-2. Assure them that if they find the method of this section unmanageable, it does not imply that they cannot solve inequations.

15-5
Pages 444-448

As mentioned before, Section 15-5 may be completed after Section 14-8. Also, this section may be treated as optional.

The only thing new in this section is that quadratic equations are now permitted as members of a system of equations to be solved by algebraic methods. The method used is essentially the *substitution method*. The major statement which must be used by students may be symbolized as follows.

$$(y = f(x) \text{ and } y = g(x)) \Rightarrow f(x) = g(x).$$

Exercises 15-5

4.
a. 2 **b.** 2

5.
a. 1 **b.** 1

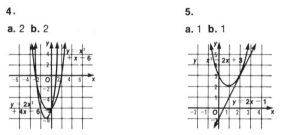

6. $x = \dfrac{3 + \sqrt{17}}{2}$, $y = \dfrac{13 + 3\sqrt{17}}{2}$

$x = \dfrac{3 - \sqrt{17}}{2}$, $y = \dfrac{13 - 3\sqrt{17}}{2}$

7. $x = 2, y = 4$

Chapter 16   Multiplying and Dividing Polynomials
Overview

The primary function of Chapter 16 is to introduce the usual long division algorithm for polynomials. Sections 16-1 and 16-2 are largely review. They relate the algebraic algorithms for multiplication to those for whole numbers. This sets the stage for the topic of Section 16-3, division of polynomials. Section 16-4 may be viewed as providing further relevance for Section 16-3. The chapter is written in such a way that able students may complete it with minimal teacher assistance. As suggested earlier, it may be assigned as supplemental work for able students while the entire class studies Chapter 14.

16-1
Pages 451-453

16-2
Pages 453-456

These two sections are primarily review, except that as preparation for Section 16-3 an analogy between whole number multiplication and multiplication of polynomials is established.

16-3
Pages 456-462

This section presents the usual long division algorithm for polynomials. A somewhat elaborate explanation which relies heavily on analogies with whole number division is presented. This elaborate explanation is present to make the amount of teacher assistance required minimal.

16-4
Pages 462-465

This section presents the proposition that $(x - c)$ is a factor of $p(x)$ if $p(c) = 0$. It is also hinted that the techniques which were used in dealing with quadratic functions and equations also may be used with those of higher degree. Thus, section 16-4 serves two purposes.

1. It adds relevance for the material presented in Section 16-3.
2. It provides a preview of work with polynomial functions of degree greater than two.

Chapter 17   Algebraic Fractions

Overview

Students may work with Chapter 17 any time after completion of Chapter 14. Able students may complete it as supplemental work while the entire class studies Chapter 15. Sections 17-1 through 17-3 are largely review of operations with rational expressions. However, they make added demands on students' abilities to factor.

There is also additional concern given to expressions which may be zero for certain replacements of the variables. In Sections 17-4 and 17-5, this same concern extends to the study of multiplying or dividing both sides of an open sentence by a polynomial. The chapter ends with a section on complex fractions which requires students to apply all concepts of Chapter 17 in a single setting.

17-1
Pages 469-472

17-2
Pages 472-474

17-3
Pages 474-476

Sections 17-1, 17-2, and 17-3 offer a very intensive review of simplifying (reducing) rational expressions and performing operations with rational expressions. No new concepts are introduced but the factoring is more difficult.

In preparation for Sections 17-4 and 17-5, attention is focused heavily on values which are not allowed for variables, namely those which make denominators zero.

17-4
Pages 476-478

17-5
Pages 478-480

These sections treat multiplying and dividing both sides of an equation by an expression containing the variable. Students should leave these sections knowing the following.

1. When both sides of an equation are multiplied by a polynomial having solution set S, $t \in S$ *may be* a solution of the resulting equation and not of the original.
2. When both sides are divided by a polynomial with solution set S, $t \in S$ *may be* a solution of the original equation and not of the resulting equation.

17-6
Pages 480-483

The work in this section on complex fractions requires the use of all concepts previously treated in the chapter. The section itself contains little that is conceptually new. However, this does not imply that the material is easy. Working with complex fractions affords students many occasions for errors which may lead to discouragement. Therefore, consider allowing students to work with each other as a means of reducing errors and raising motivation.

Chapter 18   Trigonometry
Overview

As mentioned previously, Chapter 18 may be used at any time after students complete Chapter 11. Thus, Chapter 18 may be used as supplementary work for able students while all students stay together in studying Chapters 12 through 15.

The topics are developed in such a way that able students should require minimal teacher assistance in completing the chapter. Sections 18-1 through 18-5 present right triangle trigonometry and emphasize the application of concepts. Sections 18-6 and 18-7 extend the definition for sine, cosine, and tangent to include angles such that $0° \leq m \angle A \leq 360°$.

18-1   18-2
Pages 485-489   Pages 489-491

18-3
Pages 492-495

The major concept in these sections is that of *similarity*. The instructional strategy for introducing such technical terms relies heavily on intuitive models and references to physical manipulations. For example, *similarity* is first introduced in Section 18-1 by asking students to consider photographic enlargements and reductions.

Then, in Section 18-2, rotating and flipping these figures are allowed. Finally, in Section 18-3, problems involving pictures are examined.

By using this strategy, the student is relieved of any concerns about which of the technical terms should be treated as undefined. Such concerns belong to a more formal treatment of geometry and trigonometry than is intended here.

After completing Section 18-3, students should have facility in managing the following type of problem. Let a and b name lengths of sides of polygon S and c and d name lengths of corresponding sides of polygon T, three of which are given. Find the length not given by using $\frac{a}{b} = \frac{c}{d}; \frac{a}{c} = \frac{b}{d}$; or $ad = bc$.

18-4
Pages 495-501

Many students may already be acquainted with angle measurement in degrees as presented here. The primary function of this section is to present angle measurement so as to develop the conceptual framework for defining the major trigonometric ratios for right triangles. Completing the exercises successfully should reduce the task in Section 18-5 to that of learning new vocabulary. Therefore, it is suggested that students complete *all* exercises.

18-5
Pages 501-504

The sine, cosine, and tangent are defined and their uses studied further. This section completes right triangle trigonometry. If desired, the study of trigonometry in *Algebra 1* may end here.

18-6   18-7
Pages 505-508   Pages 509-513

These two sections may be treated as optional. The goal is to extend the definitions of sine, cosine, and tangent to include angles such that $0° \leq m \angle A \leq 360°$. Students who complete these sections are adequately prepared to investigate the laws of sines, cosines, and tangents. You may suggest that able students use reference books to begin investigating these laws.

Exercises 18-7

42.

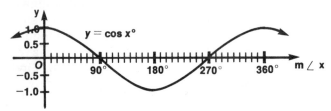

43.

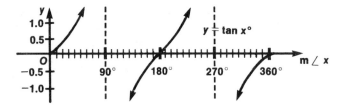

Teacher's Annotated Edition

Algebra 1

Merrill Secondary Mathematics Series

Nibbelink
Graening

CHARLES E. MERRILL PUBLISHING CO.

A Bell & Howell Company

Columbus, Ohio

AUTHORS

William H. Nibbelink
Associate Professor of Mathematics Education
University of Iowa
Iowa City, Iowa

Jay Graening
Assistant Professor of Mathematics
and Secondary Education
University of Arkansas
Fayetteville, Arkansas

CONTRIBUTING EDITORS

Leroy Sachs
Mathematics Teacher
Clayton High School
Clayton, Missouri

F. Joe Crosswhite
Professor of Mathematics Education
The Ohio State University
Columbus, Ohio

Lawrence D. Hawkinson
Curriculum Associate in Mathematics, and Teacher
Henry Gunn High School
Palo Alto, California

Project Editors: Richard Logie,
Lynn Straley
Editorial Coordinator: Bonnie Johnston
Art Coordinator: Lewis Bolen
Cover Design: John Variano
Special Interest Pages: Alan R. Osborne

ISBN O-675-05898-8

Published by
CHARLES E. MERRILL PUBLISHING CO.
A Bell & Howell Company
Columbus, Ohio 43216

PREFACE

Algebra 1 has been prepared for a general high school audience planning many different careers. It presents a balance of new and traditional mathematics in an informal setting. This approach to algebra includes a gradual transition from junior high school mathematics to the more structured mathematics characteristic of high school programs. Much of the transition is accomplished in the first seven chapters. With a minor shift of emphasis by the teacher, these seven chapters may be presented as a pre-algebra program.

The text is written in an engagingly informal style with concepts first introduced at an intuitive level. Reading level and the length of sections have been carefully controlled. The result of the attention given to these matters is a uniquely readable book: It is readable both in terms of a carefully controlled difficulty level and in terms of interest level. All of these features clearly distinguish the text from much of the material prepared in the "modern math" period.

A number of sound pedagogical features contribute to learning. First, the level of difficulty rises at a slow but steady rate. Students clearly see how current material relates to previous mathematical experiences. Second, by keeping the concept density low in each section, students do not become lost under a barrage of new material. Third, difficult concepts and procedures are presented in stages. Thus concepts and procedures frequently are encountered in several contexts before mastery is expected. This approach assures that important concepts and skills, once introduced, are revisited at appropriate points in the text.

Numerous worked examples clarify procedures and serve as models for the exercises. An unusually large number of exercises reinforce and apply the material in each section. Teachers may use these graded exercises to design programs for students of average ability or to challenge more able students.

"Chapter Summaries" and "Review Exercises" keyed to sections provide for evaluation at the end of each chapter. Further evaluation is available to the teacher in a separate testing program conveniently packaged in a spirit master format. Problems related to science, industry, and the home appear throughout the text to emphasize the role of mathematics in students' lives. The Metric System (SI units) is introduced in the first chapter and used throughout the text.

To show students that mathematics may be used in entertaining and interesting ways, special pages which highlight careers, recreation, applications, and the history of mathematics appear throughout the text. Sections entitled "Excursions in Mathematics" and "Suggested Activities" provide the teacher supplemental material to interest and challenge students.

Students will find *Algebra 1* directed to their interests, abilities, and needs. The teacher will find that this has been done without sacrificing accuracy or relying on rote drill. *Algebra 1* and the accompanying Teacher's Annotated Edition, which contains learning objectives and answers to all exercises, provide a program of great flexibility that is easily managed in the classroom.

List of Symbols

{ }	the set of	$\Leftrightarrow$	is equivalent to
$\in$	is an element of	$\doteq$	is approximately equal to
$\cap$	intersection	$\overset{?}{=}$	may be equal to (used in checks)
$\cup$	union	(x, y)	the ordered pair, x, y
ϕ	the empty set	A(x, y)	point A with coordinates x, y
$\subseteq$	is a subset of	x^n	x to the nth power
|	such that (used in set-builder notation)	$\sqrt{}$	the principal square root of
		$\sqrt[n]{}$	the nth root of
. . .	and so on (to continue a pattern)	$\rightarrow$	maps to
|x|	the absolute value of x	f(x)	f of x (functional notation)
N	the set of natural numbers	x:y	x to y (in ratios)
W	the set of whole numbers	$\pm$	plus or minus
Z	the set of integers	$\angle$	angle
Q	the set of rational numbers	m$\angle$	measure of angle
R	the set of real numbers	Q°	Q degrees
=	is equal to	$\overleftrightarrow{XY}$	line XY
<	is less than	$\overrightarrow{AB}$	ray AB
>	is greater than	$\overline{MN}$	line segment MN
$\leq$	is less than or equal to	$\cong$	is congruent to
$\geq$	is greater than or equal to	$\overset{\frown}{PQ}$	arc PQ

CONTENTS

Chapter 1   Sets of Numbers

Chapter 1 presents basic set ideas which are used in later chapters. The chapter also describes major subsets of the real numbers.

Chapter 2   Properties of Operations

Chapter 2 examines the use of letters to represent numbers and presents standard agreements on the order of operations and special punctuations.

Chapter 3   The Language of Algebra

Chapter 3 presents the main concepts and terms associated with simplifying expressions and solving open sentences.

Chapter 4   Using Whole Number Expressions

Chapter 4 provides basic practice with concepts presented in previous chapters. Algebraic skills are developed relative to whole number expressions. This gives students the security of employing previously learned skills.

Chapter 5   Exploring Integers

Chapter 5 extends previously learned concepts and skills to include the integers. By the end of the chapter, students can work with variables on the set of integers.

Chapter 6   Exploring Rational Numbers

Chapter 6 extends previously learned concepts and skills to include rational numbers. The stage is set for work with variables over the rational numbers.

Chapter 7   Solving Open Sentences

Chapter 7 introduces and provides practice with the concept of solving an open sentence by finding a more manageable equivalent open sentence.

Chapter 8   Mappings and Their Graphs

Chapter 8 defines the basic types of relations, and presents a careful examination of linear functions.

Chapter 9　Ratio and Proportion

Chapter 10　Systems of Open Sentences

Chapter 11　Using Square Roots

Chapter 12 Polynomials

Chapter 12 presents major definitions associated with polynomials and completes preparation for the study of quadratic expressions and open sentences.

Chapter 13 Quadratic Equations

Chapter 13 "builds" the quadratic formula through a unique, step-by-step presentation which clearly relates the formula to the quadratic function. The approach is both intuitive and highly applicable to a variety of problem settings.

Chapter 14 Factoring Quadratic Expressions

Chapter 14 presents concepts and skills associated with factoring expressions. The ideas developed in Chapter 13 are used to derive a factorability test for quadratic expressions.

Chapter 15 Quadratic Inequations

Chapter 15 examines techniques for solving quadratic inequations. The chapter first uses an intuitive, general approach as in Chapter 13 and then an approach which parallels that of Chapter 14.

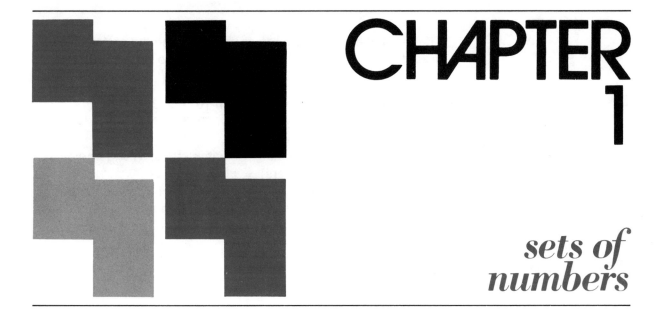

CHAPTER 1

sets of numbers

OBJECTIVES:

1. To distinguish between set and element.
2. To use standard notation for describing sets and elements.

1-1
Basic Concepts

One of the basic ideas in mathematics is that of a set. You may think of a **set** as a collection of objects which are called **elements** or **members** of the set. Sometimes the elements are said to **belong to** the set.

EXAMPLES

Set and *element of* are properly undefined terms in mathematics. Therefore the emphasis in this section is on examples and not on definitions.

1. The unicorn is an element of the set of imaginary animals.
2. The elephant is not an element of the set of rodents.
3. Peggy Fleming is a member of the set of Olympic gold-medal winners.
4. Three is not a member of the set of even numbers.
5. Willy Mays belongs to the set of former professional baseball players.
6. Six does not belong to the set of odd numbers.

You may describe a set by using the *listing method,* or *roster method.* The elements of the set are listed inside braces, { }, which are used as a symbol for *the set of.*

EXAMPLES

1. The set of vowels may be written {a, e, i, o, u}.
2. The set of the first four even numbers may be written {2, 4, 6, 8}.

If the list of elements is large or unending and the pattern is clear, three dots, . . . , may be used to mean *and so on*.

EXAMPLES

1. {whole numbers} may be written {0, 1, 2, 3, . . .}
2. {prime numbers} may be written {2, 3, 5, 7, 11, 13, . . .}

Sets may be named by single capital letters: W = {whole numbers}, N = {natural numbers} = {1, 2, 3, . . .}.

You can show that an object belongs to a set by using the symbol $\in$, which means *is an element of*. A slash through a symbol denies its meaning, so you may use $\notin$ to mean *is not an element of*.

Remind students that the slash has the same meaning in $\notin$ as in $\neq$. In both cases it inserts the word "not."

EXAMPLES

1. $3 \in$ {odd numbers}
2. $4 \notin$ {odd numbers}

EXERCISES

1. is not 2. is 3. is 4. is not
5. is not 6. A = {11, 12, 13, 14}
7. B = {red, yellow, green}
8. C = {4, 6, 8} 9. D = {11, 13, 15, 17, 19} 10. E = {Tuesday, Thursday}

Replace each ___?___ with *is* or *is not* to make a true statement.
1. The letter g ___?___ a member of the set of vowels.
2. Thirty thousand nine ___?___ a member of the set of odd numbers.
3. Thirteen ___?___ an element of the set of numbers some people call unlucky.
4. Twenty-eight ___?___ an element of the set of numbers which leave no remainder when divided by five.
5. Seven ___?___ an element of the set of factors of twelve.

Use the listing method to describe each set.

Sample   Y is the set of months whose names begin with M.
Y = {March, May}

6. A is the set of whole numbers greater than 10 but less than 15.
7. B is the set of colors in traffic lights.
8. C is the set of even numbers between 3 and 9.
9. D is the set of odd numbers between 10 and 20.
10. E is the set of days of the week whose names begin with T.

Stress the fact that *well-defined* has to do with telling others about a set. For example, if a person was living alone, {nice animals} would be defined well enough. However, two or more people are likely not to agree on the elements of such a set.

Sets which are well-defined for one group of students may not be well-defined for another group. For example, some students may want to say the spider is an insect, while others with more training in biology may insist that the spider is not an insect.

If such arguments arise among students, use the arguments to further emphasize the fact that *well-defined* has to do with people agreeing on elements of a set.

Sets should be clearly defined, or *well-defined*. This means that the description of the set should be such that people agree on which elements are in the set and which elements are not.

Write *yes* if you think people would agree on which elements are in each set. Write *no* if you think they would not agree.

11. The set of all insects
12. The set of all large numbers
13. The set of all even counting numbers larger than 1,000,000
14. The set of all excellent singers who weigh more than 100 pounds
15. The set of all small numbers between 0 and 1

16. Arrange the shapes in the following figure in sets according to the number of sides of each shape.

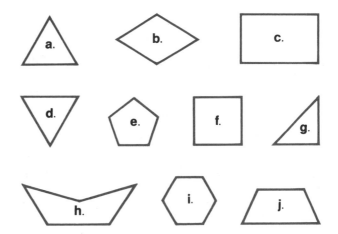

Write each new set described in Exercises **17–20** where S = {1, 2, 3, 4, 5}.

17. List the set A whose members are found by doubling each member of S.
18. List the set B of even numbers in S.
19. List the set C of the least and the greatest numbers in S.
20. List the set D whose members are found by multiplying each member of S by 5 and then subtracting 5.

Use sets A, B, and C in the following exercises.

A = {1, 2, 3, 4, 5}   B = {3, 6, 9, . . . , 99}
C = {5, 10, 15, . . .}

Replace each ___?___ with ∈ or ∉ to make a true statement.

21. 5 ___?___ A   **22.** 15 ___?___ B   **23.** 300 ___?___ B
24. 5 ___?___ B   **25.** 15 ___?___ C   **26.** 300 ___?___ C
27. Which element of A also belongs to B?
28. Which element of A also belongs to C?
29. Which elements of A do not belong to B or C?
30. Which elements of B also belong to C?

1-2

Set
Relationships

Two sets are **equal** if they have the same elements. The equal sign, =, is used to indicate that two sets are equal.

EXAMPLE

$\{a, b, c, d\}$ = {the first four letters of the alphabet}

When the listing method is used, the order of listing does not matter.

EXAMPLES

Emphasize the fact that listing an element more than once does not change the set. For example, if the catcher's name were recorded twice in a line-up, it would not change the team's membership.

1. $\{x, y, z\} = \{z, x, y\}$
2. {John, Pete, Mary, Ruth} = {Mary, Ruth, Pete, John}

In deciding which elements are in a set, only distinct elements matter. Listing the same element more than once does not change the set.

EXAMPLES

1. $\{x, y, x, z, z\} = \{x, y, z\}$
2. $\{3, 4, 5, 7\} = \{3, 1 + 4, 7, 2 + 2, 4 + 3, 5, 3\}$

Note that there is just one empty set, but that there are many ways to describe it.

There is a set which has no elements. This set is called the **empty set**. Since it has no elements to be listed, it is often symbolized { }. Another symbol for the empty set is $\varnothing$.

EXAMPLES

1. $\varnothing$ = {people in your class over 10 feet tall}
2. { } = {whole numbers between 1 and 6 which are divisible by 8}

For example, {whole numbers which cannot be used as divisors} = {0} is clearly not the empty set.

Do not confuse {0} with { }. {0} is a set which has one member, namely zero. Therefore, {0} is not the empty set.

Set B is a **subset** of set A if every element of B is also an element of A. Another way of saying this is that B is contained in A.

EXAMPLES

1. {3, 7, 11} is a subset of {1, 3, 5, 7, 11, 13}
2. {3, 7, 11} is contained in {1, 3, 5, 7, 11, 13}

The symbol $\subseteq$ means *is a subset of*. The symbol $\not\subseteq$ means *is not a subset of*.

EXAMPLES

1. $\{3, 7, 11\} \subseteq \{1, 3, 5, 7, 11, 13\}$
2. $\{2, 7, 11\} \not\subseteq \{1, 3, 5, 7, 11, 13\}$

3. $\{w, x, y, z\} \not\subseteq \{x, y, z\}$

4. $\{x\} \subseteq \{x, y, z\}$

Students might think that saying $\phi \subseteq S$ makes no sense. To help them see that it does, define sets A, B, C and S as follows.

EXAMPLE

A = {people over 4 feet tall}
B = {people over 8 feet tall}
C = {people over 12 feet tall}
S = {people}
Then ask if A $\subseteq$ S, B $\subseteq$ S, and C $\subseteq$ S. (By the way, B $\neq$ ϕ, but it is *perhaps* the case that C = ϕ.)

EXAMPLE

No matter what a set happens to be, every member of that set is a member of that set. This means that for every set S, S $\subseteq$ S.

$$\{x, y, z\} \subseteq \{x, y, z\}$$

It is agreed that for every set S, $\varnothing \subseteq$ S. That is, the empty set is a subset of every set. When listing all the possible subsets of a set S, be sure to list $\varnothing$ and S as subsets.

List all the subsets of $\{a, b\}$.

$\{ \ \}, \{a\}, \{b\}$, and $\{a, b\}$

EXERCISES

1. {2, 4, 6} = {4, 2, 6}; {y, x} = {x, y, x, y}; {1, 3, 5, 7} = {first four odd numbers}; {1, 4, 9, 16} = {1 • 1, 2 • 2, 3 • 3, 4 • 4}; {vowels in the English alphabet} = {u, e, i, o, u, a, e} **2.** A = C, B = E, D = F **3.** Y = {P, A, R, E, L}, Yes **4.** ϕ **5.** 10 **6.** The line segment with endpoints on the vertex and the base edge. **7.** ϕ **8.** {0}

1. Find pairs of equal sets. Write them as $\{p, q, r, s\} = \{s, p, r, q\}$.
$\{2, 4, 6\}$, $\{y, x\}$, $\{1, 3, 5, 7\}$, $\{x, y, x, y\}$, $\{1, 4, 9, 16\}$, {vowels in the English alphabet}, $\{2, 6\}$, $\{4, 2, 6\}$, $\{x, y, z\}$, {first four odd numbers}, $\{1 \cdot 1, 2 \cdot 2, 3 \cdot 3, 4 \cdot 4\}$, $\{u, e, i, o, u, a, e\}$

2. Find pairs of equal sets. Write them as Q = R.
A = $\{0, 1, 2, 3, 4, 5\}$
B = {whole numbers from 1 to 6 inclusive}
C = $\{5, 3, 1, 0, 2, 4\}$
D = {even numbers between 1 and 7}
E = {numbers on a die}
F = $\{2 \cdot 1, 2 \cdot 2, 2 \cdot 3\}$

3. X = {letters in the word REPEAL} = {R, E, P, A, L}
List the set Y of letters in the word PARALLEL. Is X = Y?

For each set, write $\varnothing$ if the set is the empty set. Name one element of the set if it is not the empty set.

4. The set of odd numbers which are divisible by 2

5. The set of even numbers which are divisible by 5

6. The set of straight line segments that can be drawn on the surface of a cone

7. The set of straight lines that can be drawn on a sphere

8. The set containing the number 0 as its only member

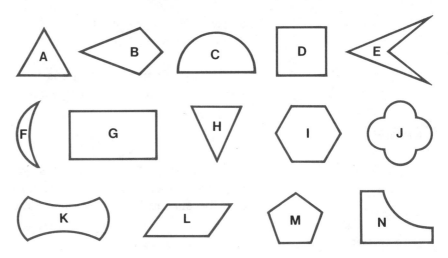

The diagram shows a set S of shapes with straight and curved sides. Use the capital letters to list the members of each subset of S described in Exercises **9–16.**

9. Members of S with straight sides only
10. Members of S with exactly three straight sides
11. Members of S with more than four straight sides
12. Members of S with curved sides only
13. Members of S with exactly two curved sides
14. Members of S with more than two curved sides
15. Members of S with some straight and some curved sides
16. Members of S with eight straight sides

List each subset of A = {1, 3, 5, 7, 9} described in Exercises **17–20.**

17. The set of prime numbers in A
18. The set of numbers in A divisible by 3
19. The set of numbers in A divisible by 2
20. The set of numbers in A greater than 5

Write true (T) or false (F) for each statement.

21. {2, 3} ⊆ {2, 3, 4}   **22.** {2, 3, 4} ⊆ {2, 3}
23. {a, b, c} ⊆ {x, y, z}   **24.** {a, b, c} ⊆ {a, b, c}
25. {0} ⊆ {0, 100}   **26.** {x, y} has four subsets
27. { } ⊆ {a, b, c}   **28.** {motor cars} ⊆ {all road vehicles}

List all the subsets of each set. Remember that for any set S, S ⊆ S and ∅ ⊆ S.

29. {p}   **30.** {p, q}   **31.** {p, q, r}   **32.** {p, q, r, s}

33.

Number of Members in Set	Subsets
1	2
2	4
3	8
4	16
5	32
10	1024

34. a, d, e, f

33. Copy this table. Use the results of Exercises **29–32** to complete it.

Set	Number of Members in Set	Number of Subsets
{p}	?	?
{p, q}	?	?
{p, q, r}	?	?
{p, q, r, s}	?	?
{p, q, r, s, t}	?	?
{p, q, . . . , x, y}	10	?

34. Which statements are true?

a. $2 \in \{1, 2, 3\}$ b. $2 \subseteq \{1, 2, 3\}$

c. $\{2\} \in \{1, 2, 3\}$ d. $\{2\} \subseteq \{1, 2, 3\}$

e. $\{2\} \subseteq \{2\}$ f. $2 \in \{2\}$

Excursions in Mathematics:
Length in the Metric System

The mathematics used in everyday situations often deals with measurement. The unit of measurement chosen depends on what is being measured and what is to be done with that measurement.

Many different units of measurement are used in the world. The most widely used system of measurement is the **metric system.** In this system, the basic unit for length is the **meter.**

The meter was used first in France in 1790. It was defined to be one ten-millionth of the distance along a meridian from the North Pole to the Equator. A bar indicating one meter is kept as a standard in most countries. Now the meter is measured in terms of the wavelength of the orange-red line of the krypton gas spectrum. One meter is defined as 1,650,764 times this wavelength.

Units in the metric system are named by adding a prefix to the name of the basic unit. This prefix gives the value of the new unit.

Unit		Meaning
*milli*meter	(mm)	a thousandth of 1 meter
*centi*meter	(cm)	a hundredth of 1 meter
*deci*meter	(dm)	a tenth of 1 meter
meter	(m)	1 meter
*deka*meter	(dkm)	ten times 1 meter
*hecto*meter	(hm)	one hundred times 1 meter
*kilo*meter	(km)	one thousand times 1 meter
*mega*meter	(Mm)	one million times 1 meter

The following diagram shows the basic relations between the more commonly used metric units of length.

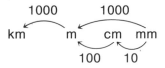

EXERCISES

1. Draw a line segment of each length. Use a meter stick or metric ruler to do this.
   a. 8 cm **b.** 17 mm **c.** 3 mm **d.** 2 cm 3 mm **e.** 10 cm 1 mm

Name the metric unit of length you would use to measure each object.

2. The distance between New York City and Washington, D.C.

3. The sleeve length of a coat

4. The inside diameter of a rifle barrel

5. The distance around a football field

6. The length of a pencil

7. The length and width of this book

8. Draw a line segment 1 inch long. Measure it in centimeters and millimeters.

9. Find the perimeter of each rectangle. The perimeter is the distance around the rectangle.

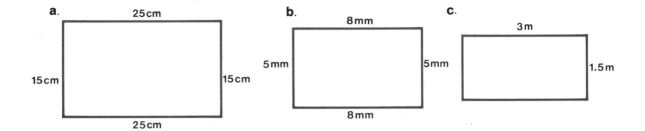

a. 25cm / 15cm / 25cm / 15cm

b. 8mm / 5mm / 15cm / 8mm

c. 3m / 5mm / 1.5m

10. 138.5 cm **11.** 1034.3 m
12. 3.150 m by 1.250 m
13. 6600 mm = 660 cm
14. 285 cm, 58 **15.** 15 **16.** .6 cm
or 6 mm **17.** 194.4 km **18.** 100
19. a. 100 **b.** 100 **c.** 100 **d.** 100
e. 100 **f.** 100 **20.** .91 cm²
21. 2.4 cm **22.** 576 mm²

10. A window is 1 m 38.5 cm wide. Express this in centimeters.

11. The distance a student has to walk to school each morning is 1 km 34.3 m. How many meters is this?

12. On a blueprint, a door is marked 3150 mm high and 1250 mm wide. What are its dimensions in meters?

13. A certain wavelength is 330 mm. Find the length of 20 waves. Express your answer in mm and then in cm.

14. Some books are 19 cm long. If 15 of them are placed end-to-end, how far will they reach? If a line of books reaches 11 m 2 cm, how many books are there?

15. How many pieces of wire 3.6 cm long can be cut from 54 cm of the wire?

16. In a month of 30 days, the total rainfall was 18 cm. What was the average daily rainfall?

17. A motorist travels 236.5 km, 168.7 km, 97.6 km, and 302.8 km. How much farther does he have to travel to complete a total distance of 1000 km?

18. Draw a square with each side 1 cm long. The area of this square is 1 square centimeter, or 1 cm². Divide each side into mm and connect the mm marks with line segments. Each small square formed is 1 mm by 1 mm, or 1 mm². How many 1 mm-squares are in the larger square?

19. Copy and complete each statement.

   a. ____?____ mm² = 1 cm²   **b.** ____?____ cm² = 1 m²
   c. ____?____ m² = 1 km²   **d.** __?__ mm² = 1 m²

20. If the length of a rectangle is .7 cm and the width is 1.3 cm, find the area of the rectangle. (Area = length times width)

21. A rectangle has area 10.8 cm² and length 4.5 cm. Find its width.

22. Find the area in mm² of a square with a side 2 cm 4 mm long. (The area of a square is equal to the length of a side times itself.)

1-3
Sets of
Numbers

OBJECTIVES:

1. To interpret and use the number line.
2. To recognize which elements are contained in the more common subsets of the integers.

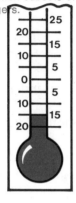

One of your first experiences with numbers was learning to count. You were using **the set of natural numbers,** {1, 2, 3, 4, 5, . . .}. In this book the letter N is used to name the set of natural numbers.

Later on you also worked with zero, which gave you another set of numbers. You then knew about **the set of whole numbers,** {0, 1, 2, 3, 4, 5, . . .}. In this book the letter W is used to name the set of whole numbers.

On a cold day the thermometer may read ''15,'' but it may be below zero. There are two points on the thermometer which use the numeral 15, but they do not represent the same temperature. When you want to say the temperature is 15 *below zero,* you may use a negative sign. The thermometer reading in the figure is $^-15$.

The emphasis in this section is to introduce negative numbers by using familiar examples.

Point out that the thermometer may be thought of as a segment of number line rotated to a vertical position. This will allow slow students to ''think temperatures'' when first working with number line representations of negative numbers.

People sometimes overdraw their checking accounts. If someone had $10.00 in an account and then wrote a check for $18.00, his or her new balance would be $^-8$ dollars.

The set written as {. . . , $^-5$, $^-4$, $^-3$, $^-2$, $^-1$, 0, 1, 2, 3, 4, 5, . . .} is called **the set of integers.** In this book, the letter Z is used to name the set of integers.

The sets N, W, and Z may be pictured on a number line. Here is the way to draw a *number line.*

1. Represent a straight line on paper.

2. Choose a point on the line and name it zero.

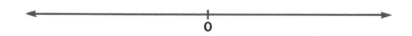

3. Choose some length and call it the *unit length*.

4. Name the point one unit length to the right of zero "1;" name the point two unit lengths to the right of zero "2;" and so on.

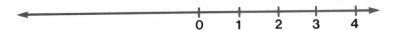

To read " −2" aloud, have students say either "minus 2" or "negative 2."

Some teachers find that allowing students to say "minus 2" tends to cause confusion with subtraction. It is completely acceptable to insist that students always say "negative 2" when being introduced to the negative number idea. However, at some point all students should be told that they probably will hear both readings.

5. Name the point one unit length to the left of zero "⁻1;" name the point two unit lengths to the left of zero "⁻2;" and so on.

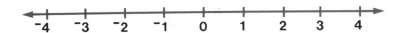

The arrows at the ends of the number line mean that you should think of the line as going on in both directions.

The dots in the three figures show the set of natural numbers, the set of whole numbers, and the set of integers, respectively.

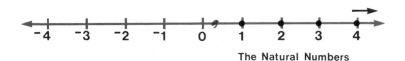

The Natural Numbers

The Whole Numbers

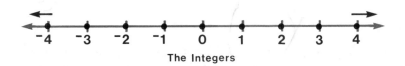

The Integers

The arrows indicate that the sets of points continue without ending in the direction shown.

Remember that every natural number is also a whole number. Every whole number is also an integer. This relationship may be stated in another way.

$$N \subseteq W \subseteq Z$$

EXERCISES

For each statement write true (T) or false (F).

1. $0 \in Z$ **2.** $0 \in N$ **3.** $^{-}3 \notin W$

4. $^{-}3 \notin Z$ **5.** $Z \subseteq W$ **6.** $N \subseteq Z$

7. $\frac{1}{3} \in Z$ **8.** $N \in W$

For Exercises **9–20,** write *yes* if it could make sense to answer the question with a negative number. Write *no* if it could not make sense to answer with a negative number.

9. What was the population of Chicago in 1937?

10. What is the record low temperature for International Falls, Minnesota?

11. What is the altitude of the lowest point in Death Valley, California?

12. How many auto accidents occurred on Christmas day last year in the United States?

13. How many sets of quintuplets were born in 1845?

14. How many days last year had temperatures below $^{-}15$ in Cut Bank, Montana?

15. In what year did the Egyptians begin building their first pyramid?

16. How much money did Greta Wildcat make playing the stock market today?

17. Compared to par, what was Henry Jackson's golf score?

18. On which floor of the new bank building is the furnace located?

19. How many accounts at the First National Bank were overdrawn on January 1?

20. How many small businesses in the United States declared bankruptcy in 1974?

1-4
The Set of Real Numbers

OBJECTIVE:

To state that there is a 1-1 correspondence between the real numbers and points on the number line.

Most work with fractions in elementary school was with whole numbers as numerators and denominators. Zero, of course, could not be used as a denominator.

On a number line, $\frac{3}{2}$ names the point midway between 1 and 2.

The point named by $\frac{9}{3}$ is also named by the numeral 3.

You also may work with fractions which name numbers less than zero. The fraction $^{-}\left(\frac{7}{3}\right)$ names the point seven thirds of a unit to the left of zero.

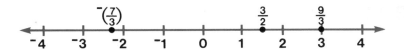

Forms $\dfrac{-m}{n}, \dfrac{m}{-n}, \dfrac{-m}{-n}$ etc. will come later in the course. The purpose of this section is simply to complete the assignment of numbers to points on the number line. Using only the form $^{-}\left(\dfrac{m}{n}\right)$ for introductory purposes allows students to see "length" and "direction" more easily when matching number names to points on the number line.

You now are considering all numbers which can be written as $\dfrac{m}{n}$ or $^{-}\left(\dfrac{m}{n}\right)$ where $m \in$ W and $n \in$ N. The set of all such numbers is called **the set of rational numbers.** In this book, the letter Q is used to name the set of rational numbers.

Remember that each integer is also a rational number. For example, 4 may be written as $\dfrac{4}{1}$, and $^{-}3$ may be written as $^{-}\left(\dfrac{6}{2}\right)$.

The special sets of numbers N, W, Z, and Q are related in a certain way.

$$N \subseteq W \subseteq Z \subseteq Q$$

Imagine that while blindfolded you are asked to pick some point on the number line.

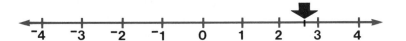

At this stage in the course, it is acceptable to leave the irrational numbers as a thing of amazement. It may be helpful for some students to name a few irrational numbers such as π and $\sqrt{2}$. It may be in order to tell students that in real life the rational numbers are used almost exclusively. For example $\dfrac{22}{7}$, 3.1416, etc. may be good enough for π, but are not exact.

Could you be absolutely sure that the point is a rational number? The answer is no. There are points on the number line which cannot be named by rational numbers. The numbers corresponding to these mysterious points are called *irrational numbers*. There are many such points. In fact, between any two rational numbers there are many such points.

You need another set if you are to have numbers for naming every point on the number line. This set of numbers is called the set of real numbers. In this book, the letter R is used to name **the set of real numbers.** To picture the real numbers, think of *all* points on the number line.

The special sets of numbers N, W, Z, Q, and R are related in the following way.

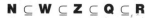

N $\subseteq$ W $\subseteq$ Z $\subseteq$ Q $\subseteq$ R

EXERCISES

1. T 2. T 3. F 4. T 5. T 6. F
7. F 8. F 9. N 10. Z 11. N 12. N
13. W 14. W 15. R 16. N 17. R
18. Q 19. R 20. R 21. N

Write true (T) or false (F) for each statement.

1. $0 \in R$

2. $^-\left(\dfrac{4}{3}\right) \in R$

3. $^-\left(\dfrac{2}{3}\right) \in Z$

4. $\dfrac{12}{2} \in N$

5. $N \subseteq Q$

6. $R \subseteq Q$

7. $N \in R$

8. $Q = R$

In the following statements, the letter m stands for the real number which makes the statement true. For each statement, name the *first* of N, W, Z, Q, and R which, for certain, contains m as an element.

9. $m + 2 = 5$

10. $8 - 10 = m$ Hint: Think of writing a $10 check on an $8 balance.

11. $2 \cdot m = 2$

12. $2 \cdot 2 = m$

13. $2 \cdot m = 0$

14. $2 \cdot m = m$

15. $m \cdot m = 2$

16. To the *nearest whole millimeter,* you are m millimeters tall.

17. You are *exactly* m millimeters tall.

18. Milk is priced at *exactly* m dollars per half gallon today.

19. The lowest point in Death Valley has an altitude of *exactly* m feet compared to sea level.

20. The lowest temperature ever reached in Lincoln, Nebraska, is *exactly* m degrees Fahrenheit.

21. The largest number of live goldfish ever swallowed by a person in one day is m.

There may be a student who will claim that the answer to Exercise 21 is R by suggesting various unpleasantries. (At least that student grasps the concept.) In such case, either insist on whole fish only, or allow R to be correct. Often a good deal of learning results from such discussions while also affording the class a good time.

Excursions in Mathematics:
The Fantastic Voyage

An inventor claims to have plans for a rocket with a marvelous engine. It gains speed (accelerates) for one hour.

In the first $\dfrac{1}{2}$ hour it goes one foot.

In the next $\dfrac{1}{4}$ hour it goes another foot.

In the next $\dfrac{1}{8}$ hour it goes another foot.

In the next $\dfrac{1}{16}$ hour it goes another foot,

and so on.

In general, each foot of distance the rocket travels after the first foot takes just half as much time as the foot before. How far will the rocket have traveled at the end of one hour?

1-5
Venn Diagrams

OBJECTIVES:

1. To state that universal set does not mean *all possible* elements.
2. To name a universal set given several sets which must be contained by it.

Strongly emphasize the fact that *universal set* means "the set of elements we are willing to consider at this time."

EXAMPLE

Some students may protest that studying things like the universal set is worthless. In that case, assure them that the concept will be useful when they give solutions to open sentences. As an example, ask which numbers make $x < 3$ a true statement. The answer, of course, will depend on whether U is defined to be N, W, Z, Q, R or some other set.

EXAMPLE

In mathematics, the set of all elements being considered is called a ***universe,*** or ***universal set.*** It is usually named by the letter U.

This item might be on a quiz.

_____ is a city on Lake Michigan.
(Choose one of the following: New York, Seattle, Chicago, Dallas.)

The student who ignores the four choices and writes Milwaukee in the blank probably will not get credit. Milwaukee is not one of the cities being considered. The universal set for the quiz item is {New York, Seattle, Chicago, Dallas}.

For any situation, there are usually many possible universal sets.

For the set {0, 2, 4, 6}, any of the following could be a universal set, U.

{even numbers}
{whole numbers}
{0, 2, 4, 6, 8}

A useful method of picturing sets uses a rectangle which you may think of as a fence enclosing all the members of the universal set. When dots are used to represent the members, they should be labeled.

Show U = {1, 2, 3, 4, 5, 6, 7, 8, 9}.

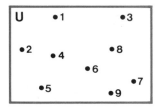

A subset of the universal set is shown by drawing a closed curve around the dots representing its members.

EXAMPLE

The purpose of including Venn diagrams is to provide picture definitions for terms. The purpose is not to teach conventions on using Venn diagrams.

Show the subset A = {4, 6, 8} of the preceding universal set.

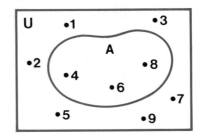

When the number of elements in a universe is large, the dots often are omitted from the diagram.

EXAMPLE

The basic idea of using bounded regions to define sets will come up again with graphing solutions to inequations and systems of inequations. For example, the solution set for $y = x$ and $y = x^2$ is a region in the plane. Therefore, it is useful that students become acquainted with the idea of picturing sets by defining regions.

Draw a diagram for U = {students in your town}, P = {students in your school}, and Q = {students in your class}.

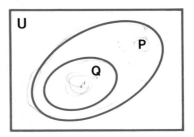

It is important to remember that a closed curve may show the empty set. In that case, all elements in the universe are outside the enclosed area.

EXAMPLE

Show U = {a, b, c, d, e} and A = ∅.

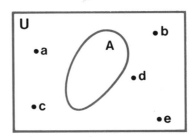

Diagrams of sets such as those in the preceding examples are called **Venn diagrams.**

EXERCISES

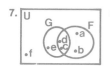

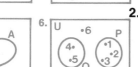

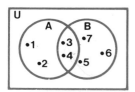

1. Consider {2, 4, 6, 8, . . .}, {4, 8, 12, 16, . . .}, and {8, 16, 24, 32, . . .}. Which of the following may serve as universal sets for all three sets being considered?
A = {even numbers}   B = {odd numbers}
C = {counting numbers}   D = {2, 4, 6, 8, 10, . . .}

2. Consider {10, 20, 30, 40, . . .}, {1, 2, 3}, and {2, 4, 6, 8, . . .}. Which of the following may serve as universal sets?
A = {even numbers}   B = {numbers less than 50}
C = {counting numbers}   D = ∅

Draw a Venn diagram for each situation. Use labeled dots to represent the members of the sets.

3. U = {vowels in the English alphabet},
   A = {the first three vowels}

4. U = {whole numbers from 1 to 9},
   C = {even numbers between 1 and 9}

Illustrate each situation with a Venn diagram.

5. U = {whole numbers}, A = {odd numbers}

6. U = {1, 2, 3, 4, 5, 6}, P = {1, 2, 3}, Q = {4, 5}

7. U = {a, b, c, d, e, f}, F = {a, b, c, d}, G = {c, d, e}

8. U = {0, 1, 2, 3, 4}, M = {1, 2, 3}, S = {2}

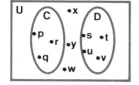

From the figure, list the members of each set in Exercises **9–13.**

9. Set A   **10.** Set B

11. The set of elements that belong to both A and B

12. The set of elements that belong to either A or B (or both A and B)

13. The set of elements that do not belong to A or B

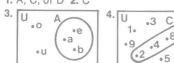

From the figure, list the members of each set in Exercises **14–18.**

14. Set C   **15.** Set D

16. The set of elements that belong to both C and D

17. The set of elements that belong to either C or D (or both C and D)

18. The set of elements that do not belong to C or D

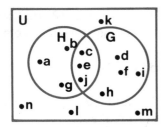

In the figure, U = {students selected from a senior class}, H = {students who like history}, and G = {students who like geography}. Each letter represents a student.

19. 6 20. 7 21. 3 22. 3 23. 4
24. 4 25. 14 26. b 27. c 28. d
29. a 30. d

19. How many students like history?
20. How many students like geography?
21. How many students like both history and geography?
22. How many students like history but not geography?
23. How many students like geography but not history?
24. How many students like neither history nor geography?
25. How many students are in U altogether?

Match each pair of sets in Exercises **26–30** with one of the following Venn diagrams. U is the set of whole numbers.

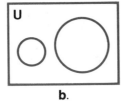

b.

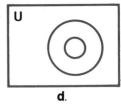

d.

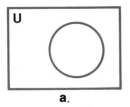

a.

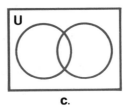

c.

26. A = {even numbers}, B = {odd numbers}
27. A = {even numbers}, P = {prime numbers}
28. D = {multiples of 2}, F = {multiples of 4}
29. S = {numbers divisible by 2 and by 5},
    T = {numbers divisible by 10}
30. M = {squares of whole numbers},
    N = {squares of natural numbers}

Excursions in Mathematics:
Mass in the Metric System

The basic unit for mass in the metric system is the ***kilogram.*** A gram is too small to use conveniently. However, each unit for mass is named by adding the necessary prefix to the base word gram.

Unit		Meaning
*milli*gram	(mg)	a thousandth of 1 gram
*centi*gram	(cg)	a hundredth of 1 gram
*deci*gram	(dg)	a tenth of 1 gram
gram	(g)	1 gram
*deka*gram	(dkg)	ten times 1 gram
*hecto*gram	(hg)	one hundred times 1 gram
*kilo*gram	(kg)	one thousand times 1 gram
*mega*gram	(Mg)	one million times 1 gram

The following diagram shows the basic relations between the most often encountered metric units of mass.

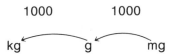

The gram is a very small measure of mass. One gram is about .04 ounce. For this reason, kilograms are used more frequently.

EXERCISES

1. g **2.** Mg **3.** kg **4.** kg
5. 2486 g **6. a.** 15.5 Mg **b.** 372 Mg

Name the metric unit you would use to measure each item.
1. Weight of a letter to be mailed
2. Mass of a truck
3. Mass of this book
4. Your weight

5. A brick weighs 2 kg 486 g. How many grams is this?
6. A railroad car can carry 15,500 kg.
   a. How many megagrams is this?
   b. How many megagrams can a train with 24 such cars carry?

7. The mass of the hammer that is used in international athletic matches is 7 kg 257 g. Express this mass in kg.

8. A box contains 72 cans of vegetables. Each can weighs 225 grams. Find the total mass of the cans in the box in kilograms.

9. A truck can carry 2500 kg. How many trips must it make to transport 18 megagrams?

10. A bin in a school kitchen contains 6.4 kg of flour. One recipe uses 160 g of flour. How many times can the recipe be made if all the flour is used?

11. A carton contains 144 cans of soup. Each can weighs 61.2 kg. Disregarding the mass of the carton, how much does each can of soup weigh in g?

12. One coin weighs .6 dg. How many cg will 200 coins weigh? How many g? How many kg?

13. Find the cost of 40 hg of candy if 1 kg costs $2.00.

14. Find the difference in price per gram of 40 dkg of tea at $.48 or 1 kg at $1.44.

1-6
Intersections and Unions

OBJECTIVE:

To identify unions and intersections of given well-defined sets.

EXAMPLES

The **intersection** of two sets A and B is the set of elements that are members of A and also members of B. The symbol ∩ is used to mean intersection. The phrase A ∩ B sometimes is read *A intersect B*.

1. If A = {p, q, r, s} and B = {r, s, t}, then A ∩ B = {r, s}.
2. If U = {whole numbers}, X = {prime numbers less than 12}, and Y = {odd numbers between 2 and 8}, then X ∩ Y = {3, 5, 7}.

Venn diagrams may be used to show set intersection. The shaded portion of the diagram shows A ∩ B.

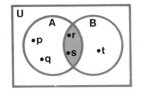

If the sets have no elements in common, they are said to be *disjoint*.

The **union** of two sets A and B is the set of elements that are either in A or in B or in both A and B. The symbol ∪ is used to mean *union*.

EXERCISES

1. If A = {p, q, r, s} and B = {r, s, t}, then A ∪ B = {p, q, r, s, t}.
2. If R = {10, 20, 30, . . .} and S = {5, 15, 25, . . .}, then R ∪ S = {5, 10, 15, 20, 25, 30, . . .}.

R ∪ S is sometimes read *R union S*. The shaded portion of the Venn diagram shows A ∪ B.

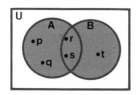

The goal here is merely to establish the basic concepts.

1. List A ∩ B and A ∩ C if A = {first five odd numbers}, B = {7, 9, 11}, and C = {1, 2, 3, 4}.

1. {7, 9}; {1, 3} 2. {2}; {2, 3, 5, 7, 11} or D

2. List D ∩ F and D ∩ W if D = {prime numbers less than 12}, F = {even numbers less than 12}, and W = {whole numbers}.

3. A ∩ B = {3, 4}

3. List the sets A ∩ B, B ∩ C, A ∩ C, and U ∩ B if U = {1, 2, 3, 4, 5, 6}, A = {1, 2, 3, 4}, B = {3, 4, 5}, and C = {5}. Show each intersection (use shading) in a separate Venn diagram.

B ∩ C = {5}

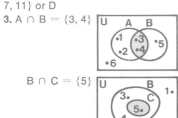

4. Copy each diagram and shade the regions that represent the given intersections.

A ∩ C = φ

U ∩ B = {3, 4, 5}

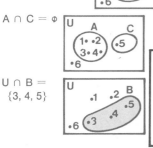

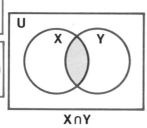

X∩Y

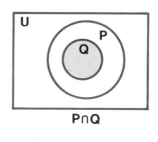

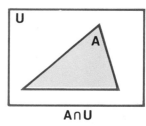

PnQ

AnU

5.
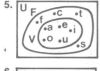

6.
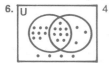

7.
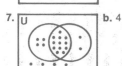
b. 4

5. Show V ∩ F in a Venn diagram if V = {vowels} and F = {f, a, c, e, t, i, o, u, s}.

6. Of 25 people, 18 like pop music, 13 like classical music, and 10 like both. Illustrate these facts in a Venn diagram. How many people do not like either pop or classical music?

7. There are 20 students in a class. Sixteen of them study physics, 14 study chemistry, and 12 study both physics and chemistry.
a. Draw a Venn diagram for this information.
b. Find the number of students in the class who do not study either physics or chemistry.

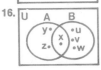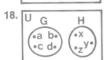
8. Write as a single set.
  a. {1, 3, 4, 7} ∩ {3, 5} ∩ {3, 9}
  b. {p, q, r} ∩ {p, r, s, t} ∩ {m, n, p, r, s}

Let P = {factors of 24} = {1, 2, 3, 4, 6, 8, 12, 24} in Exercises 9–11.
  9. List the set Q of factors of 36.
  10. List P ∩ Q.
  11. State the largest factor of both 24 and 36.

12. N is the set of natural numbers, W the set of whole numbers, Z the set of integers, Q the set of rational numbers, and R the set of real numbers.
  a. Using R as the universe, draw a Venn diagram to show N, W, Z, and Q.
  b. Use a single letter to indicate each intersection.
    (1) N ∩ W   **(2)** W ∩ Z
    (3) Z ∩ Q   **(4)** N ∩ W ∩ Z
    (5) W ∩ Z ∩ Q   **(6)** N ∩ W ∩ Z ∩ Q
  c. If S is the set of irrational numbers, what is S ∩ Q? What is R ∩ S?

13. A = {first five odd numbers}, B = {7, 9, 11}, C = {1, 2, 3, 4}. List A ∪ B and A ∪ C.

14. D = {prime numbers less than 12},
    F = {even numbers less than 12},
    W = {whole numbers}. Find D ∪ F and D ∪ W.

15. A = {a, b, c}, B = {a, b, c, d, e}, C = {x, y, z},
    D = {letters of the alphabet}, E = {2, 4, 6, 8, . . .},
    F = {1, 2, 3, 4, . . .}.
  a. Find A ∪ B, A ∩ B, C ∪ D, C ∩ D, E ∪ F, and E ∩ F.
  b. Let S and T be any sets. Look at the intersections and unions in Part **a.** Write a statement for finding S ∪ T and S ∩ T if S ⊆ T.
  c. Draw separate Venn diagrams to show S ∪ T and S ∩ T when S ⊆ T.

Draw a Venn diagram to picture each pair of sets.
  16. A = {x, y, z}, B = {u, v, w, x}
  17. C = {1, 2, 3, 4}, D = {2, 3, 4, 5}
  18. G = {a, b, c, d}, H = {x, y, z}

19. a. Copy this table and fill in the missing numbers. Use the sets in Exercises **16–18.**

Sets	Number of Elements in First Set	Number of Elements in Second Set	Number of Elements in Intersection	Number of Elements in Union
A, B	3	4	1	6
C, D	?$_4$	?$_4$	?$_3$	?$_5$
G, H	?$_4$	?$_3$	?$_0$	?$_7$

b. Study the Venn diagrams in Exercises **16–18** and the table in Part **a.** Replace each ___?___ with a number to make a true statement.

(1) If S has 4 elements, T has 5 elements, and S ∩ T has 2 elements, then S ∪ T will have ___?___ elements.

(2) If S has 7 elements, T has 8 elements, and S ∪ T has 10 elements, then S ∩ T will have ___?___ elements.

(3) If S has 6 elements, S ∩ T has 2 elements, and S ∪ T has 8 elements, T will have ___?___ elements.

(4) If S ∪ T has 10 elements, S has 6 elements, and T has 4 elements, S ∩ T will have ___?___ elements.

20. Use the letters N, W, Z, and Q to represent the special subsets of the real numbers, R.

a. Use a single letter to indicate the union.

(1) N ∪ W   **(2)** W ∪ Z   **(3)** Z ∪ Q
(4) N ∪ W ∪ Z   **(5)** W ∪ Z ∪ Q   **(6)** N ∪ W ∪ Z ∪ Q

b. If S is the set of irrational numbers, what is S ∪ Q? What is R ∪ S?

Chapter Summary

1. A set may be thought of as a collection of objects called elements or members. Elements are said to belong to the set.

2. Sets may be described by the listing or roster method.

3.

Symbol	Meaning
{ }	*the set of*
. . .	*and so on*
∈	*is an element of*
∉	*is not an element of*
⊆	*is a subset of*
⊄	*is not a subset of*
∅	*the empty set,* that is, the set with no members

4. Two sets are equal if they have the same elements.

5. Set B is a subset of set A if every element of B is also an element of A.

6. For every set S, S ⊆ S and ∅ ⊆ S.

7. N = {natural numbers} = {1, 2, 3, 4, 5, . . .}

8. W = {whole numbers} = {0, 1, 2, 3, 4, . . .}

9. Z = {integers} = {. . . −3, −2, −1, 0, 1, 2, 3, . . .}

10. Q = {rational numbers}

11. R = {real numbers}

12. N ⊆ W ⊆ Z ⊆ Q ⊆ R

13. The set of all elements being considered is called a universe, or universal set.

14. Sets, subsets, and set relationships may be illustrated in Venn diagrams. The universal set is illustrated as a rectangle. Subsets of the universal set are shown by closed curves.

15. The intersection of two sets A and B is the set of elements that are members of A and also members of B. The symbol ∩ is used to mean intersection.

16. The union of two sets A and B is the set of elements that are either in A or in B or in both A and B. The symbol ∪ is used to mean union.

REVIEW EXERCISES   1-1

1. {January, February, May, July} 2. {2, 3, 5, 7, 11, 13, 17, 19, 23, 29}

Use the listing method to describe each set.

1. A is the set of months ending in the letter y.

2. B is the set of the first ten prime numbers.

3. C is the set of letters of the alphabet between k and r.

4. D is the set of odd numbers greater than 20 but less than 30.

1-2

Use set notation to rewrite each of the following.

5. 3 is a member of W.

6. The empty set

7. x does not belong to A.

8. S is a subset of T.

9. The set P is equal to the set Q.

Write true (T) or false (F) for each statement.

10. 2 ∈ {prime numbers}

11. {x, y, z} = {p, q, r}

12. {0} is the empty set.

13. {k, l, m, n} = {m, l, k, n}

14. If A = {whole numbers greater than 50}, then 46 ∉ A.

1-3

15. Z ⊆ N   **16.** −2 ∈ W   **17.** $\frac{1}{2}$ ∉ Z

18. 0 ∈ W   **19.** Q ⊆ R   **20.** $\frac{1}{4}$ ∉ R

21. N ⊆ Q ⊆ R   **22.** R ⊄ Z

List each subset of S = {1, 2, 3, . . . , 10}.

23. The set of prime numbers in S

24. The set of odd numbers in S less than 10

25. The set of numbers in S which are factors of 70

26. The set of numbers in S which are divisible by 3

1-5

Match each Venn diagram with a sentence.

    a. A ⊆ B

    b. A = B

    c. B ⊆ A

    d. A ∩ B = ∅

27.
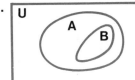

28.
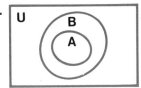

29.
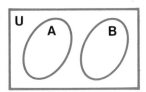

30.

31. U = {a, b, c, d, e, f, g}, P = {a, b, c}, and T = {c, b, e, d}
  a. List P ∩ T and P ∪ T.
  b. Draw a Venn diagram showing the relation between the sets. Show on your diagram the elements belonging to each set.
  c. Which elements of U do not belong to P or T?

A and B are subsets of a universal set, U. Draw a Venn diagram to show each fact.
32. Each member of A is a member of B.
33. Some members of A are also members of B.
34. A and B are disjoint.
35. Each member of A is a member of B, and each member of B is also a member of A.

36. A = {odd numbers less than 20}, B = {even numbers less than 20}, and C = {multiples of 5 less than 20}.
  a. List B ∩ C and A ∩ C.
  b. What set is A ∩ B?

A = {1, 2, 3, 5, 7, 9}, B = {2, 3, 5, 6, 8, 10}, and C = {2, 3, 4, 7, 8, 9}.
37. List A ∩ B.   **38.** List B ∩ C.   **39.** List A ∩ C.
40. List A ∩ B ∩ C.   **41.** List A ∪ B.   **42.** List B ∪ C.
43. List A ∪ C.   **44.** List A ∪ B ∪ C.

Name each union or intersection by N, W, Z, Q, or R.
45. N ∪ Z   **46.** N ∩ Z   **47.** Z ∪ R
48. Z ∩ R   **49.** W ∪ Q   **50.** W ∩ Q

31. a. {b, c}; {a, b, c, d, e}
b.

c. f, g

32.

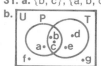

33.

34.

35.

U
A,B

36. a. B ∩ C = {10}; A ∩ C = {5, 15} **b.** A ∩ B = φ **37.** {2, 3} **38.** {2, 3, 8} **39.** {2, 3, 7, 9} **40.** {2, 3} **41.** {1, 2, 3, 5, 6, 7, 8, 9, 10} **42.** {2, 3, 4, 5, 6, 7, 8, 9, 10} **43.** {1, 2, 3, 4, 5, 7, 8, 9} **44.** {1, 2, 3, 4, 5, 6, 7, 8, 9, 10} **45.** Z **46.** N **47.** R **48.** Z **49.** Q **50.** W

CHAPTER 2

properties of operations

OBJECTIVES:

1. To use letters to represent a "quantity to be found" in a mathematical statement.
2. To use letters for real numbers in presenting a general statement about numbers.

In a strict sense there really are not two distinct uses of letters.

EXAMPLE

Rather, there are different "sizes" for truth sets. However, such a level of sophistication is appropriate for the most able students only. Most students would be overwhelmed with too heavy a concept load.

In algebra, lowercase letters often are used to stand for real numbers. Sometimes a letter stands for a number you do not know but which you are to find.

A rectangle is 5 feet long. Its area is 20 square feet. What is the width of the rectangle?

$A = 24$ sq ft	w ft

6 ft

The letter w may be used for the width. Before you decide what number w is, you may write $5 \times w = 20$. You would be using the fact that length times width equals area.

Sometimes letters are used to make statements which are true for many real numbers.

EXAMPLES

Emphasize the fact that $5 \times w = 20$ is true only for w equal to 4, but that $a \times 0 = 0$ is true for each real number replacement for a.

1. If a real number is multiplied by zero, the product is zero. This statement may be written using letters.

   If a is a real number, then $a \times 0 = 0$.

   The following statement uses even less writing to say the same thing.

   If $a \in R$, then $a \times 0 = 0$.

2. If an integer is divided by a natural number, the quotient is a rational number. This statement may be written as follows.

$$\text{If } a \in Z \text{ and } b \in N, \text{ then } a \div b \in Q.$$

Many statements in mathematics, such as those in the examples, involve products of numbers and letters representing numbers. Since the letter x is frequently used, it is confusing to use the ordinary multiplication symbol, $\times$, in algebra. Often a raised dot, $\cdot$, is used instead.

$$3 \cdot 4 \text{ and } 3 \times 4 \text{ have the same meaning.}$$
$$7 \cdot x \text{ and } 7 \times x \text{ have the same meaning.}$$

Another way to indicate multiplication is to write factors close together without any special multiplication symbol.

$$abc \text{ means } a \times b \times c \text{ or } a \cdot b \cdot c$$
$$3y \text{ means } 3 \times y \text{ or } 3 \cdot y$$
$$3(a + b) \text{ means } 3 \times (a + b) \text{ or } 3 \cdot (a + b)$$

You cannot use this symbolism when working with whole numbers. For instance, 387 does not mean $3 \cdot 8 \cdot 7$. Sometimes parentheses are used when using no symbol could lead to confusion.

$$(3)(4) = 3 \cdot 4$$
$$3(2 + 5) = 3 \cdot (2 + 5)$$

EXERCISES

Write each expression without using $\cdot$ or $\times$ for multiplication. If you use parentheses, use as few as possible.
  1. $5 \cdot a \cdot b - 4 \cdot c \cdot d$
  2. $3 \times a \times b \div c + 3 \times b$
  3. $3 \cdot y - 5 \cdot y + 8 \cdot y$
  4. $2 \times 3 \times (w)$
  5. $7 \cdot x \cdot y + 8 \cdot 3 \cdot x \cdot y$
  6. $(3) \cdot a \cdot b$

Rewrite each statement. Use only numerals, letters for numbers, the equal sign, and $+$, $-$, $\cdot$, and $\div$.
  7. 10 taken from m leaves 37.
  8. 14 times c is 70.
  9. a times b is c.
  10. x divided by 27 is 36 times y.
  11. The sum of 3, 4, and c is 5 less than d.
  12. w divided by m is 3 more than n.

13. The sum of a and b is zero.

14. r is larger than s, and their difference is 5.

Rewrite each statement. Use letters to represent real numbers. Use the letter a if you need only one letter. Use a and b if you need two letters. Use as few English words as possible.

15. If a real number is multiplied by 1, the product is the real number which was multiplied by 1.

16. If zero is added to a real number, the sum is the real number to which zero was added.

17. The sum of any two real numbers is also a real number.

18. The product of any two real numbers is also a real number.

19. The sum of any two integers is also an integer.

20. The product of any two integers is also an integer.

21. The difference of two whole numbers always will be an integer.

22. The quotient of two natural numbers always will be a rational number.

In Exercises **23–28,** write a true sentence using only numerals, letters for numbers, the equal sign, and $+$, $-$, $\cdot$, and $\div$.

23. The length of a rectangle is 6 feet. Its area is 24 square feet.

24. Mary collects \$8, Ralph collects \$7, and Matilda collects the rest (r). The three persons collect \$20.

25. The top of an antenna on a transmission tower must be 300 feet above the ground. The top of the tower is 256 feet above the ground.

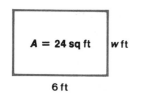

$A = 24$ sq ft w ft

6 ft

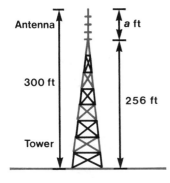

Antenna a ft

300 ft

256 ft

Tower

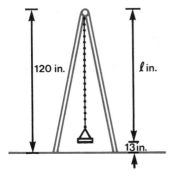

120 in. l in.

13 in.

26. The chain supporting a swing is hinged 120 inches above the ground. The swing seat is 13 inches above the ground.

27. Harry has a current bank balance of \$37. If he writes a check for an amount c, he is overdrawn by \$23.

28. If the temperature falls 15° from its present reading of $t°$, it will be a record low of 37° below zero.

29. State real number values for w, r, a, l, c, and t in Exercises **23–28.**

Write numbers that you can use to show that each statement is false.

30. If $a \in$ R and $b \in$ R, then $a - b = b - a$.

31. If $a \in$ R and $b \in$ R, then $a \div b = b \div a$.

32. If $a \in$ N and $b \in$ N, then $a \div b \in$ N.

33. If $a \in$ N and $b \in$ N, then $a - b \in$ N. Hint: Think about checking accounts.

2-2
Properties
of Operations

The four basic operations on the real numbers are addition, subtraction, multiplication, and division. There are several properties of these operations that you probably already know. If you do not, you should learn them now. In the following statements, parentheses are used as a grouping symbol to show which numbers are added or multiplied first.

1. *The Commutative Property of Addition* is illustrated by the fact that $3 + 4 = 4 + 3$.

$$3 + 4 = 7$$
$$4 + 3 = 7$$

2. *The Commutative Property of Multiplication* is illustrated by the fact that $7 \cdot 8 = 8 \cdot 7$.

$$7 \cdot 8 = 56$$
$$8 \cdot 7 = 56$$

3. *The Associative Property of Addition* is illustrated by the fact that $(8 + 3) + 2 = 8 + (3 + 2)$.

$$(8 + 3) + 2 = 11 + 2$$
$$= 13$$
$$8 + (3 + 2) = 8 + 5$$
$$= 13$$

4. *The Associative Property of Multiplication* is illustrated by the fact that $(6 \cdot 5) \cdot 3 = 6 \cdot (5 \cdot 3)$.

$$(6 \cdot 5) \cdot 3 = 30 \cdot 3$$
$$= 90$$
$$6 \cdot (5 \cdot 3) = 6 \cdot 15$$
$$= 90$$

Ask if other numbers would
have done just as well in the
examples.

5. *The Distributive Property of Multiplication over Addition* is illustrated by the fact that $3 \cdot (2 + 7) = (3 \cdot 2) + (3 \cdot 7)$.

$$3 \cdot (2 + 7) = 3 \cdot 9$$
$$= 27$$
$$(3 \cdot 2) + (3 \cdot 7) = 6 + 21$$
$$= 27$$

Upon getting an agreement that
any choices would have done as
well, remind students that the
statements using letters proclaim
that agreement. These
statements are true no matter
which number (numeral,
actually) or letter representing
a number is used for *a*, *b*, or *c*.

If the letters a, b, and c represent real numbers, these five properties may be stated as follows. The statement $a, b, c \in R$ is a way of writing $a \in R$ *and* $b \in R$ *and* $c \in R$.

If *a*, *b*, *c* ∈ R, then

1. $a + b = b + a$	**1. The Commutative Property of Addition**
2. $ab = ba$	**2. The Commutative Property of Multiplication**
3. $a + (b + c)$ $= (a + b) + c$	**3. The Associative Property of Addition**
4. $a(bc) = (ab)c$	**4. The Associative Property of Multiplication**
5. $a(b + c)$ $= (ab) + (ac)$	**5. The Distributive Property of Multiplication over Addition**

When letters are used to represent real numbers, you may use the properties in working with these letters. If x represents a real number, then $x \cdot 3$ is equal to $3 \cdot x$ because of the Commutative Property of Multiplication. If x, y, and z represent real numbers, then $x(y + z)$ is equal to $(xy) + (xz)$ because of the Distributive Property of Multiplication over Addition.

EXERCISES

1. Commutative Property of
Multiplication **2.** Distributive
Property of Multiplication over
Addition **3.** Associative Property
of Multiplication

Some students may insist that
where letters represent numbers,
nothing "can be done first."

Respond by saying, "The

Parentheses are used in these exercises to tell you which operations are to be done first.

Write the name of the property which tells you why each statement is true. All the letters represent real numbers.

1. $q \cdot 37 = 37 \cdot q$
2. $p \cdot (2 + 3) = (p \cdot 2) + (p \cdot 3)$
3. $5 \cdot (6 \cdot y) = (5 \cdot 6) \cdot y$

4. $6 + (5 + y) = (6 + 5) + y$
5. $(2 + 3)(5 + 6) = (5 + 6)(2 + 3)$
6. $3 + (4 + 6) = (4 + 6) + 3$
7. $a(b + c) = (b + c)a$
8. $(3y) + (3z) = 3(y + z)$

For each statement write true (T) or false (F). Then state if you think there is a Commutative Property for Subtraction and Division of real numbers.

9. $5 - 3 = 3 - 5$ **10.** $16 \div 8 = 8 \div 16$
11. $2 - 0 = 0 - 2$ **12.** $6 \div 2 = 2 \div 6$

For each statement write true (T) or false (F). Then state if you think there is an Associative Property for Subtraction and Division of real numbers.

13. $(4 - 3) - 2 = 4 - (3 - 2)$ **14.** $(16 \div 4) \div 2 = 16 \div (4 \div 2)$
15. $(10 \div 2) \div 5 = 10 \div (2 \div 5)$ **16.** $(6 - 3) - 3 = 6 - (3 - 3)$

For each statement write true (T) or false (F). Then state if you think $a(b - c) = (ab) - (ac)$ is true for all real numbers a, b, and c.

17. $3 \cdot (8 - 6) = (3 \cdot 8) - (3 \cdot 6)$
18. $3 \cdot (2 - 1) = (3 \cdot 2) - (3 \cdot 1)$

For each statement write true (T) or false (F). For statements which are true, name the property illustrated. The letters represent real numbers.

19. $6 + (3 \cdot 2) = (6 + 3) \cdot 2$
20. $(2 + 3)5 = 5(2 + 3)$
21. $x - (y - z) = (x - y) - z$
22. $x - y = y - x$
23. $3 \cdot (2 - x) = (3 \cdot 2) - (3 \cdot x)$
24. $(5 \cdot p) + (5 \cdot q) = 5 \cdot (p + q)$
25. $6 \cdot (3 \cdot b) = (3 \cdot b) \cdot 6$
26. $4 + (a + b) = (4 + a) + b$
27. $6 \cdot (3 \cdot b) = (6 \cdot 3) \cdot b$
28. $a - (b \cdot c) = (a - b) \cdot (a - c)$
29. $(x - y) + z = z + (x - y)$
30. $2 \cdot 36 = (2 \cdot 30) + (2 \cdot 6)$

Excursions in Mathematics: A New Operation

Think of the set S as all the points on a sheet of paper. The

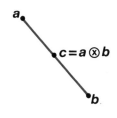

$c = a \otimes b$

operation $\otimes$ is defined as follows: $a \otimes b =$ the midpoint between a and b. In the figure, $a \otimes b = c$.

1. Does the Commutative Property hold for the operation $\otimes$? That is, does $a \otimes b = b \otimes a$ when $a \in S$ and $b \in S$?
2. Does the Associative Property hold for $\otimes$? That is, does $(a \otimes b) \otimes c = a \otimes (b \otimes c)$ when $a \in S$ and $b \in S$ and $c \in S$?

1. Yes 2. No

2-3
Real Number Statements

There are many more true statements about real numbers besides those in Section 2–2.

EXAMPLES

OBJECTIVE:

To determine whether or not a given general statement is true.

Each statement is true.
1. If $a, b, c \in R$, then $a(b - c) = (ab) - (ac)$.
2. If $a, b \in R$, then $ab \in R$.
3. If $a, b, c \in R$ and $a = b$, then $a + c = b + c$.

There are also statements about real numbers which are false. One way to show that a statement about real numbers is false is to find specific real numbers for which the statement is not true.

EXAMPLES

1. If $a, b \in R$, then $a - b = b - a$.
   To show that this statement is false, you may use 7 in place of a and 2 in place of b. Both 7 and 2 are real numbers, but $7 - 2$ and $2 - 7$ are not equal.

2. If $a, b \in R$, then $a \div b = b \div a$.
   To show that this statement is false, you may use 4 in place of a and 2 in place of b. Both 4 and 2 are real numbers, but $4 \div 2$ and $2 \div 4$ are not equal.

EXERCISES

1. - 5. Answers will vary.

Select numbers to replace each a, b, and c to show that a statement is false.
1. If $a, b, c \in R$, then $a - (b - c) = (a - b) - c$.
2. If $a, b, c \in R$, then $a + (bc) = (a + b)(a + c)$.
3. If $a, b, c \in R$, then $a \div (b \div c) = (a \div b) \div c$.
4. If $a, b \in W$, then $a \div b \in W$.
5. If $a, b \in R$ and $ab = 0$, then $a = 0$ and $b = 0$.

If there are slow students in the
class, it may be best to allow
them to work with more able
students on Exercises 6-15.

In each statement $a, b, c \in W$. Write true (T) or false (F) for each statement.

6. If $a \cdot b = 0$, then either $a = 0$ or $b = 0$. (This is the mathematical use of *or* that permits both $a = 0$ *and* $b = 0$.)

7. If $a + c = b + c$, then $a = b$.

8. If $a \cdot b = 0$, then $a = 0$.

9. If $a - b = b - a$, then $a = b$.

10. If $2 \cdot a = 3 \cdot b$, then $a \neq b$.

11. If $a - c = b - c$, then $a = b$.

12. If $a + b = a - b$, then $a = 0$.

13. If $a \cdot c = b \cdot c$, than $a = b$.

14. If $a \cdot c = b \cdot c$ and $c \neq 0$, then $a = b$.

15. If $a \div c = b \div c$ and $c \neq 0$, then $a = b$.

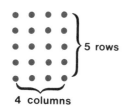

4 columns

16. Imagine that the members of a band are marching in perfect rows and columns. To find out how many members there are, you could multiply the number of rows by the number of columns; or you could multiply the number of columns by the number of rows. Which property of real numbers gives you this choice?

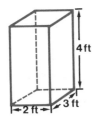

17. Suppose a student is asked to add 829 and 1065. He always writes the larger number on top. Which property of real numbers allows him to do this?

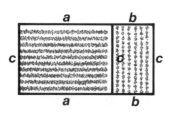

18. A rectangular solid has edges which measure 2 feet, 3 feet, and 4 feet. To find the volume in cubic feet, Martha calculated as follows: $(2 \cdot 3) \cdot 4 = 6 \cdot 4 = 24$ cu ft. Marvin calculated this way: $(2 \cdot 4) \cdot 3 = 8 \cdot 3 = 24$ cu ft. Which properties of real numbers are needed to guarantee that the two methods give the same product?

19. Two rectangular fields of farmland have a common side of length c. The owner wants to know the total area of the two fields. She will use the formula area = length × width. She could use c as the length and $a + b$ as the width. Or she could compute the area of each field and then add the two areas. Which property of real numbers gives her this choice?

34

Excursions in Mathematics: Closure

A set S is closed relative to the operation $*$ if $a * b \in S$ whenever $a, b \in S$. For example, W is closed relative to $\cdot$ because the product of any two whole numbers is a whole number.

For each statement, write true (T) or false (F).
1. W is closed relative to $-$.
2. N is closed relative to $\cdot$.
3. N is closed relative to $\div$.
4. $\{3, 6, 9, 12, \ldots\}$ is closed relative to $+$.
5. $\{3, 6, 9, 12, \ldots\}$ is closed relative to $\cdot$.
6. $\{1, 3, 5, 7, \ldots\}$ is closed relative to $+$.
7. $\{2, 4, 6, 8, \ldots\}$ is closed relative to $+$.
8. $\{1, 3, 5, 7, \ldots\}$ is closed relative to $\cdot$.
9. $\{2, 4, 6, 8, \ldots\}$ is closed relative to $\cdot$.

Let $\otimes$ be an operation on points such that $a \otimes b$ is the midpoint between a and b.
10. If S is the set of points inside a circle, is S closed relative to $\otimes$?
11. If S is the set of points outside a circle, is S closed relative to $\otimes$?
12. Which of the following sets of points inside the curves are closed relative to $\otimes$?

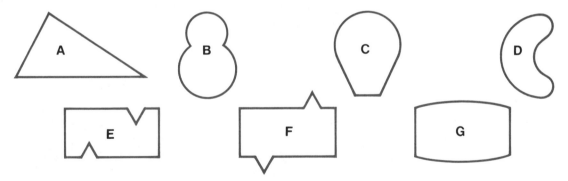

2-4
Punctuation in Mathematics

OBJECTIVE:
To simplify a given numerical expression containing parentheses.

How many members are there in the committee described by this English sentence?

The committee members are John, the fellow with the blue shirt, Harriet, the girl without glasses, Jane, and Harold.

Are there six members? If there are four members, then perhaps the sentence should be punctuated this way.

> The committee members are John, the fellow with the blue shirt; Harriet, the girl without glasses; Jane; and Harold.

Punctuation also is useful for giving precise meaning to expressions and sentences in mathematics.

EXAMPLE

Find the value of x if $x = 8 - 4 - 3$.

1. $x = 8 - 4 - 3$
$x = 4 - 3$
$x = 1$

2. $x = 8 - 4 - 3$
$x = 8 - 1$
$x = 7$

The confusion in the example may be avoided by using *parentheses,* ( ), as punctuation. In expressions and sentences, parentheses usually mean one of two things.

---

1. **The operations in parentheses are to be done first.**
2. **The expression in parentheses is to be treated as a single number.**

By using parentheses, you may show exactly how you want $8 - 4 - 3$ to be calculated.

1. $x = (8 - 4) - 3$
$x = 4 - 3$
$x = 1$

2. $x = 8 - (4 - 3)$
$x = 8 - 1$
$x = 7$

The English sentence at the beginning of the section has punctuation within punctuation. There are commas between semicolons. The same thing occurs in mathematics. Brackets, [ ], sometimes are used with parentheses.

EXAMPLE

Find the value of x if $x = 8 - [4 - (3 - 2)]$.

$$x = 8 - [4 - (3 - 2)]$$
$$x = 8 - [4 - 1]$$
$$x = 8 - 3$$
$$x = 5$$

If more punctuation is needed, braces, { }, sometimes are used. *Remember to begin working with the punctuation within punctuation.*

EXAMPLE

Find the value of y if $y = 10 \div \{8 - [4 - (3 - 2)]\}$.

$$y = 10 \div \{8 - [4 - (3 - 2)]\}$$
$$= 10 \div \{8 - [4 - 1]\}$$
$$= 10 \div \{8 - 3\}$$
$$= 10 \div 5$$
$$y = 2$$

EXERCISES

Write a whole number value for each expression.

Sample $5 + [6 - (3 + 2)] + 1 = 5 + [6 - 5] + 1$
$$= 5 + 1 + 1$$
$$= 7$$

1. $3(2 + 5)$ **2.** $(3 \cdot 2) + 5$
3. $[8 - (6 - 2)] \div 2$ **4.** $2 - \{2 - [2 - (2 - 1)]\}$
5. $16 \div 4 \cdot (2 \div 2)$ **6.** $[(16 \div 4) \div 2] \div 2$
7. $3[(5 + 3) - (8 \div 2)]$
8. $2 + \{[(8 - 2) \div 3] - (5 - 4)\}$
9. $5\{[16 \div (5 + 3)] - (4 \div 2)\}$
10. $7 + \{3 \cdot [7 - (9 - 3)] \cdot (6 \div 3)\} + 3$

Write a numerical value for each expression. If there is not enough punctuation to assure only one value, then state all possible numerical values. Imagine that the only agreement for telling the order in which to do the operations is the use of parentheses, brackets, and braces.

11. $5 - 2 + 3$ **12.** $6 + 3 - 2$
13. $8 + (7 + 6) + 3$ **14.** $8 - [2 - (2 - 1) + 1]$
15. $7 \cdot 2 - 3$ **16.** $(2 + 3)7$
17. $8 \div 4 \div 2$ **18.** $8 - \{[2 - (2 - 1)] + 1\}$
19. $2\{[2 \cdot (2 \cdot 2)] - 2\}$ **20.** $8 + [3 + (4 - 1)] - 2$
21. $(5 - 2) - [3 - (2 - 1)]$ **22.** $3 \cdot 3 + 3 \div 3$

23. Do any of the expressions in Exercises **11–22** have punctuation that is not needed? If so, rewrite these expressions using no more punctuation than is needed.

Sometimes only parentheses are used for punctuation. However, the rule for punctuation still holds. Begin by working with the punctuation within punctuation. Evaluate each expression.

24. $5(3 − (4 ÷ 2))$ **25.** $((2 · 3) + (4 · 3)) ÷ 6$

26. $5 − (4 − (3 − (2 − 1)))$ **27.** $5 − ((4 − 3) − (2 − 1))$

28. $(5 − (4 − 3)) − (2 − 1)$ **29.** $((5 + 4) − 3) − (2 − 1)$

30. $((2 + 2)2) ÷ 2$ **31.** $2 + (2(2 ÷ 2))$

32. $(((3 − 2)3) + 6) ÷ 9$

33. $1 − (((6 ÷ 3) + (9 ÷ 3)) ÷ 5)$

Insert punctuation to make each sentence true. Imagine that the only agreement for telling the order in which to do the operations is the use of parentheses.

34. $8 − 4 − 2 = 2$ **35.** $8 − 4 − 2 − 1 = 3$

36. $5 · 3 − 2 + 6 = 11$ **37.** $9 − 2 · 3 + 6 ÷ 2 = 0$

Excursions in Mathematics:
Volume in the Metric System

The standard unit of capacity or volume in the metric system is the cubic meter. However, a more commonly encountered unit of capacity is the liter. There are 1000 liters in a cubic meter. The same prefixes are used.

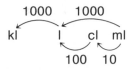

One liter is approximately equal to 1.06 quarts. One liter is equal to one thousand cm^3. (One cm^3 is the capacity of a cube 1 cm by 1 cm by 1 cm.)

EXAMPLE

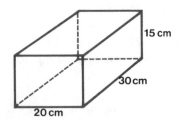

How many liters of water will a metal box hold if its dimensions are 30 cm by 20 cm by 15 cm?

To find the capacity, or volume, of this box multiply length times width times height.

$$V = lwh$$
$$V = 30 \text{ cm} · 20 \text{ cm} · 15 \text{ cm}$$
$$V = 9000 \text{ cm}^3$$

Since $1000 \text{ cm}^3 = 1$ l, the box will hold 9 liters of water.

EXERCISES

1. liter 2. liter, kiloliter 3. cubic
centimeters 4. cubic centimeters
5. cubic meters 6. liter
7. 2125 ml 8. 23153 ml 9. 15.75
kilometers/liter 10. 24 liters,
18 kg 11. $\frac{1}{2}$ liter, 500

milliliters, $\frac{1}{200}$ hectoliter
12. Answers will vary.
13. 600 kg 14. 100,000 kg

Name the metric unit you might use to measure each item.

1. Amount of milk in a carton
2. Volume of a cardboard box
3. Displacement of a motorcycle engine
4. Amount of penicillin in a hypodermic syringe
5. Amount of ready-mix concrete needed to pour the footing for a house
6. The amount of punch needed at a party

7. A bottle contains 2 l 125 ml of liquid. How many ml is this?
8. Three bottles contain 2 l 38 ml, 12 l 107 ml, and 9 l 8 ml of liquid. How many ml of the liquid are there altogether?
9. A car gas tank holds 60 liters. The car travels 945 kilometers on a full tank of gas. How far does it go on 1 liter?
10. The volume of an aquarium is 24,000 cm³. How many liters of water does it hold? If 1 l of water weighs 1 kg, how many kg does the water weigh if the aquarium is two-thirds full?
11. Express in liters the volume of a 500 cm³ can of soup. In milliliters. In hectoliters.
12. A person occupies about 1000 cm³ of space for each kg of mass. Find your mass in kg and determine the amount of space you take up in cm³. (1 kg is approximately 2.2 lb.)
13. A dump truck holds 3 cm³ of dirt. If one dm³ of dirt weighs 20 kg, what is the mass of a truckload of dirt?
14. Rainfall measures 1 cm on a field with area 10,000 m². If water weighs approximately 1 kg per liter, what is the mass in kg of water on the field?

2-5
Order
of Operations

OBJECTIVE:
To simplify a given numerical
expression using the order of
operations agreements.

The expression $3 \cdot 4 + 2 \cdot 2$ can represent several different numbers unless there is agreement on the order in which operations are done.

$$(3 \cdot 4) + (2 \cdot 2) = 16$$
$$3 \cdot (4 + (2 \cdot 2)) = 24$$
$$(3 \cdot (4 + 2)) \cdot 2 = 36$$

Fortunately, there are order of operations agreements that permit the use of less punctuation. These agreements assure that different persons will give the same value for an expression.

Stress the point that these
agreements are used in the
following situations.
1. If there are no parentheses
   in the expression
2. After parentheses have been
   removed as in Section 2-4
In other words, *remove
parentheses first.*

Order of Operations Agreements
1. Perform multiplications and divisions, moving from left to right.
2. Perform additions and subtractions, moving from left to right.

You can apply the order of operations agreements directly to an expression. You also can use the agreements to insert punctuation to be sure you make no errors.

EXAMPLES

Stress the fact that the
*agreements must be applied in
order.* To show that the order of
application makes a difference,
show the result of reversing the
order using Example 1:
$3 \cdot 4 + 2 \cdot 2 = 3 \cdot 6 \cdot 2$
$\qquad = 18 \cdot 2$
$\qquad = 36$

Insert punctuation and find the value of each expression.
1. $3 \cdot 4 + 2 \cdot 2 = (3 \cdot 4) + (2 \cdot 2) = 16$
2. $8 \div 4 \div 2 \ = (8 \div 4) \div 2 \qquad = 1$
3. $8 - 4 - 2 \ = (8 - 4) - 2 \qquad = 2$
4. $16 \div 4 \cdot 2 \div 8 = (16 \div 4) \cdot 2 \div 8$
   $\qquad\qquad\quad = 4 \cdot 2 \div 8$
   $\qquad\qquad\quad = (4 \cdot 2) \div 8$
   $\qquad\qquad\quad = 8 \div 8$
   $\qquad\qquad\quad = 1$
5. $16 - 4 + 2 - 8 = 12 + 2 - 8$
   $\qquad\qquad\quad = 14 - 8$
   $\qquad\qquad\quad = 6$

EXERCISES

1. 4 2. 1 3. 0 4. 4 5. 4 6. 5
7. 6 8. 3 9. 1 10. 4 11. 9 12. 5
13. 7 14. 6 15. 2 16. 2 17. 2
18. 3 19. 2 20. 15

Write a whole number value for each expression. Use the Order of Operations Agreements. Remember to work within parentheses first.

1. $8 + 4 - 6 - 3 + 1$
2. $13 - 10 - 2$
3. $13 - 10 - 2 - 1$
4. $13 - (10 - 2) - 1$
5. $8 - 5 + 3 - 2$
6. $3 \cdot 2 \div 6 \cdot 5$
7. $81 \div 9 \div 3 \cdot 2$
8. $5 \cdot 3 \div 5$
9. $16 \div 4 \div 2 \div 2$
10. $16 \div (4 \div 2) \div 2$
11. $8 - 4 \div 2 + 1 \cdot 3$
12. $2 + 2 \cdot 2 - 2 \div 2$
13. $(2 + 2) \cdot 2 - 2 \div 2$
14. $(8 - 2) \cdot 3 \div (9 - 6)$
15. $15 \div 5 - 3 \cdot 2 + 5$
16. $6 \cdot 3 \div 9 + 6 + 3 - 9$
17. $2 \cdot 2 - 3 + 15 \div 3 - 2 \cdot 2$
18. $15 \div 3 + 2 - 3 \cdot 2 + 8 \div 4$
19. $15 \div (1 + 2) - 3 \cdot (2 + 3) \div 5$
20. $36 \div 4 - 2 + 5 \cdot 2 - 8 \div 4$

Encourage students to write a
step for each computation.
Promise that as their skills
become refined such tedium
may be abandoned.

Put in all the parentheses needed if there were no Order of Operations Agreements.

21. $8 - 4 - 2 = 2$

22. $16 \div 2 \div 4 = 2$

23. $2 \cdot 3 \cdot 4 - 5 = 19$

24. $4 \cdot 4 \div 8 + 15 \div 5 = 5$

25. $2 \cdot 2 + 2 \div 2 - 2 = 3$

26. $2 + 2 \div 2 \cdot 2 - 2 = 2$

27. $2 \cdot 2 - 2 \div 2 + 2 = 5$

28. $2 - 2 \div 2 + 2 \cdot 2 = 5$

29. $16 - 2 - 2 - 2 = 10$

30. $16 \div 2 \div 2 \div 2 = 2$

31. $3 \cdot 2 + 2 \cdot 2 + 5 \cdot 2 = 20$

32. $5 \cdot 2 - 3 \cdot 2 + 2 \cdot 2 = 8$

Use the Order of Operations Agreements to place parentheses correctly in each expression.

Sample $a \div b + c \cdot d = (a \div b) + (c \cdot d)$

33. $a \cdot b - c \cdot d$

34. $3 \cdot x + 2 \cdot y + 5 \cdot z$

35. $x \cdot y + (3 \cdot y - 4 \cdot z)$

36. $p \div q + c \cdot d$

37. $a \div b + (2 - 8 \div c)$

38. $((x - y \div z) \div q) \cdot a + b$

Use the Order of Operations Agreements to remove parentheses that are not needed.

Sample $(c \div d) - (x \div y) = c \div d - x \div y$

39. $3 \div b + (4 \cdot c)$

40. $(a \cdot b) + (c \cdot d)$

41. $(3 \cdot y) + 3 \cdot (a + b)$

42. $(a - b) \cdot 5 + 5 + (a \cdot b)$

43. $((x + y) \cdot z) + q$

44. $8 \cdot (a - b) + (b - (c \cdot d)) + (a \div d)$

Study the following method of finding the value of an expression which uses only addition and subtraction of whole numbers.

$$8 - 3 - 2 + 5 - 1 = 7 \qquad 18 - 17 + 6 + 9 - 10 - 2 = 4$$

$$
\begin{array}{cc}
 & 3 \\
8 & 2 \\
+5 & +1 \\
\hline
13 & -\ 6 = 7
\end{array}
\qquad
\begin{array}{cc}
18 & 17 \\
6 & 10 \\
+9 & +2 \\
\hline
33 & -\ 29 = 4
\end{array}
$$

Find whole number values for each expression in two ways.

a. By moving from left to right using the Order of Operations Agreements.

b. By first combining numbers to be added, then combining numbers to be subtracted, and then finding the difference (as in the examples).

These exercises may be treated as class discussion, especially for slow students. These exercises offer preparation for Section 2-7.

45. $16 - 8 + 4 + 2 - 10 - 3$

46. $16 - 3 + 4 - 8 + 2 - 10$

47. $16 - 10 - 3 + 4 + 2 - 8$　　**48.** $16 + 4 + 2 - 8 - 10 - 3$
49. $8 - 5 + 3 + 2 - 1$　　　　　**50.** $8 - 5 - 1 + 2 + 3$
51. $13 + 2 - 3 - 5 - 2$　　　　　**52.** $13 - 5 - 3 - 2 + 2$

Are your answers in Exercises **45–52** the same for both methods? If your answer is no, then you have made an arithmetic error.

2-6
Simplifying Numerical Expressions

OBJECTIVE:

To simplify a given numerical expression by following a flow chart.

Finding a single numerical value for a numerical expression is called *simplifying the numerical expression*. Here is a flow chart for simplifying numerical expressions which do not contain parentheses.

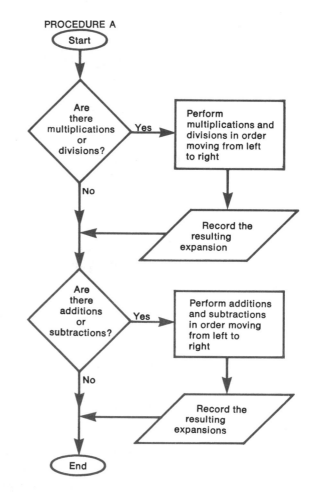

A **flow chart** is a follow-the-arrows method of giving instructions for a procedure. The shape of each box has special meaning.

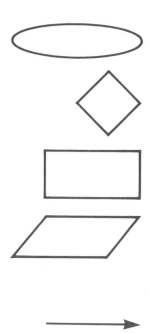

1. The *oval* is used to signal the *start* or *end* of the instructions.

2. The *diamond* is used to tell you that a question is being asked. You should be able to answer the question with *yes* or *no*. The diamond indicates a decision point.

3. The *rectangle* is used to tell you that some process must be carried out. The rectangle indicates a do-something point.

4. The *parallelogram* tells you to record or copy or remember something. If you were writing flow charts for giving instructions to a computer, you would be very careful to use enough of these. The computer is a quick accurate machine, but it is also absolutely without imagination. It needs to be told everything it must do down to the smallest detail.

5. The *arrow* indicates the sequence of the steps in a flow chart. The arrow tells you which box to go to next.

Here is a flow chart for simplifying numerical expressions which contain parentheses. The flow chart on page 42 is referred to as "Procedure A."

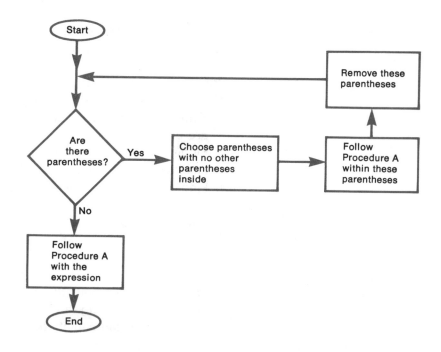

If flow-charting is not to be taught or is not considered to be important, assign only Exercises 1 and 3 with instructions that a numerical value is to be found.

EXERCISES

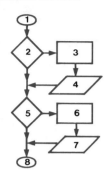

Copy the flow chart on page 42 and number the parts as shown in the figure.

1. For each expression, write the numbers of the steps in order which would be used to simplify the expression.

Sample $3 + 2 - 5 + 2$ would use $1 \to 2 \to 5 \to 6 \to 7 \to 8$

a. $5 - 3$ **b.** $2 \cdot 3 - 1$

c. 2 **d.** $2 \cdot 3 \div 4$

e. $2 \cdot 3 \cdot 5 \cdot 6 \cdot 8 \cdot 15$ **f.** $2 \div 3 \cdot 5 + 6$

g. $2 \div 3 \cdot 5 \cdot 6$ **h.** $1 \cdot 1 + 1$

2. Using the flow chart on page 42, what is the greatest number of steps there can be in simplifying an expression?

Copy the flow chart on page 43 and number the parts as shown in the figure.

3. For each expression given, write the number of each step in the order which would be used to simplify the expression.

Sample $10 - [2 - (1 + 1)]$ would use $1 \to 2 \to 3 \to 4 \to 5 \to 2 \to 3 \to 4 \to 5 \to 2 \to 6 \to 7$

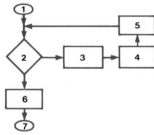

a. $3 - (5 - 4)$ **b.** $2 \cdot 3 - 5 \div 4$

c. $2 \cdot [10 - (2 + 2)]$ **d.** $(2 + 5) \cdot (4 - 2)$

e. $3 \cdot 5$ **f.** $(2 \cdot (5 - 3) + 1) \cdot 7$

g. $10 - (13 - (16 - (10 - 3)))$

h. $8 \div \{[1 + (4 - 3) - 2] \cdot 3 + 1\} - 2$

4. Using the flow chart of Exercise **3**, what is the greatest number of steps there can be in simplifying an expression?

1. a. $1 \to 2 \to 5 \to 6 \to 7 \to 8$
b. $1 \to 2 \to 3 \to 4 \to 5 \to 6 \to 7 \to 8$ **c.** $1 \to 2 \to 5 \to 8$
d. $1 \to 2 \to 3 \to 4 \to 5 \to 8$
e. $1 \to 2 \to 3 \to 4 \to 5 \to 8$
f. $1 \to 2 \to 3 \to 4 \to 5 \to 6 \to 7 \to 8$ **g.** $1 \to 2 \to 3 \to 4 \to 5 \to 8$ **h.** $1 \to 2 \to 3 \to 4 \to 5 \to 6 \to 7 \to 8$ **2.** 8 **3. a.** $1 \to 2 \to 3 \to 4 \to 5 \to 2 \to 6 \to 7$
b. $1 \to 2 \to 6 \to 7$ **c.** $1 \to 2 \to 3 \to 4 \to 5 \to 2 \to 3 \to 4 \to 5 \to 2 \to 6 \to 7$ **d.** $1 \to 2 \to 3 \to 4 \to 5 \to 2 \to 3 \to 4 \to 5 \to 2 \to 6 \to 7$ **e.** $1 \to 2 \to 6 \to 7$ **f.** $1 \to 2 \to 3 \to 4 \to 5 \to 2 \to 3 \to 4 \to 5 \to 2 \to 6 \to 7$ **g.** $1 \to 2 \to 3 \to 4 \to 5 \to 2 \to 3 \to 4 \to 5 \to 2 \to 3 \to 4 \to 5 \to 2 \to 6 \to 7$
h. $1 \to 2 \to 3 \to 4 \to 5 \to 2 \to 3 \to 4 \to 5 \to 2 \to 3 \to 4 \to 5 \to 2 \to 6 \to 7$ **4.** 4 times the number of sets of parentheses plus 4 more steps.
5. Answers will vary. **6. a.** 6
b. ∞ **c.** ∞ **d.** 8

5. Construct a flow chart for the procedure or task given.

  a. Crossing a street at an intersection which has traffic lights.

  b. Finding the area of a rectangle when the length and width are given.

  c. Finding out if a natural number is an even number.

  d. Finding out if a natural number has 7 as one of its factors.

  e. Finding the volume of a rectangular solid when length, width, and height are given.

  f. Simplifying expressions of the form $a - b + c$ where $a, b, c \in \mathrm{N}$.

6. For each flow chart, state the greatest possible number of steps there could be in using the flow chart. If there is no limit to the number of steps there might be, write ∞, the symbol for infinity.

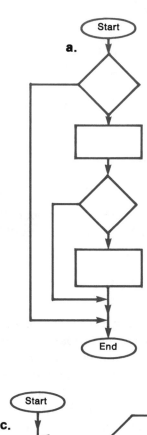

a.

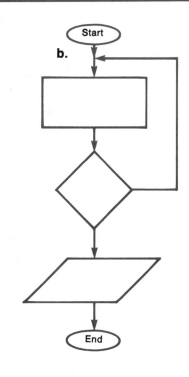

b.

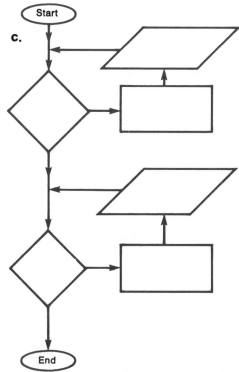

c.

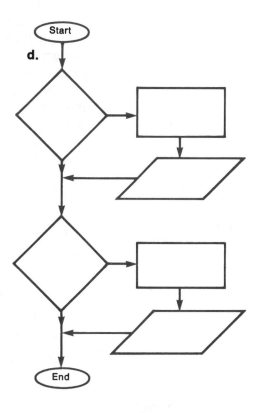

d.

2-7
Generalized Properties

Suppose someone has a checking account balance of $16. This person withdraws $8, then deposits $4, then deposits $2, withdraws $10, and finally withdraws $3. To find the balance the person does the following calculation. Withdrawals are preceded by a − sign. Deposits are preceded by a + sign.

$$16 - 8 + 4 + 2 - 10 - 3 = 1$$
The balance is $1.

However, the bank may receive the checks and deposit slips in a different order than written. The bank's statement could look like this.

$$16 + 4 - 8 + 2 - 3 - 10 = 1$$

In each case the same balance of $1 was found. This is an example of what will be called **The Rearrangement Property for Addition and Subtraction.** This property says that you may *rearrange numbers to be added or subtracted in any order as long as you keep the same operation sign before each number*. This property results from having the Order of Operations Agreements.

Suppose you are asked to think of subtracting 8 as adding the integer (⁻8). That is, $16 - 8$ is really $16 + (^-8)$. If you think of subtraction in this way, then the Rearrangement Property is a generalization of both the Commutative and Associative Properties for Addition.

The Rearrangement Property also allows you to move the first term of an expression.

EXAMPLES

1. $16 + 4 + 2 - 8 - 10 - 3$

Use the Commutative Property: $= 4 + 16 + 2 - 8 - 10 - 3$

Rearrange the numbers. $= 4 - 3 + 16 - 10 + 2 - 8$

2. $16 + 4 + 2 - 8 - 10 - 3$

Use the fact $0 + 16 = 16$. $= 0 + 16 + 4 + 2 - 8 - 10 - 3$

Rearrange the numbers. $= 0 + 4 - 3 + 16 - 10 + 2 - 8$

Use the fact $0 + 4 = 4$. $= 4 - 3 + 16 - 10 + 2 - 8$

The Distributive Property for multiplication over addition or subtraction also can be generalized.

EXAMPLE

Give a whole number value for each expression.

$$3 \cdot 5 - 3 \cdot 2 + 3 \cdot 6 - 3 \cdot 1 = 15 - 6 + 18 - 3$$
$$= 24$$
$$3 \cdot (5 - 2 + 6 - 1) = 3 \cdot (8)$$
$$= 24$$

The example shows that $3 \cdot (5 - 2 + 6 - 1) = 3 \cdot 5 - 3 \cdot 2 + 3 \cdot 6 - 3 \cdot 1$. The property illustrated is called ***The Generalized Distributive Property for Real Numbers.***

When letters are used to represent real numbers, both the Rearrangement Property and the Generalized Distributive Property still apply.

EXAMPLES

If anyone raises the issue of a universe for the variables, instruct students to think of the variables as standing for whole numbers which allow them to make sense of the expression.

1. $a - 3 - b + 5 + c = a + c - b + 5 - 3$
2. $m - 3 + n - g = n - g + m - 3$
3. $3 + (a - b) - 5y = (a - b) - 5y + 3$
4. $a(b + c - d - e + f) = ab + ac - ad - ae + af$
5. $(r - s + t - u)v = rv - sv + tv - uv$
6. $2t + 3t - t = (2 + 3 - 1)t = 4t$

EXERCISES

It may help to remind slow students of the deposit-withdrawal examples before assigning these.

Use the Rearrangement Property to rewrite each expression so that numbers to be added come first and numbers to be subtracted come later.

Samples $6 - 3 + 2 - 5 = 6 + 2 - 3 - 5$
$10 - 6x + 3x = 10 + 3x - 6x$

1. $8 - 3 - 2 + 1$ **2.** $a - b - c + d$
3. $48 - 36 + 24 - 8 - 2$ **4.** $a - b + c - d - e$
5. $3 \cdot 5 - 6 \cdot 2 + 3 \cdot 2 - 2$ **6.** $ab - cd + ad - d$
7. $25s + 2s - 5s + 3s$ **8.** $17 - 3t + 8t - 2t$
9. $5 \cdot 2 - 2 \cdot 2 + 6 \cdot 2 - 4 \cdot 2 + 2$
10. $5b - 2b + 6b - 4b + b$

Use the Generalized Distributive Property to rewrite each expression with only one multiplication.

Samples $3 \cdot 2 + 3 \cdot 5 - 3 \cdot 4 - 3 \cdot 1 = 3(2 + 5 - 4 - 1)$
$5a - 3a + 2a = (5 - 3 + 2)a$

11. $8 \cdot 5 - 8 \cdot 4 + 8 \cdot 3 - 8 \cdot 2$

12. $6t - 3t - 2t + t$ (Note: $t = 1 \cdot t$)

13. $12a + 5a - 16a$

14. $3b + 5b - 7b + b$ (Note: $b = 1 \cdot b$)

15. $bt + ct - dt$

16. $13y - 8y - 5y + y$

17. $ab - ac - ad + ae$

18. $5 \cdot 3 - 4 \cdot 3 + 2 \cdot 3 - 3$

Use the Generalized Distributive Property to write each expression as the product of a whole number and a letter which stands for a real number.

Sample $8b - 5b + 2b - 3b = (8 - 5 + 2 - 3)b$
$$= 2b$$

19. $13t - 8t - 2t$

20. $8y - 7y + 2y$

21. $5b - 3b - b$

22. $c + 2c + 5c - 4c$

23. $7s - 2s + 5s - 10s$

24. $8s - 7s - s$

25. $13t + 7t - 9t - 9t$

26. $-10p + 8p - 2p + 6p$

For each sentence, find a real number replacement for the letter to make a true statement.

Samples   **1.** $10t - 8t - t = 3$
$$(10 - 8 - 1)t = 3$$
$$1t = 3$$
$$t = 3$$

2. $5y + 2y - 3y = 12$
$$(5 + 2 - 3)y = 12$$
$$4y = 12$$
$$y = 3$$

27. $5p - 3p = 8$

28. $s \cdot 7 - s \cdot 5 - s = 5$

29. $2t - 5t + 6t = 15$

30. $5q - 3q = 1$

31. $y \cdot 7 - y \cdot 3 - y \cdot 2 = 2$

32. $10b + 7b - 15b + b = 2$

33. $3y - 2y + y + 2 = 8$

34. $t \cdot 9 - t \cdot 5 - 3 = 1$

To make sure your answers for Exercises **27–34** are correct, you can replace the letter in the original sentence with the real number replacement that you found.

Sample   Test $t = 3$ as the value for t in $10 \cdot t - 8 \cdot t - t = 3$.

$$10t - 8t - t = 10 \cdot 3 - 8 \cdot 3 - 3$$
$$= 30 - 24 - 3$$
$$= 3$$

35. Test your answers for Exercises **27–34.**

Excursions in Mathematics:
Rearrangements in Multiplication and Division

There is no Rearrangement Property for Multiplication and Division.

Review the Rearrangement Property for Addition and Subtraction on page 46. Then test different orders for $16 \div 2 \cdot 4 \div 8$. Is there also a Rearrangement Property for Multiplication and Division?

2-8
Exponents

OBJECTIVES:

1. To use exponents to indicate a repeated factor in a product.
2. To expand a given product using exponents.

In writing English sentences, abbreviations sometimes are used to save time or space. For example, you may say that the U.S. sold wheat at $3/bu. In mathematics, a special notation is used to show that a number is to be multiplied by itself several times.

$$x^2 \text{ means } xx$$
$$4^3 \text{ means } 4 \cdot 4 \cdot 4$$
$$y^4 \text{ means } yyyy$$
$$\text{and so on}$$

When a natural number is written to the upper right of a symbol, it tells how many times the symbol is used as a factor in a product.

$$(a - b)^3 \text{ means } (a - b)(a - b)(a - b)$$
$$6x^5 \text{ means } 6xxxxx$$
$$(3y)^2 \text{ means } 3y \cdot 3y$$
$$7(x + y)^3 \text{ means } 7(x + y)(x + y)(x + y)$$

Stress this emphatically!   Notice that $5x^3$ and $(5x)^3$ are not the same.

$$5x^3 \text{ means } 5xxx$$
$$(5x)^3 \text{ means } 5x \cdot 5x \cdot 5x$$

Whenever you want the number to the upper right to apply to more than one symbol, you must use parentheses. Remember that one meaning for parentheses is that the expression inside is to be considered as a single number.

Here are a few more examples, some with parentheses and some without.

$$3(ab)^2 = 3abab$$

$$3ab^2 = 3abb$$

$$(3ab)^2 = 3ab \cdot 3ab$$

$$(a^3 + b)^2 = (a^3 + b)(a^3 + b)$$
$$= (aaa + b)(aaa + b)$$

$$7x^2y^3 = 7xxyyy$$

$$\frac{(7x)^2}{y^3} = \frac{7x \cdot 7x}{yyy}$$

$$\left(\frac{x}{y}\right)^2 = \frac{x}{y} \cdot \frac{x}{y}$$

The number written at the upper right of a symbol is called an **exponent.** The symbol which is to be used as the factor is called the **base.**

Expression	Base	Exponent
x^3	x	3
$(3y)^2$	$3y$	2
$(3a + 2b)^5$	$3a + 2b$	5
$\left(\dfrac{2a}{3b}\right)^5$	$\dfrac{2a}{3b}$	5

EXERCISES

Rewrite each expression without using exponents.

Sample $(3x)^2y^3 = (3x)(3x)yyy$

1. x^5

2. $(a - 2b)^3$

3. $a - 2b^3$

4. $a - (2b)^3$

5. $a^3 - 2b$

6. $a - 2^3b$

7. $\dfrac{a^2}{3}$

8. $\left(\dfrac{a}{3}\right)^2$

9. $\dfrac{a}{3^2}$

10. $3x^3 - 2y^2$

11. $\dfrac{3a + b^2}{(a + b)^2}$

12. $\dfrac{a^2 - b^2}{(a + b)^2}$

Rewrite each expression using exponents where possible. Keep in mind the meaning of parentheses.

13. yyy **14.** $3x \cdot 3x \cdot 3x \cdot 3x$ **15.** $(2x)(2x)yyy$

16. $\dfrac{xxx}{yyy}$ **17.** $\dfrac{x}{y}\dfrac{x}{y}\dfrac{x}{y}$ **18.** $(xxx)(xx)$

19. $(x - 2y)(x - 2y)(x - 2y)(x - 2y)(x + y)(x + y)$

Use exponents to rewrite the formula in each exercise.

20. If a square has a side of length s, then the area, A, of the square is given by $A = s \cdot s$.

21. For a circle with radius r, the area, A, is given fairly accurately by $A = \dfrac{22}{7}rr$.

22. For a sphere with radius r, the volume, V, is very close to $V = \dfrac{4}{3} \cdot \dfrac{22}{7}rrr$.

23. The volume, V, of a cube with a side of length s is given by $V = sss$.

Rewrite each expression using a single exponent.

Sample $5^3 \cdot 5^4 = 5 \cdot 5 \cdot 5 \cdot 5 \cdot 5 \cdot 5 \cdot 5 = 5^7$

24. $2^2 \cdot 2^3$ **25.** $3^1 \cdot 3^4$ **26.** $n^5 \cdot n^2$
27. $x^3 \cdot x^4$ **28.** $2^x \cdot 2^y$ **29.** $x^n \cdot x^m$

Rewrite each expression using a single exponent.

Sample $2^7 \div 2^3 = \dfrac{2 \cdot 2 \cdot 2 \cdot 2 \cdot 2 \cdot 2 \cdot 2}{2 \cdot 2 \cdot 2} = 2^4$

30. $3^3 \div 3^2$ **31.** $4^5 \div 4^4$ **32.** $y^7 \div y^2$
33. $a^6 \div a^3$ **34.** $2^n \div 2^m, n > m$ **35.** $x^n \div x^m, n > m$

Rewrite each expression using exponents but not parentheses.

Sample $(2x)^2 = (2x)(2x) = (2 \cdot 2)xx = 4x^2$

36. $(3y)^2$ **37.** $(4x)^3$ **38.** $(xy)^4$
39. $(pq)^2$ **40.** $(2x)^n$ **41.** $(xy)^n$

13. y^3

14. $(3x)^4$ 15. $(2x)^2y^3$ 16. $\dfrac{x^3}{y^3}$

17. $\left(\dfrac{x}{y}\right)^3$ 18. $x^3 x^2$ or x^5

19. $(x - 2y)^4 (x + y)^2$ 20. $A = s^2$
21. $A = \dfrac{22}{7}r^2$ 22. $V = \dfrac{4}{3} \cdot \dfrac{22}{7} \cdot r^3$
23. $V = s^3$ 24. 2^5 25. 3^5 26. n^7
27. x^7 28. 2^{x+y} 29. x^{n+m} 30. 3^1 or 3
31. 4^1 or 4 32. y^5 33. a^3 34. 2^{n-m}
35. x^{n-m} 36. $9y^2$ 37. $64x^3$ 38. x^4y^4
39. p^2q^2 40. 2^nx^n 41. x^ny^n

Find a natural number replacement for the letter which makes a true sentence.

42. $3^x = 9$

43. $2^y = 16$

44. $x^3 = 8$

45. $x^5 = 1$

46. $2x^2 = 18$

47. $3^2 \cdot 3^3 = 3^x$

48. $2^2 \cdot 2^y = 16$

49. $3^2 \cdot 3^t = 3^5$

50. $\dfrac{2^4}{2^x} = 4$

51. $\dfrac{3^4}{3^2} = 3^y$

52. $2x^2 = 50$

53. $3y^6 = 3$

Simplify each expression to the form nx^m, where n and m are whole numbers.

Sample
$$
\begin{aligned}
6x^2 - (2x)^2 + 3^2x^2 &= 6x^2 - (2x)(2x) + 9x^2 \\
&= 6x^2 - 2 \cdot 2xx + 9x^2 \\
&= 6x^2 - 4x^2 + 9x^2 \\
&= (6 - 4 + 9)x^2 \\
&= 11x^2
\end{aligned}
$$

54. $3x^2 + 2x^2 - 4x^2$

55. $(2x)^3 - 5x^3$

56. $(2x)^3x^2 - 5x^5 + x^5$

57. $16x^4 - (2x)^2x^2 - 3x^4$

58. $3x(2 + 3)x - 7x^2$

59. $5x^5 - (2x)^2x^3 + x^5 - (2x)x^4 + 2x^5$

These may be treated as class discussion exercises.

For each sentence, write true (T) or false (F). The letters x, y, n, and m represent natural numbers. If you are having difficulty making up your mind, try values for x, y, n, and m. You might try $x = 2$, $y = 3$, $n = 6$, $m = 4$.

60. $x^n \cdot x^m = x^{(n+m)}$

61. $x^n \div x^m = x^{(n-m)}$ when n is larger than m

62. $(x^n)^m = x^{n \cdot m}$

63. $x^n + x^m = x^{(n+m)}$

64. $x^n - x^m = x^{n-m}$ when n is larger than m

65. $(xy)^n = x^n y^n$

66. $x^n \cdot x^n = x^{(n \cdot n)}$

67. $x^n \cdot y^m = (xy)^{(n+m)}$

Excursions in Mathematics:
Flow Charts

Assume that you know that an open sentence does not have more than one solution. The variable, x, is on the set of whole numbers.

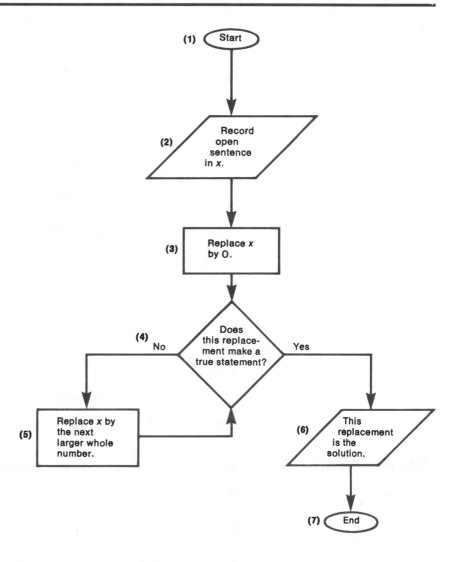

(1) Start

(2) Record open sentence in x.

(3) Replace x by 0.

(4) Does this replacement make a true statement?

No

Yes

(5) Replace x by the next larger whole number.

(6) This replacement is the solution.

(7) End

EXERCISES

1. Each move along an arrow is a step. Is there a maximum number of steps which will give a solution for all such open sentences?

2. Is it possible to have an open sentence which would use the following steps to find its solution?

   $1 \rightarrow 2 \rightarrow 3 \rightarrow 4 \rightarrow 5 \rightarrow 4 \rightarrow 5 \rightarrow 4 \rightarrow 5$ and so on, never reaching **6**

3. Use the flow chart to try to find the solution for each equation.

   a. $8 - x = 5$ **b.** $2x + 1 = 2(x + 1)$

2-9
Radicals

OBJECTIVE:

To state the value of $\sqrt[n]{x}$ where $x \geq 0$ and n, $\sqrt[n]{x} \in$ N.

Formally define *principal nth root* only for students who happen to know how to work with negative numbers and who raise the issue.
Otherwise, treat this section as dealing exclusively with $\sqrt[n]{x}$ where $x \geq 0$ and $n \in$ N.

You already may be acquainted with the symbol $\sqrt{}$. It is called a **radical**. The symbol $\sqrt{4}$ means a nonnegative number which gives 4 when squared.

$$\sqrt{4} = 2 \text{ because } 2^2 = 4$$
$$\sqrt{9} = 3 \text{ because } 3^2 = 9$$
$$\sqrt{16} = 4 \text{ because } 4^2 = 16$$

The number 3 is called a *square root* of 9; 2 is called a square root of 4; 4 is called a square root of 16; and so on.

You also may work with cube roots. The symbol $\sqrt[3]{}$ is read *the cube root of* and $\sqrt[3]{64}$ means a number which gives 64 when cubed.

$$\sqrt[3]{64} = 4 \text{ because } 4^3 = 64$$
$$\sqrt[3]{8} = 2 \text{ because } 2^2 = 8$$
$$\sqrt[3]{27} = 3 \text{ because } 3^3 = 27$$

The number 4 is called a *cube root* of 64; 3 is called a cube root of 27; 2 is called a cube root of 8; and so on.

The symbol $\sqrt[n]{}$ is read *the nth root of*. If $\sqrt[n]{b} = a$, then $a^n = b$.

$$\sqrt[5]{243} = 3 \text{ because } 3^5 = 3 \cdot 3 \cdot 3 \cdot 3 \cdot 3 = 243$$

The number 3 is a *fifth root* of 243.

EXERCISES

1. 6 2. 8 3. 4 4. 2 5. 5 6. 2
7. 3 8. 4 9. 2 10. 8 11. 2 12. 3
13. $x = 9$ 14. $x = 3$ 15. $x = 5$
16. $x = 5$ 17. $x = 64$ 18. $x = 2$
19. $x = 3$ 20. $x = 9$ 21. $x = 1$
22. $\sqrt[3]{x}$ ft 23. 5 ft

Write a whole number for each expression.

1. $\sqrt{36}$ **2.** $\sqrt{64}$ **3.** $\sqrt[3]{64}$ **4.** $\sqrt[5]{32}$

5. $\sqrt[3]{125}$ **6.** $\sqrt{2^2}$ **7.** $\sqrt[4]{3^4}$ **8.** $\sqrt{2^4}$

9. $\sqrt[4]{4^2}$ **10.** $\sqrt{4^3}$ **11.** $\sqrt[4]{16}$ **12.** $\sqrt[4]{81}$

Find a natural number replacement for x which makes each sentence true.

13. $\sqrt{x} = 3$ **14.** $\sqrt[x]{8} = 2$ **15.** $\sqrt[3]{125} = x$

16. $\sqrt[x]{32} = 2$ **17.** $\sqrt[3]{x} = 4$ **18.** $\sqrt{16} = 2^x$

19. $\sqrt[3]{27} = x$ **20.** $\sqrt{81} = x^2$ **21.** $\sqrt{x} = x^2$

22. If the volume of a cube is x cubic feet, how high is the cube?

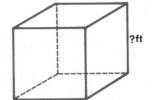
?ft

23. If the volume of a cube is 125 cubic feet, how high is the cube?

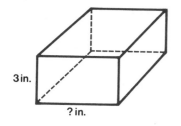

3 in.

? in.

24. A rectangular solid has a square base. It is 3 inches high. Its volume is 12x cubic inches. How wide is the base?

25. If the rectangular solid in Exercise **24** were 3x inches high, how wide would the base be?

24. $\sqrt{4x}$ **25.** 2 in.

Excursions in Mathematics:
A Flow Chart for Square Roots

Here is a flow chart for finding square roots. The method presented in the flow chart usually does not give you the exact square root. However, it can approximate a root as closely as you wish.

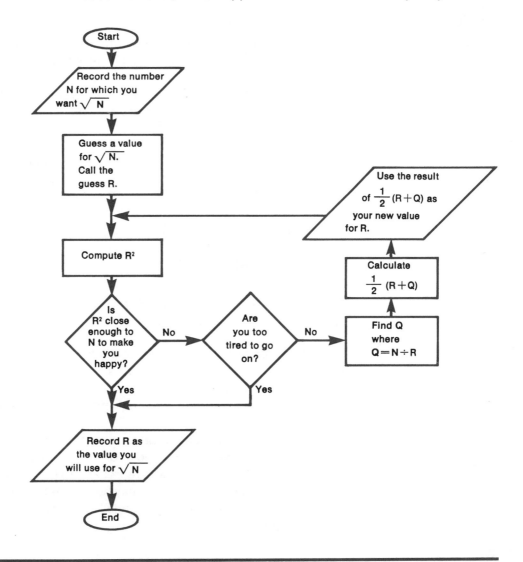

EXERCISES

1. 12.24745; 4.123106;
1.414214 **2.** Yes **3.** No

1. Use the flow chart to find approximations for $\sqrt{150}$, $\sqrt{17}$, and $\sqrt{2}$.
2. If n is a whole number and if the first r is a whole number, will all r's after that be rational numbers?
3. If $\sqrt{n}$ is an irrational number, n is a whole number, and the first r is a whole number, could you ever find $\sqrt{n}$ exactly?

Chapter Summary

1. Lowercase letters are used to stand for real numbers.
2. A raised dot, $\cdot$, often replaces the ordinary multiplication symbol, $\times$.
3. Factors may be written without any special multiplication symbol. Parentheses are used when the lack of a symbol could lead to confusion.
4. If $a, b, c \in$ R, then

I. $a + b = b + a$	Commutative Property of Addition
II. $ab = ba$	Commutative Property of Multiplication
III. $a + (b + c) = (a + b) + c$	Associative Property of Addition
IV. $a(bc) = (ab)c$	Associative Property of Multiplication
V. $a(b + c) = (ab) + (ac)$	Distributive Property of Multiplication over Addition

5. Order of Operations Agreements
    I. Perform operations in parentheses beginning with the innermost set.
    II. Perform multiplications and divisions, moving from left to right.
    III. Perform additions and subtractions, moving from left to right.
6. Flow charts may be used to describe a procedure step-by-step.
7. Real numbers, or letters representing them, connected by addition or subtraction signs may be rearranged in any order as long as the same operation sign is kept before each real number or letter.

8. The Distributive Property for Multiplication over Addition may be generalized to the following form:

$$a(b + c - d + e - f - g + i + \cdots)$$
$$= ab + ac - ad + ae - af - ag + ai + \cdots$$

9. In the expression x^2, 2 is the exponent and x is the base.

$$x^2 = xx$$
$$y^3 = yyy$$
$$z^4 = zzzz$$

10. The sentence $\sqrt[n]{m} = p$ means that $p^n = m$. The number p is an nth root of m. The symbol $\sqrt{}$ without a number means *the nonnegative square root of*.

REVIEW
EXERCISES   2-1

1. $5 + 7 = t$ **2.** $x + 6 = w$
3. $c + d = 2$ **4.** $ab > a + b$
5. $y \div 4 = x - 3$ **6.** $y \geq a + b$
7. $3d = 21$ **8.** $60a + 15 = 255$
9. $100d - (500 + 89) = 311$
10. $140 + n = 193$
11. Distributive Property of Multiplication over Addition
12. Associative Property of Addition **13.** Commutative Property of Multiplication
14. Commutative Property of Multiplication **15.** Distributive Property of Multiplication over Addition **16.** Associative Property of Multiplication

Write each expression in symbols. Do not use $\cdot$ or $\times$ for multiplication.

1. Five plus seven is t.
2. x increased by 6 is w.
3. The sum of c and d is two.
4. The product of a and b is greater than their sum.
5. y divided by 4 is 3 less than x.
6. y is greater than or equal to the sum of a and b.

In Exercises **7–10,** write a sentence using only numerals, letters for numbers, and $=$, $+$, $-$, $\cdot$, and $\div$.

7. A number of books, d, cost \$3 each. The total amount paid for the books is \$21.
8. The sum of a hours and 15 minutes is 255 minutes.
9. A boy has d dollars. He pays \$5 for a hat and \$.89 for socks. He now has \$3.11.
10. Jane has a bank balance of \$140. If she deposits n dollars, she has a balance of \$193.

2-2   Write the name of the property which tells you why each statement is true. All letters represent real numbers.

11. $s \cdot (2 + 5) = (s \cdot 2) + (s \cdot 5)$
12. $(3 + 7) + 2 = 3 + (7 + 2)$
13. $23 \cdot t = t \cdot 23$
14. $(y + z)x = x(y + z)$
15. $(2a) + (2b) = 2(a + b)$
16. $p \cdot (q \cdot r) = (p \cdot q) \cdot r$

17. T 18. T 19. F 20. F 21. T
22. F 23. 32 24. 9 25. 20 26. 2
27. 0 28. 5 29. $(x \cdot y) + (a \cdot b)$
30. $(4 \cdot y) + (3 \cdot x) - (2 \cdot z)$
31. $((d \div c) + f) - (g \cdot h)$
32. $a + (b \div ((2 \cdot 8) - c))$
33. Answers will vary. 34. $12t$
35. $3s$ 36. $1w$ 37. $2c$ 38. x^3
39. $(2x)^2$ 40. 3^2y^2 or $(3y)^2$

2-5

41. $z^4 + (2t)^2$ 42. $3y^2 - 2w^3$
43. $(a - 2b)^3 (a + 2b)$ 44. $p = 6$
45. $r = 4$ 46. $t = 7$ 47. $a = 3$
48. $x = 2$ 49. $y = 4$ 50. $x = 2$
51. $y = 6$ 52. 5 53. 5
54. 24 55. 10

Write true (T) or false (F) for each statement. $x, y, z \in R$
17. If $x = 0$, then $x \cdot y = 0$.
18. If $3 \cdot x = 3 \cdot y$, then $x = y$.
19. If $a \div 4 = b \div 4$, then $a \neq b$.
20. If $a + 6 = a - 6$, then $a = 0$.
21. $[(2 \cdot 3) - 4] + 2 = 4$
22. $[3 - (2 - 1)] + [7 - (2 \cdot 1)] = 5$

Write a whole number value for each expression. Use the Order of Operations Agreements.
23. $5 \cdot 6 + 8 \cdot 4 \div 16$
24. $18 - 6 \div 2 \cdot 3$
25. $10 \div 2 \cdot 8 - 4 \cdot 10 \div 2$
26. $17 - 9 + 2 + 8 - 6 - 10$
27. $10 - 2 - 3 + 5 - 8 - 2$
28. $2 - 1 + 7 + 3 - 4 - 2$

Use the Order of Operations Agreements to place parentheses correctly in each expression.
29. $x \cdot y + a \cdot b$
30. $4 \cdot y + 3 \cdot x - 2 \cdot z$
31. $d \div c + f - g \cdot h$
32. $a + b \div (2 \cdot 8 - c)$

2-6
33. Construct a flow chart for finding out if a natural number is prime.

2-7
Rewrite each expression as a product of a whole number and a letter which stands for a real number.
34. $10t + 4t - 2t$
35. $6s + 2s - 5s$
36. $4w - 2w + w - 3w + w$
37. $c + c + 2c - 3c + c$

2-8
Rewrite each expression using exponents when possible.
38. $x \cdot x \cdot x$
39. $2x \cdot 2x$
40. $3 \cdot 3 \cdot 3 \cdot y \cdot y \cdot y$
41. $(zzz) \cdot z + 2 \cdot 2 \cdot t \cdot t$
42. $3 \cdot yy - 2 \cdot www$
43. $(a - 2b)(a - 2b)(a - 2b)(a + 2b)$

Find a real number replacement for the letter which makes each sentence true.
44. $2p - p = 6$
45. $3r + 2r - r = 16$
46. $t \cdot 2 - t \cdot 4 + 3t = 7$
47. $14a - 2a - 6a + a = 21$
48. $4^x = 16$
49. $3^y = 81$
50. $x^5 = 32$
51. $2y^2 = 72$

2-9
Write a whole number for each expression.
52. $\sqrt{25}$
53. $\sqrt[3]{125}$
54. $2^3 \cdot 3$
55. $(4^2 - 2^3) + (3^3 - 5^2)$

CHAPTER 3

the language of algebra

3-1
Open Sentences

Suppose you are asked to decide whether each of the following sentences is true or false.

1. Henry VIII had ___?___ wives.
2. *It* is more than 100 feet tall.
3. $8 - x = 5$
4. Denver is in Alabama.
5. $8 - 2 = 5$
6. $3 + 7 = 10$

In order to make a decision for the first three sentences, you must know what will replace ___?___, *It,* and *x*. These sentences are called **open sentences.** If ___?___ is replaced by 5, the sentence Henry VIII had 5 wives is false. If, however, ___?___ is replaced by 6, the sentence is true. The table shows possible replacements for *It* and *x*.

Sentence	Replacement	True or False
It is more than 100 feet tall.	The Eiffel Tower	T
It is more than 100 feet tall.	Your teacher	F
$8 - x = 5$	4	F
$8 - x = 5$	3	T

You can say that the fourth and fifth sentences are false and the sixth sentence is true. These sentences are called statements. A ***statement*** is a sentence written in either words or symbols. A statement needs no replacements to decide if it is true or false. A statement *must* be true or false, but not both.

EXAMPLES

Sentence	Statement?	True or False
Worms are not insects.	Yes	T
February is a summer month.	Yes	F
Ben Franklin invented it.	No	
___?___ is the capital of Iowa.	No	

In an open sentence the symbol to be replaced is called a ***variable.*** In algebra, letters of the alphabet often are used as variables. A specific number written in place of a variable is called a ***replacement.*** An open sentence can be changed into a statement by replacing the variable. Depending on the specific replacement, the statement then will be true or false.

Open sentence	Variable	Replacements	True statement	False statement
___?___ is the capital of Alaska.	___?___	Juneau, Miami	*Juneau* is the capital of Alaska.	*Miami* is the capital of Alaska.
$x + 2 = 7$	x	5, 13	$5 + 2 = 7$	$13 + 2 = 7$
$y \in \{\text{even numbers}\}$	y	$6, \frac{1}{3}$	$6 \in \{\text{even numbers}\}$	$\frac{1}{3} \in \{\text{even numbers}\}$

An open sentence can be converted into a *general* statement. This is done by using such words as *all, every, each, there is, for some,* and *for at least one.*

EXAMPLE

These examples are inserted to keep students from concluding that every statement containing a variable is an open sentence. These are statements, all true.

Convert the open sentence *2y is an even number* into a true statement in several ways.

1. For all natural numbers *y*, 2*y* is an even number.
2. For each natural number *y*, 2*y* is an even number.
3. For every natural number *y*, 2*y* is an even number.
4. For some natural number *y*, 2*y* is an even number.

EXERCISES

For each statement write true (T) or false (F). For each open sentence, write the variable(s).

1. The cow is the fastest animal alive.

2. $2 = 8$

3. It is red.

4. $A \cap \{1, 2, 3\} = \varnothing$

5. $8 \cdot y = 8$

6. She is smarter than Egbert.

7. $3 < 7$

8. One of the vowels is the letter u.

9. He simply does not enjoy it.

10. $2 \cdot x = y$

11. That town is a county seat.

12. $3 \notin B$

13. $5 \in \{1, 3, 5, 7, \ldots\}$

14. Seven is the sum of two and four.

15. The sentence you are reading now is false.

Copy each open sentence. Fill in replacements to make one true statement and one false statement.

16. $x + 5 = 8$

17. $x - 2 = 1$

18. $y \in \{\text{odd numbers}\}$

19. For the natural number z, z is greater than 10.

20. $a \in \{\text{prime numbers}\}$

21. For the whole number c, $2c$ is divisible by 4.

22. The number d is greater than one million.

23. For the natural number n, $n \cdot n = 36$.

24. For the natural number p, $2 \cdot p = 30$.

Write the set of replacements which makes each open sentence into a true statement. Choose all possible replacements from N.

25. The number y is a divisor of 15.

26. $w + 12 = 20$

27. For the natural number z, z is less than 8.

28. $x - 5 = 15$

29. The number m is a multiple of 4 and is less than 21.

30. Look again at Exercise **15.** Is it possible to have a sentence which is neither an open sentence nor a statement?

Try to design some other math doodles.

3-2
Solution Sets

OBJECTIVE:

To name solutions for an open sentence when a universe is specified for the variable.

For students with a flare for set theory, saying "*x* is a variable on S" is like saying S is being adopted as the universe.

When a symbol may be replaced only by elements of a certain set, S, then the symbol is called a *variable on set S*.

More than one replacement may make an open sentence true. Consider the open sentence *x is a divisor of 12 when x is a variable on N*. The numbers 1, 2, 3, 4, 6, and 12 make the sentence true. Each of these replacements is said to *satisfy* the open sentence and is called a *solution* to the open sentence. The set of all solutions of an open sentence is called the **solution set** or **truth set.**

The solution set of *x is a divisor of 12 when x is a variable on N* is {1, 2, 3, 4, 6, 12}.

Sometimes no solution can be found for an open sentence. In such cases, the solution set is the empty set, { } or ∅.

EXAMPLE

Ask what solution set would result if *q* were a variable on Q.

Let *q* be a variable on N. There are no natural numbers which satisfy $3 \cdot q = 1$. Therefore, the solution set of $3 \cdot q = 1$ is { }, or ∅.

EXERCISES

1. 60 **2.** 6 **3.** 2 **4.** 7 **5.** 6 **6.** {3, 9, 15} **7.** {6, 12} **8.** {3, 6, 9, 12, 15} **9.** {3, 6} **10.** {15} **11.** $x \in$ {3, 6, 9, 12, 15}, $y \in$ {0, 3, 6, 9, 12}; or {(3, 0), (3, 3), (3, 6), (3, 9), (3, 12), (6, 0), (6, 3), (6, 6), (9, 0), (9, 3), (9, 6), (12, 0), (12, 3), (15, 0)} **12.** {4, 10} **13.** {7, 13} **14.** {4, 7} **15.** ∅ **16.** {4, 7, 10, 13}

In Exercises **1–5,** *x* is a variable on N. Write any replacements for *x* which make each open sentence true.

1. There are *x* minutes in one hour.

2. When the number *x* is doubled, the result is one-fourth of 48.

3. The number *x* is an even prime number.

4. In a year, there are *x* months which have 31 days.

5. There are *x* possible scores in a toss of a die.

Write the solution set for each open sentence. In Exercises **6–11,** *x* is a variable on A = {3, 6, 9, 12, 15} and *y* is a variable on W.

6. The number *x* is an odd number.

7. The number *x* is divisible by 6.

8. The number *x* is a multiple of 3.

9. The number *x* is less than 8.

10. $x + 10 = 25$

11. $x + y \in A$

For students who do not know about ordered pairs, avoid Exercise 11.

In Exercises **12–16,** *y* is a variable on B = {4, 7, 10, 13}. Write the solution set for each open sentence.

12. The number *y* is an even number.

13. The number *y* is a prime number.

14. The number *y* + 4 is less than 14.

15. The number *y* is greater than 20.

16. $y + y = 2 \cdot y$

In Exercises **17–22**, p, q, r, and s are variables on C = {1, 3, 5, 7, 9}. Write the solution set for each open sentence.

17. $p + 5 = 8$

18. $s + 2 \in C$

19. $q > 6$

20. $r < 6$

21. $p \cdot p \in C$

22. $q - 8 = 0$

In Exercises **23–29,** n is a variable on D = {1, 2, 3, 4, . . . , 10}. Write the solution set for each open sentence.

23. $n + 2 = 10$

24. $5 + n > 10$

25. $n + n + n \in D$

26. $n + 3 < 4$

27. The number n is a perfect square.

28. $2 \cdot n = n + 2$

29. $n + 3 = 11 - n$

30. x, y, and z are variables on {1, 2, 3, 4, 5}. Find the replacements for x, y, and z, with x less than y, for which $x^2 + y^2 = z^2$.

3-3
Equations

OBJECTIVE:

To name the solution set of a simple linear equation with variables on N or the positive rationals.

EXAMPLE

Remind students that it is important to know the set of elements by which the variable may be replaced.

An open sentence containing the verb *is equal to* ($=$) is called an **equation.** The verb *is equal to* may be shortened to *is* in some open sentences. To **solve an equation** means to find its solution set.

Let x be a variable on N. To solve the equation $x + 2 = 5$, test replacements for x.

Replacements for x	$x + 2 = 5$	True or False
1	$1 + 2 = 5$	F
2	$2 + 2 = 5$	F
3	$3 + 2 = 5$	T
4 ↓	$4 + 2 = 5$ ↓	F ↓

Trying all possible replacements for a variable usually takes too much time. It is an impossible task when x is a variable on an infinite set, such as N.

You may think of the equation $x + 2 = 5$ as saying, *What number added to 2 gives 5?* From your work in arithmetic, you know that the only possible solution is 3.

EXAMPLES

Ask what the solution set would be in Example 1 if x were a variable on W.

1. Solve the equation $x - 5 = 2\frac{1}{2}$, when x is a variable on the set of rational numbers, Q.

What number minus 5 is $2\frac{1}{2}$? Only when x is replaced by $7\frac{1}{2}$ is the sentence true. The solution set of the equation is $\left\{7\frac{1}{2}\right\}$.

2. Solve the equation $3 + x = 1$, when x is a variable on N.

What number added to 3 is 1? There is no natural number which can replace x to make the sentence true. Therefore, the solution set is $\varnothing$ when x is a variable on N.

EXERCISES

1. $x = 7$ **2.** $m = 6$ **3.** $y = 10$
4. $p = 9$ **5.** $x = 17$ **6.** $a = 5$
7. $z = 10$ **8.** $a = 11$ **9.** $x = 9$
10. ϕ **11.** $x = 18$ **12.** $x = 4$
13. $m = 49$ **14.** ϕ **15.** $x = 27$
16. $x = 18$ **17.** $y = 54$ **18.** $m = 5$ **19.** $p = 8$ **20.** $p = 1$
21. $n = 11$ **22.** $x = 7$ **23.** ϕ
24. $x = 3$ **25.** $y = 10$ **26.** $z = 25$
27. $w = 13$ **28.** $y = 3$ **29.** $d = 6$
30. $y = 10$ **31.** $v = 1000$
32. $x = 9$ **33.** $x = 2$ **34.** $t = 17$
35. $\{1\frac{1}{2}\}$ **36.** $\{\frac{1}{4}\}$

Solve each equation if each variable is on N. If there is just one solution as in $5 + x = 7$, write your answer as an equation, $x = 2$.

1. $x + 2 = 9$ **2.** $m + 1 = 7$

3. $y + 2 = 12$ **4.** $p - 6 = 3$

5. $x + 4 = 21$ **6.** $4 = 9 - a$

7. $21 = z + 11$ **8.** $8 = a - 3$

9. $x + 7 = 16$ **10.** $x + 10 = 0$

11. $x + 2 = 20$ **12.** $16 - x = 12$

13. $m + 5 = 54$ **14.** $p + 1 = 0$

15. $x + 2 = 29$ **16.** $x - 4 = 14$

17. $y - 27 = 27$ **18.** $3 \cdot m = 15$

19. $12 \cdot p = 96$ **20.** $4 \cdot p = 4$

21. $4 \cdot n = 44$ **22.** $x \cdot x = 49$

23. $2 \cdot x = 1$ **24.** $\dfrac{12}{x} = 4$

25. $\dfrac{20}{y} = 2$ **26.** $\dfrac{100}{z} = 4$

27. $12\frac{1}{2} = w - \frac{1}{2}$ **28.** $y \cdot \frac{1}{3} = 1$

29. $\frac{1}{2} \cdot d = 3$ **30.** $\dfrac{100}{v} = 10$

31. $\dfrac{1}{100} \cdot v = 10$ **32.** $\dfrac{3}{x} = \dfrac{1}{3}$

33. $\dfrac{3}{x} = 1\frac{1}{2}$ **34.** $\frac{1}{2} \cdot t = 8\frac{1}{2}$

Write the solution set for each equation. Each variable is on the set of positive rationals.

35. $x + 1 = 2\frac{1}{2}$ **36.** $y + 4 = 4\frac{1}{4}$

37. $z + 4 = 7\dfrac{1}{2}$

38. $p - 1 = \dfrac{1}{2}$

39. $q - 2 = 1\dfrac{1}{2}$

40. $y - 3 = 3\dfrac{1}{4}$

41. $t + \dfrac{1}{4} = 5\dfrac{3}{4}$

42. $m + \dfrac{3}{4} = \dfrac{1}{2}$

43. $m - \dfrac{1}{4} = \dfrac{1}{2}$

44. $w + \dfrac{1}{2} = 0$

45. $w + \dfrac{1}{2} = 1$

46. $x + x = \dfrac{1}{2}$

47. $2 \cdot x = \dfrac{1}{2}$

48. $q \cdot \dfrac{4}{3} = 1$

49. $q \cdot 2 = \dfrac{1}{4}$

50. $\dfrac{1}{2} \cdot y = \dfrac{1}{4}$

3-4
Writing Open Sentences

The first step in the solution of a problem often is to write a mathematical sentence about the problem. Sometimes the written words are *translated* into mathematical sentences.

EXAMPLES

OBJECTIVES:

1. To translate a verbal sentence into a mathematical one.
2. To write a mathematical sentence (using given data) which is based on a familiar formula.

1. **Words:** 4 subtracted from some number is 7.
   Translation: $x - 4 = 7$

2. **Words:** 4 times 27 is larger than some number.
   Translation: $4 \cdot 27 > z$

Sometimes when writing a mathematical sentence, you will use something that you already know. The words of the problem and what you already know may *imply* a mathematical sentence.

EXAMPLES

To clarify this, ask students to try to translate these problems as in the previous set of examples. That is, have them try without using a "What you know" statement.

1. **Words:** A rectangle has a length of 4 feet and width of y feet. Its area is 20 square feet.
   What you know: Area of a rectangle = length · width
   Implied: $20 = 4 \cdot y$

2. **Words:** The perimeter of a triangle of sides of lengths a inches, b inches, and c inches is 34 inches.
   What you know: To find the perimeter of a triangle, add the lengths of the sides.
   Implied: $a + b + c = 34$

EXERCISES

Write an equation for each problem. The equation either may be translated from the words or implied by the words and what you know.

1. Some number added to 4 is equal to 11.

2. Four added to a number is equal to 9.

3. Seven subtracted from a number is equal to 12.

4. Eleven subtracted from a number is 2.

5. If 5 is added to some number, the answer is 14.

6. Three less than a number is 8.

7. Some number added to 4 gives 10.

8. When 4 is subtracted from some number, the answer is 2.

9. When 4 is subtracted from a number, the answer is 6.

10. Some number added to itself gives 4.

11. A number x minus a number y is equal to zero.

12. A number n is 4 more than 15.

13. If n is an even number, the next even number m is 2 more than n.

14. The sum of x and y is 12.

15. The difference between p and q is 29, where p is greater than q.

16. The length, a, of a rectangle is 5 more than the width, b.

17. Adding 35 to the sum of a and b gives 360.

18. The sum of x, y, and z is 180.

19. Solve each equation you obtained in Exercises **1–10.**

Write an equation for each problem and then solve it.

20. There are 30 students in a class. If x students are absent then 25 students are present. Find x.

21. There are 21 passengers on a bus. At the next stop, x people board the bus. The number of passengers is now 30. Find x.

22. An army regiment consists of n men. Then 100 recruits join up. The total number of men is now 850. Find n.

23. A book contains 325 pages. After p pages are read, the number still to be read is 84. Find p.

24. A farmer has 250 sheep. He buys x more sheep at the market. His flock now has 320 sheep. Find x.

25. The same number is represented by a and $b + 5$. If $b = 45$, find a.

26. The same number is represented by p and $q - 20$. If $p = 80$, find q.

27. Adding $r + 5$ and 15 gives 80. Find r.

28. Tom weighs 5 lb more than Jack who weighs x lb. If Tom weighs 145 lb, how much does Jack weigh?

29. $x + y = 100$, $x + 45 = 100$, $x = 55$ **30.** $4 + x = q$, $q = 14$ **31.** $4 + x = q$, $x = 32$ **32.** $x = 21$ **33.** $z = 8$ **34.** $y = 12$

29. The sum of x and y is 100. If y is 45, what is x?
30. The sum of 4 and x is q. If $x = 10$, find q.
31. The sum of 4 and x is q. If $q = 36$, find x.

In Exercises **32–34,** the sum of y and z is x.
32. If $y = 12$ and $z = 9$, find x.
33. If $x = 15$ and $y = 7$, find z.
34. If $x = 31$ and $z = 19$, find y.

3-5
Number Pairs

OBJECTIVES:

1. To name an ordered pair, given its location in the graph of W × W.
2. To identify a point's location in the graph of W × W, given an ordered pair.

EXPLORATORY
EXERCISES

1. Student action

1. Find Casper, Wyoming, on the map. The index gives its location as G-4.

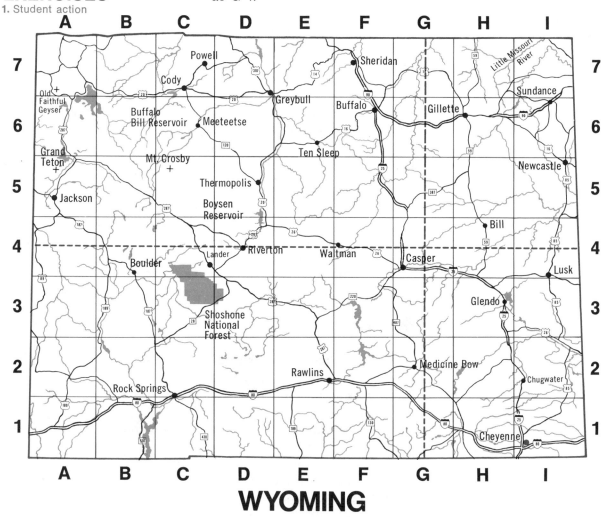

WYOMING

Imagine a vertical line (–·–·–·–·–) through G and a horizontal line (– – – – –) through 4. Casper lies near the intersection of these two lines.

2. a. I — 1 b. D — 4 c. D — 5
d. A — 5 e. C — 2 f. F — 7
g. H — 3

2. Pretend that you are writing the index for the map of Wyoming. Use vertical and horizontal lines to name the letter-number pair for each location.

   a. Cheyenne   **b.** Riverton   **c.** Thermopolis
   d. Jackson   **e.** Rock Springs   **f.** Sheridan
   g. Glendo

This map is indexed using only numbers for both vertical and horizontal locations.

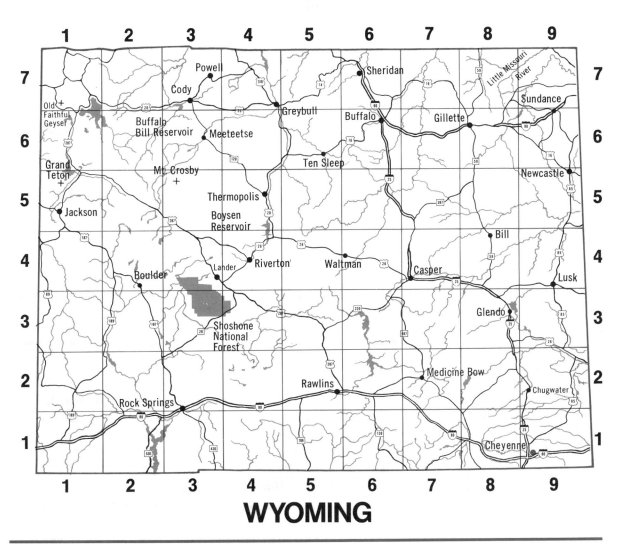

WYOMING

There could be confusion over the location of 7-4. This pair could locate either Casper or Greybull, depending on which number gives the vertical location and which gives the horizontal location. If the horizontal (side-to-side) location on the map is given first and the vertical (up-and-down) location is given second, then 7-4 locates Casper.

3. Name the location given by each number pair.

a. 4-4	**b.** 5-2	**c.** 3-6
d. 7-2	**e.** 2-4	**f.** 5-6
g. 3-7	**h.** 1-7	**i.** 3-3
j. 9-2		

When a pair of numbers is given and it makes a difference which one comes first, the pair is called an **ordered pair.** Ordered pairs usually are written in parentheses with the numbers separated by a comma. Instead of 7-3, (7, 3) should be written.

4. Giving the horizontal location first and the vertical location second, write an ordered pair for each location.

a. Old Faithful Geyser	**b.** Meeteetse
c. Rawlins	**d.** Buffalo
e. Newcastle	**f.** Boysen Reservoir
g. Lander	**h.** Intersection of Highway 187 and Highway 189

5. Name the location given by each ordered pair.

a. (1, 5)	**b.** (3, 4)	**c.** (6, 7)
d. (9, 6)	**e.** (9, 4)	**f.** (3, 5)
g. (3, 2)	**h.** (8, 6)	**i.** (9, 1)
j. (3, 7)	**k.** (6, 6)	**l.** (4, 7)

Suppose the map is removed but the index numbers and their lines are kept. The result is a picture of a part of the **Cartesian plane** or **coordinate plane.**

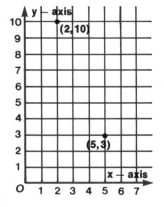

The special point O, identified by (0, 0), is called the **origin.** The horizontal line which includes the origin is called the **x-axis.** The vertical line which includes the origin is called the **y-axis.** The x-axis and y-axis usually are drawn so that they form a corner of a square. In an ordered pair, the first number is called the **x-coordinate** or **abscissa.** The second number is called the **y-coordinate** or **ordinate.**

EXAMPLES

1. (5, 3)   The x-coordinate is 5.
         The y-coordinate is 3.
2. (2, 10)   The abscissa is 2.
         The ordinate is 10.

EXERCISES

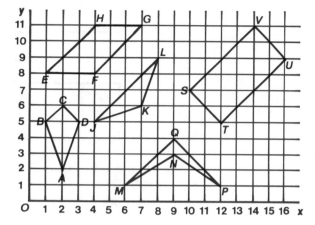

1. Name the points in the figure whose first coordinate is 4.
2. Name the points in the figure whose second coordinate is 4.
3. Write the coordinates of H, J, K, L, M, and Q in the form A(3, 2).
4. On a sheet of graph paper, mark the origin O in the lower left-hand corner. Mark the x-axis and y-axis, and number the scales on the axes from 0 to 20. Plot each set of points. Join the points in each set in the order given. Join the last point to the first.
  a. {A(5, 1), B(8, 6), C(2, 6)}
  b. {E(14, 2), F(20, 2), G(20, 8), H(14, 8)}
  c. {P(5, 10), Q(10, 13), R(15, 10), S(12, 15), T(15, 20), U(10, 17), V(5, 20), W(8, 15)}
5. In the same Cartesian plane, join each set of points in the order given. Also, join the last point of each set to the first point of that set. Describe the shape which is outlined.
  a. {(7, 3), (17, 3), (18, 5), (5, 5)}
  b. {(10, 5), (10, 21)}
  c. {(5, 5), (10, 17), (9, 7)}
  d. {(10, 6), (19, 7), (10, 21)}

Use the map for Exercises **6–8**.

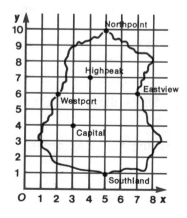

6. Use coordinates to give the positions of Capital, Eastview, and Northpoint.
7. What places are located at (4, 7), (5, 1), and (2, 6)?
8. If each unit represents 5 mi, how far is it from Northpoint to Southland? How far is it from Westport to Eastview?

71

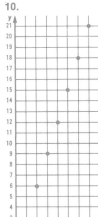
9. An ordered pair (x, y) can be plotted when x and y are replaced by numbers. Plot the ordered pairs from this table.

x	2	6	7	0	3	1
y	1	6	0	7	5	4

10. Plot the ordered pairs from this table.

x	0	2	3	4	5	6	7
y	0	6	9	12	15	18	21

11. What are the x-coordinates of the ordered pairs $(0, 5)$, $(3, 14)$, $(205, 6)$?

12. What are the y-coordinates of the ordered pairs $(6, 8)$, $(0, 4)$, $(3, 2)$?

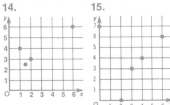
13. Write the next four ordered pairs in the sequence $(0, 0)$, $(2, 2)$, $(4, 4)$, $(6, 6)$, ...

14. Plot the ordered pairs given in the table.

x	$1\frac{1}{2}$	5	1	2	6
y	$2\frac{1}{2}$	0	4	3	6

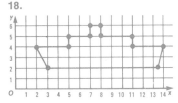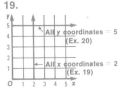
15. Plot ordered pairs to show $S = \{(3, 3), (6, 6), (2, 0), (0, 7), (4, 4)\}$. Is the second member of the given list of elements the same distance from the x-axis and the y-axis? Which other members of S are equidistant from the axes?

16. Write the coordinates of six ordered pairs which are equidistant from the x-axis and the y-axis.

17. If (a, b) is equidistant from the x-axis and the y-axis, what can you say about a and b?

18. Join the ordered pairs in order. Then describe the shape. $(3, 2)$, $\left(13\frac{1}{2}, 2\right)$, $(14, 4)$, $(11, 4)$, $(11, 5)$, $(8, 5)$, $(8, 6)$, $(7, 6)$, $(7, 5)$, $(5, 5)$, $(5, 4)$, $(2, 4)$, $(3, 2)$

19. On graph paper, do your best to show the set of all ordered pairs whose x-coordinate is 2.
   a. Is $(2, 10)$ a member of this set? Is $(2, 2000)$? Is $(2, 105,679)$?
   b. Can you say how many members this set has?

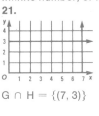
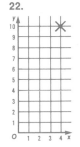
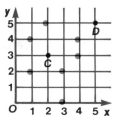
20. On the same diagram as the one for Exercise **19,** show the set
of ordered pairs whose y-coordinate is 5.
  a. Is (5, 5) a member of this set? Is (18, 5)? Is (37,321, 5)?
  b. Can you say how many members this set has?

21. Let G be the set of all ordered pairs with x-coordinate 7. Let
H be the set of all ordered pairs with y-coordinate 3. On graph
paper, show G and H. List the elements in G ∩ H.

22. In a treasure hunt, the treasure is at the point which belongs
to the set of ordered pairs with x-coordinate 4, and also to the
set of ordered pairs with y-coordinate 10. Show the position of
the treasure on a diagram.

23. The lines of the graph paper represent a network of roads.
Robbers based at C rob a bank at D. The police set up road
blocks at the crossroads (1, 2), (1, 4), (3, 0), (2, 5), (3, 2), (4, 4),
and (4, 3). Make a diagram to show this information. Can the
robbers escape by car to their base?

24. Show on graph paper S = {(4, 5), (6, 6), (6, 12), (10, 0), (10, 5),
(13, 13)}. If (x, y) is a member of S, list the ordered pairs which
satisfy each statement.
  a. $x = y$ **b.** $x = 2y$ **c.** $x > y$

25. Write the coordinates of the next four ordered pairs in the
sequence (1, 1), (3, 3), (5, 5), (7, 7), ...
  a. Plot the eight ordered pairs and draw a line through them.
  b. If (r, s) belongs to the sequence, what can you say about r
  or s, or both?
  c. Which ordered pairs lie above the line drawn in Part **a**?
    (1) $K(7, 8)$ **(2)** $L(11, 11)$ **(3)** $M(3, 2)$ **(4)** $N(106, 108)$
  d. $T(p, q)$ lies above the line. Which statement is true?
    (1) $p = q$ **(2)** $p > q$ **(3)** $p < q$

26. The set of all ordered pairs with first coordinate 5 is K and
M = {(5, 1), (5, 2), (5, 11), (5, 4)}. Which, if either, is correct:
M ⊆ K or K ⊆ M?

  Plot the points for each set on the same Cartesian plane.
27. The set P of ordered pairs for which $x = 7$
28. The set V of ordered pairs for which $x = 9$
29. The set T of ordered pairs for which $y = 2$
30. The set S of ordered pairs for which $y = 6$

31. Write the coordinates from Exercises **27–30** of the single point
in each of the sets P ∩ T, T ∩ V, V ∩ S and S ∩ P. What are
the sets P ∩ V and T ∩ S?

32. See section notes in T.G. $0 \leq b < 3$ and $a \in W$. Above the line

32. Show on graph paper the set of ordered pairs with *y*-coordinate 3. If $P(a, b)$ lies below this line, what can you say about *a* or *b*, or both? If $Q(c, d)$ is an ordered pair such that *d* is greater than 3, where does *Q* lie relative to the line?

3-6
Sentences in Two Variables

Open sentences may have two variables. Solutions for such sentences must be *ordered pairs* which give a value for each variable in the sentence.

EXAMPLE

OBJECTIVE:

To find solutions for a given linear equation in two variables over W and graph the equation.

Remind students that ordered pairs are *usually* written in the order which would be alphabetical for the corresponding variables. That is, if $x = 1$ and $y = 4$, write (1, 4), not (4, 1).

Let *x* be a variable on {0, 1, 2, 3, 4}. Solve the open sentence $y = 3 + x$.

Replacement for *x*	$y = 3 + x$	Solution
0	$y = 3 + 0 = 3$	(0, 3)
1	$y = 3 + 1 = 4$	(1, 4)
2	$y = 3 + 2 = 5$	(2, 5)
3	$y = 3 + 3 = 6$	(3, 6)
4	$y = 3 + 4 = 7$	(4, 7)

The set of solutions for $y = 3 + x$ could be given in a table.

x	0	1	2	3	4
y	3	4	5	6	7

The solution set for $y = 3 + x$ can be pictured by plotting the solutions on a part of the Cartesian plane. The picture of solutions is called a **graph**. The graph of $y = 3 + x$ when *x* is a variable on {0, 1, 2, 3, 4} shows the solution set for the equation.

EXERCISES

See section notes in T.G.

1.
x	0	1	2	3	4	5
y	0	1	2	3	4	5

See section notes in T.G.

2.
x	0	1	2	3	4	5
y	5	4	3	2	1	0

See section notes in T.G.

3.
x	0	1	2	3	4	5
y	0	2	4	6	8	10

See section notes in T.G.

4.
x	0	1	2	3	4	5
y	10	8	6	4	2	0

See section notes in T.G.

5.
x	0	1	2	3	4	5
y	0	3	6	9	12	15

See section notes in T.G.

6.
x	0	1	2	3	4	5
y	15	12	9	6	3	0

See section notes in T.G.

Exercise 9 is an early experience in solving a system of equations. If students ask that a universe be specified, tell them to make x and y variables on W.

7. a.
x	0	1	2	3
y	0	1	2	3

b.
x	0	1	2	3
y	0	1	4	9

8. See section notes in T.G.
9. $A \cap B = \{(1, 1)\}$ **10.** $y = x$
11. straight line **12.** straight line
13. not a straight line **14.** not a straight line **15.** not a straight line **16.** straight line

2 mi   **x** mi

17. a.
x	1	2	3	4	5	6
y	2	3	4	5	6	7

b. $A \cap B = \phi$

c.
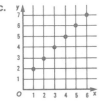

The variables x and y are on W. For each open sentence, complete this table.

x	0	1	2	3	4	5
y	?	?	?	?	?	?

Draw a graph showing the solutions.
1. $y = x$
2. $y = 5 - x$
3. $y = 2 \cdot x$
4. $y = 10 - 2 \cdot x$
5. $y = 3 \cdot x$
6. $y = 15 - 3 \cdot x$

In Exercises **7–10,** x is a variable on $\{0, 1, 2, 3\}$ and y is a variable on W.
7. Complete a table for each equation.
    a. $y = x$ **b.** $y = x^2$
8. Draw graphs on the same Cartesian plane for the two equations.
9. If A = {solutions for $y = x$} and B = {solutions for $y = x^2$}, list the elements of A ∩ B.
10. Which of the two graphs in Exercise **8** has the points lying in a straight line?

By thinking about the equations in Exercises **11–16** or by plotting a few points, name the equations that would give graphs with all points in a straight line. Let x and y be variables on W.
11. $y = 4 \cdot x$ **12.** $y = 3 \cdot x + 5$
13. $y = x^2 + 5$ **14.** $y = x^3$
15. $y = x^2 + x$ **16.** $y = 100 \cdot x + 26$

17. Sample A ship sails 2 miles east from one marker buoy to another. Then it continues to sail east for x miles.
A mathematical sentence for the total distance, y miles, that the ship sails is written $y = 2 + x$. If x is a variable on $\{1, 2, 3, 4, 5, 6\}$ and y is a variable on W, this table can be made.

x	1	2	3	4	5	6
y	3	4	5	6	7	8

18. a. $y = x - 1$
b.
x	1	2	3	4	5	6
y	0	1	2	3	4	5

c.

19. a. $y = 2x$
b.
x	1	2	3	4	5	6
y	2	4	6	8	10	12

c.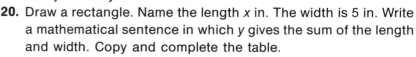

20.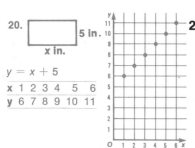
5 in.
x in.
$y = x + 5$
x	1	2	3	4	5	6
y	6	7	8	9	10	11

21.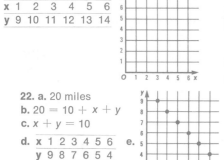
8 in.
x in.
$y = x + 8$
x	1	2	3	4	5	6
y	9	10	11	12	13	14

22. a. 20 miles
b. $20 = 10 + x + y$
c. $x + y = 10$
d.
x	1	2	3	4	5	6
y	9	8	7	6	5	4

e.

The solution set of $y = 2 + x$ can be shown as a graph obtained by plotting the ordered pairs from the table.
a. Complete a table and a graph when the distances sailed are one mile and x miles, where x is a variable on {1, 2, 3, 4, 5, 6}.
b. If A = {solutions for the sample} and B = {solutions for Part a}, what is A ∩ B?

18. The variables x and y are on W. The relation between x and y is such that y is always 1 less than x.
a. Write an equation in x and y.
b. If x is a variable on S = {1, 2, 3, 4, 5, 6}, find y when x is replaced by elements from S. Copy and complete this table.

x	1	2	3	4	5	6
y	0	1	?	?	?	?

c. Show the solution set as a graph.
19. Repeat Exercise 18 when the relation between x and y is such that y is always two times x.
20. Draw a rectangle. Name the length x in. The width is 5 in. Write a mathematical sentence in which y gives the sum of the length and width. Copy and complete the table.

x	1	2	3	4	5	6
y	?	?	?	?	?	?

Show the solution set as a graph.
21. Repeat Exercise 20 for a rectangle with length x in. and width 8 in.
22. A large boat uses 1 gallon of fuel every 4 miles it sails. One day the boat made 3 trips and used 5 gallons of fuel.
a. What was the total length of the 3 trips?
b. If the first trip was 10 mi, the second x mi, and the third y mi, write a mathematical sentence containing x and y.
c. Now write this sentence in the form $x + y = $ ___?___ .
d. Copy and complete the table.

x	1	2	3	4	5	6
y	?	?	?	?	?	?

e. Show the solution set as a graph.

OBJECTIVES:

1. To name the coefficient of a monomial expression.
2. To identify the terms of a polynomial.

EXPLORATORY EXERCISES

Solve each equation if x is a variable on W.

1. $4 \cdot x = 24$
2. $3 \cdot x = 15$
3. $3 \cdot x = 6$
4. $2 \cdot x = 12$
5. $1 \cdot x = 5$
6. $4 \cdot x = 20$
7. $x \cdot 4 = 24$
8. $x \cdot 3 = 15$
9. $x \cdot 3 = 6$
10. $x \cdot 2 = 12$
11. $x \cdot 1 = 5$
12. $x \cdot 4 = 20$

Notice that the solutions for Exercises **1** and **7, 2** and **8,** and so on, are the same.

This is what you would expect by the Commutative Property of Multiplication for whole numbers. If x is a whole number, then $4 \cdot x$ should equal $x \cdot 4$, $3 \cdot x$ should equal $x \cdot 3$, and so on.

In a product that contains a numerical factor and variables, the numerical factor is called the *numerical coefficient*. In this chapter, the word **coefficient** always will mean numerical coefficient.

EXAMPLES

1. In $3 \cdot m$, 3 is the numerical coefficient.
2. In $y \cdot 5$, 5 is the numerical coefficient.
3. In $p \cdot 21 \cdot q$, 21 is the numerical coefficient.
4. Since $x = 1 \cdot x$, 1 is the coefficient of x.
5. Since $x \cdot y = 1 \cdot x \cdot y$, 1 is the coefficient of $x \cdot y$.
6. In $3 \cdot a + 2 \cdot b + c$, 3 is the coefficient of a, 2 is the coefficient of b, and 1 is the coefficient of c.

It is usual to omit the multiplication sign between a coefficient and a variable and also between two variables. In a product, it is usual to write the coefficient first and then the variables in alphabetical order.

EXAMPLES

1. $3x$ means $3 \cdot x$
2. xyz means $x \cdot y \cdot z$
3. $abc27$ would be written $27abc$
4. $3yzx$ would be written $3xyz$

Often in algebra combinations of numbers and variables represent numbers. Such combinations result from operations such as addition, subtraction, multiplication, and division. These combinations are called **algebraic expressions.**

An expression or part of an expression which involves only a product or root of numbers, variables, or both is called a **term.**

EXAMPLES

Do not worry too much now if students are not completely sure what "term" means. Most will learn by seeing the word repeatedly in context while studying simple expressions.

Expression	Terms
$3x - 5$	$3x, -5$
$ax^2 + bx + c$	ax^2, bx, c
$6aby$	$6aby$
$\sqrt{x} - 8$	$\sqrt{x}, -8$

Many open sentences and statements in algebra are formed by connecting two expressions by symbols such as $=$, $<$, $>$, $\leq$, or $\geq$. These symbols provide a relationship between the two expressions.

EXAMPLES

These examples are review. They probably need no commentary except possibly for slow students.

1. Solve the equation $2x + 7 = 33$, where x is a variable on N. To solve this equation think, *What number added to 7 gives 33?* The answer is 26. To make $2x + 7 = 33$ a true sentence, $2x$ must equal 26, so $x = 13$. The work may look like this.

$$2x + 7 = 33$$
$$2x = 26$$
$$x = 13$$

2. Solve the equation $4x - 6 = 33$, where x is a variable on Q. To solve this equation think, *What number gives 33 when 6 is subtracted from it?* The number is 39. To make $4x - 6 = 33$ a true sentence, $4x$ must equal 39, or $x = 9\frac{3}{4}$. The work may look like this.

$$4x - 6 = 33$$
$$4x = 39$$
$$x = 9\frac{3}{4}$$

Exercises 2, 4, 6, and 8 may be done as in-class examples before making an assignment.

EXERCISES

1. x^2, $2x$, 5 **2.** $3x$, xy^2
3. $5x$ **4.** x, $-2x$, 3 **5.** a, $-b$,
c, $-d$ **6.** x^3, x^4 **7.** $3xy$, $2xz$
8. $25xyz$

List the terms in each expression.

1. $x^2 + 2x + 5$　　　　　　　**2.** $3 \cdot x + x \cdot y \cdot 2$
3. $x \cdot 5$　　　　　　　　　　**4.** $x - 2y + 3$
5. $a - b + c - d$　　　　　　**6.** $x \cdot x^2 + x^4$
7. $y \cdot 3x + z \cdot 2x$　　　　　**8.** $25 \cdot x \cdot y \cdot z$

9. $5x$ 10. $5y$ 11. $2wy$ 12. $10k$
13. $3y$ 14. $3wx$ 15. $7x$, 7
16. xy, 1 17. xy, -1 18. w, -5
19. a. 8 b. 4 c. 9 d. 9 e. 4
f. 4 20. a. 4 b. 0 c. 11 d. 20
e. 10 f. 5 21. $m = 4$ 22. $p = 2$
23. $y = 7$ 24. $c = 12$ 25. $y = 3$
26. $t = 9$ 27. $v = 15$ 28. $w = 42$
29. $x = 3$ 30. $z = 6$ 31. $x = 4$
32. $x = 1$ 33. $x = 5$ 34. $x = 6$
35. $y = 3$ 36. $t = 4$ 37. $x = 0$
38. $y = 7$ 39. $m = 25$ 40. $t = 9$
41. $x = 5/2$ 42. $x = 15/2$
43. $x = 27/2$ 44. $x = 24$
45. $x = 6$ 46. {0, 4} 47. {0}
48. {1} 49. {1, 5}

Write each expression as one term.

9. $2x + 3x$

10. $y + y + y + y + y$

11. $7wy - 6wy + wy$

12. $k + 2k + 3k + 4k$

13. $2x + 3y - x - x$

14. $xw + 2wx$

Name the term which contains the variables in each expression. Then name the coefficient of that term.

15. $7x - 8$

16. $18 + xy$

17. $16 - xy$

18. $18 - 5w + 3$

19. Find the value of each expression when $n = 2$.

a. $n + 6$ b. $2n$ c. $3n + 1$

d. $5n - 1$ e. n^2 f. $20 - 8n$

20. Find the value of each expression when $a = 0$, $b = 1$, and $c = 3$.

a. $a + b + c$ b. abc c. $a + 2b + 3c$

d. $5a + 5b + 5c$ e. $a^2 + b^2 + c^2$

f. $11b - 2c$

Solve each equation. The variables are on N.

21. $3m = 12$

22. $7p = 14$

23. $5y = 35$

24. $8c = 96$

25. $y^2 = 9$

26. $t^2 = 81$

27. $45 = 3v$

28. $3 + w = 45$

Solve each equation, where x, y, z, and so on, are variables on W.

29. $2x + 1 = 7$

30. $5z + 5 = 35$

31. $6x + 1 = 25$

32. $3x + 2 = 5$

33. $2x - 1 = 9$

34. $4x - 5 = 19$

35. $7y - 4 = 17$

36. $12 - 2t = 4$

37. $3x + 4 = 4$

38. $47 - 6y = 5$

39. $101 = 4m + 1$

40. $13t + 142 = 259$

Solve each equation, where x is a variable on Q.

41. $2x + 6 = 11$

42. $2x - 3 = 12$

43. $34 - 2x = 7$

44. $\frac{1}{2}x = 12$

45. $\frac{2}{3}x - 1 = 3$

Find the solution set of each equation if x is a variable on {0, 1, 2, 3, 4, 5}.

46. $x^2 = 4x$

47. $x^2 + 2x = 0$

48. $(x + 1)^2 = 4$

49. $x^2 + 5 = 6x$

50. If x and y are variables on $\{1, 2, 3\}$, can you find the two pairs of replacements for x and y such that $x + 2y = 7$?

3-8 Rearranging Factors

OBJECTIVE:

To express a given monomial in simplest form.

When there are more than two factors in a product, you may wish to change the order in which they are written. It is possible to change the order by using the Commutative and Associative Properties of Multiplication.

The Commutative and Associative Properties of Multiplication also let you omit the parentheses when there are several factors and when only multiplication is involved. For example, by using the Associative Property, you may think of $3 \cdot 4 \cdot 5$ as $(3 \cdot 4) \cdot 5$ or as $3 \cdot (4 \cdot 5)$. When you also use the Commutative Property, you can change the order in any way you please.

$$3 \cdot 4 \cdot 5 = (3 \cdot 4) \cdot 5 = (4 \cdot 3) \cdot 5 = 5 \cdot (4 \cdot 3) = 5 \cdot 4 \cdot 3 = 60$$
$$3 \cdot 4 \cdot 5 = 3 \cdot (4 \cdot 5) = 3 \cdot (5 \cdot 4) = (5 \cdot 4) \cdot 3 = 5 \cdot 4 \cdot 3 = 60$$
$$3 \cdot 4 \cdot 5 = (3 \cdot 4) \cdot 5 = 5 \cdot (3 \cdot 4) = \quad 5 \cdot 3 \cdot 4 = 60$$
$$3 \cdot 4 \cdot 5 = 3 \cdot (4 \cdot 5) = (4 \cdot 5) \cdot 3 = \quad 4 \cdot 5 \cdot 3 = 60$$

By using more examples, you can see that the factors in $3 \cdot 4 \cdot 5$ may be written in any order without changing the product. The same thing can be done for any number of factors.

EXAMPLES

Remind students that when letters represent numbers, the letters may be rearranged in products in the same way as numerals.

1. $3 \cdot 4 \cdot 5 \cdot 6 = 6 \cdot 3 \cdot 5 \cdot 4 = 360$
2. $2a \cdot 3b \cdot 4c = 2 \cdot 3 \cdot 4 \cdot a \cdot b \cdot c = 24abc$
3. $3x \cdot 5x \cdot 2x = 3 \cdot 5 \cdot 2 \cdot x \cdot x \cdot x = 30xxx = 30x^3$

A product is said to be in **simplest form** when two conditions are met.
1. **Only one numerical factor, the coefficient, appears in the product.**
2. **Variable factors which appear more than once are written using exponents. Thus, each different variable factor is written only once.**

The products in the examples are in simplest form when written as 360, $24abc$, and $30x^3$.

EXERCISES

By first changing the order, calculate each of the following as easily as possible.

Sample $5 \cdot 7 \cdot 2 = (5 \cdot 2) \cdot 7 = 10 \cdot 7 = 70$

1. $2 \cdot 9 \cdot 5$	**2.** $5 \cdot 38 \cdot 20$	**3.** $50 \cdot 7 \cdot 2$
4. $25 \cdot 15 \cdot 4$	**5.** $20 \cdot 26 \cdot 5$	**6.** $2 \cdot 5 \cdot 19 \cdot 10$

Write each expression in its simplest form.

Sample $5 \cdot a \cdot 3 = (5 \cdot 3) \cdot a = 15a$

7. $3 \cdot 2 \cdot a$	**8.** $4 \cdot 1 \cdot p$	**9.** $8 \cdot 5 \cdot r$
10. $5 \cdot a \cdot b$	**11.** $3 \cdot m \cdot n$	**12.** $4 \cdot 2 \cdot t$
13. $2 \cdot x \cdot 3$	**14.** $1 \cdot x$	**15.** $g \cdot h \cdot 7$
16. $a \cdot a \cdot b$	**17.** $c \cdot c \cdot c$	**18.** $5 \cdot 3w$
19. $u \cdot 8v$	**20.** $2x \cdot 4y$	**21.** $5m \cdot 2n$

In each diagram, the unit of length is the centimeter. Volume will be measured in cubic centimeters. The symbol for cubic centimeters is cm³.

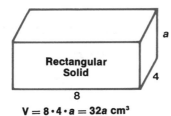

Rectangular Solid

$V = 8 \cdot 4 \cdot a = 32a$ cm³

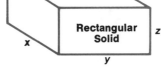

Rectangular Solid

$V = x \cdot y \cdot z = xyz$ cm³

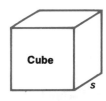

Cube

$V = s \cdot s \cdot s = s^3$ cm³

22. Write an expression in simplest form for the volume of each object.

a.
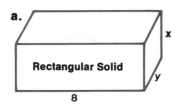

Rectangular Solid

b.
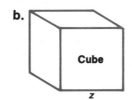

Cube

c.
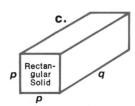

Rectangular Solid

23. If $x = 2$, $y = 3$, and $z = 5$, calculate the value of each expression.
  a. $(x + y) \cdot (y + z) \cdot (z + x)$
  b. $x^2 \cdot y^2 \cdot z^2$

24. When $x = 2$ and $y = 3$, calculate the value of each expression.
  a. $x^2 + 3xy + 1$ **b.** $3x^2 + 2xy + y^2$ **c.** $10x^2y^3$

3-9
Simplifying
Expressions

OBJECTIVE:
To find the simplified form for
a given polynomial.

An expression such as $3x + 4x$ may be written as $7x$ by using the Distributive Property.

$$3x + 4x = (3 + 4)x = 7x$$

Here are more examples of the use of the Distributive Property with expressions.

EXAMPLES

These examples should be review. However, some slow students may need to study the examples carefully.

1. $2 \cdot 5 + 3 \cdot 5 + 7 \cdot 5 = (2 + 3 + 7) \cdot 5 = 12 \cdot 5 = 60$
2. $2x + 3x + 7x = (2 + 3 + 7)x = 12x$
3. $2ab + 3ab + 7ab = (2 + 3 + 7)ab = 12ab$
4. $2z^2 + 3z^2 + 7z^2 = (2 + 3 + 7)z^2 = 12z^2$
5. $5abc - 2abc - abc = (5 - 2 - 1)abc = 2abc$

When you rewrite the expression $3x + 4x$ as $7x$, you *simplify* the algebraic expression. An expression with two or more terms can be simplified only if at least two of the terms contain a common factor.

Terms which contain *exactly the same variable factor* are called **like terms.**

EXAMPLES

Study these examples in pairs: 1 and 2; 3 and 4; 5 and 6.

1. $4x$ and $5x$ are like terms.
2. $4x^2$ and $5x$ are not like terms.
3. $2abc$ and $3abc$ are like terms.
4. $2ab$ and $3abc$ are not like terms.
5. $10x^2y^2$ and x^2y^2 are like terms.
6. $10x^2y^2$ and xy^2 are not like terms.

Stress this paragraph. → Only like terms may be combined when expressions are simplified. You may think of simplifying as combining coefficients of like terms.

EXAMPLES

1. $3x + 6y + 4x - 5y = (3x + 4x) + (6y - 5y)$
$$= (3 + 4)x + (6 - 5)y$$
$$= 7x + y$$
2. $3x + 5y + 4z + 2z = 3x + 5y + 6z$
3. $3x - 2y - 3z + 7x = 10x - 2y - 3z$
4. The expression $3x - 2y - 3z + 7q$ cannot be simplified because there are no terms with the same variable factors.

Remember, when a variable has no numerical coefficient written before it, the coefficient is 1.

EXAMPLE

$3x + x = (3 + 1)x = 4x$

EXERCISES

Simplify each expression if possible.

1. $8x + 7x$ **2.** $12y - 7y$

3. $6a + 5a - 3a$ **4.** $10b - 7b + 2b$

5. $8c - 6c - 2c$ **6.** $5x + 6y$

7. $5x + 3x + 6y$ **8.** $5x + 6y - 2y$

9. $5x + 3x + 6y - 2y$ **10.** $4a + 9a - 6a$

11. $3a + 5a + 7b - 2b$ **12.** $6c + 2d + 3c - d$

13. $2x^2 + 4y^2 + 3x^2 - 2y^2$ **14.** $x^2 + y^2 + 8x^2$

15. $a^2 + b^2 + 2a^2 - b^2$

Solve each equation where x, y, z, and so on, are variables on W.

16. $2x + 3x = 40$ **17.** $8y - 5y = 24$ **18.** $7z + 7z = 14$

19. $9p - 5p = 4$ **20.** $6q + 12q = 54$ **21.** $5r + 5r = 0$

Find a simple expression for the total length of each line. The unit of length is the centimeter.

Samples

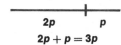

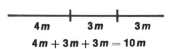

$2p + p = 3p$ $4m + 3m + 3m = 10m$

A $3a$ B $2a$ C

22. From the figure, write the length of $\overline{AC}$ in terms of a. If $AC = 40$ cm, find a.

P $5n$ Q $3n$ R $2n$ S

23. From the figure, write the length of $\overline{PS}$ in terms of n. If $PS = 95$ cm, find n.

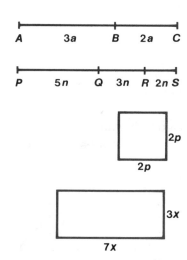

$2p$

$2p$

$3x$

$7x$

24. A square has sides $2p$ cm in length.
   a. Write the perimeter in terms of p.
   b. If $p = 5$, what is the perimeter?
   c. If the perimeter is 32 cm, find p.

25. A rectangle is $7x$ meters long and $3x$ meters wide.
   a. What is the total length of a long and a short side?
   b. What is the perimeter?
   c. If the perimeter is 100 meters, find x and then state the length and width of the rectangle.

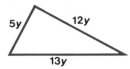

Exercise 27 lends itself to helping make the point that $x = 1 \cdot x$, $q = 1 \cdot q$, etc.

26. a. $30y$ **b.** $Y = 3$ cm
27. a. $P = 2x + 2y + 2z$
b. $P = 2r + 2s + 2t$ **c.** $P = 6p + 4q$
28. a.

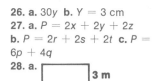

b. $P = 2x + 6$ **c.** $2x + 6 = 16$
d. $x = 5$ m, 15 m² **29. a.** $10d$ meters **b.** $10d = 80$, $d = 8$ meters **c.** 56 meters **30. a.** $x + 15$ **b.** $2x + 15$ **c.** $2x + 15 = 137$, 61

26. A triangle has sides $5y$, $12y$, and $13y$ centimeters long.
    a. Write the perimeter in terms of y.
    b. If the perimeter is 90 cm, find y.

27. In this exercise, the unit of length is a meter. Write the perimeter of each figure in simplest form.

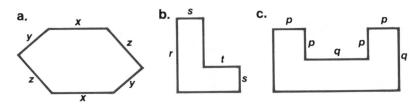

28. A rectangular carpet is x meters long and 3 meters wide.
    a. Make a sketch of the carpet and mark the dimensions.
    b. Write the perimeter in terms of x in simplest form.
    c. If the perimeter is 16 meters, write an equation in x.
    d. Find x and state the area of the carpet.

29. A boy ran $3d$ meters and then swam $7d$ meters.
    a. What total distance did he travel?
    b. If he covered a total distance of 80 meters, write an equation in d and solve it.
    c. What distance did he swim for this value of d?

30. Betty scores 15 points more than Ann on a mathematics test.
    a. Suppose that Ann's score is x. What is Betty's score in terms of x?
    b. Write their combined score in terms of x.
    c. If their combined score is 137, write an equation in x. Solve it to find Betty's score.

3-10 Formulas

OBJECTIVE:

To find the value for the remaining variable when given a formula and values for other variables.

An equation which is used often is called a **formula.**

The equation $A = lw$ is a formula for finding the area of a rectangle.

$$A = \text{area}$$
$$l = \text{length}$$
$$w = \text{width}$$

The equation $n = 2x - 1$ is a formula for finding the odd counting numbers where x is a variable on $\{1, 2, 3, 4, 5, \ldots\}$.

Replace x by 1: $n = (2 \cdot 1) - 1 = 1$
Replace x by 2: $n = (2 \cdot 2) - 1 = 3$
Replace x by 3: $n = (2 \cdot 3) - 1 = 5$
Replace x by 4: $n = (2 \cdot 4) - 1 = 7$

The set of values for n will be $\{1, 3, 5, 7, \ldots\}$.

Remember that a formula is simply an equation. To use a formula, replace all but one of the variables with numerical values in order to find the value of the remaining variable.

EXAMPLE

A rectangle is 3 feet long and 5 feet wide. Find the area of the rectangle. In the formula $A = lw$, l is replaced by 3 and w is replaced by 5.

$$a = lw$$
$$A = 3 \cdot 5$$
$$A = 15 \text{ sq ft}$$

If the length is 6 feet and the width 7 feet, then l is replaced by 6 and w by 7.

$$A = lw$$
$$A = 6 \cdot 7$$
$$A = 42 \text{ sq ft}$$

EXERCISES

Find the value of each expression when $x = 3$.

1. $x + 2$ **2.** $x^2 - 2$ **3.** $5x$ **4.** $4x - 7$

5. $2 + 3x$ **6.** $10 - 2x$ **7.** x^2 **8.** $2x^3$

In Exercises **9–14,** state whether each is true (T) or false (F).

9. $b + 4 = 4$, when $b = 0$ **10.** $3d - 1 = 10$, when $d = 3$

11. $2p = p + 3$, when $p = 3$ **12.** $\frac{1}{2} a = 15$, when $a = 30$

13. $\frac{1}{2}(a + 5) = 6\frac{1}{2}$, when $a = 8$

14. $\frac{1}{3}(b - 4) = 3$, when $b = 10$

Find the value of each expression if $p = 3$ and $q = 2$.

15. $p^2 + q^2$ **16.** $(p - q)^2$ **17.** $p^2 - q^2$

18. $(p + q)^2$ **19.** $4q^2$ **20.** $2p^2 + 3q^2$

21. If x is a variable on {1, 2, 3, 4, 5}, find the set of values of n given by $n = 3x$. Describe this set in words.

22. Find the set of values of n given by $n = 6x - 1$ if x is a variable on {1, 2, 3, 4, 5}. Describe the kind of numbers you obtain. If x is a variable on {1, 2, 3, . . . , 10}, would your description still be true? Give a reason for your answer.

23. Repeat Exercise **22** for the formula $n = 6x + 1$.

24. Find the set of all possible values of v when $v = 10 + 2t^2$, and t is a variable on {0, 1, 2, 3, 4, 5}.

25. The distance s km traveled by an airplane flying at a steady speed of v km/h for t hours is given by $s = vt$. If $v = 1600$, find s when $t = 4$ and also when $t = 1\frac{1}{2}$.

26. A distance M miles can be expressed approximately as K kilometers by the formula $K = 1.6M$.
    a. Find K when $M = 250$.
    b. Use the formula to express a speed of 30 miles per hour in kilometers per hour.

Study these formulas. Calculate the values of the stated items.

Formula	Meaning	Calculation
27. $P = 4s$	P cm = Perimeter of square s cm = length of side	The perimeters of squares with $s = 12$ and $s = 15$.
28. $A = s^2$	A cm² = Area of square s cm = length of side	The areas of squares with $s = 10$ and $s = 22$.
29. $A = lw$	A cm² = Area of rectangle l cm = length of rectangle w cm = width of rectangle	The area of a rectangle with the following dimensions. **a.** $l = 15, w = 8$ **b.** $l = 2.5, w = 1.5$
30. $V = lwh$	V m³ = Volume of a rectangular solid l m = length of a rectangular solid w m = width of a rectangular solid h m = height of a rectangular solid	The volume of a rectangular solid with the following dimensions. **a.** $l = 15, w = 8, h = 2$ **b.** $l = w = h = 10$
31. $c = 90° - x$	Angle c is the complement of angle x.	The complement of angles of 10°, 55°, and 79°.
32. $s = 180° - y$	Angle s is the supplement of angle y.	The supplement of angles of 100°, 55°, and 123°.

Formula	Meaning	Calculation
33. $d = rt$	d km is the distance traveled at r km/h in t hours.	**a.** d when $r = 65$, $t = 4$ **b.** r when $d = 250$, $t = 5$
34. $v = \frac{1}{2}(m + n)$	v is the average of two numbers represented by m and n.	The average of each pair of numbers **a.** 12 and 16 **b.** 23 and 37 **c.** 8.7 and 5.5
35. $C = \frac{83n}{100}$	C is the total cost in dollars of n books costing 83 cents each.	The total cost of 10 books. The total cost of 80 books.
36. $T = 42 - 2N - 2P$	T hours is the time after noon for month N (Jan. = 1, Dec. = 12) given by the position P of the pointer stars of the Great Bear.	The time after noon in December, if $P = 5$; in April, if $P = 7$.

33. a. 260 km **b.** 50 km/hr
34. a. 14 **b.** 30 **c.** 7.1
35. $8.30, $66.40 **36.** 8 PM, 8 AM

3-11
Using Formulas

OBJECTIVES:
To write a formula stating the relationship between quantities from a verbal or pictorial statement of the relationship.

This first example is meant to stress that formulas are made by people for convenience. Stress that there is no mystery in this practice.

Stress the importance of paying attention to which units are used.

People often create formulas when they must work with many problems of the same type. For example, a motorcycle dealer may want to have 25% of the selling price on each cycle as profit. After thinking about it, the dealer may write this formula.

$$P = \frac{4}{3}(w + s)$$

$P =$ Price of cycle
$w =$ wholesale cost
$s =$ shipping charge

A more familiar formula is the one for finding the perimeter of a rectangle. If the length is x and the width is y, the formula $P = 2x + 2y$ may be used to find the perimeter. If x and y are in inches, P also will be in inches.

In using formulas, always *pay close attention to the units of measure*. The formula $P = 2x + 2y$ will not give a reasonable answer if x is in inches and y is in feet. The motorcycle dealer's formula, $P = \frac{4}{3}(w + s)$, will not give a reasonable answer if w is in cents and s is in dollars.

EXERCISES

1.

	a.	b.
Perimeter	10 ft	34 ft
Area	6 ft²	60 ft²

c.	d.	e.
18 cm	(8 + 2t) mi	(2q + 2p) mm
16.25 cm²	4t mi²	pq mm²

2. a. $P = 4x$ **b.** $P = x + 2y$
c. $P = 4p + 2q$ **d.** $P = 2a + 2b$
e. $P = 2a + 2b + 2c$ **f.** $P = 8x + 4t$ **3. a.** $P = 3m$ cm
b. **(1)** $P = 24$ cm **(2)** $P = 16.5$ cm **(3)** $P = 31.2$ cm
4. a. $d = x + y$ **b.** 1300 km
5. a. $d = 3x + 3y$ **b.** $d = 1515$ m

1. Use the formulas $P = 2x + 2y$ and $A = lw$ to complete the following table.

	a.	b.	c.	d.	e.
Length	3 ft	12 in.	6.5 cm	4 mi	p mm
Width	2 ft	5 ft	2.5 cm	t mi	q mm
Perimeter	?	?	?	?	?
Area	?	?	?	?	?

2. Write a formula for the perimeter P of each shape in the figure. All units are centimeters.

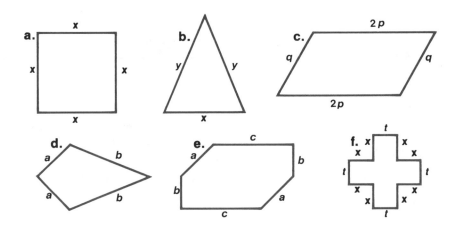

3. The perimeter of a triangle is P cm. Each side has length m cm.
   a. Write a formula for the perimeter.
   b. Calculate P when m has each of the following values.
      (1) 8   **(2)** 5.5   **(3)** 10.4

4. An airplane flies x km east, then y km north. The total distance it flies from 0 to E to N is d km.
   a. Write a formula for d.
   b. Calculate d if $x = 840$ and $y = 460$.

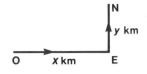

5. The figure shows a network of city streets.
   a. Write a formula for the distance d along the streets shown from A to B. All units are meters.
   b. Calculate d if $x = 325$ and $y = 180$.

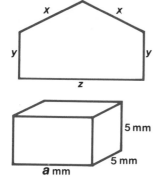

6. $w = x + y$ **a.** $w = 5.25$
b. $w = 9.50 \ \mu g$
7. $L = p - q$, $L = 3.5$
meters 8. $P = 2x + 2y + 4z$
a. $P = 112$ **b.** $z = 20$ **c.** $x = 7$
9. **a.** $S = 4a + 40$ **b.** $S = 100$ mm **10.** P cm $= 10K$ cm,
A cm$^2 = 4 \ k^2$ cm^2, $P = 75$ cm,
$A = 225$ cm^2
11. a.

	Area of Whole Square	Area of Unshaded Part
(1)	x^2	$4x$
(2)	x^2	y^2
(3)	x^2	yz

Area of Shaded Part	Formula for Area of Shaded Part
$x^2 - 4x$	$A = x^2 - 4x$
$x^2 - y^2$	$A = x^2 - y^2$
$x^2 - yz$	$A = x^2 - yz$

b. (1) $A = 60$ cm^2 (2) $A = 84$ cm^2 (3) $A = 72$ cm^2

6. A truck weighs x metric tons when empty. If y metric tons of coal are added, its loaded weight is W metric tons. Write a formula for W.
   a. Find W when $x = 2.75$ and $y = 2.50$.
   b. Find y when $x = 3\frac{1}{2}$ and $W = 6$.

7. A piece of lumber is p meters long. When q meters are sawed off, the remaining length is L meters. Write a formula for L. Find L when $p = 5$ and $q = 1.5$.

8. Write a formula for P in the figure in terms of x, y, and z.
   a. Find P when $x = 35$, $y = 15$, and $z = 12$.
   b. Find z when $P = 64$, $x = 12$, and $y = 10$.
   c. Find x when $P = 36$, $y = 5$, and $z = 12$.

9. The figure shows a rectangular solid with length a mm, width 5 mm, and height 5 mm.
   a. Write a formula for the sum S of the lengths of all the edges of the cube.
   b. Calculate S if $a = 15$.

10. A rectangle is $4k$ cm long and k cm wide. Use a sketch to write a formula for its perimeter P cm; its area A cm^2. Calculate the perimeter and area of the rectangle when $k = 7.5$.

11. The figure shows three squares of side x cm. All units are centimeters.

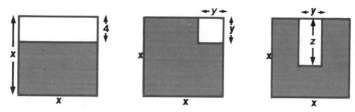

   a. Copy and complete the following table. Work along each row from left to right.

	Area of whole square (cm²)	Area of unshaded part (cm²)	Area of shaded part (cm²)	Formula for area of shaded part
(1)	x^2	$4x$	$x^2 - 4x$	$A = x^2 - 4x$
(2)	x^2	?	?	?
(3)	?	?	?	?

12. a.

(1) ab	cd	$ab - cd$	$A = ab - cd$
(2) ab	$2ef$	$ab - 2ef$	$A = ab - 2ef$
(3) ab	$4g^2$	$ab - 4g^2$	$A = ab - 4g^2$

b. (1) 120 mm² **(2)** 72 mm²
(3) 116 mm² **13. a.** 2*f*, 3*f*, *hf*
b. $W = t - hf$ **c.** $W = 10\frac{1}{4}$ tons
14. a. 30°, 10°, 0° **b.** $C =$

$(F - 32°)$, 100°, 540°

15. a. 19, 23, 27, 31 **b.** Answers
will vary. **c.** 399, 3999 **16. a.** 12
b. 20 **c. (1)** $S = xy$ **(2)** $P =$
$(x + 1)(y + 1)$ **(3)** $S = 870$,
$P = 930$

For Exercise 14, remind students
that the formula may become
more important as the English
system is replaced by the
Metric system.

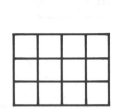

b. Use your formulas to find the area of the shaded part of each square if $x = 10$, $y = 4$, and $z = 7$.

12. Three rectangles of length a mm and width b mm are shown.

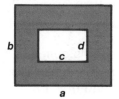 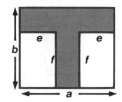 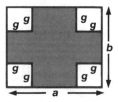

a. Make a table as in Exercise **11**. Write a formula for the area (A mm²) of the shaded part of each rectangle.

b. Use your formulas to find each shaded area if $a = 15$, $b = 12$, $c = 10$, $d = 6$, $e = 6$, $f = 9$, and $g = 4$.

13. An airplane weighs t tons when fully loaded. It uses f tons of fuel per hour.

a. How many tons of fuel does it use in 2 hours? 3 hours? h hours?

b. If W tons is the weight of the airplane after h hours, write a formula for W. Assume that the airplane was fully loaded at the start.

c. Use your formula to calculate W when $t = 12$, $f = \frac{1}{4}$, and $h = 5$.

14. The rule for expressing a Fahrenheit temperature as a Celsius (Centigrade) temperature is *Subtract 32 and multiply the result by* $\frac{5}{9}$.

a. Use this rule to find the reading, °C, on a Celsius thermometer when the reading, °F, on a Fahrenheit thermometer is 86°; 50°; 32°.

b. Write a formula for C in terms of F. Use it to calculate C when $F = 212$; when $F = 1004$.

15. a. Find the 5th, 6th, and 7th numbers of the sequence 3, 7, 11, 15, ...

b. Can you write the 100th number?

c. The nth number N is given by the formula $N = 4n - 1$. Check that this formula is true for the 5th, 6th, and 7th numbers. Use it to find the 100th and the 1000th numbers.

16. The figure shows a network of squares, each of side 1 cm.

a. How many 1-cm squares are there?

b. How many points are there where two lines cross or meet?

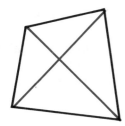

c. Assume there are x squares across and y squares up.
    (1) Write a formula for the number S of 1-cm squares.
    (2) Write a formula for the number P of points where two lines cross or meet.
    (3) Find S and P for the case when $x = 29$ and $y = 30$.

17. How many squares are there altogether in the 2-by-2 square network shown? (Not four!)
    a. Draw a 3-by-3 network. How many squares does it contain? (Not nine or ten!)
    b. For an a-by-a network, the number of squares N is given by the formula $N = \dfrac{1}{6}a(a + 1)(2a + 1)$. Use this formula to check your answers for the 2-by-2 and 3-by-3 network.
    c. Calculate the number of squares in a 100-by-100 network.

18. The figure shows a quadrilateral (four sides) and a pentagon (five sides) with all the diagonals drawn.
    a. What is the total number of diagonals in each figure?
    b. Draw a hexagon (six sides) with all its diagonals. How many diagonals are there?
    c. For a figure with n sides (a polygon), the number of diagonals N is given by the formula $N = \dfrac{1}{2}n(n - 3)$. Use this formula to check your answers to Parts **a** and **b**.
    d. How many diagonals would a figure of 20 sides have?
    e. How many sides would a polygon with 54 diagonals have?

Chapter Summary

1. A statement is a sentence written in either words or symbols. A statement is either true or false, but not both.
2. Open sentences contain variables which are symbols to be replaced by numbers. Replacements are numbers written in place of variables.
3. If a replacement makes an open sentence true, it satisfies the open sentence. A replacement which satisfies an open sentence is a solution. The set of all solutions is called the solution set or truth set of the open sentence.

4. An equation is an open sentence containing the verb *is equal to*. Solving an equation means finding its solution set.
5. A pair of numbers in which it matters which number comes first is called an ordered pair.
6. The Cartesian or coordinate plane has an *x*-axis and a *y*-axis. The intersection of these two axes is a point called the origin. The ordered pair which locates the origin is (0, 0).
7. The solutions for open sentences with two variables are ordered pairs. Such a solution set may be pictured by a graph on a Cartesian plane.
8. In a product that contains a numerical factor and variables, the numerical factor is called the numerical coefficient.
9. Multiplication signs usually are omitted between a coefficient and a variable and between variables.
10. The Commutative and Associative Properties of Multiplication may be used to rearrange the factors in a product. The Distributive Property may be used to combine like terms in an algebraic expression.
11. A formula is an equation which is used often.

REVIEW EXERCISES 3–1

1. T 2. T 3. F 4. T 5. T 6. F
7. T 8. T 9. T 10. F 11. F
12. T 13. T 14. {8} 15. {4}

Write true (T) or false (F) for each statement.
1. $14 + 19 = 33$
2. $8 \cdot 0 = 0$
3. The product of two odd numbers is always an even number.
4. The year 1996 will be a leap year.
5. 15 meters = 1500 centimeters
6. Every year contains exactly 365 days.
7. If *a* is an odd number and *b* is an even number, then $a + b$ is an odd number.
8. The coefficient of $4xy$ is 4.
9. $\{0\} \neq \varnothing$

3–2

For each open sentence, write true (T) or false (F) for the statement obtained by replacement of the variable.
10. $z + 1 = 0$; $z = 0$
11. $x - 25 = 50$; $x = 25$
12. *p* is a factor of 57; $p = 3$
13. $5y = 0$; $y = 0$

3–3

Find the solution set of each open sentence. The variables are on $S = \{1, 2, 3, 4, 5, 6, 7, 8, 9, 10\}$.
14. $x + 1 = 9$
15. $7 - a = 3$

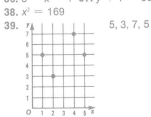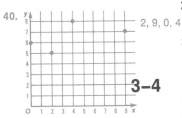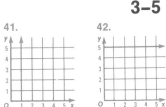
16. $n + n = 10$ **17.** $m + 6 \in S$
18. $r > 7$ **19.** $a + a \notin S$
20. $x - 1$ is an even number.
21. p divided by 12 belongs to S.

Find the solution set of each open sentence. The variables are on W.

22. The number x divides 12 exactly.
23. The number z is a common factor of 24 and 30.
24. A number p is a prime number between 20 and 30.
25. Some number n is an odd number between 2 and 10.
26. $x - 7 = 12$ **27.** $y - 8 = 15$ **28.** $8 - y = 15$
29. $\dfrac{6}{n} = 2$ **30.** $\dfrac{1}{3}x = 3$ **31.** $\dfrac{1}{5}n = 20$
32. $\dfrac{5}{n} = 20$ **33.** $\dfrac{x}{x} = 1$ **34.** $w^2 = 225$

Write each open sentence in the form of an equation. Use algebraic notation.

35. t added to 10 gives 24. **36.** x subtracted from 5 gives 1.
37. y increased by 7 gives 35. **38.** x times x is equal to 169.

39. Show on graph paper P $= \{(1, 5), (2, 3), (4, 7), (5, 5)\}$. Write the y-coordinate for each ordered pair.
40. Show on graph paper Q $= \{(2, 5), (9, 7), (0, 6), (4, 8)\}$. Write the x-coordinate for each ordered pair.
41. Plot the set S of ordered pairs for which $x = 1$.
42. Plot the set T of ordered pairs for which $y = 5$.
43. Write the coordinates of the element (s) in S ∩ T.
44. Write the next four ordered pairs in the sequence (4, 4), (8, 8), (16, 16), (32, 32), ...

The variable x is on $\{1, 2, 3, \ldots, 9, 10\}$. Let $y = x + 10$.

45. a. Find y when x is replaced by 1.
 b. Find y when x is replaced by 2.
 c. Copy and complete this table which shows the set of ordered pairs (x, y) such that $y = x + 10$.

x	1	2	3	4	5	6	7	8	9	10
y	11	12	?	?	?	?	?	?	?	?

 d. Draw a graph to show the relation between y and x.

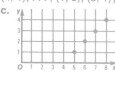
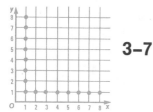
List the set of ordered pairs (x, y) that satisfy each equation. The variable x is on $\{1, 2, 3, 4\}$ and the variable y is on $\{7, 8, 9, 10\}$.

46. $x + y = 12$

47. $x + y$ has its greatest value.

48. $x + y$ has its least value.

49. $xy > 30$

50. List the set of ordered pairs (p, q) that satisfy each equation. The variables p and q are on $\{1, 2, 3, 4, 5, 6, 7, 8\}$.

  a. $p - q = 4$

  b. $p + q > pq$

  c. Draw a graph for the solution of each equation.

3–7

Use $\{1, 2, 3, 4, 5, 6, 7, 8\}$ as a replacement set. Invent an open sentence for each solution set.

51. $\{3\}$ **52.** $\{1, 2, 3\}$ **53.** $\{2, 4, 6, 8\}$

54. $\{2, 3, 5, 7\}$ **55.** $\varnothing$

3–9

Simplify each expression.

56. $4n + 9n$ **57.** $3x^2 + 5x^2$ **58.** $2p + 2p + 2p$

59. $\dfrac{1}{2} ab + \dfrac{1}{2} ba$ **60.** $5p + 3q - 3p + 6q$

Find the solution set of each open sentence. The variables are on W.

61. $5x + 4 + 3x = 36$

62. $\dfrac{1}{2} n + \dfrac{1}{3} n = 5$

63. $5x + 3x = 24$

3–10

3–11

64. Use the formula $A = lw$ to find the area of a rectangle with length 7 inches and width 3 inches.

65. a. A flashlight costs x cents and a battery y cents. Each flashlight requires 3 batteries to operate it. Write the cost of a flashlight and its 3 batteries in terms of x and y.

  b. Write a formula for the cost c cents of n flashlights, each supplied with 3 batteries.

  c. Use the formula from Part **b** to find c when $n = 6$, $x = 95$, and $y = 25$. Express the cost in dollars.

66. Write a formula for the perimeter of the pentagon in the figure. Calculate its perimeter when $a = 4.5$ cm and $b = 3.3$ cm.

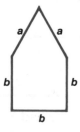

CHAPTER 4

using whole number expressions

4-1
Order for
Whole Numbers

OBJECTIVES:

1. To replace o in $a \circ b$ with the correct relation symbol when a and b are specified whole numbers.
2. To determine the truth value of a simple inequality.

The whole numbers have the property of order. For example, think of the two numbers 3 and 9. The fact that 9 is more than 3 is written $9 > 3$ or $3 < 9$. The symbol $<$ means *is less than*. The symbol $>$ means *is greater than*. Numerical statements which contain $<$ or $>$ are called ***inequalities.***

For any two whole numbers, *a* and *b*, exactly one of the statements $a = b$, $a < b$, or $a > b$ is true. If $a < b$ or $a > b$, then $a \neq b$. If $a \neq b$, then either $a < b$ or $a > b$.

Sometimes you may want to say that *a* is less than *b* or *a* is equal to *b*. You could write $a < b$ or $a = b$. However, you can say the same thing by using just one symbol, $\leq$. The inequality $a \leq b$ means $a < b$ or $a = b$. Likewise, $a \geq b$ means $a > b$ or $a = b$.

Study these examples to help you understand the meaning of $\leq$ and $\geq$.

Stress the fact that $a \leq b$ means $a < b$ or $a = b$.

EXAMPLES

With $3 \leq 4$, the statement of form $a < b$ or $a = b$ is true because $a < b$.

With $3 \leq 3$, the statement of form $a < b$ or $a = b$ is true because $a = b$.

Statement	True or False
$3 < 4$	T
$3 \leq 4$	T
$3 \leq 3$	T
$3 < 3$	F
$3 > 3$	F
$3 \geq 3$	T
$4 \geq 3$	T
$4 > 3$	T

Emphasize that for $a < b < c$ to be true it must be that *both* $a < b$ and $b < c$.

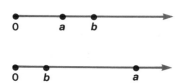

When two expressions are connected by $\geq$ or $\leq$ the statement is called an inequality. The two expressions, however, may be equal.

Sometimes two or more inequalities are written in one sentence. The statement $3 < 5 < 8$ means $3 < 5$ and $5 < 8$ or 5 *is between* 3 and 8. The sentence $6 < x \leq 10$ means that $6 < x$ and $x \leq 10$.

The order of the whole numbers may be shown by using a number line. To say that $a < b$ means that a is to the left of b on the number line.

The statement $a > b$ means that a is to the right of b on the number line.

Subsets of the whole numbers may be shown by marking points on the number line.

The picture on the number line is called the **graph** of {2, 3, 4, 6}. From this graph you can see that $2 < 3 < 4$.

EXERCISES

1. $7 > 4$ 2. $5 > 1$ 3. $2 < 3$
4. $10 < 100$ 5. $3 < 6 < 8$
6. $1 < 10 < 12$ 7. $1 < 3 < 5$
8. $a < 4 < b$

Write each statement as an inequality.

1. 7 is greater than 4.
2. 5 is greater than 1.
3. 2 is less than 3.
4. 10 is less than 100.
5. 6 is between 3 and 8.
6. 10 is between 1 and 12.
7. 3 is between 1 and 5.
8. 4 is between a and b.

Clarify this instruction if
necessary by saying "Do not use
the word 'and,' but use as many
inequality signs as required."

Copy each statement and place one of the symbols $>$, $=$, or $<$
in each blank to make a true statement.

9. 199 ___?___ 200

10. $2 \cdot 7$ ___?___ $13 + 1$

11. 2^3 ___?___ 3^2

12. 0 ___?___ 1

13. 91 ___?___ 19

14. 35 ___?___ 34

15. 0.1 ___?___ $(0.1)^2$

16. $\frac{1}{4}$ ___?___ $\frac{1}{2}$

17. $3 + 0$ ___?___ $3 \cdot 0$

Arrange each triple in order. First use the symbol $<$ only; then
use the symbol $>$ only.

18. 3, 1, 5   **19.** 1 cm, 1 mm, 1 m   **20.** 0.2, 0.02, 2.0

Write whether each statement is true (T) or false (F).

21. $9 + 7 > 8 + 8$ **22.** $5 \cdot 1 > 5 \cdot 0$ **23.** $\$12 = 1200\cent$

24. $6 \cdot 5 \cdot 4 = 4 \cdot 5 \cdot 6$ **25.** $\frac{3}{2} \neq \frac{2}{3}$ **26.** 2.5 cm $>$ 25 mm

27. $0 \leq 1$ **28.** $0 < 3 \leq 5$ **29.** $5 \geq 5$

30. $6 \leq 6 < 7$

Combine each pair of inequalities into one statement. Use only
the symbol $<$.

31. $5 < 6$ and $6 < 7$ **32.** $9 > 5$ and $5 > 1$ **33.** $2 < 3$ and $5 > 3$

34. Draw a number line from 0 to 10. Graph the whole numbers
between 1 and 7 and the number 9.

Use a number line to help you complete each statement.
35. If $a > 4$, a lies to the ___?___ of 4.
36. If $b < 7$, b lies to the ___?___ of 7.
37. If $c = 5$, c lies ___?___ 4 and 6.

If n represents a whole number, mark all possible positions of n
on a number line for each inequation.

38. $n < 4$ **39.** $n = 6$ **40.** $7 < n < 10$

41. Show E = {1, 2, 3, . . . , 10) on a number line. On this number
line mark the members of $\{1 < p < 5\}$ where p is a variable on
E. Likewise mark the subset $\{8 < p < 10\}$.

42. a. $0 \le p < 4$ **b.** $2 < q \le 6$
43. c.

42. E = {0, 1, 2, 3, 4, 5, 6}. Two subsets of E are shown by the dots. Express each subset in the form used in Exercise **41.**

a.

b.

43. Which of the following statements is false?
   a. 1 m > 10 cm   **b.** $12 ≠ $15   **c.** 1 kg > 1000 g

4-2
Inequations

EXAMPLES

OBJECTIVE:

To name the solution set of a simple linear inequation with one variable on W.

Numerical statements which contain inequality symbols may be either true or false.

Statement	True or False
$2 < 3$	T
$7 > 3$	T
$7 > 3 + 5$	F
$7 \ge 3 + 3$	T

Stress that the task in solving equations and inequations is basically the same. Both are open sentences for which a solution set must be found.

Inequalities also may contain variables. Such inequalities are called inequations. An inequation is true or false depending on what number replaces the variable. For example, $n > 3$ is true when n is replaced by 5 but false when n is replaced by 2.

An *inequation* may be defined as an open sentence which contains $≠$, $<$, $\le$, $>$, or $\ge$.

Just as with equations, the set of replacements which make an inequation true is called the *solution set*.

EXAMPLES

1. If x is a variable on W, then the solution set for $x > 3$ is {4, 5, 6, 7, ...}. This solution set is shown in the following graph.

2. If x is a variable on W, then the solution set for $x + 2 \leq 6$ is $\{0, 1, 2, 3, 4\}$.

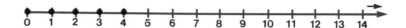

3. If x is a variable on W, then the solution set for $x + 2 < 1$ is $\varnothing$, the empty set. The solution set is shown in the following graph.

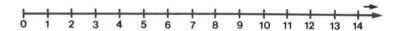

To find the solution set for an inequation, you can try substituting each member of the replacement set for the variable in the inequation. The replacements which make a sentence true are solutions.

EXAMPLE

The number 3 is the solution for $2x + 1 = 7$. Ask if knowing this fact is helpful in knowing when $2x + 1$ is greater than 7.

If x is a variable on $\{1, 2, 3, \ldots, 10\}$, find the solution set of $2x + 1 > 7$.

Replacement for x	$2x + 1 > 7$	True or False
1	$2 \cdot 1 + 1 > 7; 3 > 7$	False
2	$2 \cdot 2 + 1 > 7; 5 > 7$	False
3	$2 \cdot 3 + 1 > 7; 7 > 7$	False
4	$2 \cdot 4 + 1 > 7; 9 > 7$	True
5	$2 \cdot 5 + 1 > 7; 11 > 7$	True
6	$2 \cdot 6 + 1 > 7; 13 > 7$	True
7	$2 \cdot 7 + 1 > 7; 15 > 7$	True
8	$2 \cdot 8 + 1 > 7; 17 > 7$	True
9	$2 \cdot 9 + 1 > 7; 19 > 7$	True
10	$2 \cdot 10 + 1 > 7; 21 > 7$	True

The only replacements for x which give a true sentence are 4, 5, 6, 7, 8, 9, 10. Hence, the solution set is {4, 5, 6, . . . , 10}.

When x is a variable on an infinite set such as W, then you will not be able to check all replacements for x. The inequation, however, may be solved by checking some replacements and studying the pattern.

EXAMPLE

The rational number $3\frac{2}{3}$ is a solution to $3x - 4 = 7$. Ask if knowing this fact is helpful in deciding when $3x - 4$ will be greater than 7.

If x is a variable on W, what is the solution set for $3x - 4 > 7$? Study the table.

Replacement for x	$3x - 4 > 7$	True or False
0	$3 \cdot 0 - 4 > 7; \ ^{-}4 > 7$	False
1	$3 \cdot 1 - 4 > 7; \ ^{-}1 > 7$	False
2	$3 \cdot 2 - 4 > 7; 2 > 7$	False
3	$3 \cdot 3 - 4 > 7; 5 > 7$	False
4	$3 \cdot 4 - 4 > 7; 8 > 7$	True
5	$3 \cdot 5 - 4 > 7; 11 > 7$	True
6	$3 \cdot 6 - 4 > 7; 14 > 7$	True
↓		↓

For any number larger than 6, it appears certain that $3x - 4$ will be greater than 7. Therefore, the solution set for $3x - 4 > 7$ must be {4, 5, 6, 7, . . .}.

Trial-and-error solution methods are acceptable at this introductory level.

EXERCISES

1.-15. See section notes in T.G.

If x is a variable on {0, 1, 2, 3, 4, 5}, find the solution set of each inequation. Show the graph of each solution set on a number line.

1. $x \leq 3$ **2.** $x < 1$ **3.** $x + 1 < 5$

4. $x + 4 < 6$ **5.** $x + 5 < 10$ **6.** $x > 1$ and $x < 5$

7. $2 < x < 6$ **8.** $4 + x \geq 8$ **9.** $x + 5 > 5$

10. $x - 1 > 7$ **11.** $5 > x > 1$ **12.** $x > 0$

13. $x - 3 < 6$ **14.** $x - 1 \leq 2$ **15.** $3 < x - 4$

If x and m are variables on $\{1, 2, 3, \ldots, 10\}$ find the solution set of each inequation.

16. $2x > 8$ **17.** $2x < 10$ **18.** $3x < 10$
19. $4x > 19$ **20.** $5x < 18$ **21.** $x^2 < 20$
22. $2x + 1 > 5$ **23.** $2x - 1 < 5$ **24.** $2x + 5 < 15$
25. $2x + 8 < 9$ **26.** $2x < x + 4$ **27.** $4x + 5 > 9$
28. $11 + 3m \leq 26$ **29.** $11 + 3m < 19$ **30.** $11 - 3m < 9$
31. $11 - 3m > 9$ **32.** $3m^2 > 20$ **33.** $m^3 < 50$

If x is a variable on $\{0, 1, 2, \ldots, 10\}$, write the solution set of each inequation. Find the intersection of the solution sets in each pair of inequations.

34. $x > 3, x < 8$ **35.** $x < 7, x > 4$
36. $x > 5, x < 4$ **37.** $x + 2 < 6, x - 1 > 1$

Use inequality symbols to write each statement as an inequation.
38. The number p exceeds 50.
39. The number g is less than or equal to 10.
40. Three times t is less than 25.
41. If 2 is added to x the sum is less than y.
42. The number y is greater than 5 and less than 15.
43. The number h is less than 10 and greater than 0.

If x is a variable on W, find the solution set of each inequation.
44. $x + 7 > 11$ **45.** $x + 11 > 7$ **46.** $x - 11 > 7$
47. $x - 7 < 11$ **48.** $11 - x < 7$ **49.** $7 - x < 11$
50. $x + 11 < 7$ **51.** $x + 2 \geq 5$ **52.** $2x + 1 \leq 5$
53. $2x + 1 \geq 5$ **54.** $2x + 1 < 5$ **55.** $20 \geq 2x - 10$

Excursions in Mathematics: Series

Let S_r denote the sum of the first r terms of the series of numbers $2 + 4 + 6 + 8 + \ldots$.

$$S_1 = 2 = 1 \cdot 2$$
$$S_2 = 2 + 4 = 6 = 2 \cdot 3$$
$$S_3 = 2 + 4 + 6 = 12 = 3 \cdot 4$$

Study this pattern. Then do the following exercises.

1. Express S_5 and S_6 as a product of two factors.
2. Find the greatest number r such that $S_r < 100$.
3. Find the least number r such that $S_r > 400$.
4. Write a formula for S_r as a product of two factors. Test your formula for S_4.

4-3
Writing Inequations

To write an inequation when given a real life situation involving upper and/or lower bounds.

SPEED LIMIT
55
MIN
45

Many situations in everyday life can be described by inequations. In some states a person must be at least sixteen years old to apply for a driver's license. An inequation which describes this situation is $z \geq 16$. The legal driving ages in these states are the elements of the solution set for $z \geq 16$. The solution set for $z < 16$ gives the ages at which it is not legal to hold a license.

On some highways, speed limits are posted which give both a maximum and a minimum speed.

The set of legal speeds shown by this sign is the solution set for $45 \leq s \leq 55$.

EXERCISES

1. $s \geq 5$, $\{5, 6\}$ **2.** $h \geq 1.72$ meters, $\{1.72, 1.73, 1.74, \ldots\}$ **3.** $w \geq 326$, $\{326, 327, 328, \ldots\}$ **4.** $l \leq 101,001$, $\{0,1,2,3,\ldots, 101,001\}$ **5.** $54 \leq s \leq 275$, $\{54, 55, \ldots, 275\}$ **6.** $180 \leq m \leq 1250$, $\{180, 181, 182, \ldots, 1250\}$ **7.** $d \leq 2.2$, $d \geq 2.4$, $\{\ldots 2.2, 2.4, \ldots\}$ **8.** $7.998 < d < 8.002$, $\{7.999, 8.000, 8.001\}$ **9.** S = $\{2, 3, 4, 5, 6, 7, 8, 9, 10, 11, 12\}$, $7 \leq x \leq 12$, $\{7, 8, 9, 10, 11, 12\}$ **10.** $x + x > 10$, $x > 5$

Write a mathematical sentence to describe each situation. Use the indicated variable. Then write the solution set for each inequation.

1. In tossing a die, a score (s) of 5 or over wins.
2. Police recruits must be at least 172 centimeters in height (h meters).
3. The minimum weight of a package of cookies is 326 grams. Use w grams for the weight of a package.
4. The crowd limit (l) at a football game is 101,001.
5. In a golf match, a score (s) of 275 or less is required after 54 holes to qualify for the final round.
6. The minimum flying speed of an airplane is 180 km/h and the maximum speed is 1250 km/h. The speed of the airplane is m km/h.
7. A slot in a coin-operated machine will not accept a coin with diameter (d) equal to or greater than 2.4 cm. The machine also will not work if the diameter of the coin is 2.2 cm or less.
8. A factory makes pistons for car engines. The diameter of each piston has to be approximately 8 cm. If the diameter is 0.002 cm greater or less than this, the piston is not accepted. Use d for the diameter of the piston.
9. Two dice are tossed. Write the set S of possible scores on tossing the dice. In a game, the winning score is 7 or over. If x is a variable on S, write an inequation to express this condition. Write the solution set of this inequation.
10. The sum of the lengths of any two sides of a triangle is always greater than the length of the third side. The sides of a triangle are x cm, x cm, and 10 cm. Write an inequation in x. Express the inequation as $x >$ (a number).

4-4
Determining Order

OBJECTIVES:
1. To name $c \in W$ such that $a + c = b$ when given $a, b \in W$ such that $a < b$.
2. To state that $a < b$ when given $a, b, c \in W$ such that $a + c = b$.

These definitions divorce the concepts of less than, $<$, and greater than, $>$, from the number line. For students still very dependent on the number line, point out that c is the distance between a and b.

You have seen the meaning of $<$ and $>$ on the number line. *Less than* and *greater than* also may be defined in terms of numbers.

The statement $a < b$ means that there is a number c which is greater than zero such that $a + c = b$.

The statement $a > b$ means that there is a number c which is greater than zero such that $a = b + c$.

Thus, $2 < 5$ because $2 + 3 = 5$ and $3 > 0$. Likewise, $8 > 6$ because $8 = 6 + 2$ and $2 > 0$.

EXERCISES

1. 5 2. 19, 15 3. 7, 4 4. 5, 4, 9
5. $>$ 6. $=$ 7. $<$ 8. $<$ 9. $<$
10. $<$ 11. $<$ 12. $>$ 13. $<$
14. $>$ 15. $>$ 16. $>$

Remind students to keep in mind the allowable values for the variables.

Copy and complete each statement.
1. Because $8 = 3 +$ ___?___, $8 > 3$.
2. Because $34 =$ ___?___ $+$ ___?___, $34 > 19$.
3. Because ___?___ $+$ ___?___ $= 11$, $7 < 11$.
4. Because ___?___ $+$ ___?___ $=$ ___?___, $5 < 9$.

Copy and complete each statement where p and q are variables on N. Use $>$, $<$, or $=$ for each blank.
5. If $p = q + 5$, then p ___?___ q.
6. If $p - q = 0$, then p ___?___ q.
7. If $p + 1 = q$, then p ___?___ q.
8. If $p + p = q$, then p ___?___ q.
9. If $p = 11$ and $q = 15$, then p ___?___ q.
10. If $q = p + 3$, then p ___?___ q.

Copy and complete each statement where a and b are variables on the set of whole numbers. Use $>$, $<$, or $=$ for each blank.
11. Since $2a < 2b$, a ___?___ b.
12. Since $a - 1 > b$, a ___?___ b.
13. Since $a + 1 < b$, a ___?___ b.
14. Since $a - b = 7$, a ___?___ b.
15. Since $a + 5 > b + 5$, a ___?___ b.
16. Since $a + 7 = b + 10$, a ___?___ b.

17. Find the whole number c such that the solution set of the inequation $x + c < 20$ is $\{0, 1, 2, \ldots, 14\}$.

Given that x is a variable on $\{0, 1, 2, 3, 4, 5\}$, find the solution set of each inequation.

18. $x^2 < 15$ **19.** $x^2 \geq 3x$ **20.** $x^2 + 4 > 4x$

If x is a variable on W, copy and complete each statement.

21. $2x + 1 = 7$
$2x = \underline{\quad?\quad}$
$x = \underline{\quad?\quad}$

22. $2x + 1 > 7$
$2x > \underline{\quad?\quad}$
$x > \underline{\quad?\quad}$

23. $4x + 5 = 9$
$4x = \underline{\quad?\quad}$
$x = \underline{\quad?\quad}$

24. $4x + 5 < 9$
$4x < \underline{\quad?\quad}$
$x < \underline{\quad?\quad}$

25. $3x + 2 = 20$
$3x = \underline{\quad?\quad}$
$x = \underline{\quad?\quad}$

26. $3x + 2 \geq 20$
$3x \geq \underline{\quad?\quad}$
$x \geq \underline{\quad?\quad}$

27. $2x + 7 = 15$
$2x = \underline{\quad?\quad}$
$x = \underline{\quad?\quad}$

28. $2x + 7 \leq 15$
$2x \leq \underline{\quad?\quad}$
$x \leq \underline{\quad?\quad}$

29. A rectangle has an area of 24 cm². If its length is p cm and its width is q cm, copy and complete the table.

p	1	2	3	4	6	8	12	24
q	24	12	?	?	?	?	?	?

Using the table, complete $p + q \geq \underline{\quad?\quad}$ and $p + q \leq \underline{\quad?\quad}$.

30. Repeat Exercise **29** for a rectangle of area 36 cm², if p and q are variables on $\{1, 2, 3, 4, 6, 9, 12, 18, 36\}$.

The perimeter of a rectangle is 16 cm (the sum of the lengths of its four sides is 16 cm). Its length and width are p cm and q cm, respectively. Copy and complete each sentence.

31. $2p + 2q = \underline{\quad?\quad}$ **32.** $p + q = \underline{\quad?\quad}$ **33.** $p = \underline{\quad?\quad}$

34.

p	1	2	3	4	5	6	7
q	7	6	?	?	?	?	?

35. $pq \geq \underline{\quad?\quad}$ and $pq \leq \underline{\quad?\quad}$

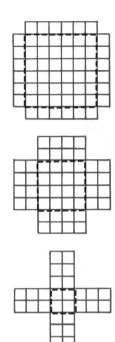

36. Repeat Exercises **31–35** for a rectangle whose perimeter is 12 cm. For the table, assume that p and q are variables on $\{1, 2, 3, 4, 5\}$.

A man walks 24 km from a place A to a place B. His average speed is greater than 4 km/h but less than 6 km/h. He takes t hours for the journey. Copy and complete each inequation.

37. $t > \underline{\quad?\quad}$ **38.** $t < \underline{\quad?\quad}$

A square is 8 units on a side. Equal squares of side x units are cut from the four corners, where $x \in \{1, 2, 3, 4\}$. In each case, this gives the net of an open box as shown. When the box is made from the net, it can be filled exactly with n unit cubes.

Copy and complete the table and open sentence.

39.

x	1	2	3	4
n	36	?	?	?

40. $\underline{\quad?\quad} \le n \le \underline{\quad?\quad}$

36. $2p + 2q = 12$, $p + q = 6$, $p = 6 - q$

p	1	2	3	4	5
q	5	4	3	2	1

$pq \ge 5$, $pq \le 9$ **37.** $t > 4$

38. $t < 6$

39.

x	1	2	3	4
n	36	32	12	0

40. 0, 36

4-5
Using the Distributive Property

1.

(b + c)	a(b + c)	ab	ac	ab + ac
6	18	6	12	18
8	16	10	6	16
9	36	12	24	36
11	0	0	0	0
6	48	8	40	48
12	120	50	70	120
3/4	3	2	1	3

Yes

1. Copy and complete the table.

a	b	c	$(b + c)$	$a(b + c)$	ab	ac	$ab + ac$
3	2	4	6	18	6	12	18
2	5	3	?	?	?	?	?
4	3	6	?	?	?	?	?
0	3	8	?	?	?	?	?
8	1	5	?	?	?	?	?
10	5	7	?	?	?	?	?
4	$\frac{1}{2}$	$\frac{1}{4}$	?	?	?	?	?

Compare the numbers in Column 5 and Column 8. Do you see that in each case $a(b + c) = ab + ac$?

2. Copy and complete the table.

a	b	c	(b − c)	a(b − c)	ab	ac	ab − ac
5	4	2	2	10	20	10	10
3	5	2	?	?	?	?	?
1	8	3	?	?	?	?	?
0	7	5	?	?	?	?	?
4	9	2	?	?	?	?	?
5	10	6	?	?	?	?	?
3	$\frac{1}{2}$	$\frac{1}{4}$	?	?	?	?	?

Do you find that $a(b - c) = ab - ac$ in each case?

The Distributive Property also applies when more than two terms are included in the parentheses.

EXAMPLE

$$5(3 - 1 + 2 + 8 - 5) = 5 \cdot 7$$
$$= 35$$

$$5 \cdot 3 - 5 \cdot 1 + 5 \cdot 2 + 5 \cdot 8 - 5 \cdot 5 = 15 - 5 + 10 + 40 - 25$$
$$= 35$$

Thus, it seems that $a(b + c + \cdots) = ab + ac + \cdots$.

The Distributive Property also applies when letters are used to represent numbers.

EXAMPLES

1. $3(2p + 3q + r) = 6p + 9q + 3r$
2. $4(2a - 3b) = 8a - 12b$
3. $m(m - 2a) = m^2 - 2am$

EXERCISES

1. $2a + 2$ **2.** $7c + 14$ **3.** $5 + 5p$
4. $8m + 8n$ **5.** $a + b$ **6.** $2n + 16$
7. $3x^2 + 3$ **8.** $4p - 8q$ **9.** $10 -$
$10x$ **10.** $21m + 28v$ **11.** $12x -$
$6y$ **12.** $9c + 6d$ **13.** $3y^3 - 3$
14. $4p + pq$ **15.** $5ah + 2ak$
16. $10m - 50n$ **17.** $a^2 + ab$
18. $2h + 2hb$ **19.** $4a^2 - 4ab$
20. $2x - 3x^2$ **21.** $2x^2 + 2xy$
22. $2p^2 - 3pq$ **23.** $abc + 2ab$
24. $rs - r^2s$ **25.** $3a + 3b + 3c$
26. $2a - 2b + 2c$ **27.** $a^2 + ab +$
ac **28.** $x^2 + xy - xz$ **29.** $6p -$
$9q + 12r$ **30.** $xy - x^2y + xy^2$
31. $15p + 10q$ **32.** $4px - 2py$
33. $9a^2 + 15a$ **34.** $r^3 - r^2s$
35. $a^2b + ab^2$ **36.** $x^2 - 7x^3$
37. $2xy + 2yz + 2zx$ **38.** $2a^2 +$
$3ab + a$ **39.** $2p^2 + 2pq - 4pr$
40. $1/2\, m + 1/2\, n$ **41.** $2x + 4y$
42. $a - 3b$ **43.** $9x + 3y$
44. $2h - 4$ **45.** $6u + 8.4v$

Write each expression as a sum or difference of terms. Use the Distributive Property.

1. $2(a + 1)$ **2.** $7(c + 2)$ **3.** $5(1 + p)$

4. $8(m + n)$ **5.** $1(a + b)$ **6.** $2(n + 8)$

7. $3(x^2 + 1)$ **8.** $4(p - 2q)$ **9.** $5(2 - 2x)$

10. $7(3u + 4v)$ **11.** $6(2x - y)$ **12.** $3(3c + 2d)$

13. $3(y^3 - 1)$ **14.** $p(4 + q)$ **15.** $a(5h + 2k)$

16. $10(m - 5n)$ **17.** $a(a + b)$ **18.** $2h(1 + b)$

19. $4a(a - b)$ **20.** $x(2 - 3x)$ **21.** $2x(x + y)$

22. $p(2p - 3q)$ **23.** $ab(c + 2)$ **24.** $rs(1 - r)$

25. $3(a + b + c)$ **26.** $2(a - b + c)$ **27.** $a(a + b + c)$

28. $x(x + 2y - z)$ **29.** $3(2p - 3q + 4r)$ **30.** $xy(1 - x + y)$

31. $5(3p + 2q)$ **32.** $2p(2x - y)$ **33.** $3a(3a + 5)$

34. $r^2(r - s)$ **35.** $ab(a + b)$ **36.** $x^2(1 - 7x)$

37. $2(xy + yz + zx)$ **38.** $a(2a + 3b + 1)$ **39.** $2p(p + q - 2r)$

40. $\dfrac{1}{2}(m + n)$ **41.** $\dfrac{1}{2}(4x + 8y)$ **42.** $\dfrac{1}{4}(4a - 12b)$

43. $\dfrac{3}{4}(12x + 4y)$ **44.** $0.4(5h - 10)$ **45.** $1.2(5u + 7v)$

Excursions in Mathematics:
Modular Arithmetic

Here is an arithmetic system containing a set of five whole numbers $\{0, 1, 2, 3, 4\}$. For this system, two operations $\oplus$ and $\otimes$ are defined.

$a \oplus b$ means divide the sum of a and b by 5 and write the remainder. For example, $2 \oplus 4 = 1$.

$a \otimes b$ means divide the product of a and b by 5 and write the remainder. For example, $2 \otimes 4 = 3$.

EXERCISES

1. Copy and complete the addition and multiplication tables.

1.

$\oplus$	0	1	2	3	4
0	0	1	2	3	4
1	1	2	3	4	0
2	2	3	4	0	1
3	3	4	0	1	2
4	4	0	1	2	3

$\otimes$	0	1	2	3	4
0	0	0	0	0	0
1	0	1	2	3	4
2	0	2	4	1	3
3	0	3	1	4	2
4	0	4	3	2	1

$\oplus$	0	1	2	3	4
0	0	1	2	3	4
1	?	?	?	4	0
2	?	?	?	?	?
3	?	?	?	?	?
4	?	?	?	?	?

$\otimes$	0	1	2	3	4
0	0	0	0	0	0
1	?	?	?	3	4
2	?	?	?	1	?
3	?	?	?	?	?
4	?	?	?	?	?

2. See section notes in T.G.
3. Yes

2. Copy and complete this table using the results from the table in Exercise **1.**

a	b	c	$b \oplus c$	$a \otimes (b \oplus c)$	$a \otimes b$	$a \otimes c$	$(a \otimes b) \oplus (a \otimes c)$
2	1	3	4	3	2	1	3
4	2	1	?	?	?	?	?
1	4	3	?	?	?	?	?
3	3	3	?	?	?	?	?
4	2	3	?	?	?	?	?

3. Study Columns 5 and 8. Is the multiplication $\otimes$ distributive over the addition $\oplus$?

4-6
Common Factors

OBJECTIVE:

To apply the Distributive Property to removing the common factor from a polynomial.

To find the sum $300 + 1500 + 600$ you could add $3 + 15 + 6$ and think of the sum as a number of hundreds. If you did this, you would be using the Distributive Property.

$$300 + 1500 + 600 = 100 \cdot 3 + 100 \cdot 15 + 100 \cdot 6$$
$$= 100 (3 + 15 + 6)$$

The same method often is used in algebra. Remember, if a property is true for numbers, it also is true when letters are used to represent numbers.

EXAMPLES

1. $4x + 4y$ may be written $4(x + y)$
2. $4 \cdot 3 + 4 \cdot 7$ may be written $4(3 + 7)$
3. $12 + 28$ may be written $4(3 + 7)$
4. $4x - 20y = 4(x - 5y)$
5. $2a^2 + 6ab = 2a(a + 3b)$

When you use the Distributive Property in this way, you are expressing a sum or difference as a product. To do this, you need to find a factor that is common to each term. If there are no common factors other than the one you find, then you have found the **_greatest common factor._** The greatest common factor may be a product of several common factors.

EXAMPLES

1. In $4x - 20y$, the greatest common factor is 4.
$4x - 20y = 4 \cdot x - 4 \cdot 5y = 4(x - 5y)$
The terms x and $5y$ have no common factor.

2. In $2a^2 + 6ab$, the greatest common factor is $2a$.
$2a^2 + 6ab = 2a \cdot a + 2a \cdot 3b = 2a(a + 3b)$.
The terms a and $3b$ have no common factor.

Using the Distributive Property in this way often is called *factoring by removing a common factor*. The greatest common factor is not always obvious. To find the greatest common factor, look at each term and ask: What is the greatest term which divides evenly into each term? In the following examples, each highlighted factor is an answer to that question.

EXAMPLES

1. $81 + 36 = \mathbf{9} \cdot 9 + \mathbf{9} \cdot 4 = 9(9 + 4)$
2. $5x - 15xy + 10 = \mathbf{5} \cdot x - \mathbf{5} \cdot 3xy + \mathbf{5} \cdot 2 = 5(x - 3xy + 2)$
3. $3ab - 3a = \mathbf{3a} \cdot b - \mathbf{3a} \cdot 1 = 3a(b - 1)$
4. $xy + 5xy = \mathbf{xy} \cdot 1 + \mathbf{xy} \cdot 5 = xy(1 + 5)$
5. $81ab + 36bc = \mathbf{9b} \cdot 9a + \mathbf{9b} \cdot 4c = 9b(9a + 4c)$
6. $3x^3 + 6x^2 + 9x = \mathbf{3x} \cdot x^2 + \mathbf{3x} \cdot 2x + \mathbf{3x} \cdot 3 = 3x(x^2 + 2x + 3)$

EXERCISES

1. $p + q$ **2.** $p + 5$ **3.** $c + 3$
4. $x - y$ **5.** $2m - 3$ **6.** $2a + 3$
7. $n - 2m$ **8.** $2 + b$ **9.** $x - 1$
10. $2(x + 2)$ **11.** $3(a + b)$
12. $4(c + 3d)$ **13.** $3(y + 2z)$
14. $4(p + 3)$ **15.** $a(x + y)$
16. $4(x - 8)$ **17.** $7(m - 7)$
18. $8(2t - 3)$ **19.** $p(q - s)$
20. $q(p - r)$ **21.** $5x(3 + 4y)$
22. $9(a + 2b)$ **23.** $x(x + 1)$
24. $y(y - 1)$ **25.** $y(x + z)$
26. $(7 \cdot 11) + (7 \cdot 9) = 7(11 + 9) = 7 \cdot 20 = 140$ **27.** $(14 \cdot 13) + (16 \cdot 13) = (14 + 16)13 = 30 \cdot 13 = 390$

Copy each sentence and insert the missing expression in the blank.

1. $2p + 2q = 2(\underline{\quad?\quad})$ **2.** $2p + 10 = 2(\underline{\quad?\quad})$
3. $3c + 9 = 3(\underline{\quad?\quad})$ **4.** $7x - 7y = 7(\underline{\quad?\quad})$
5. $4m - 6 = 2(\underline{\quad?\quad})$ **6.** $8a + 12 = 4(\underline{\quad?\quad})$
7. $5n - 10m = 5(\underline{\quad?\quad})$ **8.** $2a + ab = a(\underline{\quad?\quad})$
9. $x^2 - x = x(\underline{\quad?\quad})$

Write each expression as a product of factors.

10. $2x + 4$ **11.** $3a + 3b$ **12.** $4c + 12d$
13. $3y + 6z$ **14.** $4p + 12$ **15.** $ax + ay$
16. $4x - 32$ **17.** $7m - 49$ **18.** $16t - 24$
19. $pq - ps$ **20.** $pq - qr$ **21.** $15x + 20xy$
22. $6a + 12b$ **23.** $x^2 + x$ **24.** $y^2 - y$
25. $xy + yz$

Copy each expression and underline the greatest common factor. Then form a product of factors and calculate the value of the product.

26. $(7 \cdot 11) + (7 \cdot 9)$ **27.** $(14 \cdot 13) + (16 \cdot 13)$

28. $(38 \cdot 14) + (14 \cdot 12) =$
$14(38 + 12) = 14 \cdot 50 = 700$
29. $(15 \cdot 23) - (15 \cdot 19) =$
$15(23 - 19) = 15 \cdot 4 = 60$
30. $(16 \cdot 16) - (16 \cdot 11) =$
$16(16 - 11) = 16 \cdot 5 = 80$
31. $(3/4 \cdot 27) - (23 \cdot 3/4) =$
$3/4 (27 - 23) = 3/4 \cdot 4 = 3$
32. $S = 3(u + v)$, $S = 510$
33. $Q = 15(x + y)$, $Q = 300$
34. $A = 2h(a + b)$, $A = 200$

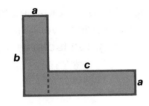

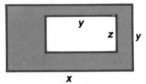

35. $A = ab + ac = a(b + c)$,
$A = 26$ m² **36.** $A = xy - yz =$
$y(x - z)$, $A = 9600$ mm²

28. $(38 \cdot 14) + (14 \cdot 12)$

29. $(15 \cdot 23) - (15 \cdot 19)$

30. $(16 \cdot 16) - (16 \cdot 11)$

31. $\left(\dfrac{3}{4} \cdot 27\right) - \left(23 \cdot \dfrac{3}{4}\right)$

Express the right side of each equation as a product of factors. Then carry out the calculation.

32. $s = 3u + 3v$ Find s when $u = 10$ and $v = 160$.

33. $Q = 15x + 15y$ Find Q when $x = 17.5$ and $y = 2.5$.

34. $A = 2ah + 2bh$ Find A when $a = 15$, $b = 10$, and $h = 4$.

35. The plan shows a hallway which is a meters wide. Measures b and c are in meters also. The dotted line divides the plan into two rectangular parts. Find a formula for the area A m² of the whole corridor. Express the formula in factored form. Calculate the area of the hallway if $a = 2$, $b = 5$, and $c = 8$.

36. A rectangle has length x mm and width y mm. From it a rectangle of length y mm and width z mm is removed to form a frame. Find a formula for the area A mm² of the frame. Express the formula in factored form. Calculate A if $x = 175$, $y = 80$, and $z = 55$.

4-7
Dividing
With Variables

OBJECTIVE:

To write the quotient of a polynomial divided by one of its common monomial factors.

EXAMPLES

Remind students who might "cancel" $\left(\dfrac{\cancel{2} \cdot 2}{\cancel{2}}\right) = 2$ that they have indeed used the fact that $a \cdot b \div b = a$.

One way to divide two numbers is to express the dividend as the divisor times another factor. That other factor is the quotient.

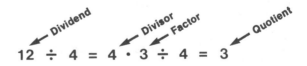

$$12 \div 4 = 4 \cdot 3 \div 4 = 3$$

1. $12 \div 4 \quad = 4 \cdot 3 \div 4 \quad = 3$

2. $104 \div 13 = 13 \cdot 8 \div 13 = 8$

3. $\dfrac{18}{9} \qquad = \dfrac{9 \cdot 2}{9} \qquad = 2$

4. $\dfrac{104}{13} \qquad = \dfrac{13 \cdot 8}{13} \qquad = 8$

The same method of division may be used when letters are used to represent numbers.

EXAMPLES

1. $\dfrac{ab}{a} = \dfrac{a \cdot b}{a} = b$

2. $\dfrac{x^2 - 3x}{x} = \dfrac{x(x - 3)}{x} = x - 3$

3. $\dfrac{7a + 21b}{7} = \dfrac{7(a + 3b)}{7} = a + 3b$

EXERCISES

Copy and complete each statement.

1. $\dfrac{1}{2}(8a + 4b) = \left(\dfrac{1}{2} \cdot \underline{}\right) + \left(\dfrac{1}{2} \cdot \underline{}\right)$

$\qquad = \underline{} + \underline{}$

2. $\dfrac{8a + 4b}{2} = \dfrac{4(\underline{} + \underline{})}{2}$

$\qquad = 2(\underline{} + \underline{})$

$\qquad = \underline{} + \underline{}$

3. What do you notice about your results in Exercises **1** and **2?**

Simplify each expression. Use the two ways shown in Exercises **1** and **2.**

4. $\dfrac{2x + 2y}{2}$ **5.** $\dfrac{6p + 6q}{3}$ **6.** $\dfrac{6a + 9b}{3}$ **7.** $\dfrac{4m - 8n}{4}$

8. $\dfrac{9x - 15}{3}$ **9.** $\dfrac{10c - 15d}{5}$ **10.** $\dfrac{3a + 6b}{3}$ **11.** $\dfrac{20x - 20y}{10}$

12. $\dfrac{5c + 5d}{5}$ **13.** $\dfrac{x^2 + xy}{x}$ **14.** $\dfrac{4t^2 + 6t}{2t}$ **15.** $\dfrac{6p^2 - 24p}{6p}$

Evaluate each expression. Use factors to help you.

16. $\dfrac{(8 \cdot 11) + (8 \cdot 19)}{15}$ **17.** $\dfrac{(1.5 \cdot 13) + (2.5 \cdot 13)}{4}$

18. $\dfrac{(49 \cdot 18) - (18 \cdot 24)}{45}$ **19.** $\dfrac{45^2 - (45 \cdot 30)}{75}$

Simplify each expression.

20. $\dfrac{5a + 10b}{5}$ **21.** $\dfrac{6a - 12b}{2}$ **22.** $\dfrac{a^2 - 4a}{a}$

23. $\dfrac{x^3 + x^2 + x}{x}$ **24.** $\dfrac{y^3 - y^2}{y}$ **25.** $\dfrac{2z^3 + 3z^2 + 4z}{z}$

4-8
Simplifying Expressions

In order to simplify some expressions, you may have to use the Distributive Property two ways. In the following example, first multiply to remove the parentheses. Then look for like terms.

EXAMPLE

Simplify $3(3a + 2b) + 2(2a - 2b)$.

$$3(3a + 2b) + 2(2a - 2b)$$

Use the Distributive Property.

$$= 9a + 6b + 4a - 4b$$

Use the Distributive Property.

$$= 9a + 4a + 6b - 4b$$
$$= 13a + 2b$$

EXERCISES

1. $(2 + 3)m = 5m$
2. $(12 - 7)p = 5p$ 3. $7a$
4. $4c$ 5. $10x$ 6. $23p$ 7. $2w$ 8. $6n$
9. $7c$ 10. 0 11. b 12. $1/2p$ 13. $6x$
14. $11q$ 15. m 16. $6ab$ 17. $10x^2$
18. xy 19. $14pq$ 20. $11cd$
21. $6a$ 22. $5x + 3$ 23. $6x + 6$
24. $8x - 3$ 25. $15m + 10$
26. $24m + 4n$ 27. $2a + b$
28. $6x$ 29. $3y + 6$ 30. $5a + k$
31. $3x$ 32. $2x^2 + x$ 33. $6q$
34. $x + 2y$ 35. a^2 36. $5x^2 + 8x$
37. $5a + 7$

Copy and complete each sentence.

1. $2m + 3m = (2 + \underline{\ ?\ })m = \underline{\ ?\ }$
2. $12p - 7p = (12 - \underline{\ ?\ })p = \underline{\ ?\ }$

Now that you are familiar with the Distributive Property, simplify Exercises **3–21** by inspection. That is, look at the expression and give the answer without writing the steps you may be thinking.

3. $4a + 3a$

4. $3c + c$

5. $x + 9x$

6. $10p + 13p$

7. $5w - 3w$

8. $8n - 2n$

9. $8c - c$

10. $7k - 7k$

11. $\frac{1}{2}b + \frac{1}{2}b$

12. $\frac{3}{4}p - \frac{1}{4}p$

13. $2.6x + 3.4x$

14. $7.5q + 3.5q$

15. $5.9m - 4.9m$

16. $2ab + 4ab$

17. $7x^2 + 3x^2$

18. $8xy - 7xy$

19. $4pq + 10qp$

20. $14cd - 3dc$

21. $a + 2a + 3a$

Simplify each expression.

22. $4x + 1(x + 3)$

23. $4x + 2(x + 3)$

24. $3(2x - 1) + 2x$

25. $7m + 2(4m + 5)$

26. $3(8m - 2n) + 10n$

27. $a + (a + b)$

28. $x + (2x + 3x)$

29. $5y + 2(3 - y)$

30. $5(a - 3k) + 16k$

31. $x(y + 3) - xy$

32. $x(x + 1) + x^2$

33. $3(p^2 + 2q) - 3p^2$

34. $3x + 2(y - x)$

35. $a(a - 1) + a$

36. $2x(x + 4) + 3x^2$

37. $2(a + 2) + 3(a + 1)$

38. $3(5a + 2) + 2(a - 3)$ **39.** $3(a - 1) + 2(a + 2)$

40. $4(2x + 7) + 7(x - 4)$ **41.** $6(3c + 4d) + 3(2c - 5d)$

42. $2(p + 3) + 3(5p - 2)$ **43.** $2a(a^2 + 1) + a^2(2a - 1)$

44. $3(a + 2b + 3c) + 2(a + b + c)$

45. $5(x + y + 4z) + 2(x + y - 3z)$

46. $2(a - 3b - 3c) + 3(a + 2b + 2c)$

47. $4a(3 + b) + 3b(3 + a) + 5c(1 + b)$

48. $5a(a - b) + 3b(2 - a) + 8ab$

49. If $P = a^2 + 2b$ and $Q = b^2 - 2a$, express $aP + bQ$ in simplest form.

Excursions in Mathematics:
The Distributive Property

An operation * means multiply the first number by itself and then add the second number.

$$2 * 3 = 4 + 3 = 7$$
$$5 * a = 25 + a$$
$$a * b = a^2 + b$$

EXERCISES

Write an expression for each operation.

1. $3 * x$ **2.** $3 * y$ **3.** $x * 3$ **4.** $y * 3$

5. $3 * (x + y)$, where $+$ has its usual meaning.

6. Is the operation * commutative?

7. Is the operation * associative?

8. Does $3 * (x + y) = (3 * x) + (3 * y)$? What does this suggest?

4-9
Solving
Open Sentences

The Distributive Property often is used to help in solving equations and inequations. Sometimes collecting like terms makes an equation easier to solve.

EXAMPLE

OBJECTIVE:

To solve linear open sentences in one variable which contain terms of the form (monomial) · (polynomial).

Solve $2x + 3x = 15$ where x is a variable on W.

$$2x + 3x = 15$$

Collect like terms. $5x = 15$

$$x = 3$$

The solution set is $\{3\}$.

Sometimes you should multiply to remove parentheses before collecting like terms.

EXAMPLES

1. If x is a variable on W, solve $4x + 4(2x - 1) = 20$.

$$4x + 4(2x - 1) = 20$$

Use the Distributive Property. $4x + 8x - 4 = 20$

Collect like terms. $12x - 4 = 20$

$$12x = 24$$

$$x = 2$$

The solution set is $\{2\}$.

2. Solve $y + 2(y - 1) > 3$ where y is a variable on W.

$$y + 2(y - 1) > 3$$

Use the Distributive Property. $y + 2y - 2 > 3$

Collect like terms. $3y - 2 > 3$

$$3y > 5$$

$$y > \frac{5}{3}$$

The solution set is $\{2, 3, 4, 5, \ldots\}$.

EXERCISES

1. $x = 3$ **2.** $y = 7$ **3.** $z = 6$
4. $p = 1$ **5.** $x = 15$ **6.** $y = 12$
7. $m = 2$ **8.** $p = 2$ **9.** $x = 1$
10. $x = 5$ **11.** $x = 3$ **12.** $y = 1$
13. $x = 1$ **14.** $x = 2$ **15.** $y = 2$
16. $y = 9$ **17.** $z = 2$ **18.** $z = 1$
19. $\{1, 2\}$ **20.** $\{1, 2, 3, 4\}$
21. $\{4, 5, 6, 7, \ldots\}$ **22.** $\{1, 2, 3\}$
23. $\{2, 3, 4, 5, \ldots\}$ **24.** $\{1, 2, 3,$
$4, 5\}$ **25.** $\{1, 2, 3, 4\}$ **26.** $\{1, 2\}$
27. $\{5, 6, 7, \ldots\}$ **28.** ϕ
29. $\{1, 2, 3, 4\}$ **30.** $\{1, 2, 3, 4, \ldots\}$
31. $\{3, 4, 5, 6, \ldots\}$ **32.** $t < 4$

Solve each equation. Each variable is a variable on N.

1. $3x + 2x = 15$
2. $4y + y = 35$
3. $7z - 4z = 18$
4. $11p - 8p = 3$
5. $9x + 2x - 8x = 45$
6. $9y - 5y + 2y = 72$
7. $7m + 2m + 3m = 24$
8. $3p + 2p + 5p = 20$
9. $3(x + 2) = 9$
10. $2(x + 5) = 20$
11. $2(x - 1) = 4$
12. $5(y + 1) = 10$
13. $5(x + 2) - 2x = 13$
14. $3(x - 2) + 4x = 8$
15. $4(y + 1) - 3y = 6$
16. $2(y + 5) - y = 19$
17. $z + 2(z + 3) = 12$
18. $6(z - 1) + z = 1$

Find the solution set of each inequation. Each variable is a variable on N.

19. $3x + 5x < 24$
20. $4x - x < 15$
21. $5x + 2x > 22$
22. $x + 2x < 10$
23. $3y + 4y > 10$
24. $8x - 3x < 30$
25. $9v + 5v - 2v < 50$
26. $m + m < 6$
27. $3y + 2(y + 1) \geq 12$
28. $5p + 3(2 + p) \leq 8$
29. $4(x + 2) + 7 \leq 31$
30. $5(y - 1) + 3y \geq 3$

Find the solution set of each open sentence. Each variable is a variable on W.

31. $5(v + 3) + 2v > 30$
32. $8t + 2(t + 5) < 50$

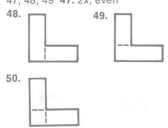
33. $2x + (x - 3) < 7$
35. $2(n + 1) + 3(2n + 3) \geq 18$
37. $(n - 1) + 3(2n + 1) < 18$

39. $\frac{1}{2}(8x + 4) = 10$

41. $\frac{1}{2}(8x + 6) > 7$

34. $5(n - 2) + 5n = 60$
36. $3(2n + 1) + 2(n + 6) \leq 47$
38. $7(x + 1) + 3(x + 2) > 23$

40. $\frac{1}{3}(12x + 15) < 17$

42. From k subtract 1. Then multiply the difference by 3. If the value of this expression is 72, find k.

43. Suppose n is a variable on N. To n add 5, and then multiply your answer by 3. If the result is greater than 33, write an inequation in n and find its solution set.

44. A rectangle has length $(x + 1)$ cm and width 4 cm. Write expressions for **(a)** its perimeter in cm, and **(b)** its area in cm^2. If the perimeter exceeds 12 cm, what can you say about x? What can you say about the area?

45. Suppose x belongs to the set of even natural numbers. From x subtract 2, and multiply your answer by 4. The value of this expression is less than 40. Write an inequation in x and find its solution set.

46. Suppose n is a whole number. Write a number 1 more than n. Write a number 1 less than n. If the sum of these three consecutive numbers is 144, find n. Write the three numbers in ascending order.

47. To x add 2, multiply the sum by 2, then subtract 4. Write a simple expression for the result. If x represents a whole number, is the result even or odd?

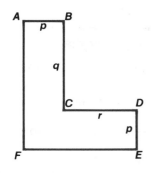

In the L shape, $AB = p$ cm, $DE = p$ cm, $BC = q$ cm, and $CD = r$ cm. Show by drawing sketches how each expression for the area is obtained. Add lines if you need to.

48. $p(q + p) + pr$ **49.** $p(r + p) + pq$
50. $pq + pr + p^2$ **51.** $p(p + q + r)$

52. Use the Distributive Property to show that all the expressions in Exercises **48–51** are equivalent.

53. On a bus trip there are x boys and two more girls than boys. Each pays \$.35. Write an expression for the total bus fares. Simplify it as much as possible. If the total fares are \$4.20, write an equation in x and solve it. How many are going on the trip?

54. A collection of coins consists of $3x$ nickels, $(x + 2)$ dimes, and $(x - 6)$ quarters. Write an expression in simplest form for the value in cents of the coins. If the value of the collection is $2.70, write an equation in x and solve it. If each person gives one coin only, find the number of contributors.

55. A rectangle has length $(x + 9)$ cm and width x cm. Write expressions for **(a)** its perimeter in cm, and **(b)** its area in cm². If its perimeter exceeds 30 cm but is less than 42 cm, write two inequations in x. Complete the inequation ___?___ $< x <$ ___?___ .

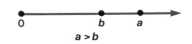

Chapter Summary

1. The whole numbers have order which can be shown on the number line.

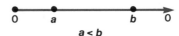

2. If a and b are any two whole numbers, then $a > b$, $a = b$, or $a < b$.

3.

Inequality Symbols	Meaning
$>$	is greater than
$\geq$	is greater than or equal to
$<$	is less than
$\leq$	is less than or equal to
$\neq$	is not equal to

4. An inequality is a numerical statement which contains an inequality symbol. An inequation is an open sentence which contains an inequality symbol.

5. The solution set of an inequation is the set of replacements for the variable which make a true sentence.
6. The Distributive Property: $a(b + c + \cdots) = ab + ac + \cdots$. The Distributive Property may be used to remove parentheses or to write an expression as a product. The Distributive Property is useful in solving open sentences.

REVIEW
EXERCISES 4-1

1. Zero is less than one. 2. Four is greater than two. 3. Five is less than or equal to ten.
4. Three is greater than one and less than twenty. 5. T 6. F 7. F
8. T 9. < 10. > 11. = 12. =
13. > 14. = 15. $2 < 3 < 5$,
$5 > 3 > 2$ 16. $0 < 1 < 4, 4 >$
$1 > 0$ 17. $4 < 10 < 20, 20 >$
$10 > 4$ 18. $3 < 7 < 11, 11 > 7$
> 3 19. {5, 6} 20. {0, 1, 2, 3, 4}
21. {1, 2, 3, 4, 5} 22. {2, 3, 4,}
23. {2, 3} 24. {3} 25. {1, 2, 3, 4, 5, 6} 26. φ 27. {1} 28. {0, 1}
29. {3, 4, 5, 6, . . .} 30. {0, 1, 2, . . . , 9} 31. {0, 1, 2, 3, . . .}
32. {5, 6, 7, . . .} 33. {5, 6, 7, 8, . . .} 34. {0, 1, 2, 3, . . ., 10}
35. {4, 5, 6, 7, . . .} 36. >
37. < 38. < 39. > **4-2**

Write each statement in words.
1. $0 < 1$ **2.** $4 > 2$ **3.** $5 \le 10$ **4.** $1 < 3 < 20$

Tell whether each statement is true (T) or false (F).
5. $6 \ge 6$ **6.** $2 < 1 < 4$ **7.** $8 < 8$ **8.** $10 > 3$

Copy each statement. Place one of the symbols $>$, $=$, or $<$ in each blank to make a true statement.
9. $4 \underline{\quad?\quad} 5$ **10.** $1 \underline{\quad?\quad} 0$ **11.** $9 \underline{\quad?\quad} 9$
12. $a \underline{\quad?\quad} a$ **13.** $2 + 0 \underline{\quad?\quad} 2 \cdot 0$ **14.** $ab \underline{\quad?\quad} ba$

Combine each pair of inequalities into one statement. First use only the $<$ symbol. Then use only $>$.
15. $2 < 3$ and $3 < 5$ **16.** $0 < 1$ and $4 > 1$
17. $4 < 10$ and $10 < 20$ **18.** $7 > 3$ and $11 > 7$

If x is a variable on {0, 1, 2, 3, 4, 5, 6}, find the solution set of each inequation.
19. $x > 4$ **20.** $x < 5$ **21.** $1 \le x \le 5$
22. $2 \le x \le 4$ **23.** $2 \le x < 4$ **24.** $3 \le x \le 3$
25. $x > 0$ **26.** $x > 7$ **27.** $0 < x \le 1$

If w is a variable on W, find the solution set of each inequation.
28. $w + 3 < 5$ **29.** $w + 3 > 5$ **30.** $w - 2 < 8$
31. $w < w + 1$ **32.** $w \le w + 1$ **33.** $3w + 1 > 13$
34. $w - 5 \le 5$ **35.** $4w - 3 > 9$

4-4

Copy and complete each statement where a and b are variables on W. Use $>$, $<$, or $=$ for each blank.
36. If $a = b + 1$, then $a \underline{\quad?\quad} b$.
37. If $a + 2 = b$, then $a \underline{\quad?\quad} b$.
38. If $3a < 3b$, then $a \underline{\quad?\quad} b$.
39. If $a + 6 = b + 9$, then $a \underline{\quad?\quad} b$.

40. $3p + 3$ **41.** $7r - 21$
42. $10r - 5$ **43.** $12x + 18y$
44. $ac + 4a$ **45.** $qc + 5dq$
46. $x^2y - xy^2$ **47.** $r + 3s - 2t$
48. $mn + m^2 - mr$ **49.** $5(x + 3y)$
50. $2(4y + 9)$ **51.** $3(x^2 + 2)$

52. $p(p + r)$ **53.** $a(a - 2b)$
54. $p(p - q)$ **55.** $x(xy + 1)$
56. $5x(3x + 1)$ **57.** $3p(3p - 5q)$
58. $a(x + y + z)$ **59.** $2(2p + 3q - 4r)$ **60.** $a(a^2 + a + 1)$
61. $x(1 - x^2)$ **62.** $x^2(y + z)$
63. $2ab(1 + 2ab)$ **64.** 3300
65. 13,390 **66.** -300 **67.** $13a$
68. $9x$ **69.** $2x^2 + y$ **70.** $6a - 7b$
71. $7pq$ **72.** $4xy$ **73.** $9a$ **74.** $9c$
75. $5m$ **76.** $15r + s$ **77.** $9n - 3$
78. $11y$ **79.** $13a^2 - 3$ **80.** $10x + 2y$ **81.** φ **82.** {1, 2, 3, 4, 5}
83. {3, 4, 5} **84.** {0} **85.** {0, 1, 2}

86. {4} **87.** {1} **88.** {0, 1}
89. {0, 1, 3} **90.** {0, 1, 3}
91. φ **92.** {3, 5}

4-5

Write each expression as a sum or difference of terms.

40. $3(p + 1)$ **41.** $7(r - 3)$ **42.** $5(2r - 1)$

43. $6(2x + 3y)$ **44.** $a(c + 4)$ **45.** $q(c + 5d)$

46. $xy(x - y)$ **47.** $1(r + 3s - 2t)$ **48.** $m(n + m - r)$

4-6

Write each expression as a product of factors.

49. $5x + 15y$ **50.** $8y + 18$ **51.** $3x^2 + 6$

52. $p^2 + pr$ **53.** $a^2 - 2ab$ **54.** $qp^2 - pq$

55. $x^2y + x$ **56.** $15x^2 + 5x$ **57.** $9p^2 - 15pq$

58. $ax + ay + az$ **59.** $4p + 6q - 8r$ **60.** $a^3 + a^2 + a$

61. $x - x^3$ **62.** $x^2y + x^2z$ **63.** $2ab + 4a^2b^2$

Write the common factor for each expression. Then use factors to calculate mentally if you can.

64. $(3 \cdot 25) + (3 \cdot 75)$ **65.** $13^2 + (13 \cdot 17)$

66. $l = mv - vu$, find l when $m = 4$, $v = 50$, and $u = 10$.

4-7, 4-8

Simplify each expression if possible.

67. $6a + 7a$ **68.** $10x - x$

69. $2x^2 + y$ **70.** $6a - 7b$

71. $5pq + 2qp$ **72.** $7yx - 3xy$

73. $2a + 3a + 4a$ **74.** $8c + 3c - 2c$

75. $6m - 2m + m$ **76.** $12r + 3r + s$

77. $5n + 4n - 3$ **78.** $7y + 5y - y$

79. $13a^2 - 3$ **80.** $6x + 2y + 4x$

4-9

If x is a variable on {0, 1, 2, 3, 4, 5}, find the solution set for each open sentence.

81. $7x + 2x + 2x = 24$ **82.** $4x - 2x + x > 2$

83. $\dfrac{1}{2}x + \dfrac{1}{2}x > 2$ **84.** $\dfrac{3}{4}x + \dfrac{1}{4}x = 0$

85. $x + x < 5$ **86.** $\dfrac{3}{4}x - \dfrac{1}{2}x = 1$

If p is a variable on {0, 1, 3, 5}, find the solution set for each open sentence.

87. $3(7p - 5) - 2p = 4$ **88.** $p - \dfrac{1}{4}p < 2$

89. $\dfrac{1}{4}p - \dfrac{1}{5}p < \dfrac{1}{4}$ **90.** $0.4p - 0.1p < 1$

91. $\dfrac{1}{2}p + \dfrac{3}{4}p = 5$ **92.** $\dfrac{1}{2}(4p + 10) > 10$

93. {6} **94.** {10, 11, 12, . . .}
95. {0, 1, 2, 3, . . . , 20} **96.** {21, 22, 23, . . .} **97.** {0, 1, 2, . . . , 12}
98. {0, 1, 2, . . . , 6} **99.** {10}
100. {6, 7, 8, 9, . . .} **101.** $y \geq 4$
102. $4x < 16$, $x < 4$ cm
103. $250 + w \leq 410$, $w \leq 160$

If y is a variable on W, find the solution set for each open sentence.

93. $3y + 4y = 42$

94. $7y + 3y \geq 100$

95. $8y + 2y - 5y < 105$

96. $3(y + 1) > 63$

97. $6(y - 3) \leq 54$

98. $2(y + 1) + 5y < 51$

99. $5(y - 4) + 8y = 110$

100. $2(y + 3) + 3(2y + 1) > 49$

101. $3(y + 2) + \dfrac{1}{2}(8y + y) \geq 44$

102. The perimeter of a square is less than 16 cm. Each side is x cm long. Write an inequation in x and find its solution. How long is each side of the square?

103. The maximum safe load for Mr. Brown's car is 410 kg. He and his passengers for a trip weigh 250 kg. Mr. Brown decides to restrict the weight of luggage, w kg, so as to be under the maximum safe load. Write an inequation in w to describe this situation. Express it in simplest form.

MATHEMATICS AND RECREATION

scuba DIVING

Have you ever thought of scuba diving as a mathematical recreation? Most people only consider scuba diving in terms of the beauty of an alien underwater world. This alien world is not safe, however, if you do not understand it. To know the safe limits of yourself and of your diving equipment, you must know the mathematics of air pressure.

Air pressure at sea level is normally 14.7 pounds per square inch (psi). For each foot you descend under water, the pressure increases 0.445 psi. Thus, if you dive to a depth of 33 feet, the pressure is almost doubled, since 33×0.445 psi $= 14.685$ psi. If you were to take a balloon with you to a depth of 33 feet, it would have half the volume it had at the surface.

Your lungs behave just like a balloon. The lungs of a typical adult have a volume of about 10 pints at sea level. If the volume is reduced to less than 3 pints, the lungs will be damaged. Try to compute a reasonable maximum depth for a safe dive without equipment.

Scuba equipment is designed to equalize the pressure in the lungs and the pressure of the water. A diver must breathe constantly to maintain this balance of pressures. The lungs will probably rupture if the gas pressure in them becomes as much as 2 psi greater than the pressure of the surrounding water.

There are many factors requiring a knowledge of mathematics and science involved in making sure of your margin of safety in diving. Before diving make sure you have enough instruction and enough understanding of these factors.

Scuba diving is exciting! It is a safe sport if you understand the limitations of your body and your diving equipment in the alien underwater world.

Photo by Ron Church, Photography Unlimited

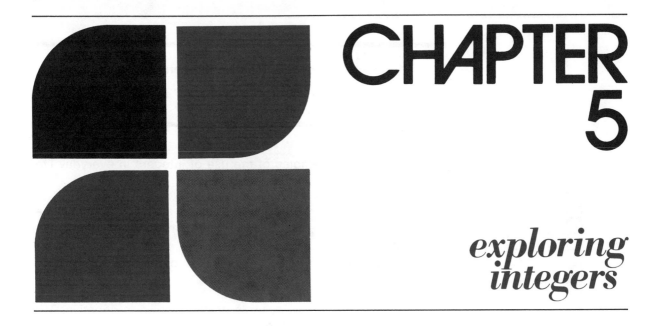

CHAPTER 5

exploring integers

5-1
Extending the Number Line

The number line can be extended to the left of zero.

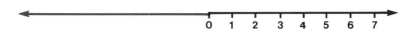

The points to the left of zero are named by starting at zero and moving left. The unit length is the same as for whole numbers.

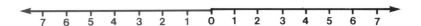

Numbers to the left of zero are called *negative integers* and numbers to the right of zero are called *positive integers.* The negative integers are written with a negative sign, ⁻3. Positive integers usually are written with no sign.

The numeral ⁻3 is read *negative three,* and 3 is read *positive three.* Sometimes the positive integers are written using the positive sign.

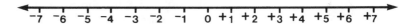

The positive integers, negative integers, and zero form the *set of integers,* $Z = \{\ldots, ^-4, ^-3, ^-2, ^-1, 0, 1, 2, 3, 4, \ldots\}$.

Here are a few examples of the use of integers in everyday life.

Temperature

The thermometer may be considered as a vertical number line. On the thermometer, the positive direction is up. The negative direction is down.

A temperature reading of $^-15°$ is 15 degrees below zero.

Altitude

In talking about altitudes, up is positive; down is negative. The top of the Grand Teton Mountain is about 13,766 feet above sea level. Its altitude is $^+13{,}766$. The floor of Death Valley is about 276 feet below sea level. Its altitude is $^-276$. The altitude of the surface of the ocean is 0.

Debits and Credits

If a person writes too many checks on his checking account, he may be overdrawn by $67.32. In this case his bank statement says that his balance is $^-67.32$. If he then deposits a hundred dollars, his balance becomes positive again, 32.68.

EXERCISES

Write the next three numbers in each sequence. Use a number line if you wish.

1. 12, 9, 6, 3, ___?___, ___?___, ___?___, . . .

2. 5, 3, 1, ___?___, ___?___, ___?___, . . .

3. $^-12$, $^-10$, $^-8$, ___?___, ___?___, ___?___, . . .

4. $^-13$, $^-9$, $^-5$, ___?___, ___?___, ___?___, . . .

5. Part of a Celsius thermometer scale is shown. Copy the figure and complete the marking of the scale. What temperature is the thermometer showing?

Write each temperature as an integer.

6. 5° below zero   **7.** 5° above zero

What is the meaning of each temperature?

8. $^-10°$ **9.** 0°   **10.** 20°

Which reading indicates a warmer temperature?

11. 0° or 3°   **12.** $^-15°$ or $^-10°$

13. The countdown to the time of launch of a rocket is given in seconds by the sequence $^-10, ^-9, ^-8, \ldots$. Write the rest of the sequence to the time of firing. Continue the sequence for the first four numbers after launch.

14. The key to a shading of a map of Holland is shown. Copy the figure and complete the missing numbers. What can you say about the land marked as in the highest rectangle? What can you say about the land marked as in the lowest rectangle?

15. If $^+10$ km means 10 km north of a place, what will $^-10$ km mean?

16. If $^+15$ newtons means a force of 15 newtons to the right, what will a force of $^-15$ newtons indicate?

17. If $^+10$ meters per second means a speed of 10 meters per second upwards, what will a speed of $^-25$ meters per second mean?

18. Suggest a way of showing that your watch is 1 minute fast. How would you write that your watch is 2 minutes slow?

19. At 4 P.M. the temperature in Portland was 5°C. At 6 P.M. a cold front passed over, and the temperature fell 7°. What was the temperature then? Your thermometer drawing for Exercise **5** should help you here. Later the temperature rose 2°. What was the temperature then?

Height Above High Water in Meters

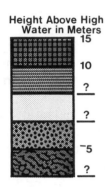

OBJECTIVES:

1. To locate (a, b) in a plane given $(a, b) \in Z \times Z$.
2. To name $(a, b) \in Z \times Z$ given its location in a plane.

5-2
Extending the Axes

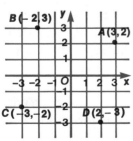

By using the negative integers, the x-axis and y-axis of the Cartesian plane also can be extended from the origin. As is usual, up and to the right are positive. Down and to the left are negative.

The coordinates of A are $(3, 2)$, and the coordinates of B are $(^-2, 3)$. What are the coordinates of C and D?

EXERCISES

1. What are the coordinates of points *B*, *C*, and *D* in the figure?

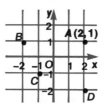

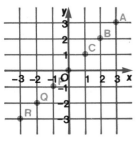

2. Copy the axes, marked as shown. Plot the points *A*(3, 3), *B*(2, 2), *C*(1, 1), *O*(0, 0), *P*(⁻1, ⁻1), *Q*(⁻2, ⁻2), *R*(⁻3, ⁻3). Write the coordinates of the next three points in this sequence and plot the points.

3. Suppose that your diagram for Exercise **2** is folded along the *y*-axis so that *A*, *B*, and *C* touch the paper at *A'*, *B'*, and *C'*. Write the coordinates of *A'*, *B'*, and *C'*. Points *A'*, *B'*, and *C'* are the images of *A*, *B*, and *C* in the *y*-axis.

4. Suppose that your diagram for Exercise **2** is folded along the *x*-axis, so that *P*, *Q*, and *R* touch the paper at *P'*, *Q'*, and *R'*. Write the coordinates of *P'*, *Q'*, and *R'*. Points *P'*, *Q'*, and *R'* are the images of *P*, *Q*, and *R* in the *x*-axis.

5. Point *A* has coordinates (4, 2), *B*(⁻1, 1), *C*(⁻3, ⁻5) and *D*(6, 0). Write the coordinates of the image of each point in the *y*-axis and in the *x*-axis.

Write the next three numbers in each sequence.

6. 12, 8, 4, ____?____, ____?____, ____?____, ...

7. 4, 1, ⁻2, ____?____, ____?____, ____?____, ...

8. ⁻9, ⁻7, ⁻5, ____?____, ____?____, ____?____, ...

9. The temperature on a thermometer was 2°F. What would the reading be if the temperature fell 2° from the first reading? What would the reading be if the temperature fell 9° from the first reading?

10. Copy the axes, marked as in Exercise **2**. Draw the triangle *ABC* with corners *A*(1, 1), *B*(3, 1), *C*(2, 4). If your diagram is folded along the *y*-axis until *A*, *B*, and *C* touch the paper at *A'*, *B'*, and *C'*, then *A'*, *B'*, and *C'* are the images of *A*, *B*, and *C* in the *y*-axis. Write the coordinates of *A'*, *B'*, and *C'*.

11. Plot the points *P*(⁻3, 1), *Q*(1, 1), *R*(1, 2), *S*(⁻3, 2) on graph paper. What shape is *PQRS*? Show the image of *PQRS* in the *x*-axis, and write the coordinates of its corners.

12. $R''(-1,2)$, $Q''(-1,1)$, $P''(3,1)$, $S''(3,2)$ **13.** $2, -$2$
14. lose one minute per day

12. Show the image of *PQRS* from Exercise **11** in the *y*-axis, and write the coordinates of its corners.
13. Mr. Smith had a balance of $10 in the bank. Write his new balance if he drew out $8. Write his new balance if he drew out $12 (the bank allows overdrafts).
14. When the regulator on a clock was set to $^+1$, the clock kept time. When it was set to $^+4$, the clock gained one minute a day. How much would it gain or lose if the regulator were set to $^-2$?

Suggested Activity

Answers will vary.

List some everyday situations involving negative integers.

5-3
Order of the Integers

OBJECTIVE:
To name which is larger given $a, b \in Z$.

Discourage student statements such as, "for negative numbers, the bigger one is less." Insist rather stubbornly on *is left of* as the meaning for $<$.

The integers also have the *property of order*. The order of the integers may be shown by using a number line. The statement $a < b$ means that a is to the left of b. Since $^-3$ is to the left of 3 on the number line, $^-3 < 3$. Likewise, $^-4 < ^-1$, $^-2 < 0$, and $^-3 < 2$. The statement $a > b$ means that a is to the right of b on the number line. Thus, $3 > ^-3$, $^-1 > ^-4$, $0 > ^-2$, and $2 > ^-3$.

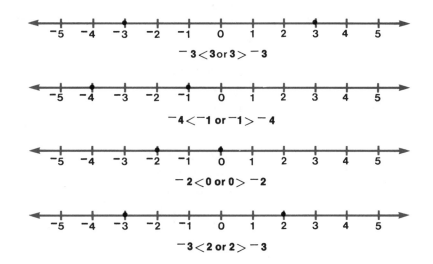

It may be helpful to remember that *all positive integers are greater than zero* and *all negative integers are less than zero.*

EXERCISES

Draw a number line. Use it to help you write the greater number in each pair.

1. 4, 3   **2.** 0, 1   **3.** ⁻1, 0   **4.** ⁻4, ⁻5

5. Which is the warmer temperature in each pair?
  a. 15°C, 12°C   **b.** 3°C, 0°C
  c. ⁻3°F, ⁻2°F   **d.** ⁻1°F, 1°F

6. Which is the greater height above sea level in each pair?
  a. 200 m, 100 m   **b.** ⁻40 m, ⁻30 m
  c. 50 m, ⁻50 m   **d.** 0 m, ⁻10 m

Use $>$ to write a true statement for each pair of numbers.

7. 5, 3   **8.** 0, ⁻1   **9.** 0, 1
10. ⁻2, 2   **11.** ⁻3, ⁻4   **12.** ⁻20, ⁻30

Use $<$ to write a true statement for each pair of numbers.

13. 5, 12   **14.** ⁻9, 9   **15.** ⁻3, ⁻5
16. ⁻6, 2   **17.** 0, ⁻1   **18.** ⁻100, ⁻99

Tell whether each statement is true (T) or false (F).

19. $1 < 3$ **20.** $⁻5 > 3$ **21.** $⁻4 \leq ⁻4$

Copy each pair of numbers in the order given. Insert the symbol $>$ or $<$ between the members of each pair to make a true statement.

22. 5 _____?_____ ⁻7   **23.** 10 _____?_____ ⁻10
24. ⁻2 _____?_____ ⁻1   **25.** ⁻7 _____?_____ ⁻100

If x is a variable on the set $\{⁻4, ⁻3, ⁻2, ⁻1, 0, 1, 2, 3, 4\}$, find the solution set of each inequation.

26. $x < 0$ **27.** $x < ⁻2$ **28.** $x > 2$
29. $x > ⁻1$ **30.** $x \geq 4$ **31.** $⁻4 < x \leq ⁻3$
32. $x \geq 0$ **33.** $⁻4 < x \leq ⁻4$

Use the inequality symbol $<$ to arrange each triple in ascending order (with the least first and the greatest last). Then use $>$ to arrange each triple in descending order (with the greatest first and the least last).

34. 3, 7, 5   **35.** 4, ⁻6, 2
36. ⁻2, ⁻1, 2   **37.** ⁻100, 10, 0

38. Every replacement which makes the open sentence $x < 0$ a true sentence is a negative number. Write five such replacements. Make a corresponding statement for the open sentence $x > 0$.

If y is a variable on the set $\{^-5, ^-4, ^-3, ^-2, ^-1, 0, 1, 2, 3\}$, solve each open sentence.

39. $^-3 < y < 0$ **40.** $^-4 < y < ^-2$ **41.** $^-3 < y < 2$

42. $y > 0$ *and* $y < 3$ **43.** $y < 0$ *and* $y < ^-3$ **44.** $^-1 < y < 1$

5-4
Combining Integers

OBJECTIVE:

To name $a + b$ given $a, b \in Z$.

If you have \$8 in your pocket but you owe \$5 to a friend, then you really have a balance of \$3.

$$8 + (^-5) = 3$$

If the temperature is $(^-5)°$F in the morning and it rises 12° by noon, then the noon temperature is 7°F.

$$(^-5) + 12 = 7$$

If a submarine is 76 feet below sea level and it dives another 48 feet, then it will be 124 feet below sea level.

$$^-76 + (^-48) = ^-124$$

Do not give "rules" for adding integers at this point. The intention here is to build up expectations which will later allow such rules to make sense.

These are examples of adding integers. When adding integers, it may be helpful to think of money, temperatures, or altitude.

The number line also may be used to add integers. When adding integers on the number line, move to the right to add a positive integer. Move to the left to add a negative integer. The steps for finding $3 + (^-9)$ are shown in the following figures.

Step 1. Locate 3 on the number line.

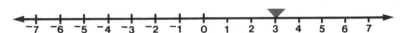

Step 2. Add $^-9$ by moving nine units to the left from 3.

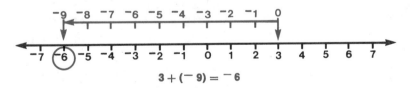

$$3 + (^-9) = ^-6$$

The following figure shows $(^-4) + (^-2)$.

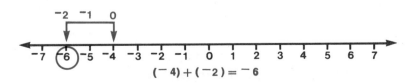

$$(^-4) + (^-2) = ^-6$$

127

EXERCISES

Find each sum by thinking about money, temperature, or altitude.

1. $5 + 3$ **2.** $3 + (^-7)$ **3.** $4 + (^-3)$
4. $3 + (^-3)$ **5.** $^-7 + 2$ **6.** $^-2 + (^-5)$
7. $^-1 + (^-8)$ **8.** $^-3 + 3$

Draw a number line to show each addition.

9. $3 + (^-2)$ **10.** $6 + 4$ **11.** $4 + (^-7)$
12. $^-6 + 6$ **13.** $^-4 + (^-4)$ **14.** $4 + (^-4)$
15. $^-4 + 4$ **16.** $^-4 + 0$

Write each sum, $a, b, c \in W$. Think about addition on the number line.

17. $^-2 + 3 + (^-3)$ **18.** $6 + (^-5) + 5$ **19.** $^-2 + (^-6) + (^-2)$
20. $^-7 + (^-4) + 11$ **21.** $7 + (^-9) + 5$ **22.** $^-8 + 3 + (^-10)$
23. $5a + (^-2a)$ **24.** $7b + (^-7b)$ **25.** $3c + (^-6c)$

26. Copy the table.

Time	6 A.M.	9 A.M	12 noon	3 P.M.	6 P.M.	9 P.M.
Temperature (°C)	$^-8$	?	?	?	?	?

The temperature rose 6° between 6 A.M. and 9 A.M., 12° between 9 A.M. and 12 noon, 4° between noon and 3 P.M., 16° between 6 A.M. and 6 P.M., and 6° between 6 A.M. and 9 P.M. Fill in the other temperatures in the table. At what times was the temperature below zero?

Find each sum. Use a number line only if you must.

27. $3 + (^-1)$ **28.** $3 + (^-5)$ **29.** $2 + (^-9)$
30. $5 + (^-5)$ **31.** $^-7 + (^-2)$ **32.** $^-3 + (^-5)$
33. $^-2 + (^-9)$ **34.** $^-5 + (^-5)$ **35.** $^-1 + (^-14)$
36. $^-12 + (^-3)$ **37.** $^-6 + 14$ **38.** $^-34 + 56$
39. $^-25 + 18$ **40.** $8 + (^-5) + (^-3)$

For each sentence write the replacement for x which will make a true sentence. $x \in Z$.

41. $x + 2 = 0$ **42.** $x + 1 = 0$ **43.** $x + (^-3) = 0$
44. $x + 100 = 0$ **45.** $x + (^-10) = 0$ **46.** $^-x + 5 = 0$

Suggested Activity

Write a situation in words to describe each addition problem in Exercises **1–8**.

5-5
Properties of Addition

EXPLORATORY EXERCISES

First Number

For most classes, this page is best managed as group discussion.

1.

+	−3	−2	−1	0	1	2	3
−3	−6	−5	−4	−3	−2	−1	0
−2	−5	−4	−3	−2	−1	0	1
−1	−4	−3	−2	−1	0	1	2
0	−3	−2	−1	0	1	2	3
1	−2	−1	0	1	2	3	4
2	−1	0	1	2	3	4	5
3	0	1	2	3	4	5	6

a. Main Diagonal — upper left corner to lower right corner.
b. Answers will vary. **c.** Sums appear from small to large.
d. Sums appear from small to large. **e.** 3 and −3, 2 and −2, 1 and −1, 0 and 0 **2.** $b + a$
3. Yes **4.** $a + (b + c)$ **5.** It checks. **6. a.** $3 = 3$ **b.** $0 = 0$

A strong commitment on students' part to the Commutative and Associative Properties will be important when letters are used to represent integers.

1. Copy and complete the addition table.

Second Number

+	⁻3	⁻2	⁻1	0	1	2	3
⁻3	?	?	?	?	?	?	?
⁻2	?	?	?	?	?	?	?
⁻1	?	?	?	?	?	?	?
0	?	?	?	?	?	?	?
1	?	?	?	?	?	?	?
2	?	?	?	?	?	?	?
3	?	?	?	?	?	?	?

a. About which diagonal is the table symmetric?
b. Make a list of patterns you can see in the table, such as where even and odd numbers occur, and so on.
c. What do you notice when you read a column from top to bottom?
d. What do you notice when you read a row from left to right?
e. List pairs of numbers which, when added together, make zero.

2. Write the Commutative Property of Addition: $a + b = $ _____?_____.

3. Check from your table that $^-3 + (^-2) = {}^-2 + (^-3)$. Is it true that $2 + (^-1) = {}^-1 + 2$?

4. Write the Associative Property of Addition: $(a + b) + c = $ _____?_____.

5. Check whether $[(^-3 + 2)] + (^-1) = (^-3) + [2 + (^-1)]$.

6. Verify each statement by calculating each side of the equality.
  a. $[(10 + 5)] + (^-12) = 10 + [5 + (^-12)]$
  b. $[7 + (^-5)] + (^-2) = 7 + [^-5 + (^-2)]$

The Exploratory Exercises suggest that addition of integers is both commutative and associative. Since the Associative and Commutative Properties apply for addition of integers, terms may be rearranged in finding sums.

For example, suppose you wish to find the sum 5 + (⁻3) + 2 + 13 + (⁻5). This problem might be easier if it were written 13 + (⁻3) + 5 + (⁻5) + 2, since 5 + (⁻5) = 0.

Changing the order of terms also may help in simplifying expressions. In the following example x, y and z are variables on W.

EXAMPLE

$3x + (⁻2y) + (⁻z) + 5y + (⁻4x) = 3x + (⁻4x) + (⁻2y) + 5y + (⁻z)$
$= (⁻x) + 3y + (⁻z)$

This is important. Since multiplication of integers has not been covered at this point, ⁻4y and ⁻4x are defined only for x, $y \in$ W. Therefore, the restrictions on the variables are made. (See the note on the next page.)

Notice that no matter what whole number value is assigned to y, $(⁻2y) + 5y = 3y$.

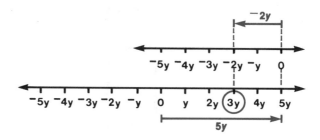

In the same way, $3x + (⁻4x) = ⁻x$ no matter what whole number value is assigned to x.

EXERCISES

1. See section notes in T.G.
2.
$-5 = (-3) + (-2) = (-2) + (-3)$

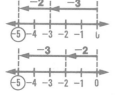

3. 8, 8; They are equal; Associative Property true.
4. −11 = −11 **5.** 6 **6.** −2
7. −3 **8.** 8 **9.** 2 **10.** 11 **11.** −21
12. −5 **13.** −21 **14.** 0 **15.** −2y
16. 4z **17.** 0 **18.** 0

Again, if $y \in$ W, then ⁻2y has meaning for students at this point in the course.

1. Show the sums 4 + (⁻6) and ⁻6 + 4 on number lines. What is each sum?
2. Calculate ⁻3 + (⁻2) and ⁻2 + (⁻3). Show these sums on the number line.
3. Calculate (5 + 6) + (⁻3) and 5 + [6 + (⁻3)]. What do you notice?
4. Show by calculation that (⁻8 + 4) + (⁻7) = ⁻8 + [4 + (⁻7)].

Simplify each expression. Rearrange the order of the terms if it will help you. The variables are on W.

5. (6 + 3) + (⁻3) **6.** (⁻2 + 3) + (⁻3)
7. ⁻8 + [8 + (⁻3)] **8.** ⁻9 + 8 + 9
9. ⁻5 + 2 + 5 **10.** 15 + (⁻12) + 8
11. ⁻9 + (⁻5) + (⁻7) **12.** ⁻8 + 15 + (⁻12)
13. ⁻7 + (⁻7) + (⁻7) **14.** 6x + (⁻3x) + (⁻3x)
15. ⁻y + y + (⁻2y) **16.** 3z + (⁻4z) + 5z
17. a + (⁻2a) + a **18.** 3b + 5b + (⁻8b)

Most students will not give a thought to the fact that variables are on W in a chapter about Z. For these students, the fact that ^-2c has not been defined for $c < 0$ need not be announced. For slow students, it is best left unannounced at this point. The jump from using $^-2$ to using ^-2c, $c \in W$, is a large enough jump.

19. $^-c + (^-2c) + (^-3c)$

20. $7 + (^-3) + (^-5) + 9$

21. $^-12 + (^-3) + 7 + 3$

22. $5x + (^-6x) + 2x + (^-3x)$

23. $^-4y + (^-4y) + 5y + (^-10y)$

24. $6a + 3b + (^-2a) + (^-2b)$

25. $^-2p + (^-3q) + (^-6p) + 3q$

If x is a variable on the set of integers, solve each equation. The table in the Exploratory Exercises may help you.

26. $^-1 + x = 2$

27. $3 + x = 1$

28. $x + 3 = ^-1$

29. $x + (^-3) = ^-2$

30. $2 + x = 0$

31. $x + (^-3) = 0$

32. On a certain test, students score 2 points for a correct answer and $^-1$ point for a wrong answer. If one student had 76 questions correct and 19 wrong, what was her score? Another student had 50 correct and 50 wrong. What was his score?

33. In a card game, the maximum possible score is 100. Negative scores are allowed. In five consecutive games, a player's scores were $^-70$, 80, $^-60$, 50, $^-30$. Calculate his total score.

34. Write an equation in y and x if y is 2 more than x. If $x \in \{^-5, ^-4, ^-3, ^-2, ^-1, 0, 1, 2\}$, write the corresponding replacements for y.

Two or more expressions may be added vertically. To add $2a - 3b$ and $4a + 7b$, you could write: $2a - 3b$
$$\underline{4a + 7b}$$

When expressions are written above each other, like terms are placed in the same column. Then you may find a sum for each column. The variables are on W.

Samples

1. ^-6x
$\underline{2x}$
^-4x

2. $2a - 3b$
$\underline{4a + 3b}$
$6a$

3. $^-p - 2q - 3r$
$\underline{^-p + 3q + 2r}$
$^-2p + q - r$

4. $^-6x + 2y$
$2x -z$
$\underline{ y + z}$
$^-4x + 3y$

Find the sum of each pair of expressions.

35. $2a$
$\underline{3a}$

36. $5b$
$\underline{b}$

37. $6c$
$\underline{^-2c}$

38. $8d$
$\underline{^-4d}$

39. $3e$
$\underline{^-5e}$

40. $2f$
$\underline{^-6f}$

41. $\begin{array}{r} {}^-3g \\ {}^-2g \\ \hline \end{array}$

42. $\begin{array}{r} {}^-4h \\ {}^-h \\ \hline \end{array}$

43. $\begin{array}{r} 7x \\ 7x \\ \hline \end{array}$

44. $\begin{array}{r} 7x \\ {}^-7x \\ \hline \end{array}$

45. $\begin{array}{r} {}^-7x \\ 7x \\ \hline \end{array}$

46. $\begin{array}{r} {}^-7x \\ {}^-7x \\ \hline \end{array}$

47. $\begin{array}{r} 3x + 4y \\ x - 2y \\ \hline \end{array}$

48. $\begin{array}{r} 2p - 3q \\ {}^-3p - 3q \\ \hline \end{array}$

49. $\begin{array}{r} k - 1 \\ k + 1 \\ \hline \end{array}$

50. $\begin{array}{r} {}^-2m \\ + 3n \\ \hline {}^-2m - 4n \\ \hline \end{array}$

51. $\begin{array}{r} a + b + \;\; c \\ a - b + 3c \\ \hline \end{array}$

52. $\begin{array}{r} 2a - 3b \\ 3b - 4c \\ \hline 2a \qquad - 4c \\ \hline \end{array}$

53. $\begin{array}{r} p + \;\; q - 3r \\ {}^-2p - 2q + 2r \\ \hline \end{array}$

54. $\begin{array}{r} 2x - 3y + 4z \\ {}^-2x + 3y - 4z \\ \hline \end{array}$

55. $\begin{array}{r} 2x + 2t \\ {}^-t + \;\; v \\ \hline {}^-3x - \;\; t + 2v \\ \hline \end{array}$

5-6
Additive Inverses

OBJECTIVE:

To name $-a$ given $a \in Z$.

If $a + b = 0$, then a and b are called ***additive inverses*** of each other; a is the additive inverse of b, and b is the additive inverse of a.

In the set of integers, each element has an additive inverse. Since $3 + (^-3) = 0$, 3 and $(^-3)$ are additive inverses of each other. Since $(^-15) + 15 = 0$, $(^-15)$ and 15 are additive inverses of each other. Since $0 + 0 = 0$, the additive inverse of 0 is 0.

For any integer a, its inverse is called the negative of a, written $-a$.

Stress the last paragraph on this page. Use more examples if necessary.

Students *must* know that $-a$ may represent a positive number, zero, or a negative number.

The negative of a does not itself have to be negative. For example, the negative of (-4) is 4. In fact, if a is positive, then negative a will be a negative integer. If a is a negative integer, then negative a will be positive. Notice that $-a$ means *the negative of a* or *negative a*.

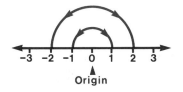

Origin

Additive inverses come in pairs which are the same distance from zero on the number line.

This distance of a number from the origin is called the **absolute value** of the number. The symbol $|x|$ means *the absolute value of x*. Since 2 and -2 are the same distance from the origin, $|2| = |-2| = 2$. Also, $|-3| = |3| = 3$. Since zero is the origin, there is no distance between zero and the origin; $|0| = 0$.

EXERCISES

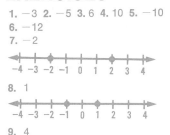

1. -3 2. -5 3. 6 4. 10 5. -10
6. -12
7. -2

8. 1

9. 4

If slow students have trouble with Exercises 1-17, spend more time with them on such problems while other students work Exercises 18-38.

10. 0

11. -7 12. 2 13. 9 14. $x = 6$
15. $x = -8$ 16. $x = 0$ 17. $x = -4$ 18. 5 19. 37 20. 37 21. 3
22. 3 23. 8 24. 2 25. 2 26. 8
27. 0 28. {7} 29. {5, -5}
30. ϕ 31. {-6, 2} 32. {-2, 2}
33. {-2, 6} 34. {-6, 6}
35. {-2} 36. {2} 37. {0, 1, 2, 3, ...}
38.

x	3	2	1	0	-1	-2	-3
$y = |x|$	3	2	1	0	1	2	3

Write the negative of each integer.

1. 3   **2.** 5   **3.** -6
4. -10 **5.** 10   **6.** 12

Graph each number. Then graph the negative of the number and name it.

7. 2   **8.** -1 **9.** -4 **10.** 0

Copy and complete each sentence.

11. $7 + \underline{\quad ? \quad} = 0$ **12.** $\underline{\quad ? \quad} + (-2) = 0$
13. $-9 + \underline{\quad ? \quad} = 0$

Solve each equation where x is a variable on Z.

14. $x + (-6) = 0$ **15.** $x + 8 = 0$
16. $x + 2 + (-2) = 0$ **17.** $x + 7 + (-3) = 0$

Write the value of each expression.

18. $|-5|$ **19.** $|37|$ **20.** $|-37|$
21. $|6 - 3|$ **22.** $|3 - 6|$ **23.** $|-3 - 5|$
24. $|-3 + 5|$ **25.** $|3 - 5|$ **26.** $|3 + 5|$
27. $|5 - 5|$

Solve each equation where x is a variable on Z. Be sure you write the complete solution set.

28. $|-7| = x$ **29.** $|x| = 5$ **30.** $|x| = -3$
31. $|x + 2| = 4$ **32.** $|x| + 2 = 4$ **33.** $|x - 2| = 4$
34. $|x| - 2 = 4$ **35.** $|x + 2| = 0$ **36.** $|x - 2| = 0$
37. $|x| = x$

38. Copy and complete the table. Draw a graph for $y = |x|$ on a coordinate plane.

x	3	2	1	0	-1	-2	-3
$y = |x|$	?	?	?	?	?	?	?

5-7
Subtraction
of Integers

The number line also may be used for subtraction. On the number line, you may think of subtraction as *going in the opposite direction*. To subtract 3 from 7, go 3 spaces in the negative direction from 7.

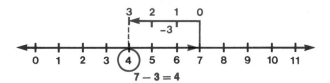

$$7 - 3 = 4$$

Students must first understand how to use the number line for subtraction. Only then is it safe to help them by giving them rules like the following: To subtract, change the number's sign and add. This is especially true for slow students who are willing to live by rules they do not understand.

To subtract -3 from 7, go 3 spaces in the positive direction from 7.

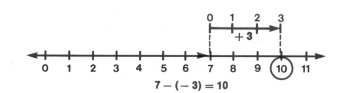

$$7 - (-3) = 10$$

The following are more examples showing addition and subtraction on the number line.

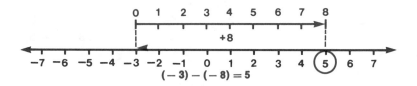

$$(-3) - (-8) = 5$$

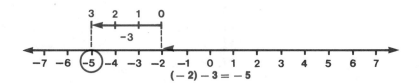

$$(-2) - 3 = -5$$

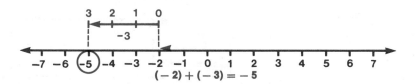

$$(-2) + (-3) = -5$$

The examples show that $a - b = a + (-b)$. This is true for any pair of integers.

Subtracting b from a is the same as adding the negative of b to a.

EXAMPLES

Variables are still being restricted to W to avoid situations that involve multiplication of integers.

1. $6 - (-5) = 6 + 5 = 11$
2. $3 - 8 = 3 + (-8) = -5$
3. $-3x - (-2x) = -3x + 2x = -x$ $(x \in W)$
4. $-7x - 5x = -7x + (-5x) = -12x$ $(x \in W)$

This means that subtraction problems may be changed to addition problems. You may change $9 - (+5)$ to $9 + (-5)$. You may change $9 - (-5)$ to $9 + (+5)$.

EXERCISES

1. 4 **2.** 14 **3.** −14 **4.** −4
5. 6 = 14 + (−8) **6.** 8 = 5 + (+3) **7.** −4 = 2 + (−6)
8. −6 = −3 + (−3) **9.** 10 = 6 + (+4) **10.** 0 = −3 + (+3)
11. −4 = 0 + (−4) **12.** −16 = 8 + (−24) **13.** 2 **14.** −5
15. −16 **16.** 5 **17.** 30 **18.** −24
19. −10 **20.** 4 **21.** 4 **22.** −4
23. 2 **24.** 8 **25.** 9 **26.** −8 **27.** 3
28. 11 **29.** −13 **30.** 5 **31.** 4c
32. 3x **33.** 5y **34.** −10h **35.** −2n
36. −6p **37.** 2n **38.** 0 **39.** −2x
40. 2m² **41.** −8y² **42.** 3t²

Watch for students who think that different things are required for Exercises 13-24 than were required for 5-12. These students likely need a bit more help understanding $a - b = a + (-b)$.

Copy each subtraction problem and fill in the blanks.

1. $9 - (+5) = 9 + (-5)$
$= \underline{\quad ? \quad}$

2. $9 - (-5) = 9 + 5$
$= \underline{\quad ? \quad}$

3. $-9 - 5 = -9 + (-5)$
$= \underline{\quad ? \quad}$

4. $-9 - (-5) = -9 + 5$
$= \underline{\quad ? \quad}$

Rewrite each subtraction as an addition and calculate the sum.

5. $14 - (+8)$ **6.** $5 - (-3)$ **7.** $2 - (+6)$
8. $-3 - (+3)$ **9.** $6 - (-4)$ **10.** $-3 - (-3)$
11. $0 - (+4)$ **12.** $8 - (+24)$

Perform each subtraction.

13. $6 - 4$ **14.** $3 - 8$ **15.** $-7 - 9$
16. $-5 - (-10)$ **17.** $13 - (-17)$ **18.** $-17 - 7$
19. $8 - 18$ **20.** $4 - 0$ **21.** $0 - (-4)$
22. $0 - 4$ **23.** $-6 - (-8)$ **24.** $17 - 9$

Simplify each expression. The variables are on W.

25. $5 + 8 - 4$ **26.** $3 + (-7) - 4$ **27.** $-3 - 2 + 8$
28. $2 - (-5) - (-4)$ **29.** $-12 - 6 + 5$ **30.** $20 - 7 - 8$
31. $6c - 2c$ **32.** $10x - 7x$ **33.** $3y - (-2y)$
34. $-4h - 6h$ **35.** $-5n - (-3n)$ **36.** $2p - 8p$
37. $0 - (-2n)$ **38.** $-5k - (-5k)$ **39.** $x - 3x$
40. $3m^2 - m^2$ **41.** $-6y^2 - 2y^2$ **42.** $10t^2 - 7t^2$

If $p = 6$, $q = -3$, and $r = 2$, find the value of each expression.

43. $p + q$ **44.** $q + r$ **45.** $p + q + r$

46. $p - r$ **47.** $p - q$ **48.** $q - r$

49. $r - p$ **50.** $p - q - r$

Tell whether each statement is true (T) or false (F).

51. $8 - (-9) = 20 - 3$ **52.** $9 + (-3) > 6 - 3$

53. $7 - (-4) = -4 - 7$ **54.** $14 + (-6) = 10 - 2$

55. $11 - 4 = 6 - (-1)$ **56.** $18 - (-10) = 30 - (-2)$

57. $3 - 7 > 10 \cdot 0$ **58.** $-2 - 4 < 0$

Simplify each expression. The variables are on W.

59. $3x + 5x - 9x$ **60.** $5y + 2y - 7y$ **61.** $3z - 2z - 6z$

62. $4a - a - 5a$ **63.** $-3b + b - 4b$ **64.** $-2c - 3c - 4c$

5-8
Subtracting Expressions

As with single terms, subtracting an expression is the same as adding its negative, or additive inverse. To find the negative of an expression, replace each term of the expression by its negative.

EXAMPLES

OBJECTIVE:

To find $a - b$ where a and b are polynomials with coefficients in Z and variables in W.

1. The negative of $(-3) + 5$ is $3 + (-5)$.

$$
\begin{aligned}
[(-3) + 5] + [3 + (-5)] &= (-3) + 5 + 3 + (-5) \\
&= (-3) + 3 + 5 + (-5) \\
&= \quad 0 \; + \; 0 \\
&= 0
\end{aligned}
$$

2. The negative of $a - b$ is $(-a) + b$.

$$
\begin{aligned}
(a - b) + [(-a) + b] &= a - b + (-a) + b \\
&= a + (-a) + b - b \\
&= 0 \qquad + \quad 0 \\
&= 0
\end{aligned}
$$

A few more numerical examples may be required for slow students.

3. The negative of $-2x + 3y + z$ is $2x - 3y - z$.

4. The negative of $-5a - 8b$ is $5a + 8b$.

For Examples **3** and **4,** think of x, y, z, a, and b as whole numbers. However, as you will see later in this chapter, the statements also are true for variables on Z.

If you use the vertical form for subtraction, you should place like terms in the same column.

EXAMPLE

$(5x - 3y + z) - (y + 2x - 3z)$ may be rewritten.

$$5x - 3y + z$$
$$-(2x + y - 3z)$$

Since subtracting a number is the same as adding its additive inverse, the difference may be found by addition.

$$5x - 3y + z$$
$$-2x - y + 3z$$
$$\overline{3x - 4y + 4z}$$

EXERCISES

1. 0 **2.** 0 **3.** 0 **4.** 0 **5.** 0
6. $-a - b$ **7.** $-2x + 3y - 7z$
8. $5x - 6y + 36$ **9.** $a + b +$
$c + d$ **10.** $-a - b - c - d$
11. $3a$ **12.** $-2b$ **13.** $9c$ **14.** $8d$
15. $-3e$ **16.** 0 **17.** $14x$ **18.** $-14x$
19. 0 **20.** $2x + 6y$ **21.** $5p$
22. -2 **23.** $7n$ **24.** $2b - 2c$
25. $8c$ **26.** $3p + 3q$
27. $4x + 6y + 8z$

Simplify each expression.

1. $(a - b) + [(-a) + b]$
2. $(-2x + 3y + z) + (2x - 3y - z)$
3. $(-5a - 8b) + (5a + 8b)$
4. $-a + b - c + a - b + c$
5. $2x - 36 + (-2x) + 36$

Write the negative (additive inverse) of each expression.

6. $a + b$ **7.** $2x - 3y + 7z$
8. $(-5x) + 6y - 36$ **9.** $-a - b - c - d$
10. $a + b + c + d$

Subtract the lower expression from the upper.

11. $5a$
$2a$

12. $2b$
$4b$

13. $6c$
$-3c$

14. $7d$
$-d$

15. $-5e$
$-2e$

16. $7x$
$7x$

17. $7x$
$-7x$

18. $-7x$
$7x$

19. $-7x$
$-7x$

20. $3x + 4y$
$x - 2y$

21. $2p - 3q$
$-3p - 3q$

22. $k - 1$
$k + 1$

23. $-2m + 3n$
$-2m - 4n$

24. $a + b + c$
$a - b + 3c$

25. $2a - 3b + 4c$
$2a - 3b - 4c$

26. $p + q - 3r$
$-(-2p - 2q - 3r)$

27. $2x + 3y + 4z$
$-(-2x - 3y - 4z)$

28. An aircraft flying at a height of 1500 m above sea level lands at an airport 600 m above sea level. What height has it lost?

29. A boy's scores in a game are 180, −100, −90, and 240. What is his total score?

30. If the temperature is −4°C and it rises 15°C, what is the new temperature? If the temperature then falls 20°C, what will it be?

31. The heights above sea level of towns A, B, and C are 100 m, −10 m, and −25 m. How much higher is A than B? B than C? A than C?

32. An airplane flying at −100 m above sea level climbs to +300 m above sea level. How much height is gained?

33. A man's account at the bank is overdrawn by $80. (He owes the bank $80.) How much must he deposit to have a balance of $150 in the bank?

34. The nth term of a sequence is given by the formula, nth term $= 8 − 5n$. For example, the second term is $8 − (5 \cdot 2) = 8 − 10 = −2$. Calculate the first six terms of the sequence.

35. Repeat Exercise **34** for the sequence for which the nth term $= 20 − 2n^2$.

36. A bird can fly through still air at 10 meters per second.
  a. The wind is blowing from the north at 11 meters per second. Explain what happens if the bird tries to fly north.
  b. Express both the northward speed of the bird through the air and the northward speed of the wind in meters per second. Copy and complete the statement, "The bird is actually traveling north at ___?___ meters per second."

37. Here is a table of times and temperatures (degrees Celsius).

Time	6 A.M.	9 A.M.	Noon	3 P.M.	6 P.M.	9 P.M.	Midnight
Temperature	−5	−1	2	8	5	0	−2

  a. What was the rise in temperature between each pair of times?
    (1) 6 A.M. and 9 A.M.   **(2)** 6 A.M. and 3 P.M.
    (3) 9 A.M. and 6 P.M.
  b. What was the fall in temperature between each pair of times?
    (1) 3 P.M. and 9 P.M.   **(2)** 6 P.M. and midnight
  c. In which 3-hour period was the rise greatest? In which was it least?

5-9
Multiplication of Integers

EXAMPLES

OBJECTIVE:

To name $a \cdot b$ given $a, b \in Z$.

The strategy here is to make or derive definitions on the basis of preserving properties of numbers.

To multiply whole numbers, you may think of multiplication as repeated addition.

1. $3 \cdot 5 = 5 + 5 + 5 = 15$
2. $5 \cdot 3 = 3 + 3 + 3 + 3 + 3 = 15$

Thinking of multiplication as repeated addition is more difficult when multiplying negative numbers. Some products, such as $5 \cdot (-3)$, may be thought of as repeated addition. $5 \cdot (-3) = (-3) + (-3) + (-3) + (-3) + (-3) = (-15)$. How can you think of $(-5) \cdot 3$? It does not make much sense to think of 3 written as an addend (-5) times.

Some decision must be made about how to find products which have negative factors. The Commutative, Associative, and Distributive Properties should apply for multiplication of integers. If these properties are to apply, there is not much choice when deciding how to multiply $(+5)(-3)$, $(-5)(+3)$, and $(-5)(-3)$.

From your work with whole numbers, you know that $(+5) \cdot (+3) = 15$.

$$(+5) \cdot (+3) = 5 \cdot 3 = 15$$

If the Distributive Property is to apply, then the following must be true. Remember that $+3$ and -3 are additive inverses.

$$[(+5) \cdot (+3)] + [(+5) \cdot (-3)] = (+5)[(+3) + (-3)]$$
$$= (+5)(0)$$
$$= 0$$

Since $(+5)(+3) = 15$, this means that $15 + (+5)(-3) = 0$. So, $(+5)(-3)$ must be the additive inverse of 15, or -15.

$$(+5)(-3) = -(5 \cdot 3) = -15$$

It may be shown in the same way that $(+3)(-5)$ is the additive inverse, or -15, of $(+3)(+5)$. If the Commutative Property is to apply, then $(-5)(+3)$ must be the same as $(+3)(-5)$.

$$(-5)(+3) = (+3)(-5)$$
$$= -(3 \cdot 5)$$
$$= -15$$

$$(-5)(+3) = -(5 \cdot 3)$$
$$= -15$$

×	−5	−4	−3	−2	−1
−5	25	20	15	10	5
−4	20	16	12	8	4
−3	15	12	9	6	3
−2	10	8	6	4	2
−1	5	4	3	2	1
0	0	0	0	0	0
1	−5	−4	−3	−2	−1
2	−10	−8	−6	−4	−2
3	−15	−12	−9	−6	−3
4	−20	−16	−12	−8	−4
5	−25	−20	−15	−10	−5

0	1	2	3	4	5
0	−5	−10	−15	−20	−25
0	−4	−8	−12	−16	−20
0	−3	−6	−9	−12	−15
0	−2	−4	−6	−8	−10
0	−1	−2	−3	−4	−5
0	0	0	0	0	0
0	1	2	3	4	5
0	2	4	6	8	10
0	3	6	9	12	15
0	4	8	12	16	20
0	5	10	15	20	25

The only remaining product to decide on is $(-5)(-3)$. In the same way that it was shown that $(+5)(-3) = -15$, it can be shown that $(0)(-3) = 0$.

$$(-5) \cdot (-3) + (+5) \cdot (-3) = [(-5) + (+5)] \cdot (-3)$$
$$= 0 \cdot (-3)$$
$$= 0$$

Thus, if the Distributive Property is to apply, $(-5) \cdot (-3) + (-15)$ must be 0. So, $(-5) \cdot (-3)$ must be the additive inverse of (-15). This means that $(-5)(-3) = 15$.

$$(-5) \cdot (-3) = 5 \cdot 3 = 15$$

No matter what numbers are used, the results will give the same pattern. For any two integers, the following multiplication rules may be used.

Stress that a and b are *any* two integers, either or both of which may be zero or negative.

$$a \cdot b = ab$$
$$a \cdot (-b) = -ab$$
$$(-a) \cdot b = -ab$$
$$(-a) \cdot (-b) = ab$$

EXERCISES

1. 0 2. −4 3. −8 4. −12
5. −16 6. −20 7. 0, −5, −10, −15, −20, −25
8. See table.

Find each product.

1. $0 \cdot (-4)$ **2.** $1 \cdot (-4)$ **3.** $2 \cdot (-4)$
4. $3 \cdot (-4)$ **5.** $4 \cdot (-4)$ **6.** $5 \cdot (-4)$

7. Write the sequence of multiples $0 \cdot (-5)$, $1 \cdot (-5)$, $2 \cdot (-5)$, $3 \cdot (-5)$, $4 \cdot (-5)$, $5 \cdot (-5)$.

8. Copy the table.

Second Number

	×	−5	−4	−3	−2	−1	0	1	2	3	4	5
	−5	?	?	?	?	?	?	?	?	?	?	?
	−4	?	?	?	?	?	?	?	?	?	?	?
	−3	?	?	?	?	?	?	?	?	?	?	?
	−2	?	?	?	?	?	?	?	?	?	?	?
First Number	**−1**	?	?	?	?	?	?	?	?	?	?	?
	0	?	?	?	?	?	?	0	0	0	0	0
	1	?	?	?	?	?	?	1	2	3	4	5
	2	?	?	?	?	?	?	2	4	6	8	10
	3	?	?	?	?	?	?	3	6	9	12	15
	4	?	?	?	?	?	?	4	8	12	16	20
	5	?	?	?	?	?	?	5	10	15	20	25

Use the results you have found to help you to fill in the bottom left part of the table. Use the Commutative Property to help you to fill in the top right part of the table. Now complete the table, using the patterns that appear in the rows and columns as a guide. The table could be expanded in either the positive or negative direction.

Use your table to write each product.

9. $-5 \cdot 3$
10. $3 \cdot (-5)$
11. $-2 \cdot (-2)$
12. $-1 \cdot 4$
13. $4 \cdot (-1)$
14. $-2 \cdot (-3)$
15. $0 \cdot (-3)$
16. $5 \cdot 0$
17. $-1 \cdot (-1)$

Students who had trouble with the introduction of this section should complete Exercises 1-17. These may be done as in-class group work.

9. -15 10. -15 11. 4 12. -4
13. 4 14. 6 15. 0 16. 0 17. 1
18. $x = 4$ 19. $x = -4$ 20. $x = 1$
21. $x = 0$ 22. $x = -5$ 23. $x = 1$
24. $x = 0$ 25. $x = 10$ 26. $x = -2$ 27. -2 28. 0 29. 2 30. 3
31. 4 32. 4 33. 9 34. -3
35. -1 36. 0 37. -8 38. 81
39. a., c., f. 40. $\{4, -4\}$ 41. ϕ
42. $\{2\}$ 43. $\{-3\}$ 44. $\{-1, 1\}$
45. $\{-11, -3\}$ 46. $\{-1, 3\}$
47. $\{\ldots, -4, -3, -2, -1\}$
48. Z 49. $\{5, 6, 7, 8, \ldots\}$
50. $a = 3$ and $b = -2$ or $a = -3$ and $b = 2$ 51. $a = 3$ and $b = 2$ or $a = -3$ and $b = -2$

Exercises **1–17** led to the following results. You should learn these rules for multiplying integers.

The product of an integer and zero is zero.
The product of two positive integers is positive.
The product of two negative integers is positive.
The product of a positive and a negative integer is negative.

Solve each equation, where x is a variable on Z.

18. $2x = 8$
19. $2x = -8$
20. $2x = 2$
21. $2x = 0$
22. $4x = -20$
23. $-4x = -4$
24. $-4x = 0$
25. $-4x = -40$
26. $-3x = 6$

If $a = -1, b = 2, c = 0, x = -2, y = -3$, calculate the value of each expression.

27. ab
28. bc
29. ax
30. ay
31. b^2
32. x^2
33. y^2
34. $a^2 - b^2$
35. a^3
36. c^3
37. x^3
38. y^4

Ask students if it is possible to have $x^n < 0$, x an integer and n an even natural number.

39. If x is replaced by an integer, which of the following can be negative?

a. x
b. x^2
c. x^3
d. x^4
e. x^8
f. x^9

Find the solution set of each equation if x is a variable on Z.

40. $x^2 = 16$
41. $x^2 = -4$
42. $x^3 = 8$
43. $x^3 = -27$
44. $x^4 = 1$
45. $(x + 7)^2 = 16$
46. $(x - 1)^2 = 4$
47. $x^3 < 0$
48. $x^2 \geq 0$
49. $x^3 > 100$

Let $S = \{-3, -2, 2, 3\}$. Let a and b be variables on S where $|a| > |b|$. Write the solutions for each equation.

50. $ab = -6$
51. $ab = 6$

141

52. A stone is dropped from a building. Its velocity v meters per second downwards after t seconds is given by the formula $v = 10t$. Calculate its velocity after 2 seconds and after 3.5 seconds.

53. A ball is thrown upward at 20 meters per second. After t seconds, its upward velocity v meters per second is given by the formula $v = 20 - 10t$. Calculate its velocity after 1 second; after 4 seconds. Explain what these results mean.

54. When a stone is thrown upward at 15 meters per second, its height h meters above the point of projection after t seconds is given by the formula $h = 15t - 5t^2$. Calculate its height after each period of time.

a. 1 second   **b.** 2 seconds   **c.** 3 seconds   **d.** 4 seconds
Explain the answer to **d.**

55. The temperature is rising steadily at 3°C per hour. At "zero hour" it is 20°C. What would the temperature be at "zero hour + 2 hours?" At "zero hour − 2 hours?" Repeat for the case where the temperature is rising at −3°C per hour. What does this mean?

56. The annual profit in dollars, P, from a boarding house was calculated from the formula $P = 10n - 600$, where n is the number of guest-weeks. Use the formula to calculate P when $n = 150$, 120, and 50. Explain what the results mean.

57. The length of a rectangle is $(x + 3)$ meters, and the width is $(x + 2)$ meters, where x is an integer. The perimeter is not more than 60 m. List the possible replacements for x.

58. A clock gains x minutes a day for seven days. The regulator is adjusted, and the clock then loses 1 minute a day for three days. If the total gain is 11 minutes, find x.

5-10
Properties of Multiplication

OBJECTIVE:

To apply the basic properties of real numbers to expressions containing only integers.

EXAMPLE

The rules for multiplying integers are determined so that the Commutative, Associative, and Distributive Properties apply. Even though the Associative Property was not used to decide how to multiply, the Associative Property applies for multiplication of integers.

$$[(-2) \cdot 3] \cdot (-4) = (-6) \cdot (-4)$$
$$= 24$$
$$(-2) \cdot [3 \cdot (-4)] = (-2) \cdot (-12)$$
$$= 24$$

The example shows that $[(-2) \cdot 3] \cdot (-4) = (-2) \cdot [3 \cdot (-4)]$.

Since both the Commutative and Associative Properties apply to multiplication of integers, you may arrange the factors in any order.

EXAMPLE

$$(-2) \cdot 3 \cdot (-4) = (-2) \cdot (-4) \cdot 3$$
$$= 3 \cdot (-4) \cdot (-2)$$

With whole numbers, you saw that two forms of the Distributive Property are true.

$$a \, (b + c) = ab + ac$$
$$a \, (b - c) = ab - ac$$

These same two forms apply to operations with the integers.

EXAMPLES

1. $-3 \, (x + 2) = -3x - 6$ $(x \in Z)$
2. $-3 \, (x - 2) = -3x + 6$ $(x \in Z)$

The Distributive Property for integers can be generalized to more than two terms inside the parentheses.

EXAMPLES

1. $5 \, (a - 2b + 3c) = 5a - 10b + 15c$ $(a, b, c \in Z)$
2. $-7 \, (a - 2b + 3c) = -7a + 14b - 21c$ $(a, b, c \in Z)$

An expression inside parentheses may have a negative sign before it, $-(-x + 2y - 3z)$. There are two ways to think of this negative sign.

1. The expression $-(-x + 2y - 3z)$ means *the additive inverse of* $(-x + 2y - 3z)$ which is $x - 2y + 3z$.

$$-(-x + 2y - 3z) = x - 2y + 3z.$$

2. Since $-a$ is the same as $(-1) \cdot a$ for any integer a, you may think of $-(-x + 2y - 3z)$ as $-1(-x + 2y - 3z)$.

EXERCISES

Verify each statement by calculation.
1. $(-3 \cdot 4) \cdot (-5) = -3 \cdot [4 \cdot (-5)]$
2. $(2 \cdot 5) \cdot (-6) = 2 \cdot [5 \cdot (-6)]$
3. $(-4 \cdot -5) \cdot (-6) = -4 \cdot [(-5) \cdot (-6)]$

4. Copy and complete this table.

a	b	c	(b + c)	a · (b + c)	ab	ac	ab + ac
2	3	−1	2	4	6	−2	4
5	−2	3	?	?	?	?	?
−2	5	−4	?	?	?	?	?
−6	−3	−2	?	?	?	?	?

By comparing the numbers in the fifth and eighth columns, do you find that in each case $a(b + c) = ab + ac$?

5. Copy and complete this table.

a	b	c	(b − c)	a · (b − c)	ab	ac	ab − ac
2	3	−4	7	14	6	8	4
5	−2	3	?	?	?	?	?
−2	5	−4	?	?	?	?	?
−6	−3	−2	?	?	?	?	?

Do you find that $a(b − c) = ab − ac$ in each case?

Simplify each product.

6. $3 \cdot (−5) \cdot (−2)$ **7.** $−2 \cdot (−7) \cdot 3$ **8.** $−5 \cdot 4 \cdot (−2)$
9. $(−3)^2 \cdot 4$ **10.** $−1 \cdot (−5)^2$ **11.** $(−2)^3 \cdot 5$
12. $(−3)^3 \cdot 4$ **13.** $(−2)^2 \cdot (−3)^2$ **14.** $2^3 \cdot (−2)^3$
15. $2^2 \cdot 5 \cdot (−3)$
16. $(−1) \cdot (−2) \cdot (−3)^2$
17. $(−1) \cdot (−2) \cdot (−3) \cdot (−4)$
18. $−4 \cdot 3 \cdot (−3) \cdot (−5)$

Write each expression as a sum or difference of terms.

19. $7(x − 2)$ **20.** $−2(a + 6)$ **21.** $−3(x − 1)$
22. $−4(4 − b)$ **23.** $−3(−x − 5)$ **24.** $x(a − 2b)$
25. $−x(−p + q)$ **26.** $−z(2a − b)$ **27.** $−x(x + y)$
28. $x(7 − 5x)$ **29.** $−(x − y)$ **30.** $−(2x − 3y)$
31. $−(5 − 4x)$ **32.** $−(3a + 2b)$ **33.** $4(a − 3b + 2c)$

34. $-3(a + 3b - 5c)$

35. $-5(1 - x - x^2)$

36. $-2(2x^2 - 3x + 4)$

37. $-(x^2 - 2x - 3)$

38. $-(5 - 4x - 3x^2)$

If $a = -1$, $b = 2$, $c = 0$, $x = -2$, and $y = -3$, evaluate each expression.

39. $3ab - 5xy$

40. $3xy - 2abc$

41. $abx^2 + y^2$

42. $ab + bc + xy$

43. $x^2y^2 - 40$

44. $2a^2 + 3b^2 - 4x^2$

Is each statement true (T) or false (F) for the replacement given?

45. $2a^2 - 3 = 5$; $a = -2$

46. $5 - 4c^2 = 9$; $c = -1$

47. $3y^2 = 48$; $y = -4$

48. $x^2 - 3x + 4 = 22$; $x = -3$

49. $x - 2x^3 = 51$; $x = -3$

50. $8y - 2y^2 < 0$; $y = -4$

5-11
Simplifying Expressions

The Distributive Property may be used to simplify expressions which contain integers. It often is convenient to rearrange the order in which the terms are written before using the Distributive Property.

EXAMPLES

OBJECTIVE:

To simplify a given expression when both coefficients and variables may represent integers.

For helping the students manage the two uses of the minus sign, see the teaching notes for this section for suggestions.

1. $-2a - 6a = (-2 - 6)a$
$$= [-2 + (-6)]a$$
$$= -8a$$

2. $2x - 3y + 4x + 5y - 8x = 2x + 4x - 8x - 3y + 5y$
$$= (2 + 4 - 8)x + (-3 + 5)y$$
$$= -2x + 2y$$

3. $5x - 2(x - 3) = 5x - 2x + 6$
$$= 3x + 6$$

Sometimes you must use the Distributive Property in two ways to simplify expressions involving integers.

EXAMPLE

Simplify $2(x^2 - 3x + y) - 5(x - 3y)$.

$$2(x^2 - 3x + y) - 5(x - 3y)$$

Use the Distributive Property to remove parentheses.

$$= 2x^2 - 6x + 2y - 5x + 15y$$

$$= 2x^2 - 6x - 5x + 2y + 15y$$

Use the Distributive Property to combine like terms.

$$= 2x^2 - 11x + 17y$$

EXERCISES

1. 7a 2. −7a 3. −3y 4. 4z
5. −6x 6. −5q 7. −4p 8. 0 9. a
10. −9b 11. 15c 12. −18k
13. 0 14. −5n 15. −x + 2y
16. −5x + y 17. 8x + 2y
18. −a + 5b 19. −2a − b
20. 2a − 3b 21. 2x + 7y
22. −a + 9b 23. a + 3b
24. 4p − 2q 25. 7x − 2y
26. 3x + 2y 27. 3x − 3y
28. 4 + 3x 29. 7 + 5x
30. −2x + 8 31. 3 − 2x
32. 3x + 3 33. 4 + x 34. 6x + 1
35. 2x − 3 36. 3 + 8x
37. 5x + y 38. x + 7y
39. 4x − 4y 40. −1 41. 4x² − 7y
42. −7a² − 3b² 43. x + 5y
44. x² − x 45. x + 5y 46. 4x −
6y 47. −3x − y 48. 6a − 2b
49. −5a − b 50. 2x² − 5x + 3
51. 4y² − 3y − 7 52. 5 −
7z + 2z² 53. 7x 54. −x − 7y
55. 2x² + 2x − 3 56. 14y² −
19y 57. 0 58. 0 59. a. 3x +
3y + 3z b. −x + y − 3z
c. −8x + 7y + z 60. Approach
may vary.

Simplify each expression.

1. $10a - 3a$
2. $3a - 10a$
3. $9y - 12y$
4. $-2z + 6z$
5. $-3x - 3x$
6. $-7q + 2q$
7. $6p - 10p$
8. $-5a + 5a$
9. $2a + 3a - 4a$
10. $5b - 6b - 8b$
11. $10c + 6c - c$
12. $-6k - 6k - 6k$
13. $-8m + 5m + 3m$
14. $n - 4n - 2n$
15. $5x - 6x + 2y$
16. $-3x - 2x + y$
17. $8x - 3y + 5y$
18. $3a - 4a + 5b$
19. $-2a + b - 2b$
20. $4a - 3b - 2a$
21. $5x - 3x + 7y$
22. $6a - 7a + 9b$
23. $a + 5b - 2b$
24. $4p + q - 3q$
25. $5x + 2(x - y)$
26. $5x - 2(x - y)$
27. $6x - 3(x + y)$
28. $10 + 3(x - 2)$
29. $12 - 5(1 - x)$
30. $4(x + 2) - 6x$
31. $1 - 2(x - 1)$
32. $5x - (2x - 3)$
33. $6 - (2 - x)$
34. $3(2x + 1) - 2$
35. $8x - 3(2x + 1)$
36. $7 - 4(1 - 2x)$
37. $3(x + y) + 2(x - y)$
38. $4(x + y) - 3(x - y)$
39. $5(x - y) - (x - y)$
40. $2(3x + 1) - 3(2x + 1)$
41. $7x^2 - 3x^2 + 2y - 9y$
42. $3a^2 + 6b^2 - 10a^2 - 9b^2$
43. $2(x + y) - x + 3y$
44. $3x^2 + 2x - 2x^2 - 3x$
45. $3(x + y) - 2(x - y)$
46. $5(x - y) - (x + y)$
47. $-2(x + y) - (x - y)$
48. $4(a - b) + 2(a + b)$
49. $3(-a + b) - 2(a + 2b)$
50. $2(x^2 - x) - 3(x - 1)$
51. $4(y^2 - 1) - 3(y + 1)$
52. $5(1 - z) - 2(z - z^2)$
53. $2(5x - y) - (3x - 2y)$
54. $5(x - 2y) - 3(2x - y)$
55. $2(x^2 - 2x) - 3(1 - 2x)$
56. $5(2y^2 - 3y) - 4(y - y^2)$
57. $(a - b) + (b - c) + (c - a)$
58. $a(b - c) + b(c - a) + c(a - b)$

59. Given $A = x + 2y$, $B = y + 2z$, $C = z + 2x$, find the simplest form of each expression.
   a. $A + B + C$
   b. $A - B - C$
   c. $2A + 3B - 5C$

60. Given $X = ap + bq$ and $Y = bq + aq$, show that each sentence is true.
   a. $X + Y = p(a + b) + q(a + b) = (a + b)(p + q)$
   b. $X - Y = p(a - b) + q(b - a) = (a - b)(p - q)$

5-12 Division of Integers

OBJECTIVE:
To name $\frac{a}{b}$ given $a, b \in Z$ such that $\frac{a}{b} \in Z$.

In arithmetic you were asked to check division by multiplication. The rule you learned was this: If $a \cdot b = c$, then $c \div b = a$.

You also could have used division to check multiplication. The rule would be this: If $c \div b = a$, then $a \cdot b = c$.

You can decide how to divide integers by insisting that these two rules apply. Writing the two rules together, the following statement results.

The words *if and only if* may need clarification for some students.

$$c \div b = a \text{ if and only if } a \cdot b = c$$

You already know how to find the product of two integers. If you apply the rule, you obtain the following quotients.

a	$\cdot$	b	$=$	c	so	c	$\div$	b	$=$	a
$(+5) \cdot (+3) = (+15)$,					so	$(+15) \div (+3) = (+5)$				
$(+5) \cdot (-3) = (-15)$,					so	$(-15) \div (-3) = (+5)$				
$(-5) \cdot (+3) = (-15)$,					so	$(-15) \div (+3) = (-5)$				
$(-5) \cdot (-3) = (+15)$,					so	$(+15) \div (-3) = (-5)$				

If you do the same thing with any pair of integers, the results will be similar. The following rules will help you divide any integers a and b, $b \neq 0$.

If necessary, examine cases to see that these statements do indeed hold for any $a, b \in Z$, $b \neq 0$. For example, let $a = -12$, $b = 3$, and check to see that $a \div (-b) = -\dfrac{a}{b}$.

$$a \div b = \frac{a}{b}$$

$$(-a) \div b = \frac{-a}{b} = -\frac{a}{b}$$

$$a \div (-b) = \frac{a}{-b} = -\frac{a}{b}$$

$$(-a) \div (-b) = \frac{-a}{-b} = \frac{a}{b}$$

A positive integer divided by a positive integer is positive.

A negative integer divided by a positive integer is negative.

A positive integer divided by a negative integer is negative.

A negative integer divided by a negative integer is positive.

147

EXERCISES

1. 3 **2.** 2 **3.** −4 **4.** −4 **5.** −5
6. −5 **7.** 5 **8.** 5 **9.** 5 **10.** 5
11. 7 **12.** 7 **13.** 7 **14.** 7
15. $x + 2y$ **16.** $-x - 2y$
17. $x + 2$ **18.** $-x + 3$

Find each quotient.

1. $\dfrac{(-12)}{(-4)}$ **2.** $\dfrac{-24}{-12}$ **3.** $\dfrac{8}{-2}$

4. $\dfrac{-8}{2}$ **5.** $\dfrac{3 \cdot 5}{-3}$ **6.** $\dfrac{-2 \cdot 5}{2}$

7. $\dfrac{-6 \cdot 5}{-6}$ **8.** $\dfrac{-30}{-6}$ **9.** $\dfrac{30}{6}$

10. $\dfrac{6 \cdot (-5)}{-6}$ **11.** $\dfrac{2 \cdot 7}{2}$ **12.** $\dfrac{-2 \cdot 7}{-2}$

13. $\dfrac{c \cdot 7}{c}$ **14.** $\dfrac{-c \cdot 7}{-c}$ **15.** $\dfrac{2x + 4y}{2}$

16. $\dfrac{2x + 4y}{-2}$ **17.** $\dfrac{-x^2 - 2x}{-x}$ **18.** $\dfrac{6x - 18}{-6}$

Chapter Summary

1. The positive integers, negative integers, and zero form the set of integers, $Z = \{\ldots, -4, -3, -2, -1, 0, 1, 2, 3, 4, \ldots\}$.
2. The x-axis and y-axis of a coordinate plane may be extended using the negative integers.
3. The integers have the property of order.
4. Addition of integers is commutative and associative.
5. If $a + b = 0$, then a and b are called additive inverses of each other.
6. For any integer a, its additive inverse is called the negative of a, written $-a$.
7. The absolute value of a number may be thought of as the distance from the number to the origin. The symbol $|x|$ means the absolute value of x.
8. Subtracting b from a is the same as adding the negative of b to a.
9. The product of two integers with the same signs is positive. The product of two integers with different signs is negative.
10. Multiplication of integers is commutative and associative.
11. The Generalized Distributive Property is true for integers.
12. The Distributive Property may be used to simplify expressions involving integers.
13. The quotient of two integers with the same signs is positive. The quotient of two integers with different signs is negative.

REVIEW EXERCISES

5-1

5-2

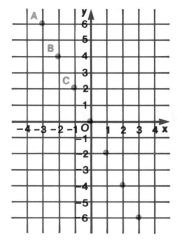

5-7

1. If $+\$10$ means a gain of \$10, what does $-\$30$ mean?
2. If $+5$ km means 5 km east, how would you write 10 km west?
3. Copy the axes, marked as shown. Plot the points $A(-3, 6)$, $B(-2, 4)$, $C(-1, 2)$, $O(0, 0)$. Write the coordinates of three more points in this sequence and plot the points.

5-3

Copy and complete each statement by placing one of the symbols $>$, $=$, or $<$ in the blank.

4. 6 ___?___ 4	**5.** 0 ___?___ −1	**6.** −2 ___?___ (−2)
7. −3 ___?___ 3	**8.** −3 ___?___ −5	**9.** −2000 ___?___ 2

If x is a variable on $\{-4, -3, -2, -1, 0, 1, 2\}$, solve each equation or inequation.

10. $x > -2$	**11.** $x \le 1$	**12.** $x < 0$
13. $x + (-3) = 0$	**14.** $-1 + x = 1$	**15.** $x + x = -4$

Simplify each expression.

16. $-4 + (-9)$	**17.** $15 + (-8)$	**18.** $7 + (-13)$
19. $14 - 9$	**20.** $-20 - 12$	**21.** $6 - 34$
22. $0 - 4$	**23.** $0 - (-4)$	**24.** $-15 - (-8)$
25. $10a - 3a$	**26.** $2a - 9a$	**27.** $24m - (-12m)$

If $x = 8$, $y = -5$, and $z = -3$, find the value of each expression.

28. $x + y$	**29.** $x - y$	**30.** $y - x$
31. $x - z$	**32.** $x + y - z$	**33.** $x - y + z$

5-8

Simplify each expression.

34. $3p + 5p - 2p$	**35.** $9m - 4m - 3m$
36. $6y - (10y + y)$	**37.** $7p - (3p + p) + 2p$
38. $-4k - 3k + (k - 6k)$	**39.** $n - n + n + (n - n)$

40. Using sea level as 0, a point A has a height of $+254$ m and a point B has a height of -35 m. How many meters higher is A than B?
41. If the temperature of a liquid changes from $-10°C$ to $-3°C$, how many degrees did the temperature rise?

5-9

42. On an exam a student scores 3 points for each correct answer and -2 points for each wrong answer. If the student has 33 correct answers and 17 wrong answers, what is her total score?

Solve each equation, when x is a variable on Z.

43. $2x = 30$ **44.** $2x = -14$ **45.** $-8x = -8$

46. $-5x = 0$

If $p = 2$, $q = -3$, $r = -4$, find the value of each expression.

47. $pq + qr + rp$

48. $\dfrac{p - q}{q - r}$

49. $\dfrac{8q}{pr}$

50. $3p + 2q - 4r$

5-11, 5-12

Simplify each expression.

51. $10 + 2(x - 7)$

52. $-3(4x - 5)$

53. $3(x + 3) - 9$

54. $4(2a - 3b) - 3(4a - 4b)$

55. $-\dfrac{1}{3}(6p - 21q)$

56. $\dfrac{-8a + 4b}{2}$

57. $\dfrac{9a - 24b}{-3}$

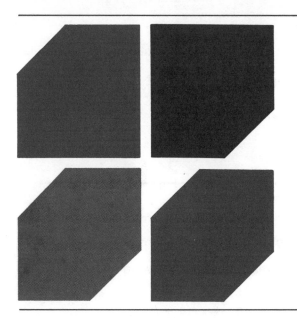

CHAPTER 6

exploring rational numbers

6-1
Introduction

OBJECTIVE:
To state if $\frac{a}{b}$ and $\frac{c}{d}$ name the same rational number for $a, b, c, d \in Z$, b and d nonzero.

EXAMPLE
In Chapter 1, $\frac{3}{-6}, \frac{-2}{-12}$, etc., were not defined.

Ask students to keep in mind the work of Section 5-12 while reading this.

In Chapter 1 you briefly looked at the set of all numbers which may be named as $\frac{m}{n}$ or $-\left(\frac{m}{n}\right)$ where $m \in W$ and $n \in N$. This set is the set of rational numbers, Q. You saw that $N \subseteq W \subseteq Z \subseteq Q$. You may think of the rational numbers as naming points on the number line.

Locate $-\left(\frac{5}{3}\right), \frac{3}{2}, -\left(\frac{7}{7}\right), \frac{12}{4}$, and $\frac{0}{2}$ on a number line.

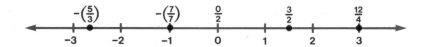

The elements of Q usually are described another way. The set of **rational numbers,** Q, is the set of all numbers which may be named as $\frac{m}{n}$ where $m, n \in Z$ and $n \neq 0$. However, using this definition creates a question. Which numbers are named by $\frac{-5}{3}, \frac{5}{-3},$

It seems *reasonable* because of the work done in Section 5-12. Remind students of this.

and $\dfrac{-5}{-3}$? It seems reasonable that these fractions should be elements of $\left\{-\dfrac{5}{3}, \dfrac{5}{3}\right\}$. In other words, $\dfrac{-5}{3}$, $\dfrac{5}{-3}$, and $\dfrac{-5}{-3}$ should be different ways of writing either $-\dfrac{5}{3}$ or $\dfrac{5}{3}$.

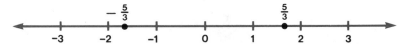

In elementary school you often thought of a fraction as a quotient: $\dfrac{a}{b} = a \div b$. By thinking of fractions as quotients, the question may be answered easily. You already have the following rules for dividing integers where $b \neq 0$.

See section notes in T.G. on $\dfrac{a}{b} \in Q - Z$. Such numbers were carefully avoided in Section 5-12.

$$(-a) \div b = -(a \div b)$$
$$a \div (-b) = -(a \div b)$$
$$(-a) \div (-b) = a \div b$$

You may write these rules in fractional form.

$$\frac{-a}{b} = -\frac{a}{b}$$

$$\frac{a}{-b} = -\frac{a}{b}$$

$$\frac{-a}{-b} = \frac{a}{b}$$

Using these rules, the point named by $-\dfrac{5}{3}$ also may be named by $\dfrac{-5}{3}$ and $\dfrac{5}{-3}$. The point named by $\dfrac{5}{3}$ also may be named by $\dfrac{-5}{-3}$. These rules provide the answer to the question.

Fractions which name the same point on the number line are called **equivalent fractions.** An equal sign is used to indicate that fractions are equivalent.

EXAMPLES

1. $\dfrac{5}{3} = \dfrac{-5}{-3} = \dfrac{10}{6} = \dfrac{-10}{-6} = \dfrac{20}{12} = \dfrac{-20}{12} = \cdots$

2. $\dfrac{-5}{3} = \dfrac{5}{-3} = \dfrac{-10}{6} = \dfrac{10}{-6} = \dfrac{-20}{12} = \dfrac{20}{-12} = \cdots$

Given a fraction, other equivalent fractions may be obtained by using one of the following rules.

1. The numerator and denominator of a fraction may be multiplied by the same nonzero integer to obtain an equivalent fraction.
2. The numerator and denominator of a fraction may be divided by the same nonzero integer to obtain an equivalent fraction.

EXAMPLES

1. $\dfrac{2}{3} = \dfrac{2 \cdot 5}{3 \cdot 5} = \dfrac{10}{15}$

2. $\dfrac{2x}{3y} = \dfrac{2x \cdot 4}{3y \cdot 4} = \dfrac{8x}{12y}$

3. $\dfrac{-12}{16} = \dfrac{-12 \div 4}{16 \div 4} = \dfrac{-3}{4}$

4. $\dfrac{4x}{3x} = \dfrac{4x \div x}{3x \div x} = \dfrac{4}{3}$

These rules may be stated in the following form.

If $a, b, c \in \mathbf{Z}$, $b \neq 0$, and $c \neq 0$, then

$$\textbf{1.} \ \frac{a}{b} = \frac{a \cdot c}{b \cdot c} \qquad \textbf{2.} \ \frac{a}{b} = \frac{a \div c}{b \div c}$$

EXERCISES

Solve each equation where n and d are variables on Z, $d \neq 0$.

1. $n = 3$ **2.** $d = -4$ **3.** $d = -8$
4. $d = 1$ **5.** $n = -16$
6. $n = -18$ **7.** $n = -21$
8. $d = -4$ **9.** $n \in \mathbf{Z}$ **10.** Answers will vary. **11.** Answers will vary.
12. Answers will vary.
13. Answers will vary.

1. $\dfrac{-3}{-5} = \dfrac{n}{5}$ 　　 **2.** $\dfrac{-2}{4} = \dfrac{2}{d}$ 　　 **3.** $\dfrac{-2}{4} = \dfrac{4}{d}$

4. $\dfrac{-8}{-4} = \dfrac{2}{d}$ 　　 **5.** $\dfrac{-8}{-4} = \dfrac{n}{-8}$ 　　 **6.** $\dfrac{6}{-1} = \dfrac{n}{3}$

7. $3 = \dfrac{n}{-7}$ 　　 **8.** $-2 = \dfrac{8}{d}$ 　　 **9.** $\dfrac{n}{3} = \dfrac{-n}{-3}$

For each fraction, write two equivalent fractions. The variables are on Z, $y \neq 0$ and $m \neq 0$.

10. $\dfrac{16}{24}$ 　　 **11.** $\dfrac{2}{3}$ 　　 **12.** $\dfrac{x}{y}$ 　　 **13.** $\dfrac{3m}{4m}$

153

For each fraction, write an equivalent fraction which has the indicated denominator. The variables are nonzero integers.

Sample $\dfrac{-2}{2x}$; $-6x^2$

$$\frac{-2}{2x} = \frac{(-2) \cdot (-3x)}{2x \cdot (-3x)} = \frac{6x}{-6x^2}$$

14. $\dfrac{45}{60}$; 4

15. $\dfrac{30x}{5x}$; 5xy

16. $\dfrac{-30x}{-5x}$; 1

17. $\dfrac{-14c}{-2c}$; 4c

18. $\dfrac{0}{2x}$; −2

19. $\dfrac{85pq}{25pq^2}$; 25q

20. $\dfrac{5a^2}{5b^2}$; −b²

21. $\dfrac{-5}{3}$; −12xy

Express each fraction as an integer. The variables are on Z, x ≠ 0.

See if students understand that each fraction is already an integer. This may be done by asking if there is any difference between the given instruction line and, "Express each without using a denominator."

Sample $\dfrac{6x - 4y}{2} = \dfrac{2(3x - 2y)}{2}$

$$= \frac{2(3x - 2y) \div 2}{2 \div 2}$$

$$= \frac{3x - 2y}{1}$$

$$= 3x - 2y$$

22. $\dfrac{2x - 2y}{2}$

23. $\dfrac{15t - 20}{5}$

24. $\dfrac{2p + 8q}{-2}$

25. $\dfrac{x - xy}{x}$

26. $\dfrac{-4x - 12xy}{-4x}$

27. Which two of these fractions are equivalent?

$$\frac{45}{65} \qquad \frac{75}{105p} \qquad \frac{63}{90} \qquad \frac{54s^2}{78s^2}$$

28. Name the fraction with the smallest possible whole number denominator that is equivalent to all of these fractions.

$$\frac{15}{18}, \frac{20}{24}, \frac{65}{78}, \cdots$$

Do not assign Exercise 29 to slow students as individual work. If it is to be considered by slow students, treat it as a discussion exercise.

29. a. If denominators are the same, add the numerators. Since $(-a)$ is the additive inverse of (a), it follows that $\dfrac{-a}{b}$ is the additive inverse of $\dfrac{a}{b}$. **b.** Again, the denominators are the same and the numerators are additive inverses. Therefore, the fractions are additive inverses.

c. $\dfrac{-a}{-b}$ and $\dfrac{a}{-b}$ are additive inverses of each other. They will be equal if the negative of one is found. $-\left(\dfrac{-a}{-b}\right) = \dfrac{a}{-b}$.

d. Using the same reasoning as in Part c, $\dfrac{a}{b}$ and $\dfrac{-a}{b}$ are additive inverses. Therefore, $\dfrac{a}{b} = -\dfrac{-a}{b}$. **e.** In Part a, $\dfrac{a}{b}$ and $\dfrac{-a}{b}$ were shown to be additive inverses. This implies $-\dfrac{-a}{b} = \dfrac{-a}{b}$.

Exercise 30 makes the point that agreeing to the procedure for finding equivalent fractions automatically gives the equations listed on page 152.

30. a. -1 **b. (1)** $-(a/b)$ **(2)** $-(a/b)$ **(3)** a/b **(4)** a/b **(5)** a/b **(6)** $-(a/b)$

---

29. To add $\dfrac{3}{4}$ and $\dfrac{2}{4}$, add the numerators and use the same denominator.

$$\frac{3}{4} + \frac{2}{4} = \frac{3+2}{4} = \frac{5}{4}$$

Imagine that you insist on using this method to add fractions with *equal*, nonzero denominators. Numerators and denominators are integers.

a. By looking at $\dfrac{a}{b} + \dfrac{-a}{b}$, explain why $\dfrac{-a}{b}$ must be the additive inverse of $\dfrac{a}{b}$. Hint: Remember that for integers, x and y are *additive inverses* if $x + y = 0$.

b. By looking at $\dfrac{-a}{-b} + \dfrac{a}{-b}$, explain why $\dfrac{a}{-b}$ must be the additive inverse of $\dfrac{-a}{-b}$.

c. Placing a negative sign in front of a real number name indicates the additive inverse of that real number. If $x \in R$, then $x + (-x) = (-x) + x = 0$. How does your work for Part **b** show that $-\dfrac{-a}{-b} = \dfrac{a}{-b}$?

d. How does your work for Part **a** show that $\dfrac{a}{b} = -\dfrac{-a}{b}$?

e. In which part of this exercise did you show that $-\dfrac{a}{b} = \dfrac{-a}{b}$?

30. It seems reasonable to insist that $\dfrac{a}{b} = \dfrac{ac}{bc}$ when $a, b, c \in Z$, $b \neq 0$ and $c \neq 0$.

a. Which value for c would be used to show that $\dfrac{-a}{b} = \dfrac{a}{-b}$?

b. For each fraction, state if it names the point $\dfrac{a}{b}$ or the point $-\dfrac{a}{b}$; $a, b \in Z, b \neq 0$.

(1) $\dfrac{-a}{b}$ **(2)** $\dfrac{a}{-b}$ **(3)** $\dfrac{-a}{-b}$

(4) $-\dfrac{-a}{b}$ **(5)** $-\dfrac{a}{-b}$ **(6)** $-\dfrac{-a}{-b}$

6-2
Simplest Form

To express $\dfrac{a}{b}$ in simplest form
where the greatest common
divisor of a and b is a monomial.

EXAMPLES

A fraction is said to be in **simplest form** if numerator and denominator have no common factors except 1 and -1.

1. The fraction $\dfrac{2}{3}$ is in simplest form.

2. The fraction $\dfrac{12}{-16}$ is not in simplest form since 4 and -4 are common factors of numerator and denominator.

$$\frac{12}{-16} = \frac{12 \div (-4)}{-16 \div (-4)} = \frac{-3}{4}$$

Suggest to slow students that this means, "no minus sign allowed in front of the denominator." Then remind them that $\dfrac{a}{-b} = \dfrac{-a}{b}$ and $\dfrac{-a}{-b} = \dfrac{a}{b}$.

In writing the simplest form of a fraction, use the forms $\dfrac{a}{b}$ or $\dfrac{-a}{b}$.

The forms $\dfrac{a}{-b}$ or $\dfrac{-a}{-b}$ are not said to be in simplest form. Thus, $\dfrac{-3}{4}$ is preferred to $\dfrac{3}{-4}$ as the simplest form of $\dfrac{12}{-16}$.

Fractions often have variables in the numerator or denominator. Saying that such fractions are in simplest form does not mean that they are in simplest form for all replacements for the variables.

EXAMPLES

See section notes in T.G. on dealing with the question, "If you don't know what x and y are, how can you say $\dfrac{2x}{y}$ is in simplest form?" This can be very important to students.

1. The fraction $\dfrac{2x}{y}$, $y \neq 0$, is in simplest form because -1 and 1 are the only common factors of numerator and denominator.

2. The fraction $\dfrac{2x^2}{4xy}$, $x \neq 0$ and $y \neq 0$, is not in simplest form. Both numerator and denominator have $2x$ as a factor.

$$\frac{2x^2}{4xy} = \frac{2x \cdot x}{2x \cdot 2y}$$
$$= \frac{2x \cdot x \div 2x}{2x \cdot 2y \div 2x}$$
$$= \frac{x}{2y}$$

3. The fraction $\dfrac{2y + 1}{4}$ is the simplest form of $\dfrac{-8xy - 4x}{-16x}$.

$$\frac{-8xy - 4x}{-16x} = \frac{-4x(2y + 1)}{-4x \cdot 4}$$

$$= \frac{-4x(2y + 1) \div (-4x)}{-4x \cdot 4 \quad \div (-4x)}$$

$$= \frac{2y + 1}{4}$$

You may find it easier to change a fraction to the form $\frac{-a}{b}$ or $\frac{a}{b}$ first and then find its simplest form. The last example may be done in this way.

$$\frac{-8xy - 4x}{-16x} = \frac{-(-8xy - 4x)}{-(-16x)}$$

$$= \frac{8xy + 4x}{16x}$$

$$= \frac{4x(2y + 1)}{4x \cdot 4}$$

$$= \frac{4x(2y + 1) \div 4x}{4x \cdot 4 \quad \div 4x}$$

$$= \frac{2y + 1}{4}$$

Remember the following facts when simplifying fractions: $a, b \in Z, b \neq 0$.

$$\frac{-a}{b} = -\frac{a}{b} = \frac{a}{-b} = -\frac{-a}{-b}$$

$$\frac{a}{b} = \frac{-a}{-b} = -\frac{a}{-b} = -\frac{-a}{b}$$

EXAMPLES

1. $\frac{2}{-3}$ may be written $\frac{-2}{3}$.

2. $\frac{-(2x + y)}{-3w}$ may be written $\frac{2x + y}{3w}$.

EXERCISES

Write the simplest form of each fraction. Do not leave a negative sign in front of a denominator.

1. $\frac{24}{36}$

2. $\frac{27p}{63p}$

3. $\frac{-5}{-15}$

4. $\dfrac{30x}{-5x}$

5. $\dfrac{-30x}{5x}$

6. $\dfrac{-10a}{5a}$

7. $\dfrac{6b}{-2b}$

8. $\dfrac{-4d}{d}$

9. $\dfrac{12x}{-12x}$

10. $\dfrac{0}{-5y}$

11. $\dfrac{-2z}{6z}$

12. $\dfrac{5a}{7b}$

13. $\dfrac{2x^2}{3x}$

14. $\dfrac{14y^3}{42xy^2}$

15. $\dfrac{7abx}{21acx}$

Change each fraction to the form $\dfrac{a}{b}$ or $\dfrac{-a}{b}$.

16. $-\dfrac{7}{8}$

17. $-\dfrac{-7}{8}$

18. $-\dfrac{-7}{-8}$

19. $\dfrac{13}{-16}$

20. $-\dfrac{13}{-16}$

21. $\dfrac{-13}{-16}$

22. $\dfrac{x}{-y}$

23. $-\dfrac{xy}{-z}$

24. $-\dfrac{-x^2}{-y}$

25. $\dfrac{-2x}{-3y}$

26. $-\dfrac{-4y}{x}$

27. $-\dfrac{y - x}{-y}$

Simplify each fraction. You will have to use the Distributive Property in the numerator.

28. $\dfrac{3c + 9}{3}$

29. $\dfrac{6 + 6a}{6}$

30. $\dfrac{4x + 5xy}{x}$

31. $\dfrac{-4c - 6}{2}$

32. $\dfrac{12x + 15}{-3}$

33. $\dfrac{-3a - 6b}{3}$

34. $\dfrac{15 - 5x}{-5}$

35. $\dfrac{a^2 - ab}{a}$

36. $\dfrac{7x - 3xy}{-x}$

37. Assume that all variables in Exercises **28–36** are integers. Do all the fractions then name integers? Explain your answer.

Write each fraction in the form $\dfrac{a}{6}$ or $\dfrac{-a}{6}$ where a is positive.

38. $-\dfrac{-1}{-3}$

39. $\dfrac{4}{-12}$

40. $\dfrac{-10}{-2}$

41. $-\dfrac{2}{12}$

42. $-\dfrac{6x}{18x}$

43. $\dfrac{-3x - 9}{6(x + 3)}$

44. $\dfrac{-4xyz^2}{-12xyz^2}$

45. $\dfrac{-(x - 3)}{3(x - 3)}$

46. $-\dfrac{6x(y + z)}{12(xy + xz)}$

6-3
Adding and Subtracting Fractions

To add or subtract fractions, the denominators must be the same.

EXAMPLE

OBJECTIVE:

To find the sum (or difference) of fractions of integers when denominators vary only in sign.

It is assumed that students will insist on having denominators the same from work in previous grades.

Using the number line, you can see that it is reasonable to give $\frac{7}{4}$ as the sum of $\frac{5}{4}$ and $\frac{2}{4}$.

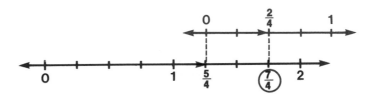

$$\frac{5}{4} + \frac{2}{4} = \frac{5+2}{4} = \frac{7}{4}$$

If $a, b, c \in \mathbf{Z}, b \neq 0$, then $\frac{a}{b} + \frac{c}{b} = \frac{a+c}{b}$.

As with integers, subtracting a number has the same result as adding that number's additive inverse.

EXAMPLE

For slow students, demonstrate this example using a number line.

Since $\frac{-5}{-3}$ and $\frac{5}{-3}$ are additive inverses, the following is true.

$$\frac{2}{-3} - \frac{-5}{-3} = \frac{2}{-3} + \frac{5}{-3}$$

$$= \frac{2+5}{-3}$$

$$= \frac{7}{-3}$$

$$= \frac{-7}{3}$$

Sometimes when adding or subtracting fractions you will find denominators that are additive inverses of each other. In such cases,

Stress that $\frac{-a}{b} = \frac{a}{-b}$.

remember that $\frac{-a}{b} = \frac{a}{-b}$.

1. $\dfrac{a}{b} - \dfrac{c}{-b} = \dfrac{a}{b} - \dfrac{-c}{b}$

$$= \dfrac{a - (-c)}{b}$$

$$= \dfrac{a + c}{b}$$

Stress that in general, $-(x - y) = y - x$. This will be useful often.

2. $\dfrac{5}{a - b} + \dfrac{2}{b - a} = \dfrac{5}{a - b} + \dfrac{-2}{a - b}$

$$= \dfrac{5 + (-2)}{a - b}$$

$$= \dfrac{3}{a - b}$$

Notice that $\dfrac{2}{b - a}$ was rewritten as $\dfrac{-2}{a - b}$. This may be done because $-(b - a) = -b + a = a - b$. Therefore:

$$\dfrac{2}{b - a} = \dfrac{-2}{-(b - a)} = \dfrac{-2}{a - b}$$

In working with fractions, it is helpful to remember the following facts.

1. The additive inverse of an expression may be found by changing the sign of *each* term of the expression. For example, $-(3x - y + 2xy) = -3x + y - 2xy$.
2. The value of an expression is not changed if the terms of the expression are written in a different order. For example, $-3x + y - 2xy = y - 2xy - 3x$.

EXERCISES

1. $\dfrac{1}{3}$ 2. $\dfrac{2}{7}$ 3. $\dfrac{-2}{3}$ 4. $\dfrac{5}{7}$ 5. $\dfrac{x}{3}$ 6. $\dfrac{3w}{5}$

Add or subtract by first restating the fractions in each exercise so that fractions of the forms $\dfrac{a}{b}$ or $\dfrac{-a}{b}$ must be added. In other words, make the denominators the same positive integer before adding.

1. $\dfrac{2}{3} - \dfrac{1}{3}$

2. $\dfrac{-5}{-7} - \dfrac{-3}{-7}$

3. $-\dfrac{-1}{-3} - \dfrac{-1}{-3}$

4. $-\dfrac{5}{-7} - \dfrac{1}{7} + \dfrac{2}{-7} - \dfrac{-3}{7}$

5. $\dfrac{2x}{3} - \dfrac{x}{3}$

6. $\dfrac{3w}{5} - \dfrac{w}{-5} + \dfrac{-w}{5}$

7. a. Yes **b.** Because the additive inverse of a number is unique (Part a) and $-\left(-\frac{a}{b}\right)$ and $\frac{a}{b}$ are additive inverses of $-\frac{a}{B}$, they are equal.

8. $\frac{2}{7}$ **9.** $\frac{4}{5}$ **10.** $\frac{1}{3}$ **11.** a **12.** $\frac{3}{z}$

13. $\frac{-3y}{x^2}$ **14.** y **15.** $\frac{(-4a + 3)}{5}$

16. $\frac{-x}{a}$ **17.** $\frac{(4a - 2)}{3ab}$

18. $\frac{(2a + 2b)}{(a + b)^2} = \frac{2}{(a + b)}$

19. $\frac{x}{3y}$ **20.** 0 **21.** $\frac{3r + 3s}{r + s} = 3$

(7.) The symbol $-\left(-\frac{a}{b}\right)$ means the *additive inverse* of $-\frac{a}{b}$.

   a. Do you agree that if $x + s = 0$ and $x + t = 0$, then $s = t$ for $x, s, t \in Q$?

   b. Why does it make sense to insist that $-\left(-\frac{a}{b}\right) = \frac{a}{b}$? Hint:

   Use Part **a.** If you do not agree with Part **a,** you should not agree with Part **b.**

Write each expression in the form $\frac{a}{b}$ or $\frac{-a}{b}$ where $a, b \in Z, b \neq 0$.

(8.) $-\left(-\frac{5}{7}\right) - \left(-\frac{-3}{7}\right)$ **(9.)** $\frac{3}{5} - \left(-\frac{-1}{-5}\right)$

(10.) $\frac{1}{3} - \frac{2}{3} - \left(-\frac{2}{-3}\right) - \left(-\frac{-2}{-3}\right) - \left(-\frac{2}{3}\right)$

Add or subtract. If not already done, first restate the fractions in each exercise so that fractions of the form $\frac{a}{b}$ or $\frac{-a}{b}$ must be added.

(11.) $\frac{a}{3} + \frac{2a}{3}$ **12.** $\frac{8}{3z} - \frac{-1}{3z}$ **(13.)** $\frac{-5y}{x^2} - \frac{2y}{-x^2}$

14. $\frac{x + y}{2} - \frac{x - y}{2}$ **(15.)** $\frac{-(2a + 1)}{5} - \frac{4 - 2a}{-5}$

16. $\frac{5x}{-2a} + \frac{-3x}{-2a}$ **(17.)** $\frac{5}{3ab} + \frac{1 - 2a}{-3ab} - \frac{6 - 2a}{3ab}$

18. $\frac{7a}{(a+b)^2} - \frac{5a+4b}{(a+b)^2} + \frac{6b}{(a+b)^2}$

(19.) $\frac{4x}{-3y} - \frac{-5x}{3y} + \frac{x}{3y} - \frac{-x}{-3y}$ **20.** $\frac{3a}{-2b} + \frac{a}{2b} + \frac{-5a}{2b} - \frac{-7a}{-2b}$

(21.) $\frac{3r}{r + s} + \frac{-3s}{-s - r}$

6-4
Least Common Denominators

OBJECTIVE:

To find the sum or difference of fractions of integers when denominators are monomials.

It is not reasonable to add or subtract numerators when fractions have different denominators.

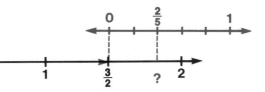

$\frac{3}{2} + \frac{2}{5} = \underline{\quad ? \quad}$

To add $\frac{3}{2}$ and $\frac{2}{5}$, the fractions must be changed to equivalent fractions which have the same denominator.

EXAMPLES

This should be a review of grade school arithmetic. However, remind students of the procedures for finding equivalent fractions on page 153.

1. $\dfrac{3}{2} = \dfrac{3 \cdot 5}{2 \cdot 5} = \dfrac{15}{10}$ $\qquad \dfrac{2}{5} = \dfrac{2 \cdot 2}{5 \cdot 2} = \dfrac{4}{10}$

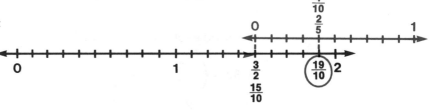

$$\frac{3}{2} + \frac{2}{5} = \frac{15}{10} + \frac{4}{10}$$

$$= \frac{15 + 4}{10}$$

$$= \frac{19}{10}$$

Ask which pairs of fractions are equivalent in line 1.

2. $\dfrac{3}{a} - \dfrac{3}{b} = \dfrac{3 \cdot b}{a \cdot b} - \dfrac{3 \cdot a}{b \cdot a}$

$$= \frac{3b}{ab} - \frac{3a}{ab}$$

$$= \frac{3b - 3a}{ab}$$

$$= \frac{3(b - a)}{ab}$$

When two or more fractions have the same denominator, it is said they have a **common denominator.** For any set of fractions, there is an infinite number of common denominators.

EXAMPLES

1. $\dfrac{3}{4} + \dfrac{5}{6} = \dfrac{9}{12} + \dfrac{10}{12}$ $\qquad$ **2.** $\dfrac{3}{4a} - \dfrac{2}{3b} = \dfrac{9b}{12ab} - \dfrac{8a}{12ab}$

$$= \frac{18}{24} + \frac{20}{24} \qquad\qquad\qquad = \frac{18b}{24ab} - \frac{16a}{24ab}$$

$$= \frac{27}{36} + \frac{30}{36} \qquad\qquad\qquad = \frac{27b}{36ab} - \frac{24a}{36ab}$$

and so on $\qquad\qquad\qquad\qquad\qquad$ and so on

3. $\dfrac{3}{x} + \dfrac{4}{y} = \dfrac{3y}{xy} + \dfrac{4x}{xy}$

$\qquad\qquad = \dfrac{3y^2}{xy^2} + \dfrac{4xy}{xy^2}$

$\qquad\qquad = \dfrac{3xy}{x^2y} + \dfrac{4x^2}{x^2y}$

$\qquad\qquad = \dfrac{3xy^2}{x^2y^2} + \dfrac{4x^2y}{x^2y^2}$

and so on

Notice that 12 is a factor of all possible common denominators for Example **1.** In Example **2,** $12ab$ is a factor of all possible common denominators. In Example **3,** xy is a factor of all possible common denominators. Each of these expressions is called the least common denominator for its corresponding set of fractions. The abbreviation **LCD** often is used to stand for *Least Common Denominator.*

EXAMPLES

1. The LCD of $\dfrac{3}{4}$ and $\dfrac{5}{6}$ is 12.

2. The LCD of $\dfrac{3}{4a}$ and $\dfrac{2}{3b}$ is $12ab$.

3. The LCD of $\dfrac{3}{x}$ and $\dfrac{4}{y}$ is xy.

Usually, LCDs are not negative numbers or variable expressions with negative signs. For example, both 12 and -12 are factors of all possible common denominators for $\dfrac{3}{4} + \dfrac{5}{6}$. However, 12 is called the LCD. Also, the expressions xy, $-xy$, $(-x)y$ and $x(-y)$ are factors of all common denominators for $\dfrac{3}{x} + \dfrac{4}{y}$. However, xy is called *the* LCD.

You always can find *a* common denominator of a set of fractions by simply multiplying the denominators together. If you wish to find *the* LCD, here is a method you may use.

EXAMPLE

Find the LCD of $\dfrac{7}{12}$ and $\dfrac{4}{9}$.

Step 1. Express each denominator as a product of prime number factors.

$$12 = 2 \cdot 2 \cdot 3 \qquad 9 = 3 \cdot 3$$

Step 2. Determine the maximum number of times each factor appears in a product.

Factors	2	3
In 12	2	1
In 9		2
Maximum	2	2

Step 3. Write the LCD as a product. Use each factor the maximum number of times it appears.

$$\text{LCD of } \frac{7}{12} \text{ and } \frac{4}{9} \text{ is } \underbrace{2 \cdot 2 \cdot \overbrace{3 \cdot 3}^{=9}}_{=12} = 36.$$

At this stage in the course, clarify the word *prime* for an expression by saying it is prime "if you can't factor it."

Each expression, x, $x + 3$, or $2x + 5$, is called **prime** because it has no factors except 1 and -1. These expressions cannot be factored using only integers as coefficients. The expression $3x^2$ is not prime because $3x^2 = (3x)x = 3 \cdot x \cdot x$. The expression $2x + 4$ is not prime because $2x + 4 = 2(x + 2)$. Notice that calling an expression prime does not mean it is a prime number for all possible replacements.

EXAMPLES

Emphasize this as *the* procedure where variables appear in denominators.

1. Find the LCD of $\dfrac{3}{4a}, \dfrac{1}{6b}, \dfrac{2}{15a^2}$

Step 1. Express each denominator as a product of prime factors.

$$4a = 2 \cdot 2 \cdot a \qquad 6b = 2 \cdot 3 \cdot b \qquad 15a^2 = 3 \cdot 5 \cdot a \cdot a$$

Step 2. Determine the maximum number of times each factor appears in a product.

Factors	2	3	5	a	b
In $4a$ In $6b$ In $15a^2$	2 1 	 1 1	 1	1 2	 1
Maximum	2	1	1	2	1

Step 3. Write the LCD as a product, using each factor the maximum number of times it appears.

The LCD of $\dfrac{3}{4a}$, $\dfrac{1}{6b}$, and $\dfrac{2}{15a^2}$ is

$$2 \cdot 2 \cdot 3 \cdot 5 \cdot a \cdot a \cdot b = 60a^2b.$$

2. Find $\dfrac{3}{x^2y} - \dfrac{1}{xy} + \dfrac{4}{3y^2}$

$$\left.\begin{array}{l} x^2y = x \cdot x \cdot y \\ xy = x \cdot y \\ 3y^2 = 3 \cdot y \cdot y \end{array}\right\} \quad LCD = 3 \cdot x \cdot x \cdot y \cdot y = 3x^2y^2$$

$$\dfrac{3}{x^2y} - \dfrac{1}{xy} + \dfrac{4}{3y^2} = \dfrac{9y}{3x^2y^2} - \dfrac{3xy}{3x^2y^2} + \dfrac{4x^2}{3x^2y^2}$$

$$= \dfrac{9 - 3xy + 4x^2}{3x^2y^2}$$

EXERCISES

1. 24 2. 30 3. 18 4. 72 5. ab
6. x^2y 7. $15x^2$ 8. $12(a+b)^2$
9. $\dfrac{9}{40}$ 10. $\dfrac{-19}{18}$ 11. $-\dfrac{1}{2}$ 12. $\dfrac{-3}{4}$
13. $\dfrac{41}{63}$ 14. $\dfrac{-59}{270}$

Find the LCD of each set of fractions.

1. $\left\{\dfrac{-3}{8}, \dfrac{15}{12}\right\}$

2. $\left\{\dfrac{-5}{6}, \dfrac{1}{10}\right\}$

3. $\left\{\dfrac{5}{6}, \dfrac{-2}{9}\right\}$

4. $\left\{\dfrac{1}{8}, \dfrac{2}{9}, \dfrac{3}{4}\right\}$

5. $\left\{\dfrac{1}{a}, \dfrac{1}{b}\right\}$

6. $\left\{\dfrac{6x}{y}, \dfrac{7}{x^2y}\right\}$

7. $\left\{\dfrac{2}{15^2}, \dfrac{3}{5x}, 4\right\}$

8. $\left\{\dfrac{1}{a+b}, \dfrac{3}{6(a+b)}, \dfrac{5}{4(a+b)^2}\right\}$

Add or subtract. When fractions have different denominators, first find equivalent fractions with the LCD.

9. $\dfrac{3}{5} - \dfrac{3}{8}$

10. $-\dfrac{5}{6} + \left(-\dfrac{2}{9}\right)$

11. $-\dfrac{5}{6} + \dfrac{1}{3}$

12. $\dfrac{0}{63} - \dfrac{3}{4}$

13. $\dfrac{5}{9} + \dfrac{2}{21}$

14. $\dfrac{4}{27} + \dfrac{-11}{30}$

15. $\frac{(10x + 3y)}{30}$ **16.** $\frac{-x}{10}$

17. $\frac{9x + 7y}{9y}$ **18.** $\frac{11x - 11y}{144}$ **19.** $\frac{11}{8x}$

20. $\frac{(12a + 2ac)}{3c^2r}$ **21.** $\frac{(7 - x)}{x^2}$

22. $\frac{(-5x - 4)}{6x^2}$ **23.** $\frac{(8y^2 - 15x)}{18x^2y^3}$

24. $\frac{(16bc + 45)}{20a^2b^2c^2}$ **25.** $\frac{(3a + 5)}{a}$

26. $\frac{7 - x^3}{x^2}$ **27.** $\frac{(15b - 2c + 6a)}{6abc}$

28. $\frac{(16m^2n^2 + 16mn^3 + 9n^4 - 2m^3)}{12m^2n^3}$

29. $\frac{(22a + 22b - 5)}{20(a + b)^2}$

In Exercise 29, remind slow students to think of $(a + b)$ as a single number.

30. $\frac{(4b + 6a + 20)}{(a + 2)(b + 2)}$ **31.** $\frac{(3x + 7y)}{3}$

32. $\frac{(-10x - 3)}{4}$ **33.** $\frac{4}{15}$ **34.** 240

35. Answers will vary.

36. Answers will vary.

15. $\frac{x}{3} + \frac{y}{10}$

16. $\frac{x}{6} - \frac{4x}{15}$

17. $\frac{x}{y} + \frac{7}{9}$

18. $\frac{x - y}{18} + \frac{x - y}{48}$

19. $\frac{3}{4x} + \frac{5}{8x}$

20. $\frac{4a}{c^2r} - \frac{-2a}{3cr}$

21. $\frac{7}{x^2} - \frac{1}{x}$

22. $\frac{-5}{6x} + \frac{-2}{3x^2}$

23. $\frac{4}{9x^2y} - \frac{5}{6xy^3}$

24. $\frac{12}{15a^2bc} + \frac{9}{4(abc)^2}$

25. $\frac{3}{1} + \frac{5}{a}$

26. $\frac{7}{x^2} - x$

27. $\frac{5}{2ac} - \frac{1}{3ab} + \frac{1}{bc}$

28. $\frac{4(m + n)}{3mn} + \frac{3n}{4m^2} - \frac{m}{6n^3}$

29. $\frac{1}{(a + b)} - \frac{1}{4(a + b)^2} + \frac{1}{10(a + b)}$

30. $\frac{4}{(a + 2)} + \frac{6}{(b + 2)}$

31. $x + \frac{y}{3} + 2y$

32. $-2x - \frac{3}{4} + \frac{-x}{2}$

33. In a garden, $\frac{1}{3}$ of the area is used for vegetables and $\frac{2}{5}$ for flowers and paths. If the rest of the garden consists of lawn, what fraction of the garden is given to the lawn?

34. In a theater, $\frac{5}{12}$ of the seating capacity is in the back seats, $\frac{1}{4}$ in the front seats, and the remainder in the balcony. If the theater can seat 720 people, how many can sit in the balcony?

35. By choosing different combinations of $a \in \left\{\frac{-2}{9}, -\frac{-5}{-9}\right\}$, $b \in \left\{-\frac{5}{6}, -\frac{1}{-6}\right\}$, and $c \in \left\{\frac{5}{-4}, -\frac{-1}{4}\right\}$, check to see that

i. $a + b = b + a$

ii. $(a + b) + c = a + (b + c)$

36. Construct a flow chart for finding the LCD.

6-5
Multiplying Fractions

OBJECTIVE:
To find $\frac{a}{b} \cdot \frac{c}{d}$ where $a, b, c,$ and d represent integers, b and d nonzero.

EXAMPLE

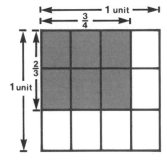

This should be a reminder of what students already know.

The formula for the area of rectangles, $A = lw$, may be used to picture the multiplication of fractions. The numerator and denominator of the fractions should be natural numbers.

In the figure, the shaded region has dimensions $\frac{3}{4}$ unit by $\frac{2}{3}$ unit.

$$\text{Area of shaded region} = lw$$

$$= \frac{3}{4} \cdot \frac{2}{3}$$

By drawing the vertical lines for fourths and the horizontal lines for thirds, the unit area is divided into twelve equal parts. The product of the denominator tells how many of these equal parts there will be in a unit. In this example, $4 \cdot 3 = 12$.

The shaded area has three columns with two of these equal parts in each column. The product of the numerators tells how many of these equal parts there will be in the shaded area. In this example, $3 \cdot 2 = 6$.

Each equal part is one-twelfth of the unit area. The shaded area is 6 of these equal parts. Therefore, the shaded area is $\frac{6}{12}$ of the unit area.

$$A = lw = \frac{3}{4} \cdot \frac{2}{3}$$

$$= \frac{3 \cdot 2}{4 \cdot 3}$$

$$= \frac{6}{12}$$

$$= \frac{1}{2}$$

From arithmetic, you remember that $\frac{a}{b} \cdot \frac{c}{d} = \frac{a \cdot c}{b \cdot d}$ when $a, b, c, d \in \text{N}$. This multiplication rule may be stated in words.

To multiply fractions, multiply the numerators together and multiply the denominators together.

This rule also applies if there are three or more factors in the product.

EXAMPLE

$$\frac{1}{5} \cdot \frac{2}{3} \cdot \frac{1}{8} = \frac{1 \cdot 2 \cdot 1}{5 \cdot 3 \cdot 8}$$

$$= \frac{2}{120}$$

$$= \frac{1}{60}$$

See the section notes in T.G. for an optional approach. As suggested there, this rule may be created or derived by students.

The same rule is used to multiply fractions with negative numerators or denominators.

EXAMPLES

1. $\dfrac{-2}{3} \cdot \dfrac{-6}{-25} \cdot \dfrac{10}{-12} = \dfrac{(-2) \cdot (-6) \cdot 10}{3 \cdot (-25) \cdot (-12)}$

$$= \frac{120}{900}$$

$$= \frac{2}{15}$$

2. $\dfrac{-2}{3} \cdot \dfrac{-5x}{-6} \cdot \dfrac{1}{-2} = \dfrac{(-2) \cdot (-5x) \cdot 1}{3 \cdot (-6) \cdot (-2)}$

$$= \frac{10x}{36}$$

$$= \frac{5x}{18}$$

3. $\dfrac{-2a}{b} \cdot \dfrac{4}{(a + b)} \cdot \dfrac{b^2}{a} = \dfrac{-2a \cdot 4 \cdot b^2}{b(a + b)a}$

$$= \frac{-8ab^2}{ab(a + b)}$$

$$= \frac{-8b}{(a + b)}$$

Remember that in your study of integers it was decided to define addition and multiplication so that the Commutative, Associative, and Distributive Properties would apply. These properties also will apply for the multiplication of fractions when it is defined as $\dfrac{a}{b} \cdot \dfrac{c}{d} = \dfrac{a \cdot c}{b \cdot d}$.

EXERCISES

1. $\frac{1}{5}$, Commutative

2. $\frac{-1}{4}$, Associative

3. $\frac{2x}{3}$, Commutative

4. $\frac{a}{2b}$, Associative

5. $\frac{(2 + x^2y)}{x^3}$, Distributive

6. $\frac{(-x^3 - 2xy)}{2y}$, Distributive

7. $\frac{2}{c}$, Associative and Commutative

8. $\frac{5}{18}$ 9. $\frac{25}{12}$ 10. $\frac{-17}{10}$ 11. -1 12. $\frac{2}{9}$

13. 1 14. $\frac{rm}{sn}$ 15. $\frac{6a^2x^2}{5y^2}$ 16. $\frac{-1}{10c^2}$

17. $\frac{-a}{d}$ 18. 0 19. $\frac{-m^2}{4}$ 20. $-y$

21. $\frac{10x}{9}$ 22. $\frac{-2}{(a-b)}$ 23. -1

24. $\frac{-1}{2}$ 25. $\frac{-(a+b)}{2}$ 26. 28

27. 1 28. $\frac{-4v}{3xy}$ 29. $\frac{-2x}{3(2x+1)}$

30. $\frac{-2y}{x}$ 31. $\frac{1}{2b^4}$

Find each product. Keep in mind the Associative, Commutative, and Distributive Properties. For each pair, name any property being demonstrated.

1. $\frac{-3}{5} \cdot \frac{2}{-6} = \frac{2}{-6} \cdot \frac{-3}{5}$

2. $\left(\frac{1}{2} \cdot \frac{-2}{3}\right) \cdot \frac{-3}{-4} = \frac{1}{2} \cdot \left(\frac{-2}{3} \cdot \frac{-3}{-4}\right)$

3. $\left(\frac{2x}{3} \cdot \frac{5}{3x}\right) \cdot \frac{3x}{5} = \frac{3x}{5} \cdot \left(\frac{2x}{3} \cdot \frac{5}{3x}\right)$

4. $\left(\frac{a}{b} \cdot \frac{-2}{ab}\right) \cdot \frac{-a}{4b} = \frac{a}{b} \cdot \left(\frac{-2}{ab} \cdot \frac{-a}{4b}\right)$

5. $\frac{2}{xy^2} \cdot \left(\frac{y}{x^2} + \frac{y^2}{2}\right) = \frac{2}{xy^2} \cdot \frac{y}{x^2} + \frac{2}{xy^2} \cdot \frac{y^2}{2}$

6. $(-x) \cdot \frac{x^2}{2y} - \frac{2y}{x} \cdot \frac{x^2}{2y} = \left(-x - \frac{2y}{x}\right) \cdot \frac{x^2}{2y}$

7. $\left(\frac{ab^2}{c} \cdot \frac{2}{cb^2}\right) \cdot \frac{c}{a} = \frac{2}{cb^2} \cdot \left(\frac{ab^2}{c} \cdot \frac{c}{a}\right)$

Find each product. Express the product in simplest form.

8. $\frac{-3}{4} \cdot \frac{5}{9} \cdot \frac{-2}{3}$ **9.** $1\frac{2}{3} \cdot 1\frac{1}{4}$ **10.** $-2\frac{1}{8} \cdot \frac{4}{5}$

11. $-\frac{5}{6} \cdot 1\frac{1}{5}$ **12.** $1\frac{5}{9} \cdot \frac{1}{7}$ **13.** $-2\frac{1}{2} \cdot \frac{-4}{5}$

14. $\frac{r}{s} \cdot \frac{m}{n}$ **15.** $\frac{6ax}{5y} \cdot \frac{ax}{y}$ **16.** $\left(-\frac{1}{2c}\right) \cdot \left(\frac{1}{5c}\right)$

17. $\frac{ab}{cd} \cdot \frac{-c}{b}$ **18.** $\frac{x}{2y^2} \cdot \frac{0}{x^2}$ **19.** $m \cdot \frac{-m}{4}$

20. $(-xy) \cdot \frac{1}{x}$ **21.** $\frac{5x^2}{3y} \cdot \frac{2y}{3x}$

22. $\frac{-(a-b)}{6} \cdot \frac{12}{(a-b)^2}$ **23.** $\frac{s}{s-r} \cdot \frac{r-s}{s}$

24. $\frac{u+v}{4} \cdot \frac{2}{-v-u}$ **25.** $\frac{a+b}{10} \cdot \frac{-5}{a}$

26. $7x \cdot \frac{x}{2} \cdot \frac{8}{x^2}$ **27.** $\frac{2a+2b}{10} \cdot \frac{5}{a+b}$

28. $\frac{-7xy}{5uv} \cdot \frac{20uv^2}{21x^2y^2}$ **29.** $\frac{2x}{3} \cdot \frac{-1}{2x+1}$

30. $\frac{x^2y}{2} \cdot \frac{4}{xy} \cdot \frac{-y}{x^2}$ **31.** $\frac{ab}{c} \cdot \frac{2}{a^3b^2c} \cdot \frac{a^2c^2}{4b^3}$

Remind students that $a = \frac{a}{1}$ for any $a \in Z$. Thus, in Exercise 19, $m \cdot \frac{-m}{4}$ may be written $\frac{m}{1} \cdot \frac{-m}{4}$.

Also, remind students that $1\frac{2}{3} = 1 + \frac{2}{3} = \frac{3}{3} + \frac{2}{3} = \frac{5}{3}$. Knowing this is necessary for Exercise 9.

Watch for difficulties with Exercises 23, 25, 27, and 29. With these, students must treat expressions as single numbers.

32. a. $(-a)b = \dfrac{a}{-1} \cdot \dfrac{-b}{-1} =$

$\dfrac{-ab}{1} = -(ab)$ **b.** $(-a)(-b) =$

$\dfrac{-a}{1} \cdot \dfrac{b}{-1} = \dfrac{-ab}{-1} = \dfrac{ab}{1} = ab$

(32.) If $a \in Z$, then a may be written as $\dfrac{a}{1}$ or $\dfrac{-a}{-1}$.

   a. When $-a$ is written as $\dfrac{a}{-1}$ and b is written as $\dfrac{-b}{-1}$, show

      that $(-a)b = -(ab)$.

   b. When $-a$ is written as $\dfrac{-a}{1}$ and $-b$ is written as $\dfrac{b}{-1}$, show

      that $(-a)(-b) = ab$.

6-6
Dividing Fractions

OBJECTIVE:

To find $\dfrac{a}{b} \div \dfrac{c}{d}$ where a, b, c, and d represent integers, b, c, and d nonzero.

When two fractions have the same denominators, it makes sense to think of dividing one fraction by the other as dividing the numerators.

EXAMPLES

These examples are leading up to $\dfrac{a}{b} \div \dfrac{c}{d} = \dfrac{a}{b} \cdot \dfrac{d}{c}$ on the next page.

1. You may think of $6 \div 2 =$ ___?___ as asking how many two's there are in six.

2. You may think of $\dfrac{6}{5} \div \dfrac{2}{5} =$ ___?___ as asking how many $\dfrac{2}{5}$'s there are in $\dfrac{6}{5}$.

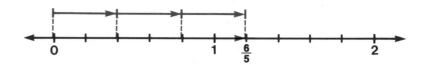

$$\frac{6}{5} \div \frac{2}{5} = 6 \div 2$$
$$= 3$$

3. You may think of $\dfrac{7}{5} \div \dfrac{2}{5} =$ ___?___ as asking how many $\dfrac{2}{5}$'s there are in $\dfrac{7}{5}$.

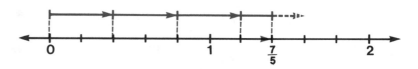

$$\frac{7}{5} \div \frac{2}{5} = 7 \div 2$$
$$= 3\frac{1}{2}$$

To divide fractions with unlike denominators, you may first change both to equivalent fractions which have the same denominator.

EXAMPLES

Allow slow students who seem confused by this merely to memorize the rule (definition) at the bottom of this page.

1. $\dfrac{2}{3} \div \dfrac{5}{7} = \dfrac{2 \cdot 7}{3 \cdot 7} \div \dfrac{3 \cdot 5}{3 \cdot 7}$

$= (2 \cdot 7) \div (3 \cdot 5)$

$= \dfrac{2 \cdot 7}{3 \cdot 5}$

$= \dfrac{2}{3} \cdot \dfrac{7}{5}$

2. $\dfrac{2}{x} \div \dfrac{2x}{3y} = \dfrac{2 \cdot 3y}{x \cdot 3y} \div \dfrac{x \cdot 2x}{x \cdot 3y}$

$= (2 \cdot 3y) \div (x \cdot 2x)$

$= \dfrac{2 \cdot 3y}{x \cdot 2x}$

$= \dfrac{2}{x} \cdot \dfrac{3y}{2x}$

3. $\dfrac{a}{b} \div \dfrac{c}{d} = \dfrac{a \cdot d}{b \cdot d} \div \dfrac{b \cdot c}{b \cdot d}$

$= (a \cdot d) \div (b \cdot c)$

$= \dfrac{a \cdot d}{b \cdot c}$

$= \dfrac{a}{b} \cdot \dfrac{d}{c}$

These examples show the rule you learned before. To divide by a nonzero fraction $\dfrac{c}{d}$, multiply by $\dfrac{d}{c}$.

By thinking of division in this way, how to divide with negative numerators or denominators is already decided. This is so because the only division which was done was with numerators, and such division is already familiar.

It is "familiar" because division of integers is an already familiar process.

Perhaps you learned a different statement of the rule for dividing fractions which used the word *reciprocal*.

To divide by a fraction, multiply by its *reciprocal* or *multiplicative inverse*.

Two rational numbers are called reciprocals or multiplicative inverses of each other if their product is 1. The only rational number that does not have a reciprocal is zero. For *any* number a, $0 \cdot a = 0$.

For a fraction that is not zero, the reciprocal is easy to find. You only have to interchange the numerator and denominator.

Stress the fact that 0 has no reciprocal.

EXAMPLES

1. The reciprocal of $\frac{2}{3}$ is $\frac{3}{2}$. $\frac{2}{3} \cdot \frac{3}{2} = \frac{2 \cdot 3}{3 \cdot 2} = \frac{6}{6} = 1$

2. The reciprocal of $-\frac{1}{2}$ is -2. $-\frac{1}{2} \cdot -\frac{2}{1} = \frac{2}{2} = 1$

Ask if $\frac{a}{b}$ has a reciprocal if $a = 0$ and $b = 3$.

3. The reciprocal of $\frac{a}{b}$ is $\frac{b}{a}$. $\frac{a}{b} \cdot \frac{b}{a} = \frac{ab}{ab} = 1$

4. The reciprocal of $\frac{1}{a}$ is a. $\frac{1}{a} \cdot \frac{a}{1} = \frac{a}{a} = 1$

Reciprocals, just as additive inverses, come in pairs. For instance, $\frac{3}{2}$ and $\frac{2}{3}$, 2 and $\frac{1}{2}$, $\frac{b}{a}$ and $\frac{a}{b}$, and a and $\frac{1}{a}$, $a \neq 0$, $b \neq 0$, are pairs of reciprocals.

Division with fractions can be summarized in one statement.

For slow students, stress again that only a may be zero if $\frac{a}{b} \div \frac{c}{d}$ is to exist.

If a, b, c, $d \in Z$, $b \neq 0$, $c \neq 0$, and $d \neq 0$, then

$$\frac{a}{b} \div \frac{c}{d} = \frac{a}{b} \cdot \frac{d}{c}$$

$$= \frac{ad}{bc}$$

EXERCISES

1. $\frac{7}{6}$ 2. $\frac{5}{6}$ 3. -4 4. $\frac{2}{3}$ 5. $\frac{-9}{4}$ 6. $\frac{5}{3}$
7. $\frac{14}{9}$ 8. 4 9. $\frac{-4}{3}$

Divide using the rule $\frac{a}{b} \div \frac{c}{d} = \frac{a}{b} \cdot \frac{d}{c}$. If there are mixed numerals, change them to fractions before dividing.

Some students may need reminding that $3 = \frac{3}{1}$, $2\frac{1}{3} = 2 + \frac{1}{3}$, etc.

1. $\frac{7}{10} \div \frac{3}{5}$ **2.** $\frac{5}{8} \div \frac{3}{4}$ **3.** $2\frac{1}{2} \div \frac{-5}{8}$

4. $2\frac{1}{3} \div 3\frac{1}{2}$ **5.** $3\frac{3}{8} \div -1\frac{1}{2}$ **6.** $3\frac{1}{3} \div 2$

7. $4\frac{2}{3} \div 3$ **8.** $5\frac{1}{3} \div 1\frac{1}{3}$ **9.** $2 \div -1\frac{1}{2}$

Use the symbols $+$, $-$, $\cdot$, $\div$, or $=$ to make at least 3 true statements about each set of fractions.

(10) $\frac{1}{2}, \frac{1}{4}, \frac{3}{4}$

(11) $\frac{2}{x^2}, \frac{y}{4x}, \frac{xy}{8}$

(12) $\frac{x}{3} + \frac{y}{3}, \frac{xy}{x+y}, \frac{xy}{3}$

Divide.

13. $\frac{a+b}{2} \div 2$

14. $\frac{c^2}{d} \div \frac{c}{d}$

15. $\frac{6a^2}{5b^3} \div \frac{3a^2}{b^2}$

16. $\frac{6x^2y}{5ab^2} \div \frac{18xy}{25a^2b^2}$

17. $\frac{3}{x^3} \cdot \frac{x^2}{5} \div \frac{6}{xy}$

18. $\frac{x-y}{2} \div \frac{(x-y)^2}{6}$

19. $\frac{(x-y)^3}{(x+y)} \div \frac{(x-y)^4}{(x+y)^2}$

20. $\frac{(y+1)^2}{15} \div \frac{(y+1)}{5} \div \frac{(y+1)}{3}$

21. $\frac{(a+1)(a-1)}{6a^3b^5} \div \frac{(a+1)}{3(ab)^3}$

Rewrite each sentence. Replace $\circ$ by $+$, $-$, $\cdot$, or $\div$ so that the statement is correct. There may be more than one possible replacement.

22. $\frac{1}{2} \circ \frac{1}{2} = 1$

23. $\frac{1}{2} \circ \frac{1}{2} = 0$

24. $\frac{1}{2} \circ \frac{1}{2} = \frac{1}{4}$

25. $1 \circ \frac{1}{4} = 1\frac{1}{4}$

26. $1 \circ \frac{1}{4} = 4$

27. $1 \circ \frac{1}{4} = \frac{3}{4}$

28. $1 \circ \frac{1}{4} = \frac{1}{4}$

29. $\frac{1}{2} \circ \frac{1}{3} = \frac{1}{6}$

30. $\frac{1}{a} \circ \frac{1}{a} = \frac{2}{a}$

31. $\frac{y}{x} \circ x^2 = xy$

32. $\frac{a}{b} \circ \frac{b}{a} = \frac{a^2 + b^2}{ab}$

33. $\frac{(y+1)^2}{15} \circ \frac{y+1}{3} = \frac{y+1}{5}$

34. $x \circ x = 1$

35. $x \circ x = 0$

If $a = 8$, $b = 1\frac{1}{2}$, $c = \frac{3}{4}$, find the values of each expression.

36. $(ab) \div c$

37. $a \cdot c \div b$

38. $1 \div a \cdot b \cdot c$

39. $(2b) \div 3 \cdot c$

40. Divide the sum of $\frac{1}{2}$ and $\frac{1}{3}$ by their difference.

6-7
More
on Inverses

OBJECTIVES:

1. To name $-a$ given $a \in Q$.
2. To name a^{-1} given $a \in Q$, $a \neq 0$.

This section is largely review except that it presents the symbol a^{-1} for $a \in Q$, $a \neq 0$.

EXAMPLES

EXAMPLES

EXAMPLES

When you studied the integers, you saw that all subtractions may be treated as additions by using the following rule.

Subtracting a number is the same as adding its additive inverse.

---

1. $6 - 8 = 6 + (-8) = -2$
2. $5 - (-3) = 5 + 3 = 8$

The same rule also is true for rational numbers.

1. $\dfrac{1}{2} - \dfrac{1}{3} = \dfrac{1}{2} + \dfrac{-1}{3}$

$= \dfrac{3}{6} + \dfrac{-2}{6}$

$= \dfrac{1}{6}$

2. $\dfrac{-5}{6} - \dfrac{-2}{6} = \dfrac{-5}{6} + \dfrac{2}{6}$

$= \dfrac{-3}{6}$

$= \dfrac{-1}{2}$

However, for the rational numbers there is a rule for multiplication and division which you did not encounter in your study of integers.

Dividing by a number is the same as multiplying its multiplicative inverse.

---

1. $\dfrac{3}{4} \div \dfrac{9}{8} = \dfrac{3}{4} \cdot \dfrac{8}{9}$

$= \dfrac{24}{36}$

$= \dfrac{2}{3}$

2. $\dfrac{-3}{5} \div (-6) = \dfrac{-3}{5} \cdot \dfrac{1}{-6}$

$= \dfrac{-3}{-30}$

$= \dfrac{1}{10}$

The reason this second rule was not given for the integers is simple. For most integers, n, the multiplicative inverse, $\dfrac{1}{n}$, is not an integer.

You remember that the notation $-a$ means the additive inverse of a.

$$a + (-a) = (-a) + a = 0$$

Definitions for $-a$ and a^{-1} should be memorized.

The notation a^{-1} often is used to mean the multiplicative inverse of a. $a^{-1} = \dfrac{1}{a^1} = \dfrac{1}{a}$

$$a \cdot a^{-1} = a^{-1} \cdot a = 1$$

For a fraction, $\dfrac{n}{m}$, you know that $\left(\dfrac{n}{m}\right)^{-1} = \dfrac{m}{n}$.

EXERCISES

1. $n = 1$ **2.** $n = 0$ **3.** $\dfrac{n}{m} = 1$

4. a. No **b.** No **c.** Yes **d.** Yes

1. If $n \in$ N and $n^{-1} \in$ N, what number must n be?

2. If $n \in$ W and $-n \in$ W, what number must n be?

3. If $\left(\dfrac{n}{m}\right)^{-1} \in$ Z, what do you know about the simplified form for $\dfrac{n}{m}$?

4. A set S is said to be *closed relative to operation* * if $a * b \in$ S whenever $a, b \in$ S.
   a. Is Z closed relative to $\div$?
   b. Is W closed relative to $-$?
   c. Is Q closed relative to $\cdot$?
   d. Is N closed relative to $+$?

If assigned to slow students, these exercises are best treated by group discussions. These exercises may be omitted.

5. Copy and complete the following table. Write *yes* if the set is closed relative to the operation given at the head of the column. Write *no* if the set is not closed relative to the given operation.

5.

	$+$	$-$	$\cdot$	$\div$
N	Yes	No	Yes	No
W	Yes	No	Yes	No
Z	Yes	Yes	Yes	No
Q	Yes	Yes	Yes	Yes
$\{-1, 0, 1\}$	No	No	Yes	No

6. 3 **7.** Yes

	$+$	$-$	$\cdot$	$\div$
N	?	?	?	?
W	?	?	?	?
Z	?	?	?	?
Q	?	?	?	?
$\{-1, 0, 1\}$	?	?	?	?

6. If $a = 3$, what number is $(a^{-1})^{-1}$?

7. Is it true that $(ab)^{-1} = a^{-1} \cdot b^{-1}$? Hint: To get started, you may want to try a specific example by letting $a = \dfrac{2}{3}$ and $b = \dfrac{5}{7}$.

8. Is it true that $(a^{-1})^3 = (a^3)^{-1}$? Hint: Begin by looking at the case when $a = \dfrac{2}{3}$.

9. The number 0 is called an *additive identity,* and the number 1 is called a *multiplicative identity.* Write each of the following statements in words.

    a. If $a \in$ Q, then $a + (-a) = 0$.

    b. If $a \in$ Q and $a \neq 0$, then $a \cdot a^{-1} = 1$.

10. Decide if each statement is true (T) or false (F).

    a. If $a \in$ Q, then $(-a)^2 = -(a^2)$.

    b. If $a \in$ Q, then $(-a)^3 = -(a^3)$.

    c. If $ab^{-1} = c$, then $a = bc$.

    d. If $a^{-1}b^{-1} = c$, then $abc = 1$.

    e. If $a > 0$, $a \in$ R, and $a^2 = 2$, then $a \in$ Q.

6-8
Order for Rational Numbers

OBJECTIVE:

To name $z \in$ Q such that $x < z < y$ given $0 < x < y$, and $x, y \in$ Q.

EXAMPLES

Order for the rational numbers may be pictured on the number line just as it was for integers. The sentence $\dfrac{a}{b} < \dfrac{c}{d}$ means that $\dfrac{a}{b}$ is to the left of $\dfrac{c}{d}$ on the number line. The sentence $\dfrac{a}{b} > \dfrac{c}{d}$ means that $\dfrac{a}{b}$ is to the right of $\dfrac{c}{d}$ on the number line.

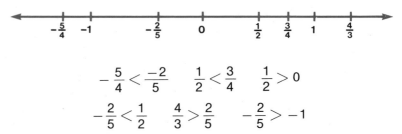

$$-\frac{5}{4} < \frac{-2}{5} \qquad \frac{1}{2} < \frac{3}{4} \qquad \frac{1}{2} > 0$$

$$-\frac{2}{5} < \frac{1}{2} \qquad \frac{4}{3} > \frac{2}{5} \qquad -\frac{2}{5} > -1$$

Sometimes it is not easy to say which of two fractions with different denominators is larger. In such a case, you may rename the numbers as equivalent fractions with the same denominators.

EXAMPLE

Find the larger of $\dfrac{3}{5}$ and $\dfrac{4}{7}$.

$$\frac{3}{5} = \frac{3 \cdot 7}{5 \cdot 7} = \frac{21}{35} \qquad \qquad \frac{4}{7} = \frac{4 \cdot 5}{7 \cdot 5} = \frac{20}{35}$$

$$\frac{21}{35} > \frac{20}{35}, \text{ and so } \frac{3}{5} > \frac{4}{7}$$

When you studied the integers, you saw that there are many unbroken segments of the number line which contain no integers.

Segments marked in red contain no integers. However, no matter how short a segment of the number line is chosen, that segment does contain many rational numbers. In fact, between any two rational numbers there are an infinite number of other rational numbers.

EXAMPLES

1. Find a rational number between $\frac{1}{5}$ and $\frac{1}{4}$.

If you add these two numbers and divide by 2, you will find the number midway between the two numbers.

$$\left(\frac{1}{5} + \frac{1}{4}\right) \div 2 = \left(\frac{1}{5} + \frac{1}{4}\right) \cdot \frac{1}{2}$$
$$= \left(\frac{4}{20} + \frac{5}{20}\right) \cdot \frac{1}{2}$$
$$= \frac{9}{20} \cdot \frac{1}{2}$$
$$= \frac{9}{40}$$

Check: $\frac{1}{5} = \frac{1 \cdot 8}{5 \cdot 8} = \frac{8}{40}$ The number is $\frac{9}{40}$. $\frac{1}{4} = \frac{1 \cdot 10}{4 \cdot 10} = \frac{10}{40}$

2. Find two rational numbers between $\frac{1}{5}$ and $\frac{1}{4}$.

Find the least common denominator, which is 20. Multiply it by one more than the number of fractions you need. In this case, use 3. The answer, 60, is the denominator you should use in converting $\frac{1}{5}$ and $\frac{1}{4}$ to equivalent fractions.

$$\frac{1}{5} = \frac{12}{60} \qquad \frac{1}{4} = \frac{15}{60}$$

The numbers $\frac{13}{60}$ and $\frac{14}{60}$ are between $\frac{12}{60}$ and $\frac{15}{60}$ and, therefore, between $\frac{1}{5}$ and $\frac{1}{4}$. Of course, they are not the only rational numbers between $\frac{1}{5}$ and $\frac{1}{4}$.

EXERCISES

1. Answers may vary. **2.** Answers may vary. **3.** Answers may vary. **4.** Answers may vary. **5.** Answers may vary. **6.** Answers may vary. **7.** Answers may vary. **8.** Answers may vary. **9.** $\frac{1}{4}, \frac{1}{2}, \frac{3}{4}$

To be assigned at teacher's discretion.

10. $\frac{3}{8}, \frac{1}{2}, \frac{5}{8}$ **11.** $\frac{1}{2}, \frac{2}{3}, \frac{3}{4}$ **12.** $\frac{2}{5}, \frac{1}{2}, \frac{3}{5}$
13. $\frac{1}{2}, \frac{1}{4}, \frac{1}{8}$ **14.** $1, \frac{11}{12}, \frac{7}{8}$
15. $1\frac{5}{6}, 1\frac{3}{4}, 1\frac{2}{3}$ **16.** $\frac{4}{5}, \frac{7}{10}, \frac{69}{100}$
17. $\frac{5}{6}, \frac{19}{24}$ **18.** Answers may vary.

a. $\frac{79}{560}, \frac{15}{112}, \frac{73}{560}, \frac{71}{560}$

b. $\frac{17}{24}, \frac{3}{4}, \frac{19}{24}, \frac{4}{5}$ **c.** $\frac{57}{70}, \frac{29}{35}, \frac{59}{70}, \frac{119}{140}$

19. Answers will vary,
$\frac{17}{100}, \frac{13}{75}, \frac{53}{300}, \frac{9}{50}, \frac{11}{60}, \frac{14}{75}, \frac{19}{100},$
$\frac{59}{300}, \frac{29}{150}$ **20.** $\frac{y}{2}$ **21.** $\frac{3}{3x}$

22. $\frac{3y^2}{y}$

23. $\frac{1}{(x + y)}$

24. $\frac{1}{(y - x)}$

25. $(y - x)(y + x)$

Name one fraction between each pair of rational numbers.

1. $\frac{1}{2}$ and 1 **2.** $\frac{1}{4}$ and $\frac{3}{4}$ **3.** $\frac{1}{2}$ and $\frac{5}{6}$ **4.** $\frac{1}{4}$ and $\frac{1}{2}$

5. $\frac{1}{5}$ and $\frac{1}{2}$ **6.** 1 and $1\frac{1}{8}$ **7.** 0 and $\frac{1}{10}$ **8.** $\frac{1}{4}$ and $\frac{1}{3}$

Arrange each group of rational numbers in increasing order.

9. $\frac{1}{2}, \frac{1}{4}, \frac{3}{4}$ **10.** $\frac{1}{2}, \frac{5}{8}, \frac{3}{8}$ **11.** $\frac{2}{3}, \frac{1}{2}, \frac{3}{4}$ **12.** $\frac{1}{2}, \frac{2}{5}, \frac{3}{5}$

Arrange each group of rational numbers in decreasing order.

13. $\frac{1}{2}, \frac{1}{8}, \frac{1}{4}$ **14.** $\frac{7}{8}, 1, \frac{11}{12}$

15. $1\frac{2}{3}, 1\frac{3}{4}, 1\frac{5}{6}$ **16.** $\frac{4}{5}, \frac{7}{10}, \frac{69}{100}$

17. Which of the following rational numbers are between $\frac{3}{4}$ and $\frac{7}{8}$.

$$\frac{1}{2}, \frac{5}{6}, \frac{19}{24}, \frac{2}{3}$$

18. Name four fractions between each pair of rational numbers.

a. $\frac{1}{7}, \frac{1}{8}$ **b.** $\frac{2}{3}, \frac{7}{8}$ **c.** $\frac{4}{5}, \frac{6}{7}$

19. Name nine rational numbers between $\frac{1}{5}$ and $\frac{1}{6}$.

If $x \in W$, $y \in W$, and $0 < x < y$, decide which fraction in each pair is the larger.

20. $\frac{3x}{6}; \frac{y}{2}$ **21.** $\frac{1}{2y}; \frac{3}{3x}$ **22.** $\frac{x + y}{2}; \frac{3y^2}{y}$

23. $\frac{1}{x + y}; \frac{1}{x - y}$ **24.** $\frac{1}{y + x}; \frac{1}{y - x}$ **25.** $\frac{y - x}{y + x}; \frac{x - y}{x + y}$

6-9
Beyond
the Rationals

In Chapter 1 it was stated that there are points on the number line which cannot be named by rational numbers. These points correspond to numbers which are called *irrational numbers*.

EXAMPLES

OBJECTIVE:
To name at least two irrational numbers.

1. Pi (π) is an irrational number.
2. $\sqrt{2}$ is an irrational number.

You probably have used the formula $C = \pi d$ to find the circumference of a circle. You may have used $\pi = \frac{22}{7}$, or $\pi = 3.14$, or $\pi = 3.1416$. None of these values is exact. When it is necessary to compute with a number such as π, a rational number that is close enough to π to suit you is used.

Even if you were very particular and used $\pi = 3.141592654$, you would miss the exact value of π. Your value would be a bit too large.

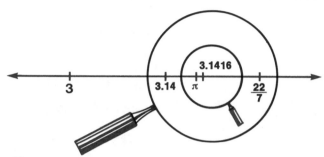

There are many irrational numbers. Between any two rational numbers, there are many irrational numbers. The union of the set of rational numbers and the set of irrational numbers is called the set of **real numbers.** The set of *all* points on a number line may be thought of as the set of real numbers.

$$R = \{\text{rational numbers}\} \cup \{\text{irrational numbers}\}$$

Another way to think about the irrational numbers is to think about decimal expansions. All irrational numbers have *nonrepeating decimal expansions*. On the other hand, all rational numbers have repeating decimal expansions.

EXAMPLES

1.
$$
\begin{array}{r}
.66 \\
3)\overline{2.00} \\
1\,8 \\
\hline
20 \\
18 \\
\hline
20 \\
18 \\
\hline
2
\end{array}
$$
$\frac{2}{3} = 0.666 \ldots$ A repeating decimal.

The number $\frac{2}{3}$ has a repeating decimal expansion. Therefore, $\frac{2}{3}$ is a rational number.

2.

$$5)\overline{3.000} \qquad \frac{3}{5} = 0.6000 \ldots \text{ A repeating decimal.}$$

```
      .600
  5)3.000
    3 0
    ──
     00
      0
    ──
     00
      0
    ──
      0
```

Notice that the division process "terminated" with the first 0 remainder, and 0 is the repeating digit. Therefore, $\frac{3}{5}$ usually is written as 0.6 and called a *terminating decimal*. You may say that because $\frac{3}{5}$ is a terminating decimal, it is a rational number.

Stress this example. → **3.** Accurate to the nearest ten billionth, the real number $\pi =$ 3.1415926536. Imagine that the value were computed further, at the rate of a digit a day, starting today, and going on forever. Even so, the expansion would never terminate, nor would it begin to repeat itself.

EXERCISES

1. $\frac{22}{7}$ **2.** Answers will vary.

3. Irrational **4. a.** 1.414214
b. 1.732051 **c.** 2.236068
d. 2.645751 **e.** 3.316625
f. 3.605551

To be assigned at teacher's discretion.

1. Which is closer to π, $\frac{22}{7}$ or 3.14? Use the fact that π is fairly close to 3.1415926536.

2. Convert $\frac{22}{7}$ to a decimal expansion. Find enough digits to convince yourself that the digits 142857 will repeat themselves in that order again and again.

3. Study the pattern in 1.0100100010000100001 . . . and decide if the number is rational or irrational.

4. If your school has a computer or calculator which can find square roots, compute each square root to as many places as possible. Each of the numbers listed is in fact irrational. You will be getting an approximation, no matter how many places you find.

a. $\sqrt{2}$ **b.** $\sqrt{3}$ **c.** $\sqrt{5}$
d. $\sqrt{7}$ **e.** $\sqrt{11}$ **f.** $\sqrt{13}$

Excursions in Mathematics:
An Irrational Number

Part I Answer with *yes* or *no*.

1. If $\frac{m}{n}$ is in simplest form and $m, n \in$ N, can both m and n be even numbers?

2. If 2 is a factor of m^2 and $m \in$ N, is 2 also a factor of m?

3. If $m^2 = 2q$ and $m, q \in$ N, is 2 a factor of m?

Part II Study the following argument which claims that if $\frac{m}{n} = \sqrt{2}$, $m, n \in$ N, then m and n are even.

An assumption!	**1.** $\frac{m}{n} = \sqrt{2}$ where $m, n \in$ N
Square both sides.	**2.** $\frac{m^2}{n^2} = 2$
From step **2**	**3.** $m^2 = 2n^2$
From step **3**	**4.** 2 is a factor of m.
From step **4**	**5.** $m = 2p$ for some $p \in$ N
From step **5**	**6.** m is an even number.
From steps **3** and **5**	**7.** $(2p)^2 = 2n^2$
From step **7**	**8.** $4p^2 = 2n^2$
From step **8**	**9.** $2p^2 = n^2$
From step **9**	**10.** 2 is a factor of n.
From step **10**	**11.** $n = 2q$ for some $q \in$ N
From step **11**	**12.** n is an even number.
From steps **6** and **12**	**13.** m and n are even numbers.

Part III Answer *yes* or *no*.

1. Can every positive rational number be expressed as $\frac{m}{n}$ where $m, n \in$ N and $\frac{m}{n}$ is in simplest form?

2. Is it possible that $\sqrt{2} = \frac{m}{n}$ where $m, n \in$ N and $\frac{m}{n}$ is in simplest form? (Look at Part **II**.)

3. Is $\sqrt{2}$ a positive rational number?

4. Since $\sqrt{2}$ is very close to 1.414214, is it likely that $\sqrt{2}$ is a negative rational number?

5. Is $\sqrt{2}$ most likely irrational?

Chapter Summary

1. Rational numbers may be thought of as the set of all numbers which can be represented by fractions. Fractions are written in the form $\frac{a}{b}$. The numerator, a, is an integer. The denominator, b, is a nonzero integer.

2. Fractions which name the same rational number are called equivalent fractions.

3. If $a, b, c \in Z$, $b \neq 0$, and $c \neq 0$, then

   i. $\dfrac{a}{b} = \dfrac{a \cdot c}{b \cdot c} = \dfrac{ac}{bc}$ ii. $\dfrac{a}{b} = \dfrac{a \div c}{b \div c}$

4. A fraction is in simplest form if the numerator and denominator have no common factor except 1 or -1.

5. If $a, b \in Z$, $b \neq 0$, then

   i. $\dfrac{a}{-b} = \dfrac{-a}{b} = -\dfrac{a}{b} = -\dfrac{-a}{-b}$ ii. $\dfrac{-a}{-b} = \dfrac{a}{b} = -\dfrac{-a}{b} = \dfrac{-a}{-b}$

6. To add or subtract fractions, the denominators must be the same. If $a, b, c \in Z$, and $b \neq 0$, then $\dfrac{a}{b} + \dfrac{c}{b} = \dfrac{a + c}{b}$.

7. The smallest common denominator for a set of fractions is called the Least Common Denominator (LCD).

8. The LCD may be found as a product. Each number or variable will appear in the product for the LCD the same number of times it appears at most in any single denominator expressed as a product of primes.

9. If $a, b, c, d \in Z$, $b \neq 0$, and $d \neq 0$, then $\dfrac{a}{b} \cdot \dfrac{c}{d} = \dfrac{ac}{bd}$.

10. If $a, b, c, d \in Z$, $b \neq 0$, $c \neq 0$, and $d \neq 0$, then $\dfrac{a}{b} \div \dfrac{c}{b} = \dfrac{a}{b} \cdot \dfrac{d}{c} = \dfrac{ad}{bc}$.

11. Two rational numbers are called reciprocals or multiplicative inverses of each other if their product is 1. Zero does not have a reciprocal.

12. Rational numbers have order. To see which of two rational numbers is larger, rename the numbers as equivalent fractions with the same denominator.

13. Between any two rational numbers, there are an infinite number of other rational numbers.

14. The decimal expansion of a rational number is a repeating or terminating decimal. A decimal expansion which is nonrepeating or nonterminating describes an irrational number.

15. The set of real numbers is the union of the set of rational numbers and the set of irrational numbers.

REVIEW EXERCISES

6-1

1. $A\left(\frac{-1}{5}\right)$, $B\left(1\frac{1}{5}\right)$,

$C\left(-1\frac{3}{5}\right)$, $D\left(2\frac{2}{5}\right)$,

$E\left(\frac{2}{5}\right)$, $F(-1)$

2. $\frac{1}{2}$ 3. $\frac{1}{3}$ 4. $\frac{1}{8}$ 5. $\frac{p}{2}$ 6. $\frac{2}{7}$ 7. $\frac{a}{2b}$

8. $\frac{d}{3f}$ 9. $\frac{y}{3x}$ 10. $x + y$

11. $\frac{1}{2}$ 12. $\frac{3x}{y}$ 13. $\frac{(4a^2 + 3b^2)}{3a^2 + 4b^2}$

14. $\frac{11}{14}$ 15. $\frac{1}{3}$ 16. $\frac{25}{24}$ 17. $\frac{-4}{3}$

18. $\frac{-3}{2}$ 19. $\frac{-3}{4}$ 20. $\frac{116}{21}$ 21. $\frac{65}{6}$

22. $\frac{285}{56}$ 23. $\frac{25}{21}$ 24. $\frac{143}{15}$ 25. $\frac{61}{16}$

26. $\frac{13}{6a}$ 27. $\frac{(4b^2 + 7a^2)}{a^2b^3}$

28. $\frac{(2 + x^2)}{x^2}$ 29. $\frac{(r^2 - 4s^2)}{4rs}$ 30. $\frac{23x}{8}$

6-3, 6-4

31. $\frac{-1}{3(x - y)}$ 32. $\frac{(2m^2 - 3p)}{6m^2p}$

33. $\frac{(12 - r)}{6r}$ 34. $\frac{(x^2 + y^2 + z^2)}{xyz}$

6-1

1. Write a fraction to name each point labeled with a letter. In each case, use the number of divisions between 0 and 1 as the denominator.

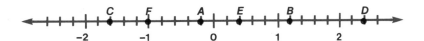

6-2 Write the simplest form of each fraction.

2. $\frac{7}{14}$

3. $\frac{8}{24}$

4. $\frac{4}{32}$

5. $\frac{2p^2}{4p}$

6. $\frac{10}{35}$

7. $\frac{5a}{10b}$

8. $\frac{7cde}{21cef}$

9. $\frac{14xy^2}{42x^2y}$

10. $\frac{3ax + 3ay}{3a}$

11. $\frac{4a + 4b}{8a + 8b}$

12. $\frac{4x^2 + 5x^2}{3xy}$

13. $\frac{4a^2 + 3b^2}{3a^2 + 4b^2}$

6-3, 6-4 Add or subtract.

14. $\frac{2}{7} + \frac{1}{2}$

15. $\frac{3}{4} - \frac{5}{12}$

16. $\frac{3}{8} - \frac{-2}{3}$

17. $-\frac{2}{3} - \frac{2}{3}$

18. $-\frac{5}{6} + \frac{-2}{3}$

19. $0 - \frac{-3}{-4}$

20. $7\frac{2}{3} + \left(-2\frac{1}{7}\right)$

21. $8\frac{1}{2} + 2\frac{1}{3}$

22. $6\frac{5}{7} - 1\frac{5}{8}$

23. $1\frac{1}{3} - \frac{1}{-7}$

24. $5\frac{1}{5} - \left(-4\frac{1}{3}\right)$

25. $3\frac{3}{4} + \left(-\frac{-1}{16}\right)$

26. $\frac{4}{3a} + \frac{5}{6a}$

27. $\frac{4}{a^2b} + \frac{7}{ab^3}$

28. $\frac{2}{x^2} + 1$

29. $\frac{r}{4s} - \frac{s}{r}$

30. $\frac{9x}{8} - \frac{3x}{4} + \frac{5x}{2}$

31. $\frac{2}{3x - 3y} - \frac{2}{2x - 2y}$

32. $\frac{m + p}{3mp} - \frac{2m + 3}{6m^2}$

33. $\frac{3}{r} + \frac{2r - 3}{6r} - \frac{r + 1}{2r}$

34. $\frac{z}{xy} + \frac{y}{xz} + \frac{x}{yz}$

6-5, 6-6

35. $\frac{16}{45}$ **36.** $\frac{1}{4}$ **37.** $\frac{64}{21}$ **38.** $\frac{-25}{8}$

39. $\frac{7}{6}$ **40.** $\frac{80}{33}$ **41.** $\frac{-4}{11}$ **42.** $\frac{3}{2}$ **43.** $\frac{ad}{bc}$

44. $\frac{9ab}{16}$ **45.** $\frac{c}{10}$ **46.** 0 **47.** $\frac{ac}{bd}$

48. $\frac{-4}{xy}$ **49.** $\frac{2a^2}{3x}$ **50.** $\frac{3(a+b)}{(a-b)}$

51. 7 **52.** $\frac{(a+2b)}{3(a+b)}$

53. $-a-2-b$ **54.** $\frac{-ab}{3}$

55. $\frac{13}{12}$ **56.** $\frac{-19}{6}$ **57.** $\frac{-9}{4}$ **58.** $\frac{-39}{4}$

59. $\frac{1}{6}$ **60.** $\frac{8}{3}$ **61.** $\frac{-20}{9}$ **62.** $\frac{-65}{4}$

63. Answers may vary.
$\frac{3}{8}, \frac{5}{12}, \frac{11}{24}$

64. Answers may vary.
$1\frac{3}{4}, 1\frac{5}{6}, 1\frac{11}{12}$

65. Answers may vary.
$\frac{13}{22}, \frac{33}{80}, \frac{67}{160}$

66. Answers may vary.

67. Answers may vary.
$\frac{13}{76}, \frac{7}{48}, \frac{5}{32}$ **68.** $\frac{1}{2}, \frac{2}{5}, \frac{1}{4}$ **69.** $\frac{3}{4}, \frac{5}{7}, \frac{2}{3}$

70. $1\frac{15}{16}, 1\frac{3}{4}, 1\frac{7}{10}$

Multiply or divide.

35. $\frac{2}{5} \cdot \frac{8}{9}$ **36.** $\frac{-2}{3} \cdot \frac{-3}{8}$ **37.** $1\frac{1}{3} \cdot 2\frac{2}{7}$

38. $-2\frac{1}{2} \cdot 1\frac{1}{4}$ **39.** $\frac{7}{8} \div \frac{3}{4}$ **40.** $5\frac{1}{3} \div 2\frac{1}{5}$

41. $-1 \div 2\frac{3}{4}$ **42.** $\frac{-5}{7} \div \frac{10}{-21}$ **43.** $\frac{a}{b} \div \frac{c}{d}$

44. $\frac{3a^2}{4b} \cdot \frac{3b^2}{4a}$ **45.** $\left(-\frac{1}{5c}\right)\left(\frac{-c^2}{2}\right)$ **46.** $\frac{x}{4} \cdot \frac{0}{-4}$

47. $\frac{a}{b} \cdot \frac{c}{d}$ **48.** $\frac{-3}{x^2} \div \frac{3xy}{4}$ **49.** $\frac{-4ax}{3by} \div \frac{-2x^2}{aby}$

50. $\frac{a-b}{3} \div \frac{(a-b)^2}{9(a+b)}$

Simplify each expression.

51. $\frac{7x - 7y}{(x - y)}$ **52.** $\frac{5a + 10b}{15(a + b)}$

53. $\frac{a^2b + 2ab + b^2a}{-ab}$ **54.** $\frac{1}{3}(5ab - 6ab)$

Evaluate each expression if $p = \frac{1}{3}$, $q = \frac{3}{4}$, $r = -5$, and $s = 2$.

55. $p + q$ **56.** $p + r + qs$ **57.** $q(r + s)$
58. $pq + rs$ **59.** $p \div s$ **60.** $s \div q$
61. $pr \div q$ **62.** $rq \div p + r$

6-8

Find three rational numbers between each pair of fractions.

63. $\frac{1}{3}; \frac{1}{2}$ **64.** $1\frac{2}{3}; 2$ **65.** $\frac{2}{5}; \frac{5}{8}$ **66.** $0; \frac{1}{7}$ **67.** $\frac{1}{6}; \frac{1}{8}$

Arrange each group of fractions in decreasing order.

68. $\frac{1}{4}, \frac{2}{5}, \frac{1}{2}$ **69.** $\frac{2}{3}, \frac{5}{7}, \frac{3}{4}$ **70.** $1\frac{3}{4}, 1\frac{13}{16}, 1\frac{7}{10}$

7-1 *Equivalent Equations*

OBJECTIVE:

To find an equivalent equation using $a = b \Leftrightarrow a + c = b + c$.

Equations which have the same solution set are called **equivalent equations.** If x is a variable on W, then the three equations in the following table are equivalent.

Equation	Solution Set
$x + 5 = 9$	$\{4\}$
$2x - 1 = 7$	$\{4\}$
$x = 4$	$\{4\}$

Stress that for open sentences the symbol $\Leftrightarrow$ means *has the same solution set as.*

The symbol $\Leftrightarrow$ means *is equivalent to*. By using this symbol, equivalent equations may be shown.

EXAMPLES

1. $x + 5 = 9 \Leftrightarrow x = 4$
2. $2x + 3 = 9 \Leftrightarrow 2x = 6$
$\Leftrightarrow x = 3$

The solution set for $x = 3$ is easier to name than the solution set for $2x + 3 = 9$. Equivalent equations which are easily solved may be found by using certain rules. One such rule concerns addition.

This rule for addition may be used with both positive and negative numbers.

EXAMPLE

Find the solution set of $x + 7 = 3$, if $x \in Z$.

Students with a flair for logic may read the symbol $\Leftrightarrow$ as *if and only if*. However, most students will be more comfortable with reading $\Leftrightarrow$ as *has the same solution set as.*

Add -7 to both sides. $\quad x + 7 = 3 \Leftrightarrow x + 7 + (-7) = 3 + (-7)$
Simplify both sides. $\qquad\qquad\qquad\quad \Leftrightarrow \qquad\qquad x = -4$

The solution set of $x = -4$ is $\{-4\}$. Since $x = -4$ and $x + 7 = 3$ are equivalent equations, the solution set of $x + 7 = 3$ is $\{-4\}$.

Each solution should be checked. To *check a solution,* replace the variable in the original equation by the solution. The symbol $\stackrel{?}{=}$ is used to show that you may be unsure of equality when using the solution. If a true statement results, then the solution is correct for the equation.

$$\text{Check: } x + 7 = 3$$
$$-4 + 7 \stackrel{?}{=} 3$$
$$3 = 3$$

Subtracting a number is the same as adding its negative. Therefore, the rule for addition also says the following.

Stress that this statement really says nothing new, since subtracting *a* is the same as adding $(-a)$.

EXAMPLE

Solve $x + 5 = 9$, if $x \in Z$.

Using addition:
$$x + 5 = 9 \Leftrightarrow x + 5 + (-5) = 9 + (-5)$$
$$\Leftrightarrow \qquad\qquad x = 4$$

Using subtraction:
$$x + 5 = 9 \Leftrightarrow x + 5 - 5 = 9 - 5$$
$$\Leftrightarrow \qquad\qquad x = 4$$

EXERCISES

1. a. Yes b. Yes c. Yes
2. a. Yes b. Yes 3. {6} They are
the same. 4. {10} They are the
same. 5. $x = 11$ 6. $x = 12$
7. $y = -3$ 8. $z = -7$ 9. $p = 7$
10. $q = 54$ 11. $t = 10$
12. $x = 20$ 13. $x = -4$
14. {1} 15. $\left\{\frac{1}{4}\right\}$ 16. $\left\{\frac{3}{4}\right\}$
17. $\left\{-\frac{1}{4}\right\}$ 18. $\left\{\frac{1}{4}\right\}$ 19. $\left\{\frac{1}{4}\right\}$
20. $\left\{\frac{3}{2}\right\}$ 21. $\left\{\frac{1}{4}\right\}$ 22. {−1}

1. **a.** Is $5 + 3 = 8$ a true statement?

   b. Is $(5 + 3) + 4 = 8 + 4$ a true statement?

   c. Is $(5 + 3) + (-12) = 8 + (-12)$ a true statement?

2. **a.** Is $\dfrac{1}{2} + \dfrac{1}{4} = \dfrac{3}{4}$ a true statement?

   b. Add $-\dfrac{1}{4}$ to both sides in Part **a** and simplify. Is the result a true statement?

3. Add -3 to both sides of $x + 3 = 9$. Simplify both sides of the new equation and write its solution set. Compare this with the solution set for the first equation.

4. Add 3 to both sides of $x - 3 = 7$. Simplify both sides of the new equation and write its solution set. Compare this with the solution set for the first equation.

Solve each equation. The variables are on Z. Check each solution.

5. $x + 4 = 15$	6. $x + 7 = 19$	7. $y + 4 = 1$
8. $z + 5 = -2$	9. $6 + p = 13$	10. $21 + q = 75$
11. $t + (-2) = 8$	12. $x + (-7) = 13$	13. $x + (-5) = -9$

Find the solution set of each equation. The variables are on Q. Check each solution.

14. $x + \dfrac{1}{2} = \dfrac{3}{2}$ 15. $y + \dfrac{1}{2} = \dfrac{3}{4}$ 16. $t + \left(-\dfrac{1}{2}\right) = \dfrac{1}{4}$

17. $z + \dfrac{1}{2} = \dfrac{1}{4}$ 18. $x - \dfrac{1}{2} = \dfrac{-1}{4}$ 19. $x - \dfrac{3}{8} = -\dfrac{1}{8}$

20. $0 = \dfrac{3}{2} - x$ 21. $\dfrac{3}{4} = 1 - x$ 22. $\dfrac{3}{2} = \dfrac{1}{2} - x$

Insist that students show each step using the symbol $\Leftrightarrow$ correctly, even if they think that the problems are not hard enough to deserve such methods.

7-2

Finding Equivalent Equations

OBJECTIVE:
To find an equivalent equation using $a = b \Leftrightarrow ac = bc$, $c \neq 0$.

In an equation, a variable may occur on both sides of the equal sign. For example, in $3x + 1 = x + 7$ and $x + 3 = 2x - 2$ the variable x occurs on both sides of the equal sign. To solve such equations, the variables are collected on one side, usually the left, and the constants on the other side of the equal sign. The rule for adding the same number to both sides of an equation may be used.

EXAMPLE

Discuss this example in class for slow students. Have them examine the goals behind each step.

Solve $5x - 2 = 4x + 7$, if $x \in Z$.

Add 2 to both sides. $\quad 5x - 2 = 4x + 7 \Leftrightarrow 5x - 2 + 2 = 4x + 7 + 2$

Simplify both sides. $\qquad\qquad\qquad \Leftrightarrow \qquad\qquad 5x = 4x + 9$

Add $(-4x)$ to both sides. $\qquad \Leftrightarrow 5x + (-4x) = 4x + 9 + (-4x)$

$\qquad\qquad\qquad\qquad\qquad\qquad \Leftrightarrow \qquad\qquad\quad x = 9$

The solution set of $5x - 2 = 4x + 7$ is $\{9\}$.

$$\text{Check:} \quad 5x - 2 = 4x + 7$$
$$(5 \cdot 9) - 2 \overset{?}{=} (4 \cdot 9) + 7$$
$$45 - 2 \overset{?}{=} 36 + 7$$
$$43 = 43$$

Another rule which can be used to find equivalent equations involves multiplication.

If both sides of an equation are multiplied by the same *nonzero* number, the resulting equation is equivalent to the first.

EXAMPLES

Stress that *in general ax = c* is followed by the step $a^{-1}(ax) = a^{-1} \cdot c$ where a and c are numerals and x is a variable.

1. Find the solution set of $3x = 7$, if $x \in Q$.

Multiply both sides by $\frac{1}{3}$. $\quad 3x = 7 \Leftrightarrow \frac{1}{3} \cdot 3x = \frac{1}{3} \cdot 7$

Simplify both sides. $\qquad\qquad\qquad \Leftrightarrow \qquad x = \frac{7}{3}$

The solution set of $x = \frac{7}{3}$ is $\left\{\frac{7}{3}\right\}$. Since $x = \frac{7}{3}$ and $3x = 7$ are equivalent equations, $\left\{\frac{7}{3}\right\}$ is the solution set of $3x = 7$.

$$\text{Check:} \quad 3x = 7$$
$$3 \cdot \frac{7}{3} \overset{?}{=} 7$$
$$7 = 7$$

2. Solve $-\frac{3}{8}x = 12$, if $x \in Q$.

$$-\frac{3}{8}x = 12 \Leftrightarrow -\frac{8}{3} \cdot \left(-\frac{3}{8}x\right) = -\frac{8}{3} \cdot 12$$
$$\Leftrightarrow \qquad\qquad x = -32$$

Dividing by a number is the same as multiplying by its reciprocal. Therefore, the rule for multiplication also says the following.

If both sides of an equation are divided by the same nonzero number, the resulting equation is equivalent to the first.

EXAMPLE

Solve $3x = 12$, if $x \in Q$.

Using multiplication:

$$3x = 12 \Leftrightarrow \frac{1}{3} \cdot 3x = \frac{1}{3} \cdot 12$$
$$\Leftrightarrow \quad x = 4$$

Using division:

$$3x = 12 \Leftrightarrow \frac{3x}{3} = \frac{12}{3}$$
$$\Leftrightarrow \quad x = 4$$

EXERCISES

See Section notes in T.G. regarding Exercises 1-4.

1. a. Yes b. Yes c. Yes d. Yes
2. a. Yes b. Yes 3. b. $\{-6\}$
c. Yes 4. b. $\left\{\frac{15}{2}\right\}$ c. Yes

1. **a.** Is $3 \cdot 4 = 12$ a true statement?
   b. Is $(3 \cdot 4) \cdot 2 = 12 \cdot 2$ a true statement?
   c. Is $(3 \cdot 4) \cdot \frac{1}{6} = 12 \cdot \frac{1}{6}$ a true statement?
   d. Is $(3 \cdot 4) \cdot (-2) = 12 \cdot (-2)$ a true statement?

2. **a.** Is $3 \cdot 7 = 21$ a true statement?
   b. Multiply both sides of the statement in Part **a** by $\frac{1}{3}$, the reciprocal of 3.
   c. Is the statement in Part **b** true?

3. **a.** Multiply both sides of $-3x = 18$ by $-\frac{1}{3}$, the reciprocal of -3.
   b. Simplify both sides of the new equation and write its solution set.
   c. Is this the solution set of the first equation?

4. **a.** Multiply both sides of $\frac{2}{3}x = 5$ by $\frac{3}{2}$, the reciprocal of $\frac{2}{3}$.
   b. Simplify both sides of the new equation and write its solution set.
   c. Is this the solution set of the first equation?

189

5. $\frac{1}{2}$ 6. $\frac{8}{5}$ 7. $-\frac{1}{13}$ 8. $-\frac{8}{5}$

9. $-\frac{1}{4}$ 10. 1 11. $-\frac{5}{6}$

12. $\frac{5}{4}$ 13. $\frac{4}{3}$ 14. {3} 15. {1}

16. {3} 17. {0} 18. $\left\{-1\frac{3}{4}\right\}$

19. $\left\{5\frac{1}{2}\right\}$ 20. {5} 21. $\left\{\frac{2}{3}\right\}$

22. $\left\{-\frac{3}{7}\right\}$ 23. $\left\{\frac{1}{4}\right\}$ 24. $\left\{\frac{2}{9}\right\}$

25. $\left\{\frac{1}{12}\right\}$ 26. {3} 27. {12}

28. {4} 29. {−10} 30. {20}

31. {21} 32. {2} 33. {6} 34. {3}

35. {−9} 36. {3}

Insist that students show steps in the solution using the symbol ⟺ correctly, even if they complain that the problems are not hard enough to deserve such methods.

Write the reciprocal, or multiplicative inverse, of each number.

5. 2   **6.** $\frac{5}{8}$ **7.** −13

8. $-\frac{5}{8}$ **9.** −4   **10.** 1

11. $\frac{-6}{5}$ **12.** $\frac{4}{5}$ **13.** $\frac{3}{4}$

Find the solution set of each equation. The variables are on Q. Check each solution.

14. $3m = 3 + 2m$ **15.** $2y + 7 = 8 + y$

16. $\frac{1}{2}x = 3 - \frac{1}{2}x$ **17.** $3x - \frac{1}{2} = 4x - \frac{1}{2}$

18. $\frac{3}{4}x + 2 = \frac{1}{4} - \frac{1}{4}x$ **19.** $6z - 4 = 1\frac{1}{2} + 5z$

20. $2x = 10$ **21.** $3x = 2$

22. $7x = -3$ **23.** $2x = \frac{1}{2}$

24. $3x = \frac{2}{3}$ **25.** $9x = \frac{3}{4}$

26. $\frac{1}{2}x = \frac{3}{2}$ **27.** $\frac{2}{3}x = 8$

28. $-\frac{1}{4}x = -1$ **29.** $-\frac{4}{5}x = 8$

30. $\frac{x}{4} = 5$ **31.** $\frac{x}{-3} = -7$

32. $\frac{x}{3} - \frac{1}{2} = \frac{x}{12}$ **33.** $\frac{1}{3}x - \frac{5}{6} = \frac{7}{6}$

34. $\frac{1}{2} + \frac{x}{5} = \frac{11}{10}$ **35.** $\frac{x}{2} = \frac{5x}{6} + 3$

36. $\frac{2x}{3} + \frac{3}{4} = 3 - \frac{x}{12}$

OBJECTIVE:
To name the solution set of a given linear equation in one variable.

7-3

Solving
Equations

To find the simplest equation equivalent to a given equation, it often is necessary to use the rule for addition *and* the rule for multiplication.

EXAMPLE

It may be helpful to some students if this same equation is solved another way in class. That is, use the steps, "Subtract $7x$ from both sides," and "Divide both sides by 4," in solving the equation.

Solve $3x - 4 = 32 + 7x$, if $x \in Q$.

Add 4 to		$3x - 4 = 32 + 7x$
both sides.	$\Leftrightarrow$	$3x - 4 + 4 = 32 + 7x + 4$
Simplify both sides.	$\Leftrightarrow$	$3x = 36 + 7x$
Add $-7x$ to both sides.	$\Leftrightarrow$	$3x + (-7x) = 36 + 7x + (-7x)$
Simplify both sides.	$\Leftrightarrow$	$-4x = 36$

Multiply both sides by $-\dfrac{1}{4}$. $\Leftrightarrow \left(-\dfrac{1}{4}\right) \cdot (-4x) = \left(-\dfrac{1}{4}\right) \cdot 36$

Simplify both sides. $\Leftrightarrow \qquad x = -9$

$$\begin{aligned}\text{Check:} \quad 3x - 4 &= 32 + 7x \\ 3 \cdot (-9) - 4 &\stackrel{?}{=} 32 + 7 \cdot (-9) \\ -27 - 4 &\stackrel{?}{=} 32 - 63 \\ -31 &= -31 \end{aligned}$$

As you gain experience, you may begin to do several steps at one time. You also may do some steps mentally. The work for the solution of $3x - 4 = 32 + 7x$ could be shortened.

$$\begin{aligned} 3x - 4 = 32 + 7x &\Leftrightarrow 3x - 7x = 32 + 4 \\ &\Leftrightarrow \quad -4x = 36 \\ &\Leftrightarrow \qquad x = -9 \end{aligned}$$

Study this example and justify each step. Check the given solution.

EXAMPLE

The example will make more sense for some students if they are asked to state what the goal is at each step, and how it is achieved.

Solve $2(x + 3) = 8 - 3(x - 4)$, if $x \in Q$.

$$\begin{aligned} 2(x + 3) = 8 - 3(x - 4) &\Leftrightarrow 2x + 6 = 8 - 3x + 12 \\ &\Leftrightarrow 2x + 6 = 20 - 3x \\ &\Leftrightarrow 2x + 3x = 20 - 6 \\ &\Leftrightarrow \qquad 5x = 14 \\ &\Leftrightarrow \qquad x = \dfrac{14}{5} \end{aligned}$$

EXERCISES

1. $x = 3$ 2. $y = \frac{1}{2}$ 3. $m = 7$

4. $t = 1$ 5. $m = 7$ 6. $z = \frac{7}{5}$

7. $n = -4$ 8. $x = \frac{8}{3}$ 9. $x = -2$

10. $x = 0$ 11. $y = \frac{5}{2}$ 12. $x = -1$

13. $t = \frac{5}{8}$ 14. $x = \frac{1}{3}$ 15. $x = 39$

Solve each equation. The variables are on Q. Check each solution.

1. $2x + 3 = 9$ **2.** $2y + 5 = 6$ **3.** $3m + 4 = 25$

4. $5t - 1 = 4$ **5.** $2m - 3 = 11$ **6.** $5z - 4 = 3$

7. $4n + 5 = -11$ **8.** $6 + 3x = 14$ **9.** $3x + 2 = -4$

10. $5x - 3 = -3$ **11.** $0 = 5 - 2y$ **12.** $7 = 4 - 3x$

13. $2t + \dfrac{1}{2} = \dfrac{3}{4}$ **14.** $5x - \dfrac{5}{3} = 0$ **15.** $\dfrac{1}{3}x + 2 = 15$

16. $4x + 3 = 2x + 15$
18. $4p + 12 = 48 - 2p$
20. $4x - 8 = 6x + 12$
22. $-7z = 3z - 30$
24. $2x + 9 = 5x + 7$

17. $7y - 3 = 3y + 17$
19. $6m - 2 = 2m - 8$
21. $3t + 6 = 5t + 7$
23. $9t + 5 = 15t - 1$

Find the solution set of each equation. The variables are on Q. Check each solution.

25. $3x + 4 = 2(x + 11)$
27. $10(y - 6) = -5y$
29. $3(5t - 3) = 5(2t + 1)$
31. $5(6 - p) + 1 = p + 1$
33. $5x + 17(2 + 3x) = 16(1 + 4x)$
35. $4 - (x - 3) = 6 - 4x$
37. $3(5 - x) = 4(3x + 2) + 27$
38. $3(2x - 3) - 2(1 - x) - (x + 1) = 0$

26. $2x = 3(5 - x)$
28. $5(z - 4) = 3(8 - z)$
30. $3x - 2 = 6 - (8 + 3x)$
32. $2(m + 3) - 1 = 8 + 3m$
34. $5t - 9(t - 1) = 3t + 5$
36. $4(13 - z) = 9z - (z - 7)$

7-4
Equivalent Inequations

Inequations are called *equivalent inequations* if they have the same solution set. If $x \in$ R, then $x + 5 < 9$, $3x + 1 < 2x + 5$, and $x < 4$ are equivalent inequations. Each of these inequations has as its solution set all real numbers less than 4.

The solution set for $x < 4$ is easier to see than the solution set for $3x + 1 < 2x + 5$. Just as for equations, a set of rules may be used for changing inequations to equivalent inequations.

If the same number is added to both sides of an inequation, the resulting inequation is equivalent to the first.

This rule for addition may be used with both positive and negative numbers.

EXAMPLES

1. $x + 3 < 8 \iff x + 3 + (-3) < 8 + (-3)$
$\iff \qquad x < 5$
2. $3x > 2x - 4 \iff 3x + (-2x) > 2x - 4 + (-2x)$
$\iff \qquad x > -4$

Since subtracting a number is the same as adding its negative, the addition rule gives the following subtraction rule.

> **If the same number is subtracted from both sides of an inequation, the resulting inequation is equivalent to the first.**

EXAMPLE

For students who like to translate the symbol ⇔ as *if and only if*, assure them that it is still permissible.

Find the solution set for $x + 5 < 9$, if $x \in Z$.

Using addition:
$$x + 5 < 9 \Leftrightarrow x + 5 + (-5) < 9 + (-5)$$
$$\Leftrightarrow \qquad x < 4$$
The solution set is $\{\ldots, -1, 0, 1, 2, 3\}$.

Using subtraction:
$$x + 5 < 9 \Leftrightarrow x + 5 - 5 < 9 - 5$$
$$\Leftrightarrow \qquad x < 4$$
The solution set is $\{\ldots, -1, 0, 1, 2, 3\}$.

EXERCISES

See section notes in T.G. regarding Exercises 1-4.

1. a. Yes **b.** Yes **c.** Yes

d.

2. a. Yes **b.** Yes **3. a.** $\{-4, -3, -2, -1, 0, 1, 2\}$ **b.** $\{-4, -3, -2, -1, 0, 1, 2\}$ **c.** They are the same.

1. a. Is $1 < 7$ a true statement?

b. Is $1 + 2 < 7 + 2$ a true statement?

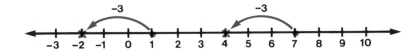

c. Is $1 + (-3) < 7 + (-3)$ a true statement?
d. How are the answers to Parts **a, b,** and **c** shown on the number line?

2. a. Is $5 + 3 > 6$ a true statement?
b. Is $(5 + 3) + (-3) > 6 + (-3)$ a true statement?

In Exercises **3** and **4,** $x \in \{-4, -3, -2, -1, 0, 1, 2, \ldots, 10\}$.
3. a. What is the solution set of $x + 3 < 6$?
b. Add -3 to both sides of the inequation in Part **a.** Simplify both sides of the new inequation and write its solution set.
c. Compare the solution set from Parts **a** and **b.**

4. a. What is the solution set of $x - 2 > 3$?

  b. Add 2 to both sides of the inequation in Part **a.** Simplify the new inequation and write its solution set.

  c. Compare the solution sets from Parts **a** and **b.**

Find the simplest equivalent inequation for each inequation. The variables are on R.

5. $x + 5 > 8$ **6.** $y + 3 < 7$ **7.** $x + 2 > -1$
8. $7 + p < 12$ **9.** $9 + t > 4$ **10.** $6 + y < 20$
11. $m - 2 < 5$ **12.** $x - 4 > 10$ **13.** $v - 8 < -3$
14. $9 < 3 - x$ **15.** $15 > 5 - y$ **16.** $-2 > 10 - x$
17. $2y < y + 12$ **18.** $4x > 3x + 15$ **19.** $3m > 2m - 1$
20. $3 + x > 3$ **21.** $3x + 1 > 2x + 5$ **22.** $5y - 4 < 4y - 4$

7-5 Set-Builder Notation

OBJECTIVE:

To name the solution set using set-builder notation when given a simple linear inequation in one variable.

The phrase, "which is $x < 5$," may also be read as "which is equivalent to $x < 5$."

Emphasize that even by using dots the listing method cannot describe the set in the paragraph.

When variables are on sets, such as Z or Q, it often is impossible to list all the members of the solution set of an inequation. The solution set can be described in several ways. For example, the solution set for $x + 3 < 8$, $x \in Z$, which is $x < 5$, can be described in three different ways.

1. The solution set can be written $\{\ldots, -1, 0, 1, 2, 3, 4\}$. Remember that the three dots mean that you continue endlessly listing negative integers.
2. You could say in words that the solution set is the set of all integers less than 5.
3. A shorter way to give such solution sets is by **set-builder notation,** $\{x \mid x < 5, x \in Z\}$. This is read *the set of all x such that x is less than 5 and x is an element of Z.*

It is impossible to write the complete solution set for $x + 3 < 8$, $x \in Q$ using the first of these three methods. For variables on Q or R, set-builder notation is the only way to write the solution set of an inequation.

$\{$	x	$\mid$	$x > 2,$	$x \in Q\}$
the set	of all x	such that	x is greater than 2	and x is an element of the set of rational numbers

EXAMPLES

1. $\{x|x < 5, x \in W\} = \{0, 1, 2, 3, 4\}$

2. $\{y|y \geq 3, y \in Z\} = \{3, 4, 5, 6, \ldots\}$

3. Find the solution set of $7x - 2 > 6x + 8$, if $x \in Q$.

$$7x - 2 > 6x + 8 \Leftrightarrow 7x - 6x > 8 + 2$$
$$\Leftrightarrow \quad\quad x > 10$$

The solution set is $\{x|x > 10, x \in Q\}$.

In Example **3** it would take forever to check all possible solutions given by $\{x|x > 10, x \in Q\}$. The best you can do is to check a finite number of the solutions. Since $14 > 10$ and $14 \in Q$, 14 is a solution.

Check: $7x - 2 > 6x + 8$

$$7 \cdot 14 - 2 \overset{?}{>} 6 \cdot 14 + 8$$
$$98 - 2 \overset{?}{>} 84 + 8$$
$$96 > 92 \quad \text{True statement}$$

It is a good idea to include the check of a negative number when such numbers are included in the solution set.

EXERCISES

1. $\{4, 5, 6\}$ **2.** $\{2, 4\}$ **3.** $\{7, 9, 11\}$
4. $\{4\}$ **5.** $\{2, 4, 6, 8\}$ **6.** $\{3, 5, 7, 11, 13\}$ **7.** $\{y \mid y < 26, y \in Q\}$

If $A = \{1, 2, 3, 4, 5, 6\}$, $B = \{2, 4, 6, 8, 10\}$, and $C = \{3, 5, 7, 9, 11, 13, 15\}$, list the elements in each set.

1. $\{x|x > 3, x \in A\}$

2. $\{x|x < 6, x \in B\}$

3. $\{y|5 < y < 13, y \in C\}$

4. $\{z|z + 3 = 7, z \in A\}$

5. $\{t|t + 1 < 10, t \in B\}$

6. $\{p|p \text{ is prime}, p \in C\}$

Insist that each solution set be written in one of the forms $\{v \mid v < c, v \in Q\}$ or $\{v \mid v > c, v \in Q\}$ where v is the variable and c is a specified rational number.

Use set-builder notation to write the solution set of each inequation. The variables are on Q.

7. $y + 4 < 30$

8. $p + 12 < 9$

9. $x + 10 > -32$

10. $24 + z > 15$

11. $m - 14 > 25$

12. $t - 4 < 4$

13. $t + 4 > 4$

14. $y + \dfrac{1}{2} < \dfrac{5}{2}$

15. $p - \dfrac{4}{5} > \dfrac{3}{5}$

16. $5x > 4x + 9$

17. $2x + 5 > x + 12$

18. $4y + 9 < 3y - 1$

19. $2m - \dfrac{3}{2} < m - \dfrac{1}{2}$

20. $3n - 1 < 8 + 2n$

21. $2x + 7 > 1 + x$

22. $\dfrac{1}{2}t + 3 < 2 - \dfrac{1}{2}t$

8. $\{p \mid p < -3, p \in Q\}$ **9.** $\{x \mid x > -42, x \in Q\}$ **10.** $\{z \mid z > -9, z \in Q\}$ **11.** $\{m \mid m > 39, m \in Q\}$ **12.** $\{t \mid t < 8, t \in Q\}$ **13.** $\{t \mid t < 0, t \in Q\}$ **14.** $\{y \mid y < 2, y \in Q\}$ **15.** $\{p \mid p > \frac{7}{5}, p \in Q\}$ **16.** $\{x \mid x > 9, x \in Q\}$ **17.** $\{x \mid x > 7, x \in Q\}$ **18.** $\{y \mid y < -10, y \in Q\}$ **19.** $\{m \mid m < 1, m \in Q\}$ **20.** $\{n \mid n < 9, n \in Q\}$ **21.** $\{x \mid x > -6, x \in Q\}$ **22.** $\{t \mid t < -1, t \in Q\}$

MATHEMATICS AND RECREATION

RACETRACK

Will you be a skilled driver? It's possible. One thing you will need to do is control speed on corners. Racetrack is a game that simulates actual driving conditions and requires that you develop a good strategy for acceleration and deceleration on corners.

Racetrack is played by two people and requires only graph paper and different-colored pencils. Any shape racecourse may be drawn on the graph paper, but the challenge comes if there are a few sharp corners. Players move their cars in turn following these rules:

1. A segment joining two successive positions of a car must be on the track. If one player's car leaves the track, the other player wins.

2. No two cars may occupy the same position at the same time. However, a player may move to a point after his opponent has left it.

3. If a player's last move was v units vertically and h units horizontally, then the next horizontal and vertical moves H and V must be such that $|V - v| \leq 1$ and $|H - h| \leq 1$.

In the sample game shown, what mistakes in strategy did the losing player make?

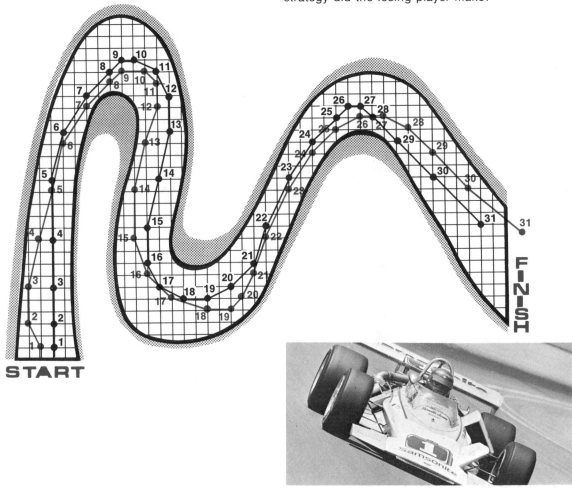

Imagine International

7-6
Finding Equivalent Inequations

OBJECTIVES:

1. To find an equivalent inequation using $a \leq b \Leftrightarrow ac < bc$ for $c > 0$.
2. To find an equivalent inequation using $a < b \Leftrightarrow ac > bc$ for $c < 0$.

You can see on the number line that $3 < 5$. If both sides of this inequality are multiplied by 2, another true statement, $6 < 10$, results.

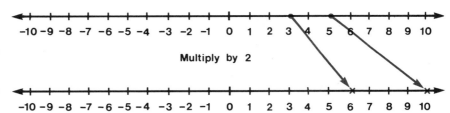

Multiply by 2

It may be helpful to consider more cases. For example, examine $a < b$ where $a < 0$, and $b > 0$, and also $a < b$ where $a < b < 0$.

If both sides of an inequation are multiplied by the same *positive* number, the resulting inequation is equivalent to the first.

EXAMPLES

Solve each inequation, if $x \in Z$.

1. Multiply both sides by $\frac{1}{6}$. $6x < 24 \Leftrightarrow \frac{1}{6} \cdot 6x < \frac{1}{6} \cdot 24$

$$\Leftrightarrow \quad x < 4$$

The solution set is $\{x \mid x < 4, x \in Z\}$.

2. Multiply both sides by 3. $\frac{x}{3} \geq 2 \Leftrightarrow 3 \cdot \frac{x}{3} \geq 3 \cdot 2$

$$\Leftrightarrow \quad x \geq 6$$

The solution set is $\{x \mid x \geq 6, x \in Z\}$.

If both sides of the inequality $3 < 5$ are multiplied by -2, a *false* statement, $-6 < -10$, results. The statement $-6 > -10$, however, is true.

It may be helpful to consider more cases for this diagram also.

Multiply by -2

> **If both sides of an inequation are multiplied by the same *negative* number *and* if the inequality symbol is reversed, the resulting inequation is equivalent to the first.**

EXAMPLES

Solve each inequation, if $x \in Q$.

1. $-4x < 20 \Leftrightarrow -\dfrac{1}{4} \cdot (-4x) > -\dfrac{1}{4} \cdot 20$ Note: The inequality symbol is reversed *when* $-4x < 20$ is

$\Leftrightarrow \qquad\qquad x > -5$ multiplied by $-\dfrac{1}{4}$.

The solution set is $\{x \mid x > -5, x \in Q\}$.

2. $-2x \geq -8 \Leftrightarrow -\dfrac{1}{2} \cdot (-2x) \leq -\dfrac{1}{2} \cdot (-8)$

$\Leftrightarrow \qquad\qquad x \leq 4$

The solution set is $\{x \mid x \leq 4, x \in Q\}$.

Dividing by a number is the same as multiplying by its reciprocal. Therefore, the rules for multiplication give the following rules for division.

> **If both sides of an inequation are divided by the same *positive* number, the resulting inequation is equivalent to the first.**

> **If both sides of an inequation are divided by the same *negative* number *and* if the inequality symbol is reversed, the resulting inequation is equivalent to the first.**

EXAMPLE

Find the solution set for $-3x < 12$, if $x \in Q$.

Using multiplication:

$$-3x < 12 \Leftrightarrow \left(-\dfrac{1}{3}\right) \cdot (-3x) > \left(-\dfrac{1}{3}\right) \cdot 12$$

$$\Leftrightarrow \qquad\qquad x > -4$$

The solution set is $\{x \mid x > -4, x \in Q\}$.

Using division:

$$-3x < 12 \Leftrightarrow \frac{-3x}{-3} > \frac{12}{-3}$$

$$\Leftrightarrow \quad x > -4$$

The solution set is $\{x \mid x > -4, x \in Q\}$.

EXERCISES

1. T 2. T 3. T 4. T 5. T 6. T
7. F 8. F 9. T 10. F 11. F
12. T 13. F 14. F 15. T 16. T
17. Answers will vary.
18. a. Yes b. No c. Yes
19. Answers will vary.
20. a. Yes b. No c. Yes
21. $x > 2$ 22. $y \leq 6$ 23. $z < 1$
24. $x > 0$ 25. $t \leq 5$ 26. $x > 4$

Write true (T) or false (F) for each statement.

1. $12 < 18$ **2.** $12 > 8$

3. $12 \cdot 2 < 18 \cdot 2$ **4.** $12 \cdot 3 > 8 \cdot 3$

5. $12 \cdot \frac{1}{6} < 18 \cdot \frac{1}{6}$ **6.** $12 \cdot \frac{1}{4} > 8 \cdot \frac{1}{4}$

7. $12 \cdot 0 < 18 \cdot 0$ **8.** $12 \cdot 0 > 8 \cdot 0$

9. $12 \cdot (-1) \geq 18 \cdot (-1)$ **10.** $12 \cdot (-1) \geq 8 \cdot (-1)$

11. $12 \cdot (-1) \leq 18 \cdot (-1)$ **12.** $12 \cdot (-1) \leq 8 \cdot (-1)$

13. $12 \cdot \left(-\frac{1}{3}\right) \leq 18 \cdot \left(-\frac{1}{3}\right)$ **14.** $12 \cdot \left(-\frac{1}{4}\right) \geq 8 \cdot \left(-\frac{1}{4}\right)$

15. $12 \cdot \left(-\frac{1}{3}\right) \geq 18 \cdot \left(-\frac{1}{3}\right)$ **16.** $12 \cdot \left(-\frac{1}{4}\right) \leq 8 \cdot \left(-\frac{1}{4}\right)$

17. Write two solutions of $x > 4$, if $x \in Q$.

18. Do the solutions from Exercise **17** belong to the solution set for each of these inequations?
     a. $2x > 8$ Multiplying both sides of $x > 4$ by 2
     b. $-x > -4$ Multiplying both sides of $x > 4$ by -1
     c. $-x < -4$ Multiplying both sides of $x > 4$ by -1 and reversing the inequality symbol

19. Write two solutions of $x \leq -3$, if $x \in Q$.

20. Do the solutions from Exercise **19** belong to the solution set for each of these inequations?
     a. $2x \leq -6$ Multiplying both sides of $x < -3$ by 2
     b. $-x \leq 3$ Multiplying both sides of $x < -3$ by -1
     c. $-x \geq 3$ Multiplying both sides of $x < -3$ by -1 and reversing the inequality symbol

Find the simplest equivalent inequation for each inequation. The variables are on Q.

If necessary, define *simplest* to mean an inequation of form $v < c, v \leq c, v > c$, or $v \geq c$ where v is the variable and c is a real number.

21. $\frac{1}{2}x > 1$ **22.** $\frac{1}{2}y \leq 3$ **23.** $\frac{1}{3}z < \frac{1}{3}$

24. $\frac{1}{4}x > 0$ **25.** $2t \leq 10$ **26.** $3x > 12$

27. $7x > 7$ **28.** $3y \leq -2$ **29.** $\frac{2}{3}w < 1$

30. $\frac{3}{4}x < 9$ **31.** $-\frac{1}{5}z \geq 1$ **32.** $-2x < 0$

33. $-x < 5$ **34.** $-x \leq -5$ **35.** $-5z < 6$

36. $-\frac{3}{4}x < -3$ **37.** $\frac{-2}{3}y \geq \frac{3}{2}$

Find the solution set of each inequation. The variables are on Q.

38. $\frac{1}{2}x > 5$ **39.** $\frac{1}{4}y < 1$ **40.** $\frac{2}{3}z > 2$

41. $\frac{3}{4}x \leq 6$ **42.** $2p \geq 18$ **43.** $3x \leq 24$

44. $2x > \frac{3}{2}$ **45.** $\frac{3}{4}y < \frac{1}{2}$ **46.** $4y < 12$

47. $\frac{1}{2}p \leq 10$ **48.** $4x \geq -28$ **49.** $9m \leq -108$

50. $72n < -72$ **51.** $-6t > 18$ **52.** $-3x > 21$

53. $-6y \leq 18$ **54.** $-5x \geq -15$ **55.** $8x \leq 0$

7-7 *Solving Inequations*

The use of more than one rule may be necessary to find the simplest inequation equivalent to a given inequation. The addition and multiplication rules may be used in the same problem. They also may be used more than once in a problem.

EXAMPLE

OBJECTIVE:

To name the solution set given a linear inequation in one variable.

While examining these, ask students to identify the goal of each step and state how it is accomplished.

Solve $6x - 5 \leq 2x + 7$, if $x \in Q$.

Add 5 to
both sides. $6x - 5 \leq 2x + 7 \Leftrightarrow 6x - 5 + 5 \leq 2x + 7 + 5$
$\Leftrightarrow \qquad 6x \leq 2x + 12$

Add $(-2x)$ to both sides. $\Leftrightarrow 6x + (-2x) \leq 2x + 12 + (-2x)$
$\Leftrightarrow \qquad 4x \leq 12$

Multiply both sides by $\frac{1}{4}$. $\Leftrightarrow \qquad \frac{1}{4} \cdot 4x \leq \frac{1}{4} \cdot 12$

$\Leftrightarrow \qquad x \leq 3$

The steps in solving an inequation may be done in different orders. The same solution will result as long as the rules are used correctly.

Study each method for solving $8 > 3x - 4$, if $x \in Z$. Justify each step in the solutions.

1. $8 > 3x - 4 \Leftrightarrow \qquad\qquad -3x > -4 - 8$

$\Leftrightarrow \qquad\qquad -3x > -12$

$\Leftrightarrow \left(-\dfrac{1}{3}\right) \cdot (-3x) < \left(-\dfrac{1}{3}\right) \cdot (-12)$

$\Leftrightarrow \qquad\qquad x < 4$

2. $8 > 3x - 4 \Leftrightarrow 3x - 4 < 8$

$\Leftrightarrow \qquad 3x < 12$

$\Leftrightarrow \qquad x < 4$

3. $8 > 3x - 4 \Leftrightarrow 4 + 8 > 3x$

$\Leftrightarrow \qquad 12 > 3x$

$\Leftrightarrow \qquad 4 > x$

$\Leftrightarrow \qquad x < 4$

The solution set is $\{x \mid x < 4,\ x \in Z\}$.

Notice that the rules for addition and multiplication were used in different orders with the same solution resulting.

EXERCISES

Find the solution set of each inequation. The variables are on Z.

1. $4x - 28 \geq 0$ **2.** $3y + 15 < 0$

3. $2x - 1 > 3$ **4.** $2y + 1 \leq 9$

5. $2t + 5 \geq 13$ **6.** $3x - 2 < 4$

7. $5m + 1 > 16$ **8.** $3x + 2 \leq 11$

9. $2x + 9 \leq 5$ **10.** $3t + 10 < 7$

11. $4z - 3 > -35$ **12.** $5t - 9 \geq -4$

13. $9x + 5 \leq 5$ **14.** $12 - 4y < 0$

15. $40 - x > x$ **16.** $x \leq 2x - 3$

17. $3y - 5 \geq 4y$ **18.** $z + 5 < 3z$

Find the solution set of each inequation. The variables are on Q.

19. $3m + 1 < -1 + m$ **20.** $3x + 1 \geq x - 2$

21. $4p - 7 \geq 2p$ **22.** $5 - 2y < 4$

23. $x - 2 > 6 + 3x$ **24.** $2y + 3 \leq 27 - 4y$

25. $5z - 4 \geq 7z + 9$ **26.** $3p + 5 < p - 11$

27. $15 - 7x > 3x + 5$ **28.** $2(x + 1) \geq 1$

29. $3(x - 2) \leq -2$ **30.** $3(x + 1) < x + 5$

31. $4(x - 3) < x + 3$ **32.** $3(2x - 1) \geq 2(2x + 3)$

33. $2(4 - 3x) \leq 4(x - 5)$ **34.** $2(4x - 1) > 4(3x + 1)$

1. $\{x \mid x \geq 7, x \in Z\}$ **2.** $\{y \mid y < -5, y \in Z\}$ **3.** $\{x \mid x > 2, x \in Z\}$ **4.** $\{y \mid y \leq 4, y \in Z\}$ **5.** $\{t \mid t \geq 4, t \in Z\}$ **6.** $\{x \mid x < 2, x \in Z\}$ **7.** $\{m \mid m > 3, m \in Z\}$ **8.** $\{x \mid x \leq 3, x \in Z\}$ **9.** $\{x \mid x \leq -2, x \in Z\}$ **10.** $\{t \mid t < -1, t \in Z\}$ **11.** $\{z \mid z > -8, z \in Z\}$ **12.** $\{t \mid t \geq 1, t \in Z\}$ **13.** $\{x \mid x \leq 0, x \in Z\}$ **14.** $\{y \mid y > 3, y \in Z\}$ **15.** $\{x \mid x < 20, x \in Z\}$ **16.** $\{x \mid x \geq 3, x \in Z\}$ **17.** $\{y \mid y \leq -5, y \in Z\}$

18. $\{z \mid z > \frac{5}{2}, z \in Z\}$ **19.** $\{m \mid m < -1, m \in Q\}$ **20.** $\{x \mid x \geq -\frac{3}{2}, x \in Q\}$ **21.** $\{p \mid p \geq \frac{7}{2}, p \in Q\}$ **22.** $\{y \mid y > \frac{1}{2}, y \in Q\}$

23. - 34. See section notes in T.G.

7-8
Fractions in Open Sentences

OBJECTIVE:

To name the solution set given a linear open sentence in one variable.

EXAMPLES

Stress repeatedly that when multiplying both sides by a number, the *entire expression* on both sides is multiplied by that number.

When an equation or inequation contains fractions, it usually is best to find an equivalent sentence without fractions. This can be done by multiplying both sides of the equation or inequation by the least common denominator of the fractions. The resulting equation or inequation then can be solved in the usual way.

1. Solve $\frac{x}{2} - 2 = 5 + \frac{x}{3}$, if $x \in Z$.

a. Use fractions to solve the equation.

$$\frac{x}{2} - 2 = 5 + \frac{x}{3} \Leftrightarrow \frac{x}{2} - \frac{x}{3} = 5 + 2$$

$$\Leftrightarrow \frac{3x}{6} - \frac{2x}{6} = 7$$

$$\Leftrightarrow \frac{3x - 2x}{6} = 7$$

$$\Leftrightarrow \frac{x}{6} = 7$$

$$\Leftrightarrow x = 42$$

b. Find an equivalent sentence without fractions and then solve the equation.

Multiply both sides by 6, the LCD for the fractions.

$$\frac{x}{2} - 2 = 5 + \frac{x}{3} \Leftrightarrow 6\left(\frac{x}{2} - 2\right) = 6\left(5 + \frac{x}{3}\right)$$

$$\Leftrightarrow 3x - 12 = 30 + 2x$$
$$\Leftrightarrow 3x - 2x = 30 + 12$$
$$\Leftrightarrow x = 42$$

Stress the importance of using parentheses and then applying the Distributive Property.

Check: $\frac{x}{2} - 2 = 5 + \frac{x}{3}$

$$\frac{42}{2} - 2 \stackrel{?}{=} 5 + \frac{42}{3}$$

$$21 - 2 \stackrel{?}{=} 5 + 14$$

$$19 = 19$$

2. Find the solution set of $\frac{2x - 3}{3} - \frac{x - 3}{2} \geq 1\frac{1}{5}$, if $x \in Q$.

$$\frac{2x - 3}{3} - \frac{x - 3}{2} \geq 1\frac{1}{5}$$

Again, slow students may profit by being asked to identify the goal of each step and state how it is accomplished.

$$\Leftrightarrow \quad \frac{1}{3}(2x - 3) - \frac{1}{2}(x - 3) \geq \frac{6}{5}$$

Multiply both sides by 30, the LCD for

$\frac{1}{3}, \frac{1}{2},$ and $\frac{6}{5}$.

$$\Leftrightarrow \frac{30}{3}(2x - 3) - \frac{30}{2}(x - 3) \geq 30 \cdot \frac{6}{5}$$

$$\Leftrightarrow \quad 10(2x - 3) - 15(x - 3) \geq 36$$

$$\Leftrightarrow \quad 20x - 30 - 15x + 45 \geq 36$$

$$\Leftrightarrow \quad 20x - 15x \geq 36 + 30 - 45$$

$$\Leftrightarrow \quad 5x \geq 21$$

$$\Leftrightarrow \quad x \geq \frac{21}{5}$$

The solution set is $\left\{ x \mid x \geq \frac{21}{5}, x \in Q \right\}$.

EXERCISES

For each equation or inequation, obtain an equivalent sentence without fractions. Then find the solution set for each equation or inequation. The variables are on Q.

1. $\{12\}$ 2. $\{30\}$ 3. $\left\{\frac{5}{2}\right\}$
4. $\{x \mid x < -\frac{3}{4}, x \in Q\}$ 5. $\{x \mid x$
$\leq -9, x \in Q\}$ 6. $\{x \mid x \geq -2,$
$x \in Q\}$ 7. $\{m \mid m < -4, m \in Q\}$
8. $\{20\}$ 9. $\{t \mid t > 6, t \in Q\}$
10. $\{-28\}$ 11. $\{s \mid s < 12,$
$s \in Q\}$ 12. $\{7\}$ 13. $\{x \mid x < 9,$
$x \in Q\}$ 14. $\{11\}$ 15. $\{y \mid y \geq \frac{1}{8},$
$y \in Q\}$ 16. $\{y \mid y \geq \frac{5}{4}, y \in Q\}$

17. $\{t \mid t > \frac{4}{7}, t \in Q\}$ 18. $\{-2\}$

1. $\frac{1}{2}x + 3 = 9$ 2. $\frac{1}{2}x - 5 = 10$

3. $\frac{1}{2}y - 1 = \frac{1}{4}$ 4. $\frac{2}{3}x + 1 < \frac{1}{2}$

5. $\frac{1}{4}x + 3 \leq \frac{3}{4}$ 6. $\frac{3}{4}x + \frac{1}{2} \leq \frac{1}{2}x$

7. $\frac{2m}{3} - \frac{1}{3} > \frac{3m}{4}$ 8. $\frac{y}{4} - \frac{y}{5} = 1$

9. $\frac{2t}{3} - \frac{t}{2} > 1$ 10. $\frac{z}{2} = \frac{z}{7} - 10$

11. $\frac{s}{3} + 2 > \frac{s}{2}$ 12. $\frac{2x}{3} + \frac{1}{3} = 5$

Watch closely for students who may fail to treat $\frac{1}{3}(2x - 3)$ as a product of two numbers.

13. $\frac{1}{3}(2x - 3) < 5$ 14. $\frac{1}{4}(3m - 1) = 8$

15. $\frac{2}{3}(y + 1) \geq \frac{3}{4}$ 16. $\frac{1}{3}(5y - 1) \geq \frac{1}{2}(2y + 1)$

17. $\frac{1}{3}(t + 2) < t + \frac{1}{2}t$ 18. $\frac{1}{3}(p + 2) - \frac{1}{4}(p - 2) = 1$

19. {1} **20.** $\{x \mid x > 3, x \in Q\}$
21. $\{n \mid n < 11, n \in Q\}$ **22.** {0}
23. $\{t \mid t \geq 6, t \in Q\}$
24. $\{y \mid y \geq 10, y \in Q\}$ **25.** $\left\{\frac{1}{2}\right\}$
26. $\left\{m \mid m < \frac{5}{3}, m \in Q\right\}$
27. $\left\{-\frac{1}{2}\right\}$ **28.** $\{x \mid x < \frac{17}{26},$
$x \in Q\}$ **29.** {12} **30.** $\left\{\frac{10}{3}\right\}$

(19.) $\frac{1}{3}(x + 2) + \frac{1}{2}(x - 1) = 1$ **20.** $\frac{1}{2}(x + 5) - \frac{1}{4}(x + 1) > 3$

(21.) $\frac{n - 3}{4} + \frac{n - 2}{3} < 5$ **22.** $\frac{n - 4}{2} - \frac{n - 5}{5} = -1$

(23.) $\frac{t - 2}{4} - \frac{t - 4}{6} \geq \frac{2}{3}$ **24.** $\frac{y + 4}{4} - \frac{3y - 9}{7} \leq \frac{1}{2}$

(25.) $\frac{m}{2} - \frac{m}{3} = \frac{1 - m}{6}$ **26.** $\frac{2m}{3} - \frac{3m - 1}{2} > 0$

(27.) $\frac{4x + 2}{3} + \frac{2x + 1}{2} = \frac{6x + 3}{4}$

28. $\frac{1 - x}{3} - \frac{1 - 2x}{4} + \frac{1 - 3x}{5} > 0$

(29.) $\frac{8}{x} = \frac{2}{3}$, $x \neq 0$ (Hint: Multiply both sides by $3x$.)

30. $\frac{2}{x} = \frac{3}{5}$, $x \neq 0$

In Exercise 29 it is specified only that $x \neq 0$. Ask why it is safe in that case to multiply both sides of an equation by x, but not to multiply both sides of an inequation by x.

7-9
Special Solution Sets

Sometimes strange statements result when you try to find the simplest equivalent sentence for an equation or inequation. When the search for a simple equivalent sentence leads to a *false statement,* then the original equation or inequation has *no solution.*

EXAMPLES

OBJECTIVE:

To name the solution set given an open sentence which is equivalent to a statement about specific numbers.

The section notes in the T.G. give several suggestions for helping students to understand open sentences like these.

In these examples, x is a variable on R.

1. $2(x + 3) = 4(x + 3) - 2x \Leftrightarrow 2x + 6 = 4x + 12 - 2x$
$\Leftrightarrow 2x + 6 = 2x + 12$
$\Leftrightarrow 2x - 2x = 12 - 6$
$\Leftrightarrow \qquad 0 = 6$

2. $3x - 2 > 3(x + 1) \Leftrightarrow 3x - 2 > 3x + 3$
$\Leftrightarrow 3x - 3x > 3 + 2$
$\Leftrightarrow \qquad 0 > 5$

The statements $0 = 6$ and $0 > 5$ are false. The solution set for each example is $\varnothing$, the empty set.

When the search for a simple equivalent sentence leads to a *statement which is true for all replacements,* then the solution set for the original equation or inequation is the *universal set,* U.

EXAMPLES

In these examples, x is a variable on R.

1. $2(x + 6) = 4(x + 3) - 2x \Leftrightarrow 2x + 12 = 4x + 12 - 2x$
$\Leftrightarrow 2x + 12 = 2x + 12$
$\Leftrightarrow 2x - 2x = 12 - 12$
$\Leftrightarrow \qquad 0 = 0$

2. $3x - 2 \leq 3(x + 1) \Leftrightarrow 3x - 2 \leq 3x + 3$
$\Leftrightarrow 3x - 3x \leq 3 + 2$
$\Leftrightarrow \qquad 0 \leq 5$

The statements $0 = 0$ and $0 \leq 5$ are true. These statements are not dependent upon the value of x. Therefore, the solution set of each example is the universal set which, in this case, is R.

Exercises 1-4 are suitable for class discussion especially with slow students.

EXERCISES

1. Copy and complete this table.

Sentence: $2(x + 3) = 4(x + 3) - 2x$			
Replacement	Statement	Simplified Statement	True or False
2	$2(2 + 3) = 4(2 + 3) - 2 \cdot 2$	$10 = 16$	F
3	?	?	?
4	?	?	?
5	?	?	?
0	?	?	?
−1	?	?	?
−2	?	?	?
−3	$2(-3 + 3) = 4(-3 + 3) - 2 \cdot (-3)$	$0 = 6$	F

1. See section notes in T.G.

2. $6 = 12$, ϕ

2. Find a simple equivalent sentence for $2(x + 3) = 4(x + 3) - 2x$. Write the solution set for this equation if $x \in$ Z.

3. Copy and complete this table.

Sentence: $3(x + 3) + 2x > 5x + 6$			
Replacement	Statement	Simplified Statement	True or False
2	$3(2 + 3) + 2 \cdot 2 > 5 \cdot 2 + 6$	$19 > 16$	T
3	?	?	?
4	?	?	?
5	?	?	?
0	?	?	?
−1	?	?	?
−2	?	?	?
−3	$3(-3 + 3) + 2 \cdot (-3) > 5 \cdot (-3) + 6$	$-6 > -9$	T

3. See section notes in T.G.

4. $9 > 6$, Z **5.** Q **6.** φ **7.** φ

8. {2} **9.** {0} **10.** $\{x \mid x > -\frac{7}{3},$ $x \in Q\}$ **11.** $\{x \mid x < 9, x \in Q\}$
12. Q **13.** Q **14.** $\{x \mid x \leq 5,$ $x \in Q\}$ **15.** φ **16.** $\left\{ \frac{-1}{2} \right\}$

17. φ **18.** $\{m \mid m > \frac{3}{5}, m \in Q\}$
19. Q **20.** Q

4. Find a simple equivalent sentence for $3(x + 3) + 2x > 5x + 6$. Write the solution set for this equation if $x \in$ Z.

Write the solution set for each equation or inequation. The variables are on Q.

5. $2(x + 2) = 2x + 4$ **6.** $2(x - 2) = 2x + 4$
7. $2(x + 1) = 2x + 4$ **8.** $2(x + 1) = x + 4$
9. $2(x + 1) = x + 2$ **10.** $2(x - 1) < 5(x + 1)$
11. $5(x - 1) < 4(x + 1)$ **12.** $5(x - 1) < 5(x + 1)$

13. $10(x + 1) + 2 \leq 6(2x + 3) - 2x$

14. $11(x + 1) + 2 \leq 6(2x + 3) - 2x$

15. $10(x + 1) + 12 < 6(2x + 3) - 2x$

16. $\dfrac{6x + 3}{4} - \dfrac{2x + 1}{2} = \dfrac{4x + 2}{3}$

17. $\dfrac{2m}{3} - \dfrac{3m - 1}{2} = m - \dfrac{11m + 3}{6}$

18. $\dfrac{2m}{3} < \dfrac{3m - 1}{2}$

19. $\dfrac{5x}{3} + \dfrac{10}{3} \geq \dfrac{10 - x}{3} + 2x$

20. $0 \geq \dfrac{5x - 1}{3} - \dfrac{3x - 1}{5} - \dfrac{16x + 7}{15}$

7-10
Applications

Equations or inequations are often used to solve practical problems. In such problems, a mathematical model must be set up using the data given. The goal is to set up an equation or inequation with a solution set which is the answer to the question in the problem. Then the equation or inequation is solved to obtain the answer to the problem.

PROBLEM 1

The length of a rectangle is twice its width. The perimeter of the rectangle is 51 cm. Find the length and width.

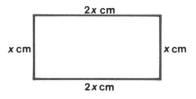

Mathematical Model
Let the width be x cm.
Then the length is $2x$ cm.

$$2x + 2x + x + x = 51 \Leftrightarrow 6x = 51$$
$$\Leftrightarrow x = 8.5$$

The width of the rectangle is 8.5 cm. The length is 17 cm.

PROBLEM 2

A boy starts walking to school at 7:30 A.M. He walks at the rate of 3 miles per hour. At 7:40 A.M. his brother starts for school on his bicycle. He cycles at the rate of 6 miles per hour. When will the boy on the bicycle overtake his brother?

The formula $d = rt$ can be used for distance-rate-time calculations.

$$d = rt \begin{cases} d = \text{distance traveled} \\ r = \text{constant rate} \\ t = \text{time in travel} \end{cases}$$

To use this formula, you must know the values of two of the variables. You may then solve an equation to find the value of the third variable.

Mathematical Model
Let t be the time in hours that it takes the first boy to walk to school.

	d	r	t	$d = r \cdot t$
Walking	d_1	3	t	$d_1 = 3t$
Bicycling	d_2	6	$t - \dfrac{1}{6}$	$d_2 = 6\left(t - \dfrac{1}{6}\right)$

The distance traveled by the boys to school is the same, that is $d_1 = d_2$. Notice that 10 minutes was written as $\frac{1}{6}$ hour in the table. In this problem, the units are miles and hours. Each of the values d, r, and t must be written in terms of miles and hours.

$$3t = 6\left(t - \frac{1}{6}\right) \Leftrightarrow 3t = 6t - 1$$
$$\Leftrightarrow -3t = -1$$
$$\Leftrightarrow t = \frac{1}{3}$$

Since $\frac{1}{3}$ hour equals 20 minutes, the boy on the bicycle will overtake his brother 20 minutes after 7:30 A.M. at 7:50 A.M.

PROBLEM 3

A chemist has a solution that is 25% acid. She wishes to increase the amount of acid to 40% by adding 100% acid. If she starts with 800 cm³ of solution, how much 100% acid must be added to give the desired concentration?

Mathematical Model

Let x be the number of cm³ of 100% acid to be added.

	Volume in cm³	Amount of acid in cm³
Original Solution	800	.25(800)
100% Acid	x	1.00(x)
Final Mixture	$800 + x$	.40($800 + x$)

The sum of the amount of acid in the original solution and the 100% acid equals the amount of acid in the final mixture.

$$.25(800) + 1.00(x) = .40(800 + x) \Leftrightarrow 200 + x = 320 + .4x$$
$$\Leftrightarrow 200 + .6x = 320$$
$$\Leftrightarrow .6x = 120$$
$$\Leftrightarrow x = 200$$

The amount of 100% acid to be added is 200 cm³. Check this answer to be sure that it is correct.

EXERCISES

1. 12, $2x + 13 = 37$

2. $3x - 3 = 17$, $x = \frac{20}{3}$

3. $2[(x + 3) + x] = 30$, $x = 6$ mm **4.** $y + (y + 2) + (y - 3) = 23$, $y = 8$ cm, $y + 2 = 10$ cm, $y - 3 = 5$ cm

5. $(2x + 3)5 = 50$, $x = 3\frac{1}{2}$ cm

6. $n + (n + 1) = 57$, $n = 28$, $n + 1 = 29$ **7.** $n + (n + 1) = -77$, $n = -39$, $n + 1 = -38$

8. $n + (n + 1) + (n + 2) = 75$, $n = 24$, $n + 1 = 25$, $n + 2 = 26$

9. $n + (n + 2) + (n + 4) = 108$, $n = 34$, $n + 2 = 36$, $n + 4 = 38$

10. $n + (n + 2) + (n + 4) = 63$, $n = 19$, $n + 2 = 21$, $n + 4 = 23$

11. $6(2x) + 15 \cdot x = 2.16$, $x = \$.08$ — pencil, $2x = \$.16$ — ruler **12.** $x + 3x = 96$, $x = 24¢$, $3x = 72¢$ **13.** $2 \cdot (x) + 1 \cdot (2x) = 3.68$, $x = \$.92$, $2x = \$1.84$

14. $3x + 5 > x + 12$, $x > 3\frac{1}{2}$ mm

15. $(x + 1) + (x - 3) > 12$, $x > 7$ cm

Write an equation for each problem and then solve it. Draw a picture if it will help you. Check each solution.

1. Think of a whole number. Double it and then add 13. The result is 37. Can you mentally find the number? Make a mathematical model using x for the number, and solve the equation. What is the number?

2. Repeat Exercise **1** if the number is first multiplied by 3, then 3 is subtracted from the product, giving an answer of 17.

3. The length of a rectangle is $(x + 3)$ mm and the width is x mm. The perimeter of the rectangle is 30 mm. Find its length and width.

4. The sides of a triangle are y cm, $(y + 2)$ cm and $(y - 3)$ cm long. The perimeter is 23 cm. Find the length of each side of the triangle.

5. The length of a rectangle is $(2x + 3)$ cm and the width is 5 cm. Given that the area is 50 cm², find the length of the rectangle. Remember that the area of a rectangle is equal to its length multiplied by its width.

6. The sum of two consecutive integers is 57. Use n and $(n + 1)$ to represent the integers. Write an equation and find the integers.

7. Repeat Exercise **6** if the sum of the two integers is -77.

8. The sum of three consecutive integers is 75. Find the integers.

9. The sum of three consecutive even numbers is 108. Use n, $n + 2$, and $n + 4$ to represent the numbers. Find them.

10. The sum of three consecutive odd numbers is 63. Find them.

11. A ruler costs twice as much as a pencil. Six rulers and fifteen pencils cost $2.16. Find the cost of a pencil and of a ruler.

12. One food package costs three times as much as another. Together they cost 96¢. Use x cents as the cost of the less expensive package. Find the cost of each package.

13. Plums cost twice as much per kg as apples. The total cost of 2 kg of apples and 1 kg of plums is $3.68. Set up a mathematical model. Use x cents as the price of 1 kg of apples and $2x$ cents as the price of 1 kg of plums. Find the price of each.

14. The distance along the curve $\overgroup{ABC}$ is greater than the distance AOC. ABC is $(3x + 5)$ mm long. AOC is $(x + 12)$ mm long. Write an inequation in x. Find x.

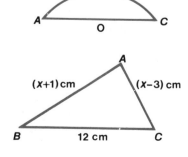

15. In the triangle, $\overline{AB} + \overline{AC} > \overline{BC}$. Write and solve an inequation in x.

16.

Number	Points
20	60
40	$-40x$
Total 60	$60 - 40x$
	$= -20$

$x = -2$

17. a.

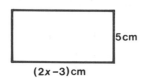

Answers to Exercises 18 and 19 will be of the form "at least c" or "at most c."

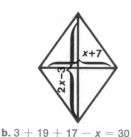

$5\,\text{cm}$

$(2x-3)\,\text{cm}$

b. $3 + 19 + 17 - x = 30$

$x = 9$ **18.** $(2x - 3)(5) < 45$,

$2x - 3 < 9 \text{ cm}^2$ **19.** $2x - 3 >$

$x + 7$, $x + 7 > 17$, $2x - 3 > 17$

Each length greater than 17 m

20. 55 mph **21. a.** $x \cdot 2$,

$(x - 10) \cdot \frac{3}{2}$ **b.** $146 = x \cdot 2 +$

$(x - 10)\frac{3}{2}$, $x = 46$ km/hr, 54 km

22. $45t = 55(t - \frac{1}{2})$, 151.25 miles,

10:15 A.M.

16. A player earns 3 points for each correct answer in a game. He also pays a penalty in points for each incorrect answer. One player scores 20 correct answers out of 60. This gives him a score of -20. Set up a model with a penalty of x points for each incorrect answer. Find the penalty.

17. In a class of 30 students, 19 play football and 17 play baseball. Three do not play either game. Suppose x pupils play both games, as shown in the Venn diagram.
  a. Copy the diagram and mark, in terms of x, the number of students who play football only. Then mark the number who play baseball only.
  b. Write an equation for x. Solve this equation to find the number of students who play both games.

18. The length of a rectangle is $(2x - 3)$ cm. The width is 5 cm. The area is less than 45 cm^2. Find the length of the rectangle.

19. One diagonal of a kite is marked $(2x - 3)$ meters. The other diagonal of the kite is marked $(x + 7)$ meters. The first diagonal is longer than the second. What is the length of each?

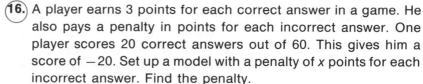

20. A distance of 180 mi was traveled on a combined bus-train trip. During its one half-hour segment, the bus averaged a speed of $(2x + 10)$ mi/hr. The train trip was 80 miles. Write an equation and find x. Remember, the distance is equal to the rate multiplied by the time.

21. A motorist makes a trip of 146 km. He drives for 2 hours in daylight and for $1\frac{1}{2}$ hours in darkness. His average speed in the dark is reduced by 10 km/hr from his daylight speed.
  a. Using x km/hr for his daylight speed, write expressions for the distances he covers in daylight and in darkness.
  b. Write an equation in x and solve it. Find his speed in daylight and how far he drives in the dark.

22. A woman leaves home at 7:00 A.M. on a business trip. She travels at a rate of 45 miles per hour. Her son discovers that his mother forgot her brief case and starts out to overtake her. The son leaves home at 7:30 A.M. He travels at 55 miles per hour. How far from home and at what time will he overtake his mother?

23. One hiking group starts out on a trail at 2:15 P.M. A second hiking group starts at 2:45 P.M. The first group travels $2\frac{1}{4}$ miles per hour. The second group travels $3\frac{3}{4}$ miles per hour. Will the second group catch up with the first if the trail is 3 miles long? If so, how far from the end of the trail? At what time?

24. A motorist drives 92 km in 2 hours. She averages 54 km/hr on the open road and 22 km/hr passing through cities. Make a mathematical model using t hours for the time passing through cities. Find t.

25. A mixture of antifreeze and water contains 40% antifreeze. How much pure (100%) antifreeze is added to bring the concentration up to 50% if 16 quarts are in the original solution?

26. How much pure water is added to 500 cm³ of 50% acid solution to decrease the concentration to 30%?

27. A car radiator holds 18 quarts. If a 20% antifreeze mixture is in the radiator, how much must be drained out and replaced by pure antifreeze to increase the concentration to 30%?

Chapter Summary

1. Equations or inequations which have the same solution set are called equivalent. The symbol $\Leftrightarrow$ means is equivalent to.
2. Two rules can be used to find equivalent equations.
   a. If the same number is added to both sides of an equation, the resulting equation is equivalent to the first.
   b. If both sides of an equation are multiplied by the same non-zero number, the resulting equation is equivalent to the first.
3. Two rules can be used to find equivalent inequations.
   1. If the same number is added to both sides of an inequation, the resulting inequation is equivalent to the first.
   2. a. If both sides of an inequation are multiplied by the same positive number, the resulting inequation is equivalent to the first.
      b. If both sides of an inequation are multiplied by the same negative number *and* if the inequality symbol is reversed, the resulting inequation is equivalent to the first.

4. More than one rule may be used to find the simplest equivalent equation or inequation.
5. Set-builder notation may be used to describe the solution sets of inequations. The solution set of $2x - 5 > x + 6$, if $x \in Z$, is $\{x \mid x > 11, x \in Z\}$. This is read *the set of all x such that x is greater than 11, and x is an element of the integers.*
6. When an equation or inequation contains fractions, you should find the simplest equivalent sentence without fractions. To do this, multiply both sides of the equation or inequation by the LCD for the fractions.
7. When the simplest equivalent sentence does not depend on the value for the variable and is true, the solution set is U. If the statement is false, however, the solution set is $\varnothing$.
8. When solving practical problems, set up a mathematical model and draw a picture if it will help.

REVIEW EXERCISES 7-1, 7-2, 7-3

1. $\{14\}$ 2. $\{-6\}$ 3. $\{-1\}$ 4. $\{7\}$
5. $\{-8\}$ 6. $\{8\}$ 7. $\{13\}$ 8. $\{-2\}$
9. ϕ 10. $\{4\}$ 11. $\{3\}$ 12. $\left\{\frac{4}{3}\right\}$

Find the solution set for each equation. The variables are on Z. Check each solution.

1. $3x - 2 = 40$
2. $5x + 7 = -23$
3. $4x + 1 = -3$
4. $5x - 4 = 3x + 10$
5. $7 - 9x = 79$
6. $3(x - 3) = x + 7$
7. $3(2c - 4) = 4c + 14$
8. $5(z + 3) = 2(z - 4) + 17$
9. $8 - 3(y + 7) = y + 5$
10. $2 + 7(2 - z) = 3z - 24$
11. $2(5 - 3x) + 11 = 3(2x - 5)$

7-4, 7-5, 7-6

13. $\{m \mid m > 12, m \in Q\}$
14. $\{y \mid y > \frac{1}{6}, y \in Q\}$
15. $\left\{\frac{3}{4}\right\}$ 16. $\{x \mid x \geq -6,$
$x \in Q\}$ 17. $\left\{\frac{2}{5}\right\}$ 18. $\{p \mid p < 15,$
$p \in Q\}$ 19. $\{x \mid x < 2, x \in Q\}$
20. $\{x \mid x < -8, x \in Q\}$
21. Q 22. $\{y \mid y < \frac{-1}{36}, y \in Q\}$
23. $\{m \mid m \geq \frac{5}{24}, m \in Q\}$

Find the solution set for each equation or inequation. The variables are on Q.

12. $3x = 4$
13. $\frac{1}{4}m > 3$
14. $2y > \frac{1}{3}$
15. $\frac{2}{3}x = \frac{1}{2}$
16. $-3x \leq 18$
17. $-5t = -2$
18. $-4p > -60$
19. $4 - x > 2$
20. $7 < -1 - x$
21. $y + 1 \geq y$
22. $7y + \frac{3}{4} < 4y + \frac{2}{3}$
23. $\frac{3}{2} - m \leq 3m + \frac{2}{3}$

7-7

24. $x > 3$ 25. $x < 2$ 26. $x < -5$
27. $x < 3$

Solve each inequation if $x \in Z$.

24. $2x - 1 > 5$
25. $3x + 5 < 2x + 7$
26. $2(x + 9) - 3 < 5$
27. $3x - 11 < x - 5$

7-8

Write true (T) or false (F) for each statement. The variables are on Q.

28. If $x + 4 \geq 8$, then $x \geq 4$

29. If $2y - 3 < 4 - y$, then $y > \dfrac{7}{3}$

30. If $7 - 5z > 3z - 9$, then $z < 2$

31. If $\dfrac{1}{2} a + 2 > \dfrac{1}{4} a + 3$, then $a > 4$

32. If $x + \dfrac{1}{2} > \dfrac{1}{4}$, then $x > -\dfrac{1}{4}$

33. If $-2y > 6$, then $y > -3$

34. If $x \geq -1$ and also $x \leq -1$, then $x = -1$

35. If $x < -2$, and $x > -4$, then $-4 < x < -2$

28. T **29.** F **30.** T **31.** T **32.** T
33. F **34.** F **35.** T **36.** $\{x \mid x < -2, x \in Q\}$ **37.** $\{y \mid y < \dfrac{1}{3}, y \in Q\}$ **38.** $\{x = \dfrac{27}{2}\}$
39. $\{t \mid t < \dfrac{6}{5}, t \in Q\}$
40. $\{t \mid t < -9, t \in Q\}$
41. $\{a \mid a < -8, a \in Q\}$

7-9

Solve each equation or inequation. The variables are on Q.

36. $8x + 12 < 5x + 6$

37. $6 - 2y > y + 5$

38. $\dfrac{1}{2} x - \dfrac{1}{3} x = \dfrac{9}{4}$

39. $\dfrac{2}{3} t + 1 > \dfrac{3}{2} t$

40. $\dfrac{1}{3} (6t + 9) < -15$

41. $\dfrac{1}{3} (a + 2) > 2 + \dfrac{a}{2}$

42. $\dfrac{x + 1}{3} + \dfrac{x + 2}{2} = 3$

43. $\dfrac{2y + 1}{5} - \dfrac{y - 1}{3} < \dfrac{2}{3}$

44. $5.9x - 2.1 = 3.4x - 1.85$

42. $\{x = 2\}$ **43.** $\{y \mid y < 2, y \in Q\}$ **44.** $\{x = \dfrac{1}{10}\}$
45. $2N + 15 = 27 - 2, N = 5$
46. $k + 2, k + 4, k + (k + 2) + (k + 4) = 78, k = 24,$ $k + 2 = 26, k + 4 = 28$
47. $x = 67$ **48.** $A \cap B = \{-2, -1, 0, 1, 2, 3, 4\}; A \cap B = \{x \mid -3 < x < 5, x \in Z\}$
49. $\dfrac{3}{2}$ hr; 12 km

7-10

45. Two times a certain number added to 15 is 2 less than 27. Can you mentally find the number? Set up a mathematical model using n for the number and solve the equation. Do you get the same answer?

46. If k is an even number, what are the next two greater even numbers? Set up a mathematical model and use it to find three consecutive even numbers whose sum is 78.

47. The altimeter of an airplane is set at zero when it is on the Teheran airfield, which is above sea level. On takeoff, the airplane climbs for $(x + 34)$ meters. Later it loses height for $3x$ meters. The altimeter now reads -100 meters. Find x.

48. The solution set of $3x + 14 > 5$ is A and the solution set of $4 - 5x > -21$ is B, if $x \in Z$. List the elements of $A \cap B$. Describe $A \cap B$ using set-builder notation.

49. A boy cycles 37 km. For part of the time he averages 8 km/hr. The rest of the time he averages 10 km/hr. He takes 4 hours altogether. Using t hours for his time at 8 km/hr, write an equation. How long does he cycle at 8 km/hr? How far does he cycle at 8 km/hr?

50. Repeat Exercise **49** using x km for the distance the boy cycles at 8 km/hr. Use your solution to answer the same questions. Which model is preferable?

51. In a league competition, each team is awarded 3 points for a win and 2 points for a tie. No points are given for a loss. At the end of a season, a team had played 24 games. It lost 7 of them and scored 45 points in all. How many games did the team win?

52. A container holds 14 liters of a 25% antifreeze solution (25% of the 14 liters is antifreeze and the rest is water). How many liters of water are in the solution? The strength of the solution becomes 30% when x liters of pure antifreeze are added. Write, in terms of x, the percentage of water in the new solution. Write an equation from your two answers to find x.

CHAPTER 8

mappings and their graphs

8-1

OBJECTIVE:

To describe a mapping by one of the methods of this section given its description by another of the methods.

Mappings and Ordered Pairs

In everyday conversation, there are many words that show a *relation* between persons or things.

EXAMPLES

1. Maria *owns* the red bicycle.
2. Leroy *loves* Fonnia.
3. Three *is less than* seven.

Mapping and *relation* may be viewed as synonyms.

In mathematics, relations between sets of objects often are called **mappings.** One way to picture a mapping is by an arrow diagram. For example, the following information may be drawn as an arrow diagram.

EXAMPLE

Four girls, Mary, Jane, Betty, and Nan, were asked if they owned a transistor radio, record player, or cassette recorder. Their answers show the following.

a. Mary and Jane each own a transistor radio (*t*).

b. Betty and Nan each own a record player (*r*).

c. Mary and Betty each own a cassette recorder (*c*).

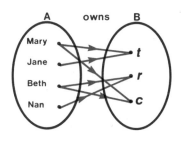

Notice that there are two sets. The first is a set of girls {Mary, Jane, Betty, Nan} which will be named A. The second is a set of instruments {*t*, *r*, *c*} which will be named B. Also, notice that there is a relation, *owns,* which pairs elements of set A with elements of set B.

Stress the fact that mappings
have direction.

The mapping in the example shows a relation from *set A to set B*. In general, relations have a *direction,* or *sense.* Mary owns a transistor radio, Mary → *t*. It would not be accurate to write *t* → Mary if the arrow means *owns.*

Instead of writing Mary → *t*, you could write the ordered pair (Mary, *t*). A mapping also may be described in terms of ordered pairs.

EXAMPLE

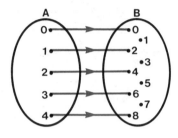

Using the information in the arrow diagram, describe the mapping, *is half of,* from set A to set B by a set of ordered pairs.

$$M = \{(0, 0), (1, 2), (2, 4), (3, 6), (4, 8)\}$$

Using ordered pairs to describe a mapping leads to the following definition.

Do not insist on understanding of
this definition all at once.
Rather, point it out often and
let it "grow" on the students.

A *mapping from set A to set B* is a set of ordered pairs with each first component from set A and each second component from set B.

If it is impossible to list all the ordered pairs that describe a mapping, set-builder notation may be used. For example, the mapping, *has as a reciprocal,* from N to Q may be described by $M = \left\{(x, y) \mid y = \dfrac{1}{x}, x \in N, y \in Q\right\}$. You may think of this set as the solution set for $y = \dfrac{1}{x}$ where *x* is a variable on N and *y* is a variable on Q. In this sense, ordered pairs are not new to you. You have used ordered pairs to locate points on road maps and to picture solution sets of equations.

EXAMPLES

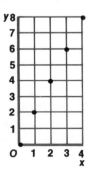

1. Let *x* be a variable on {0, 1, 2, 3, 4} and *y* be a variable on {0, 1, 2, 3, 4, 5, 6, 7, 8}. Graph the solution set of $y = 2x$.

2. If w and z are variables on $A = \{0, 1, 2, 3, 4, 5\}$, graph the mapping $M = \{(w, z)|z > w, w \in A, z \in A\}$.

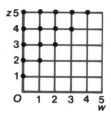

w	0	1	2	3	4	5
z	1	2	3	4	5	
	2	3	4	5		
	3	4	5			
	4	5				
	5					

Give adequate time to examining these four methods.

Thus, a mapping may be described in four ways. The four methods are: using the listing method; using set-builder notation; drawing an arrow diagram; drawing a graph.

EXAMPLE

Describe the mapping, *is half of,* from $A = \{0, 1, 2, 3, 4\}$ to $B = \{0, 1, 2, 3, 4, 5, 6, 7, 8\}$ in four ways.

1. Listing

$$M = \{(0, 0), (1, 2), (2, 4), (3, 6), (4, 8)\}$$

2. Set-builder notation

$$M = \{(x, y)|y = 2x, x \in A, y \in B\}$$

3. Arrow diagram

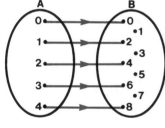

4. Graph

EXERCISES

It may be best to treat Exercises 1-4 as class discussion.

1. Answers will vary.

1. Relations may be described in words. For example: *is the brother of, is half of, lives on the same street as.* List four more examples.

217

2.

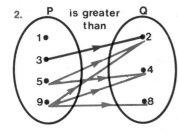

3. See section notes in T.G.

4. $\{(x, y) \mid y = 3x, y \in G, x \in H\}$

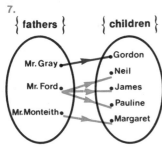

7.

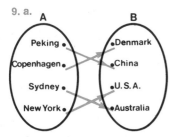

9. a.

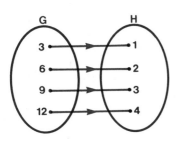

2. Two sets of numbers, P and Q, are listed in the following figure. Copy and complete the arrow diagram to show the mapping *is greater than* from set P to set Q.

3. Using the same sets as in Exercise **2,** draw an arrow diagram to show the mapping, *is less than,* from set P to set Q.

4. What mapping from set G to set H is illustrated in the figure?

5. $S = \{0, 1, 2, 5\}$, $T = \{1, 2, 3, 4, 6\}$ Make an arrow diagram to show the mapping, *is one less than,* from S to T.

6. Construct an arrow diagram to show the mapping, *is a factor of,* from $A = \{2, 3, 5, 7, 11\}$ to $B = \{1, 6, 12, 17, 30, 35\}$.

7. Mr. Gray is the father of Gordon. Mr. Ford is the father of Neil, James, and Pauline. Mr. Monteith is the father of Margaret. Copy the following figure and complete the arrow diagram to show the mapping, *is the father of,* from the set of fathers to the set of children.

8. Using the same sets as in Exercise **7,** draw an arrow diagram to show the mapping, *is the child of,* from the set of children to the set of fathers.

9. a. Copy the figure and draw an arrow from each city in set A to the country in set B in which it is situated.

  b. Complete: "The arrow diagram in Part **a** shows the mapping ____?____ from set A to set B."

10. Naomi and Jane are both clever. Jean and Jane are both tall. Naomi and Jane are both athletic.

  a. List the set G of girls and the set C of their characteristics.

  b. Draw an arrow diagram relating each girl to her characteristics.

  c. Which girl is both tall and clever?

11. $A = \{2, 3, 5, 6\}$ and $B = \{1, 2, 3, 4, 5, 6\}$

  a. Show the relation, *is a factor of,* from A to B in an arrow diagram.

  b. Express the relation as a set of ordered pairs.

12. A relation between two sets is given by $\{(-1, 2), (1, 4), (3, 6), (5, 8), (7, 10)\}$.

  List the elements of the two sets. Describe in words a possible relation from the first set to the second set.

3. See section notes in T.G.
4. $\{(x, y) \mid y = 3x, y \in G, x \in H\}$
5. See section notes in T.G.
6. See section notes in T.G.
8. See section notes in T.G.
9. b. is situated in
10. a. G = {Naomi, Jane, Jean}
C = {clever, tall, athletic}
b. See section notes in T.G.
c. Jane
11. See section notes in T.G.
b. {(2, 2), (2, 4), (2, 6), (3, 3), (3, 6), (5, 5), (6, 6)} **12.** A = {−1, 1, 3, 5, 7} and {2, 4, 6, 8, 10} = B. An element in A is 3 less than an element in B.

218

13. a. {(0, 0), (2, 1), (4, 2), (6, 3), (8, 4)}

b.
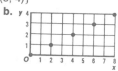

14. {(a, n), (a, s), (a, t), (i, f), (i, n), (i, s), (i, t), (o, f), (o, n), (u, s) }

15. a.

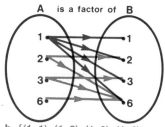

b. {(1, 1), (1, 2), (1, 3), (1, 6), (2, 2), (2, 6), (3, 3), (3, 6), (6, 6)}

16.
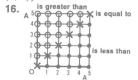

a. {(1, 2), (1, 3), (1, 4), (1, 5), (2, 3), (2, 4), (2, 5), (3, 4), (3, 5), (4, 5) } **b.** {(1, 1), (2, 2), (3, 3), (4, 4),(5, 5)} **c.** {(2, 1), (3, 1), (3, 2), (4, 1), (4, 2), (4, 3), (5, 1), (5, 2), (5, 3), (5, 4)}

17. a. $\left\{ \frac{1}{2}, 1, 2, 4, 8 \right\}$

b.
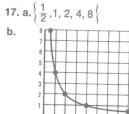

c. The product of the elements of ordered pairs equals 4.

---

13. X = {0, 2, 4, 6, 8} and Y = {0, 1, 2, 3, 4, 5}
  a. If $x \in$ X and $y \in$ Y, list the set of ordered pairs in the relation *x is double y.*
  b. Graph the relation.

14. S = {a, e, i, o, u} and T = {f, n, s, t}
  If $x \in$ S and $y \in$ T, list the set of ordered pairs in the relation *x followed by y spells a two-letter English word.* For example, (a, n) is in the relation.

15. A = B = {1, 2, 3, 6}
  a. Copy and complete the arrow diagram for the mapping, *is a factor of,* from set A to set B.
  b. Express the mapping as a set of ordered pairs.
  Note: When two sets of a mapping, A and B, are equal, it is usual to refer to a relation *on A.*

16. a. List the set of ordered pairs which describe the relation *is less than* on A = {1, 2, 3, 4, 5}, that is, from set A to set A. Also, draw a graph of the relation.
  b. Repeat Part **a** for the relation *is equal to.* Use the same coordinate plane as in Part **a,** but use a different color for the graph.
  c. Repeat Part **a** for the relation *is greater than.* Use a third color for the graph.

17. A mapping *M* is defined by $\left\{ \left(\frac{1}{2}, 8 \right), (1, 4), (2, 2), (4, 1), \left(8, \frac{1}{2} \right) \right\}$.
  a. List the set of first members of the pairs and the set of second members of the pairs.
  b. Draw a graph of the mapping *M,* and draw a smooth curve through the points.
  c. Describe in words a possible relation from the first set to the second.

8-2
Functions

A function from a set A to a set B is a special kind of mapping.

A *function* from A to B maps *each* element of A to *exactly one* element of B.

EXAMPLES

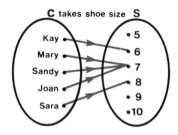

1. The arrow diagram shows the mapping, *takes shoe size,* from a set C of customers to a set S of shoe sizes.

Since each customer has only one shoe size, each element of C is paired with exactly one element of S. Since the mapping has this property, it is a function.

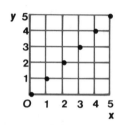

2. The graph shows the mapping $y = x$ on set $A = \{0, 1, 2, 3, 4, 5\}$. Since each x is paired with exactly one y, this mapping is a function.

If, for a mapping from S to T, s is an element of S and t is the corresponding element of T, t is called the *image* of s. You may say s *maps to t,* and write $s \rightarrow t$. You also may say this by using the ordered pair, (s, t).

EXAMPLES

In Example 1 some student may mention an acquaintance who takes a different size for each foot. Add this atypical person to set C to get an example of a nonfunction.

Which of the mappings shown are functions?

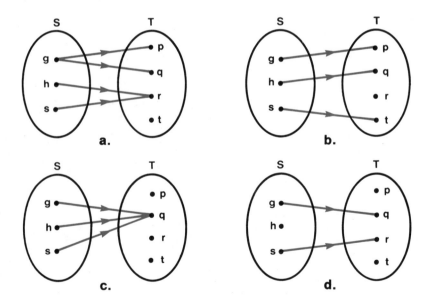

Diagram **a** is not a function since g has two images in T.
Diagrams **b** and **c** are both functions.
Diagram **d** is not a function because h does not have an image in set T.

EXERCISES

1. Each of the diagrams shows a mapping from a set P to a set Q. Which of these mappings are functions?

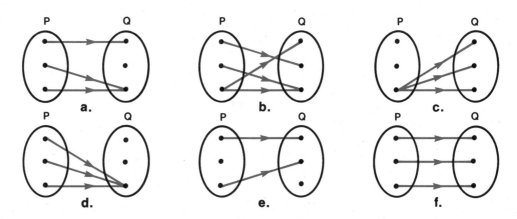

a.

b.

c.

d.

e.

f.

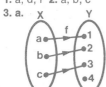

2. Each graph shows a mapping on $P = \{0, 1, 2, 3, 4, 5\}$, that is, a mapping from P to P. Which of these mappings are functions?

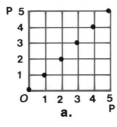

a.

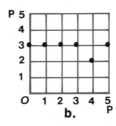

b.

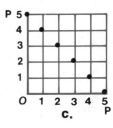

c.

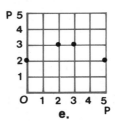

d.

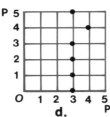

e.

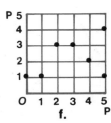

f.

3. $X = \{a, b, c,\}$ and $Y = \{1, 2, 3, 4\}$
   a. Make an arrow diagram to show the function f defined by $a \rightarrow 1$, $b \rightarrow 2$, $c \rightarrow 2$.
   b. List f as a set of ordered pairs.
   c. Graph f.

4. X and Y are the same sets as in Exercise **3.** A mapping M from X to Y is such that $a \rightarrow 3$, $b \rightarrow 2$, $b \rightarrow 4$, $c \rightarrow 1$.
   a. Show M as a set of ordered pairs and as an arrow diagram.
   b. Why is M not a function from X to Y?

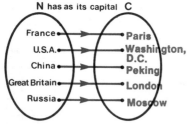
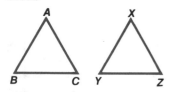
5. S = {1, 2, 3, 4} and T = {8, 9}. A mapping R maps each odd number in S to 8, and each even number in S to 9.
  a. List R as a set of ordered pairs, and draw an arrow diagram.
  b. Is R a function from S to T?
  c. Graph R.

6. The variables x and y are on the set S = {1, 2, 3, . . . , 20}. A relation on S is defined by the open sentence: *x is three times y.*
  a. List the set of ordered pairs (x, y) which describes the relation.
  b. Is this relation a function? Give a reason for your answer.

7. K = {1, 2, 3, 4, 5, 6}, and n ∈ K. A function f is such that if n is odd, n → 1, and if n is even, $n → \frac{1}{2}n$.
  a. Write the images of 1, 2, 3, 4, 5, and 6 under f.
  b. Express f as a set of ordered pairs.

8. E = {1, 2, 3, . . . , 12} and A = {1, 3, 5, 7, 9}. A function g from A to E is such that n → n + 2. Replacing n by members of A, find the set of ordered pairs in g. For example, (1, 3) ∈ g.

9. a. Copy the figure. Fill in the members of the second set (the image set) for the function, *has as its capital,* from set N to set C.
  b. Suggest an easy way of adapting the diagram to show the function, *is the capital of,* from the set of capitals to the set of countries.

10. The figure shows two equilateral triangles. List the six possible mappings of the vertices A, B, and C to the vertices X, Y, and Z in which all three of the vertices X, Y, and Z appear. For example, A → X, B → Y, C → Z.

11. a. Investigate by listing ordered pairs or by making arrow diagrams the number of functions possible from A = {a, b, c,} to B = {p, q}.
  b. Investigate the number of functions possible from B to A.

8-3
One-to-One Correspondence

EXAMPLES

OBJECTIVE:
To decide if a given mapping is or is not a one-to-one correspondence.

Functions often establish a relationship between two sets such that each element in each set is used exactly once in the function.

1. Each flag flown at the Olympic games corresponds to one of the participating nations.
2. In a certain school, each student has one book locker, and each book locker is used by one student. There is a one-to-one correspondence.

correspondence between the set of students and the set of book lockers.

3. There is a one-to-one correspondence between A = {a, e, i, o, u} and B = {1, 3, 5, 7, 9}.

A: a   e   i   o   u
       ↕   ↕   ↕   ↕   ↕
B: 1   3   5   7   9

Of course, this is not the only one-to-one correspondence from A to B.

See section notes in T.G. for more intuitive definitions for *1-1 correspondence*.

A ***one-to-one correspondence*** between set A and set B is a function from A to B for which each element of B is an image of exactly one element of A.

Consider a function from a set A to a set B which is a one-to-one correspondence. If you reverse the direction of this function, you will have a function from B to A which is also a one-to-one correspondence. Of course, it is not the same function as the original.

Now consider a function from a set A to a set B which is not a one-to-one correspondence. If you reverse the direction of this function, you have a mapping from B to A which is not a one-to-one correspondence. The mapping from B to A is not even a function.

EXAMPLES

Ask students the following question. If you have a function and reversing the direction also gives a function, what do you know?

1. The function from A to B is a one-to-one correspondence.

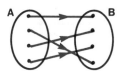

Reversing the direction produces a one-to-one correspondence from B to A.

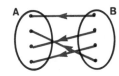

2. The function from A to B is not a one-to-one correspondence.

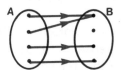

Reversing the direction produces a mapping which is not a function.

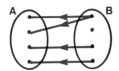

223

Two-headed arrows sometimes are used to show a one-to-one correspondence. Pointing one head of an arrow in each direction is a reminder that you have a one-to-one correspondence in both directions.

EXERCISES

1. Which of these diagrams shows a 1-1 (one-to-one) correspondence between set A and set B?

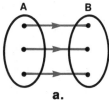

a.

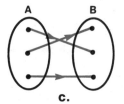

b.

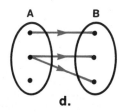

c.

d.

2. Below are graphs of mappings on P = {0, 1, 2, 3, 4}. Describe each graph by one of the following responses.
   a. A mapping, but not a function
   b. A function, but not a 1-1 correspondence
   c. A 1-1 correspondence

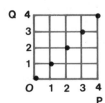 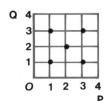 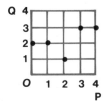

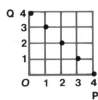 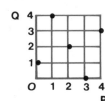 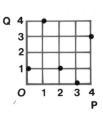

Exercise 3 may be treated as class discussion.

3. Let M represent the set of all mappings from set A to set B, F represent the set of all functions from A to B, and O represent the set of all 1-1 correspondences between A and B. Connect M, F, and O by the set inclusion sign, ⊆, to make a true statement.

4. a. Draw a diagram to show a possible 1-1 correspondence between A = {a, b} and P = {p, q}.
   b. Show the 1-1 correspondence in Part **a** in a graph.

c. Draw a diagram to show *another* possible 1-1 correspondence between A and P.

5. One copy of a book costs 90¢, two copies cost 180¢, three copies cost 270¢, and so on.
   a. What two sets of numbers are in 1-1 correspondence in the sentence?
   b. What is the cost of 7 books? How many books can be bought with $9?

6. A plane flies 500 km in 1 hour, 1000 km in 2 hours, 1500 km in 3 hours, and so on.
   a. What two sets of numbers are in 1-1 correspondence in the sentence?
   b. How far would the plane fly in 4 hours? How long would it take to fly 250 km?

7. State whether or not each pair of sets may be put in 1-1 correspondence.
   a. A = {0, 2, 4, 6}, B = {1, 3, 5, 7}
   b. P = {fingers on one hand}, Q = {days in a week}
   c. X = {a, b, c,}, Y = {c, a, b}
   d. G = {natural numbers less than 4}, T = {the vertices of △ABC}

8. List three examples from everyday life of 1-1 correspondences.

9. A shopkeeper wishes to mark prices with letters and chooses the code word *importance*. She sets up a 1-1 correspondence with the set of letters in this word and the set of numerals {0, 1, 2, 3, ... , 9}.

I	M	P	O	R	T	A	N	C	E
↕	↕	↕	↕	↕	↕	↕	↕	↕	↕
0	1	2	3	4	5	6	7	8	9

An article priced at $5.07 she marks T/IN.
   a. What would the code be for $1.32? $0.76?
   b. What would P/AI mean? M/MR?

10. In secret writing, VJG GPGOA KU KP UKIJV means THE ENEMY IS IN SIGHT. Set up a one-to-one correspondence for this code, and translate the coded message VJGA UGG OG.

11. Which of the following sets may be put in 1-1 correspondence with the set of students in your class?
    a. {desks in your classroom}
    b. {names on the class roll}
    c. {homes of students in your school}
    d. {months of the year}
    e. {dates of birth of students in your class}

12. See section notes in T.G.
13. a. None **b.** They are equal.

12. Draw diagrams to show that A = {1, 2, 3} and B = {p, q, r} can be put in a 1-1 correspondence in six ways.

13. A = {1, 2, 3, 4} and B = {p, q, r}
   a. How many mappings which give a 1-1 correspondence between A and B may be drawn on a coordinate system?
   b. Let M and N be any two sets each with a finite number of elements. Make a statement about the number of elements in sets M and N if you are told that the sets are in a one-to-one correspondence.

8-4

Graphing on the Real Numbers

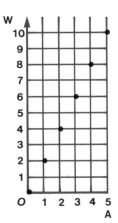

Mappings often are described using variables and an arrow. You may simply write $x \rightarrow 2x$ to indicate the mapping in which an element, x, has an image that is twice itself, or $2x$. If x is a variable on A = {0, 1, 2, 3, 4, 5}, then under the function $x \rightarrow 2x$ from A to the set of whole numbers, $0 \rightarrow 0$, $1 \rightarrow 2$, $2 \rightarrow 4$, $3 \rightarrow 6$, $4 \rightarrow 8$, and $5 \rightarrow 10$. Using ordered pairs, a graph of the function $x \rightarrow 2x$ from A to W may be drawn.

Graphs of mappings may be described by an equation in which y represents the image of x. The graph of $x \rightarrow 2x$ may be described by the equation $y = 2x$ where $x \in$ A and $y \in$ W.

While any mapping may be described by using arrow symbolism, or an equation, a function also may be written in **functional notation.** The function $x \rightarrow 2x$ may be written in functional notation as $f(x) = 2x$. The symbol $f(x)$ is read *f of x.* The symbol $f(x)$ may be thought of as the value of the image of x, that is, $y = f(x)$.

See section notes in T.G. for more intuitive approaches to providing meaning for these different methods for describing functions.

EXAMPLE

If $f(x) = 4 - x^2$, then $f(-2) = 4 - (-2)^2 = 0$
$$f(0) = 4 - (0)^2 = 4$$
$$f(1) = 4 - (1)^2 = 3$$
$$f(3) = 4 - (3)^2 = -5$$

You now have three ways to describe and denote a function.

   a. An arrow $x \rightarrow 4 - x^2$
   b. An equation using y $y = 4 - x^2$
   c. Functional notation $f(x) = 4 - x^2$

It is impossible to list or graph all ordered pairs for the function $f(x) = x^2$ on R, that is, from R to R. To graph a function on R, find enough ordered pairs which belong to the function to see a pattern. When you are fairly sure you know where the rest of the points would lie on the graph, draw a smooth line through the points you have found. If the smooth line were drawn perfectly, it would be exactly the graph of the function.

Stress this with each example done in class.

EXAMPLES

1. Graph the function $f(x) = x^2$ on R.

First, find some ordered pairs to see a pattern.

x	-3	-2	-1	0	1	2	3
$f(x)$	9	4	1	0	1	4	9

Next, graph the points and then connect them with a smooth line.

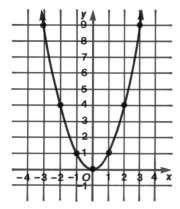

2. Graph the function $x \to \dfrac{x^3}{9}$ on R.

x	-3	-2	-1	0	1	2	3
$\dfrac{x^3}{9}$	-3	$-\dfrac{8}{9}$	$-\dfrac{1}{9}$	0	$\dfrac{1}{9}$	$\dfrac{8}{9}$	3

Every point on the line is assumed to be an element of the mapping. Of course, only a portion of the graph of a function on R may be drawn. Arrowheads at the ends of a graph indicate that the graph continues but is not drawn.

Mappings on R often involve regions of the plane. Again, it is impossible to list or graph all ordered pairs of such mappings. As before, you should find some ordered pairs to see a pattern.

EXAMPLE

Graph $y \geq x + 2$ on R.

x	-5	-2	0	1	5
y	-3	0	2	3	7
	-1	$\frac{1}{2}$	$2\frac{1}{4}$	$3\frac{1}{20}$	$7\frac{1}{10}$
	7	8	10	8	$7\frac{1}{2}$
	$\vdots$	$\vdots$	$\vdots$	$\vdots$	$\vdots$

With functional notation, $f(x)$ denotes the *unique* image of x. Ask why it would not make sense in this example to write $f(x) \geq x + 2$.

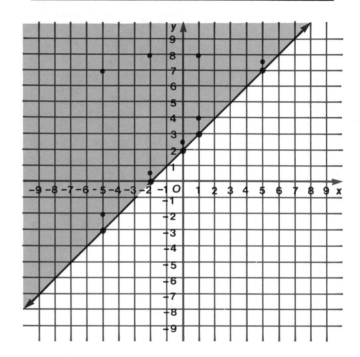

EXERCISES

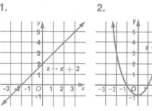

1.

2.

3.-12. See section notes in T.G.

Graph each function on R.

1. $x \rightarrow x + 2$

2. $x \rightarrow x^2 - 1$

3. $x \rightarrow x^3 - 1$

4. $x \rightarrow 1 - x^2$

5. $x \rightarrow \left| \dfrac{1}{x} \right| \ (x \neq 0)$

6. $x \rightarrow x - 4$

7. $x \rightarrow 2x$

8. $x \rightarrow 2x^3 + 2$

9. $x \rightarrow 2 - 2x$

10. $x \rightarrow -2x$

Graph each mapping on R.

11. $y = x + 1$

12. $y \leq x + 1$

Assign in pairs: 11 and 12; 13 and 14; 15 and 16.

13. $y = \dfrac{x^2}{4}$

14. $y \geq \dfrac{x^2}{4}$

15. $y = 3 - 2x$

16. $y \geq 3 - 2x$

Some of the functions described in Exercises 17-38 may be used for in-class demonstrations of constructing graphs.

Each function is denoted using one method. Write each function using the two remaining methods given on page 226.

17. $x \to 7 - x^2$

18. $y = 2x^2 - 3x + 1$

19. $g(x) = x + 2$

20. $x \to 4(x + 7)^2$

21. $y = x^2 + x$

22. $h(x) = (3 + x + x^2)^3$

23. $x \to \dfrac{x + 2}{x - 2}$

24. $y = \dfrac{5}{x + 5}$

25. $f(x) = 27 + \dfrac{1}{x} - \dfrac{3}{x^2}$

26. $x \to x$

27. $y = 1603 - 8x + 97x^2$

28. $f(x) = \dfrac{x^2 + x + 1}{x + 1}$

Compute the requested values of each function.

29. $f(x) = 9 - x^2$ — Compute $f(3)$ and $f(-2)$.

30. $g(x) = x^2 + 2x + 1$ — Compute $g(0)$ and $g(-1)$.

31. $h(x) = x^3 + 2x^2 - 2x - 1$ — Compute $h(1)$ and $h(-1)$.

32. $f(x) = x + 3$ — Compute $f(4)$ and $f(-10)$.

33. $f(x) = x^3$ — Compute $f(3)$ and $f(-3)$.

34. $f(x) = x^5 - 4x^3 + 16x - 32$ — Compute $f(0)$ and $f(1)$.

35. $p(x) = \dfrac{1}{2}x + 5$ — Compute $p\left(\dfrac{2}{3}\right)$ and $p(6)$.

36. $q(x) = 1 - x - x^2$ — Compute $q(1)$ and $q(-1)$.

37. $f(x) = x^2 - 7x + 12$ — Compute $f(3)$ and $f(4)$.

38. $f(x) = (x + 1) - (x - 1)$ — Compute $f(3)$ and $f(-3)$.

Draw the graph of each function.

39. $f(x) = x$

40. $g(x) = x^2$

41. $h(x) = x^3$

42. Look at the graphs from Exercises **1, 6, 7, 9, 10,** and **39.** What do they all have in common? What do the equations of these graphs have in common?

43. Look at the graphs from Exercises **2, 4,** and **40.** What do they all have in common? What do the equations of these graphs have in common?

44. Look at the graphs from Exercises **3, 8,** and **41.** What do they all have in common? What do the equations of these graphs have in common?

13. See section notes in T.G.
14. See section notes in T.G.
15. See section notes in T.G.
16. See section notes in T.G.
17. $y = 7 - x^2$, $f(x) = 7 - x^2$
18. $x \to 2x^2 - 3x + 1$, $f(x) = 2x^2 - 3x + 1$ 19. $y = x + 2$, $x \to x + 2$ 20. $y = 4(x + 7)^2$, $f(x) = 4(x + 7)^2$ 21. $f(x) = x^2 + x$, $x \to x^2 + x$ 22. $y = (3 + x + x^2)^3$, $x \to (3 + x + x^2)^3$
23. $y = \dfrac{x + 2}{x - 2}$, $f(x) = \dfrac{x + 2}{x - 2}$
24. $f(x) = \dfrac{5}{x + 5}$, $x \to \dfrac{5}{x + 5}$
25. $y = 27 + \dfrac{1}{x} - \dfrac{3}{x^2}$, $x \to 27 + \dfrac{1}{x} - \dfrac{3}{x^2}$ 26. $y = x$, $f(x) = x$
27. $f(x) = 1603 - 8x + 97x^2$, $x \to 1603 - 8x + 97x^2$
28. $y = \dfrac{x^2 + x + 1}{x + 1}$, $x \to \dfrac{x^2 + x + 1}{x + 1}$
29. $f(3) = 0$, $f(-2) = 5$
30. $g(0) = 1$, $g(-1) = 0$
31. $h(1) = 0$, $h(-1) = 2$
32. $f(4) = 7$, $f(-10) = -7$
33. $f(3) = 27$, $f(-3) = -27$
34. $f(0) = -32$, $f(1) = -19$
35. $p\left(\dfrac{2}{3}\right) = \dfrac{16}{3}$, $p(6) = 8$
36. $q(1) = -1$, $q(-1) = 1$
37. $f(3) = 0$, $f(4) = 0$
38. $f(3) = 2$, $f(-3) = 2$
39. See section notes in T.G.
40. See section notes in T.G.
41. See section notes in T.G.
42. They are straight lines. A term of x.
43. They are "bowl" shaped. A term of x^2.
44. They have a common (cubic) shape. A term of x^3.

8-5
Domain and Range

EXAMPLES

OBJECTIVE:

To name the range of a function f given the domain of f and a formula $f(x)$.

The functions in this book have variables on the real numbers or on some subset of the real numbers.

1. The function $f(x) = 4 - x^2$ has an image for any $x \in R$.

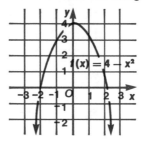

2. The mapping $x \rightarrow \dfrac{1}{x^2}$ is not a function if $x \in R$ because $\dfrac{1}{0^2}$ has no meaning. However, $f(x) = \dfrac{1}{x^2}$ is a function on $\{x \mid x \neq 0, x \in R\}$.

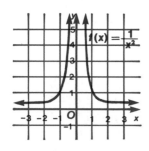

Sometimes it is desirable to limit the values of x you are willing to consider.

EXAMPLE

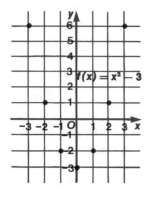

3. To sketch $f(x) = x^2 - 3$, you may let $\{-3 \leq x \leq 3, x \in Z\}$ be the replacement set for x.

The set of numbers allowed as replacements for the variable is called the **domain** of the function. In other words, if x is the variable in a function, then the domain of the function is the set of values of x that you are willing to use.

In Example **1,** the domain of $f(x) = 4 - x^2$ is $\{x \mid x \in R\}$.

In Example **2,** the domain of $f(x) = \dfrac{1}{x^2}$ is $\{x \mid x \neq 0, x \in R\}$.

In Example **3,** the domain of $f(x) = x^2 - 3$ is $\{x \mid -3 \leq x \leq 3, x \in Z\}$.

If no domain is specified for a function, you may assume the domain to be the set of real numbers which have a real number image.

Stress that students should keep this in mind when no domain is named.

See section notes in T.G. regarding these restricted definitions for domain and range.

Once a function and its domain are given, the **range** of the function is the set of values of the function for the given replacements for the variable. In other words, the range is the set of images of the values in the domain.

To find the range of a function, you may draw and investigate the graph of the function over the given domain. On the other hand, calculating certain values of the function may be enough to find the range.

EXAMPLES

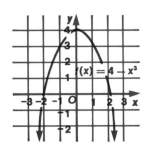

1. What is the range of $f(x) = 4 - x^2$ with domain $\{x \mid x \in R\}$?

You can see in the graph that $f(x)$ is always less than or equal to 4. Also, there is no limit on $f(x)$ in the negative direction. Therefore, the range of $f(x)$ is $\{f(x) \mid f(x) \leq 4, f(x) \in R\}$.

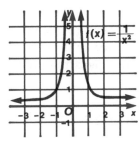

2. What is the range of $f(x) = \dfrac{1}{x^2}$ with domain $\{x \mid x \neq 0, x \in R\}$?

As you move along the x-axis away from the origin, the graph shows that $f(x)$ gets closer to 0. However, $f(x)$ never reaches 0. There is no real number solution for $\dfrac{1}{x^2} = 0$ so $f(x)$ is always greater than 0. Also, as the values of x become closer to 0, $f(x)$ becomes large without limit. The range of $f(x)$ is $\{f(x) \mid f(x) > 0, f(x) \in R\}$.

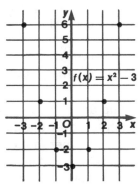

3. What is the range of $f(x) = x^2 - 3$ with domain $\{x \mid -3 \leq x \leq 3, x \in Z\}$?

By calculating each value, you will find the range to be $\{-3, -2, 1, 6\}$.

EXERCISES

1. See section notes in T.G.
2. See section notes in T.G.

Graph each function on the given domain. Mark the domain on the x-axis before drawing the graph.

1. $f(x) = x^2$ with domain $\{x \mid -1 \leq x \leq 1, x \in R\}$
2. $f(x) = |x|$ with domain $\{x \mid -3 \leq x \leq 3, x \in R\}$

3.

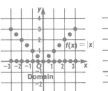

4.

5.

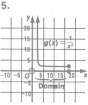

6.

7.

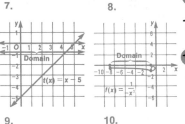

8.

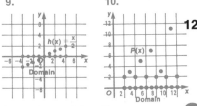

9.

10.

It may be useful to discuss why domains often are restricted to some proper subset of R. This is usually done for one of two reasons:

1. Out of necessity as with

$$f(x) = \frac{1}{x^2}$$

2. As a practical matter as in Exercise 14.

11. See section notes in T.G.
12. a. $f(x) = 5x$
b. $\{x \mid 0 \le x \le 10, x \in W\}$
13. a. $d(s) = 3s$
b. $\{s \mid 45 \le s \le 55\}$
c. $\{d(s) \mid 135 \le d(s) \le 165\}$
14. a. $c(h) = 8h + 4$
b. $\left\{ h \mid 0 \le h \le 4\frac{1}{2} \right\}$
c. $\left\{ 0, \frac{1}{2}, 1, 1\frac{1}{2}, 2, 2\frac{1}{2}, \right.$
$\left. 3, 3\frac{1}{2}, 4, 4\frac{1}{2} \right\}$
d. $4, $8, $12, $16, $20, $24, $28, $32, $36, $40

232

3. $f(x) = |x|$ with domain $\left\{ -3, -\frac{5}{2}, -2, -\frac{3}{2}, -1, -\frac{1}{2}, 0, \frac{1}{2}, \right.$ $\left. 1, \frac{3}{2}, 2, \frac{5}{2}, 3 \right\}$

4. $h(x) = 4 - x^2$ with domain $\{x \mid -1 \le x \le 1, x \in R\}$

5. $g(x) = \frac{1}{x^2}$ with domain $\{x \mid 0 < x \le 16, x \in R\}$

6. $g(x) = x + \frac{1}{x}$ with domain $\{x \mid x > 0, x \in R\}$

7. $t(x) = x - 5$ with domain R.

8. $f(x) = \frac{1}{-x^2}$ with domain $\{x \mid -9 \le x \le -1, x \in R\}$

9. $h(x) = \frac{x}{2}$ with domain $\{-4, -3, -2, -1, 0, 1, 2, 3, 4\}$.

10. $p(x) =$ the smallest prime number which is a factor of x with domain $\{2, 3, 4, 5, 6, 7, 8, 9, 10, 11, 12\}$.

11. Pearl sells a certain fabric by the yard. She refuses to accept an order for less than 5 yards. For x yards of material, the cost in dollars is given by the function $c(x) = 1 + 2x$. Draw a graph showing the cost on the y-axis and the amount of material on the x-axis.

12. During a store-closing sale, all pairs of shoes are being sold for $5.00 per pair. The limit on pairs per customer is set at ten.
a. Write an equation for the function which gives the cost for x pairs of shoes.
b. What is the domain of the function?

13. The minimum speed on an interstate highway is 45 mph and the maximum speed is 55 mph.
a. Using s for speed and $d(s)$ for distance, write an equation for the function which gives the distance a car will travel in 3 hours at constant speed s.
b. If drivers obey the laws, what is the domain of d?
c. Using set notation and the domain in Part **b**, what possible values are there for $d(s)$?

14. Labor and shop charges for a TV repair shop are computed in two parts. First, $4.00 is charged on any job to cover the cost of paper work and storage. In addition, $8.00 per hour is charged for the time a repairperson is working on the set.
a. Write the equation of a function which gives labor and shop charges for a repair job which took h hours. Let $c(h)$ be the total charge.
b. If you tell the repairperson that you will not spend more than $40.00 on labor and shop charges, what domain are you giving for the variable h?

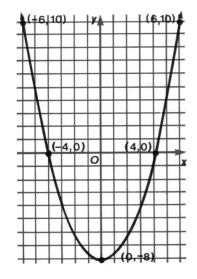

c. If the shop records h in half-hour intervals only, what domain are you giving for the variable h when you set a $40.00 maximum charge?

d. For the domain given in Part **c,** what are the different possible amounts you could be charged?

State the range of each function with the given domain.

15. $g(x) = 3x$ with domain R.

16. $h(x) = x^2 + 1$ with domain $\{x \mid -1 \le x \le 1, x \in \text{R}\}$.

17. $f(x) = 4 - x^2$ with domain $\{x \mid x \ge 2, x \in \text{R}\}$.

18. $g(x) = x^3$ with domain R.

19. $s(x) = \dfrac{1}{x^2}$ with domain $\{x \mid x \ne 0, x \in \text{Z}\}$.

20. $p(x) =$ the smallest prime number which is a factor of x with domain $\{2, 3, 4, 5, 6, 7, 8, 9, 10, 11, 12\}$

21. $p(x) =$ the smallest prime number which is a factor of x with domain $\{2, 4, 6, 8, 10, 12, \ldots\}$

22. $h(x) = |x|$ with domain R.

State a domain for each function which would give the indicated range.

Sample $f(x) = \dfrac{x^2}{2} - 8$ with range $\{f(x) \mid 0 \le f(x) \le 10, f(x) \in \text{R}\}$.

By inspecting the graph, you can see that $f(x)$ is between 0 and 10 if x is between -6 and -4 *and* between 4 and 6. The domain is $\{x \mid -6 \le x \le -4, x \in \text{R}\} \cup \{x \mid 4 \le x \le 6, x \in \text{R}\}$.

23. $f(x) = x^2 - 2x + 1$ with range $\{f(x) \mid f(x) > 0, f(x) \in \text{R}\}$.

24. $f(x) = \dfrac{1}{x}$ with range $\{f(x) \mid 0 < f(x) \le 9, f(x) \in \text{Z}\}$.

25. $f(x) = x^2$ with range $\{0, 1, 4, 9, 16, 25, \ldots\}$.

26. $f(x) = x - 10$ with range $\{f(x) \mid f(x) \ge 10, f(x) \in \text{R}\}$.

27. $f(x) = 10 - x$
The range of f is $\{f(x) \mid f(x) > 10, f(x) \in \text{Z}\}$.

28. $f(x) = 9 - x^2$
The range of f is $\{f(x) \mid 0 \le f(x) \le 9, f(x) \in \text{Q}\}$.

29. $f(x) = x^3$
The range of f is $\{f(x) \mid -8 \le f(x) \le 27, f(x) \in \text{R}\}$.

30. $f(x) = x^2 - x - 12$
The range of f is $\left\{f(x) \mid -12\dfrac{1}{4} \le f(x) \le 0, f(x) \in \text{R}\right\}$.

31. $f(x) = 9 - x^2$
The range of f is $\{f(x) \mid f(x) \le 0, f(x) \in \text{R}\}$.

32. $f(x) = \dfrac{1}{x^2 - 1}$, $x \neq -1, 1$

The range of f is $\{f(x) \mid f(x) > 0, f(x) \in R\}$.

33. Weather-treated two-by-four boards are sold by the foot. If x is the number of feet, the cost in dollars is given by $c(x) = \dfrac{x}{4}$. Boards can be bought in 6-, 8-, 10-, 12-, 14-, and 16-foot lengths only.

a. What is the domain of the function $c(x)$ for the purchase of a single board?

b. What is the range of the function $c(r)$ for the purchase of a single board?

34. A small loan company makes loans of $100.00. It never makes a loan for less than 5% interest per year. The law prohibits making loans for more than 15% interest per year.

a. The function $i(r) = 100r$ gives the amount of interest per year a person will owe on a hundred dollar loan at interest rate r. What is the domain for the function where r must be expressed as a rational number? The company's computer does not work with irrational numbers.

b. What is the range of the function $i(r)$ for $100 loans?

35. On a 100-mile stretch of tollway between two pay booths, the minimum speed limit is 40 mph and the maximum speed limit is 55 mph.

a. Use s to denote the average speed of a motorist over the 100-mile stretch. Write an equation for a function $t(s)$ where $t(s)$ is the time taken in hours to go the 100 miles.

b. State the domain of t which would include all average speeds that may result from obeying the speed laws.

c. State the range of t for the domain you gave in Part **b.**

d. Imagine that the time taken by a motorist to drive the 100 miles was not in the range of Part **c.** Could you be absolutely certain that a law was broken? Why? Assume that there are no exits and no rest stations on the 100-mile stretch.

e. If the time taken by a motorist to drive the 100 miles was in the range of Part **c,** could you be *absolutely* sure that the motorist obeyed all speed laws? Why?

8-6
OBJECTIVE:
To graph the solution set of a given linear open sentence.

Lines Parallel to Axes

The function $f(x) = 4$ with domain R is called a **constant function.** No matter what value of the domain is chosen, its image is 4.

x	. −80	$-\dfrac{1}{3}$	0	6	1000
y	4	4	4	4	4

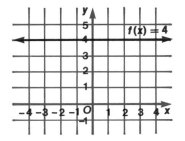

The graph of $f(x) = 4$ is a straight line 4 units above the x-axis and parallel to the x-axis.

> In general, a **constant function** is a function which has only one element in its range. Constant functions on R always may be described by an equation of the form $f(x) = c$ or $y = c$ where c is a specific real number.

Until now you have thought of an equation such as $x = 3$ as naming a single point on the number line.

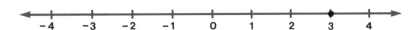

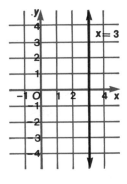

If you consider all points in a coordinate plane then there are many solutions to $x = 3$. The following graph shows the solution set for $x = 3$, $\{(x, y) \mid x = 3\}$.

In general, each straight line parallel to the y-axis can be described by an equation of the form $x = c$ where c is a specific real number.
Straight lines often are boundaries for regions in the plane. The graph of $y \geq c$ or $y \leq c$ includes the points of the line with equation $y = c$. To show that the line is part of the region, draw the boundary line with a solid line.

EXAMPLE

Graph $\{(x, y) | y \geq 2\}$.

x	−4	$-2\frac{1}{2}$	0	$\frac{3}{4}$	2	4
y	2	2	2	2	2	2
	3	$2\frac{1}{2}$				
	4	$3\frac{1}{10}$				
	5	$4\frac{1}{6}$				
	6	7				

The graph of $y > c$ or $y < c$ does *not* include the points of the line with equation $y = c$. In this case, the boundary line is broken or dashed. This shows that it does not belong to the set.

EXAMPLE

Emphasize the broken line and solid line conventions on drawing boundaries.

Graph $\{(x, y) | y > 2\}$.

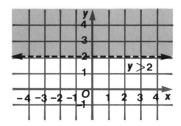

EXERCISES

1. Relation 2. Function
3. Function 4. Relation

Imagine that for functions on subsets of R, the domain is given as points on the *x*-axis. The range would be given as points on the *y*-axis. State whether each graph is a graph of a function or of a relation.

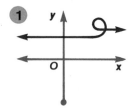
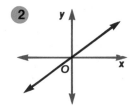
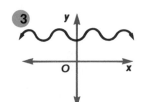
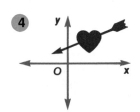

236

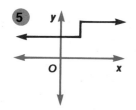 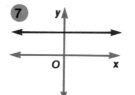 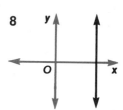

5 **6** **7** **8**

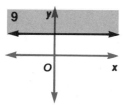 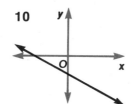 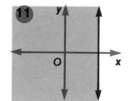 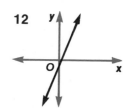

9 **10** **11** **12**

5. Relation 6. Function
7. Function 8. Relation
9. Relation 10. Function
11. Relation 12. Function
13. Answers will vary;
$x =$ constant
14. (1) Relation (2) Function
(3) Relation (4) Relation
(5) Relation (6) Relation
(7) Relation (8) Function
(9) Relation (10) Function
(11) Relation (12) Function

15.

16. See section notes in T.G.
The x and y axes

17. a. See section notes in T.G.
b. See section notes in T.G.
c. See section notes in T.G.
d. See section notes in T.G.
18. a. See section notes in T.G.
b. See section notes in T.G.
c. See section notes in T.G.
d. See section notes in T.G.
19. a. See section notes in T.G.
b. P ∩ Q = {(3,3)}
20. a See section notes in T.G.
b. P ∩ Q = {(−4, −2)}
21. a. See section notes in T.G.
b. P ∩ Q = {(x, y) | x ≥ 0
and y ≥ 2}
22. a. See section notes in T.G.
b. (2, 6), (2, −1), (6, −1),
(6, 6) c. x = 2 and x = 6
y = −1 and y = 6

13. If a straight line is not a function, what type of equation could be used to describe it?

14. Repeat Exercises **1–12** except imagine that domains are given on the y-axes and ranges are given on the x-axes. You may find it easier if you "cheat" and turn the book so that the x-axes point up-and-down.

15. Show the sets of points in the same coordinate plane.
    a. $\{(x, y) \mid x = 4\}$ **b.** $\{(x, y) \mid x = -2\}$
    c. $\left\{(x, y) \mid y = 1\frac{1}{2}\right\}$ **d.** $\{(x, y) \mid y = -5\}$

16. Show the sets of points in the same coordinate plane.
    a. $\{(x, y) \mid x = 0\}$ **b.** $\{(x, y) \mid y = 0\}$
    What special lines are these?

17. Graph each line and region in the same coordinate plane. Decide first if the line should be drawn solid or broken.
    a. $x = 1; x \geq 1$ **b.** $x = 6; x < 6$
    c. $y = 3; y > 3$ **d.** $y = -2; y \leq -2$

18. Graph each set of points in a separate coordinate plane by shading the proper region.
    a. $\{(x, y) \mid x > 0\}$ **b.** $\{(x, y) \mid y \leq 0\}$
    c. $\{(x, y) \mid x \geq 3\}$ **d.** $\{(x, y) \mid y < 6\}$

19. **a.** Graph the sets of points $P = \{(x, y) \mid x = 3\}$ and $Q = \{(x, y) \mid y = 3\}$ in the same coordinate plane.
    b. What set is given by P ∩ Q?

20. Repeat Exercise **19** for $P = \{(x, y) \mid x = -4\}$ and $Q = \{(x, y) \mid y = -2\}$.

21. Repeat Exercise **19** for $P = \{(x, y) \mid x \leq 0\}$ and $Q = \{(x, y) \mid y \geq 2\}$.

22. **a.** Graph the lines in the same coordinate plane.
    $x = 2$ $y = -1$ $x = 6$ $y = 6$

b. Give the points of intersection of each pair of lines.

c. Which pair of lines does not intersect?

23. a. Graph the sets of points in the same coordinate plane.

   $A = \{(x, y)\,|\,x = 5\}$ $B = \{(x, y)\,|\,y = -5\}$
   $C = \{(x, y)\,|\,x = -3\}$ $D = \{(x, y)\,|\,y = 2\}$

   b. Use set notation to write A ∩ B, B ∩ C, C ∩ D, and D ∩ A.

   c. What is A ∩ C and B ∩ D?

24. a. Graph the sets of points in the same coordinate plane by shading the proper regions. $M = \{(x, y)\,|\,2 < x < 6\}$, $N = \{(x, y)\,|\,-3 < y < 5\}$

   b. Color the region M ∩ N. Calculate its area.

25. Repeat Exercise **24** for the regions $0 = \{(x, y)\,|\,-3 < x < 3\}$ and $P = \{(x, y)\,|\,-2 < y < 3\}$.

26. $F = \{(x, y)\,|\,y < 3\}$, $G = \{(x, y)\,|\,y = 3\}$, $H = \{(x, y)\,|\,y > 3\}$, $I = \{(x, y)\,|\,x < 3\}$, $J = \{(x, y)\,|\,x = 3\}$, $M = \{(x, y)\,|\,x > 3\}$ Show each intersection in a separate coordinate plane.

   a. G ∩ J   **b.** G ∩ M   **c.** J ∩ H
   d. F ∩ I   **e.** F ∩ M

Excursions in Mathematics: Flow Charts

This flow chart shows the steps for graphing equations in which y is equal to some expression with x as the variable.

1. 7, 8

2. a.   b.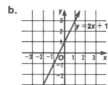

   c.

(6)

3. Answers will vary.

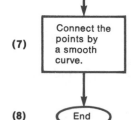

(1) Start

(2) Replace x by a real number a.

(3) Compute b, the y-value when x = a.

(4) Mark (a, b) in the plane.

(5) Do you see a pattern? No → Choose a real number, a, which you have not used as a replacement for b.

Yes

(7) Connect the points by a smooth curve.

(8) End

1. If you could not see a pattern to the points, what steps would you never reach?

2. Use this flow chart to graph each equation.

   a. $y = \dfrac{1}{2}x^2$ **b.** $y = 2x + 1$ **c.** $y = 3x^2 - 1$

3. Place steps between **(7)** and **(8)** so that the flow chart could be used to graph $y \le$ expression with x as the variable.

8-7
Lines: y=x+c
and y=−x+c

To graph the solution set of a given linear equation equivalent to $y = \pm x + c$.

Both $y = x$ and $y = -x$ are equations of straight lines that pass through the origin.

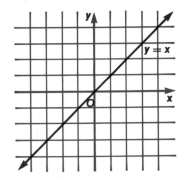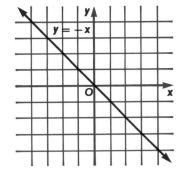

The graph of $y = x + c$ where c is a nonzero real number is a straight line parallel to the line with equation $y = x$.

For forms $y = x + c$ and $y = -x + c$, ask how it may be known at a glance at which point the equation's graph intersects the y-axis.

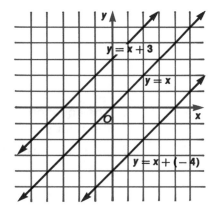

The graph of $y = -x + c$ where c is a nonzero real number is a straight line parallel to the line with equation $y = -x$.

It is assumed that students understand the concept *parallel*. If not, define lines l_1 and l_2 as parallel if they have no common points.

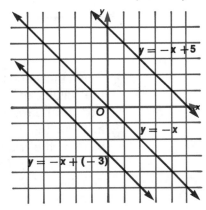

Notice that $y = x$ is of the form $y = x + c$ since $y = x$ may be written as $y = x + 0$. Also, $y = -x$ is of the form $y = x + c$ since $y = -x$ may be written as $y = -x + 0$.

It may not always be obvious that an equation is equivalent to $y = x + c$ or $y = -x + c$. In such cases, you may need to find equivalent equations to decide.

EXAMPLES

1. $6x + 6y = 0 \Leftrightarrow 6x + 6y - 6x = 0 - 6x$

$$\Leftrightarrow \qquad 6y = -6x$$

$$\Leftrightarrow \qquad \frac{1}{6}(6y) = \frac{1}{6}(-6x)$$

$$\Leftrightarrow \qquad y = -x$$

The equation $6x + 6y = 0$ is equivalent to an equation of the form $y = -x + c$.

2. $6y - 3x = 3x + 9 \Leftrightarrow 6y - 3x + 3x = 3x + 9 + 3x$

$$\Leftrightarrow \qquad 6y = 6x + 9$$

$$\Leftrightarrow \qquad \frac{1}{6}(6y) = \frac{1}{6}(6x + 9)$$

$$\Leftrightarrow \qquad y = x + \frac{3}{2}$$

The equation $6y - 3x = 3x + 9$ is equivalent to an equation of the form $y = x + c$.

3. $6y + 3x = 5x + 9 \Leftrightarrow 6y + 3x - 3x = 5x + 9 - 3x$

$$\Leftrightarrow \qquad 6y = 2x + 9$$

$$\Leftrightarrow \qquad \frac{1}{6}(6y) = \frac{1}{6}(2x + 9)$$

$$\Leftrightarrow \qquad y = \frac{1}{3}x + \frac{3}{2}$$

The equation $6y + 3x = 5x + 9$ is not equivalent to an equation of the form $y = x + c$ or $y = -x + c$.

EXERCISES

1. $-6, 4, -1, -100, 0, 14$

2. a. b.

c. D, E, and F above line; A, B, and G below line **d.** (3)

1. Given that each point lies on the line with equation $y = -x$, write the values of a, b, c, d, e, and f. $A(6, a)$, $B(-4, b)$, $C(1, c)$, $D(d, 100)$, $E(e, 0)$, $F(f, -14)$

2. a. Draw the line with equation $y = x$.
   b. Plot the points $A(4, 2)$, $B(5, 1)$, $C(3, 3)$, $D(3, 5)$, $E(1, 2)$, $F(-4, -1)$, $G(-2, -5)$.
   c. Which of these points lie above the line, and which lie below the line?

3. a.

b. Answers will vary.

4.   **5.**

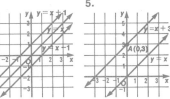

6.

7. Answers will vary.

8. $(0, 3)$ **9.** $(0, -3)$

10. $\left(0, \dfrac{1}{2}\right)$

11. $(0, 5)$ **12.** $(0, 1)$ **13.** $(0, 2)$
14. $y = x - 5$ **15.** $y = x + 5$
16. $y = x + 2$ **17.** $y = x + 3$
18. $y = x + 3$ **19.** $y = x + 3$
20. $y = -x + 7$
21. $y = -x - 2$ **22.** $y = -x - 2$
23. $y = -x + 4$
24. Equivalent **25.** Equivalent
26. Equivalent **27.** Not equivalent
28. Equivalent **29.** Equivalent

d. If the point (r, s) lies above the line in Part **a,** which statements are true?
   (1) $r > s$ **(2)** $r = s$ **(3)** $r < s$

3. a. Graph each set of points in the same coordinate plane.
   $\{(x, y)\,|\,y > x\}$, $\{(x, y)\,|\,y = x\}$, $\{(x, y)\,|\,y < x\}$
  b. List the coordinates of two points in each set.

4. Graph the line with equation $y = x$. In the same coordinate plane, draw the lines with equations $y = x + 1$ and $y = x - 1$. Give the coordinates of the points on the y-axis through which these lines pass.

5. Draw the line through $A(0, 3)$ parallel to the line $y = x$. What is the equation of this line?

6. Repeat Exercise **5** for the line through $B(0, -6)$ parallel to the line $y = x$.

7. Say as much as you can about each line.
  a. $y = x$ **b.** $y = x + 100$ **c.** $y = x - 10$

Name the point on the y-axis that is on the line described by each equation.

8. $y = x + 3$ **9.** $y = -x - 3$

10. $y = -x + \dfrac{1}{2}$ **11.** $y - x = 5$

12. $x + y = 1$ **13.** $2y = 2x + 4$

Write the equation of a line which passes through the point and is parallel to $y = x$.

14. $(0, -5)$ **15.** $(0, 5)$
16. $(0, 2)$ **17.** $(0, 3)$
18. $(1, 4)$ **19.** $(7, 10)$

Write the equation of a line which passes through the point and is parallel to $y = -x$.

20. $(0, 7)$ **21.** $(0, -2)$
22. $(1, -3)$ **23.** $(3, 1)$

State whether or not each equation is equivalent to an equation of the form $y = x + c$ or $y = -x + c$.

24. $\dfrac{y}{2} = 2 - \dfrac{x}{2}$ **25.** $3(x + y) = 6$

26. $2x + y = x$ **27.** $y - 2x = x + 2$

28. $\dfrac{x + y}{3} = 1$ **29.** $\dfrac{x + y + 3}{3} = 1$

30. $10x - y = 10y - x$

31. $\dfrac{y - x}{5} = 0$

32. $\dfrac{x + 2y + 3}{4} = \dfrac{x + y + 2}{2}$

33. $\dfrac{x + y}{2} = \dfrac{2x - 2y}{4}$

34. $\dfrac{x + 3}{3} = \dfrac{2y + 3}{6}$

35. $\dfrac{2}{3}x = \dfrac{2y + 1}{3}$

36. $\dfrac{x + 2y}{2} = y + \dfrac{x}{2}$

37. $x + y + 3 = x + y + 5$

8-8
Lines: y=mx

OBJECTIVES:

1. To name the slope of its graph given a linear equation.
2. To name the slope of a line given two points in the line.

Sometimes along mountain roads there are signs which tell how steep the road is. These signs may give the measure of an angle or they may give a rational number for the slope or grade of the hill. *Slope* or *grade* may be described by $\dfrac{\text{rise}}{\text{run}}$.

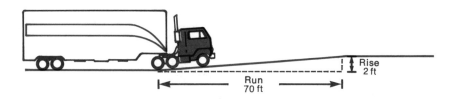

Mention that $\dfrac{1}{35}$ gives the same slope as $\dfrac{2}{70}$.

If a road rises 2 feet in a horizontal distance of 70 feet, the slope would be $\dfrac{2}{70}$.

A graph of a straight line also has steepness. The steepness is called the **slope** or **gradient** of the line. Slope usually is given by **$\dfrac{rise}{run}$**.

$$\text{slope} = \dfrac{\textbf{change in } \textit{y}\textbf{-coordinates between points } \textit{A} \textbf{ and } \textit{B}}{\textbf{change in } \textit{x}\textbf{-coordinates between points } \textit{A} \textbf{ and } \textit{B}}$$

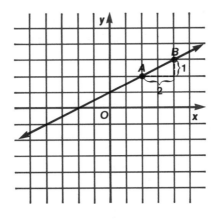

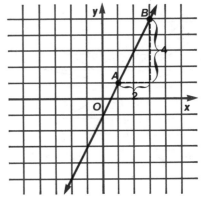

Slope $= \dfrac{1}{2}$

Slope $= \dfrac{4}{2} = 2$

The slope may be calculated using the coordinates of the points $A(1, 1)$ and $B(3, 5)$.

$$\text{slope} = \frac{\text{change in } y\text{-coordinates}}{\text{change in } x\text{-coordinates}}$$

$$= \frac{1 - 5}{1 - 3}$$

$$= \frac{-4}{-2}$$

$$= 2$$

If a line runs *downhill* as you move to the right across the plane, its slope will be a negative number.

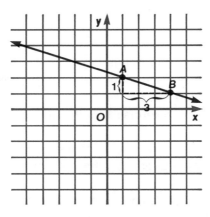

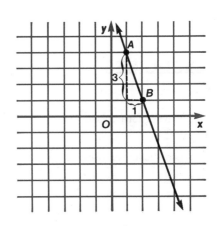

Slope $= -\dfrac{1}{3}$

Slope $= -\dfrac{3}{1} = -3$

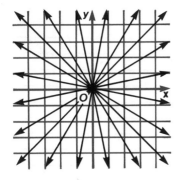

There are infinitely many lines which pass through the origin. In fact, for each possible slope there is a unique straight line which passes through (0, 0).

All straight lines which pass through the origin, except one, may be written in the form $y = mx$, where m is a real number representing the slope of a line.

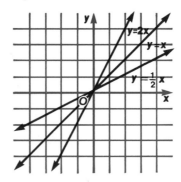 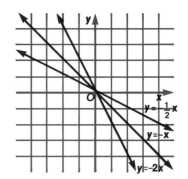

If necessary, allow discussion time for the concepts *no slope* and *zero slope*.

The only straight line through the origin which cannot be written as $y = mx$ is the y-axis itself. The equation of the y-axis must be written as $x = 0$ or an equivalent equation. The y-axis does not have a slope since the run is zero, and division by zero is impossible.

The equation of the x-axis may be written as $y = 0x$. This means that the slope of the x-axis is zero.

EXERCISES

1. a. See section notes in T.G.
b. $y = 2x$
2. a. See section notes in T.G.
b. $y = \frac{1}{2}x$
3. a. See section notes in T.G.
b. $y = \frac{2}{3}x$
4. a. See section notes in T.G.
b. $y = -\frac{1}{2}x$
5. Slope $= 1$ 6. Slope $= 2$
7. Slope $= 3$ 8. Slope $= \frac{1}{3}$
   See section notes in T.G.

1. **a.** Plot the points (1, 2), (2, 4), (3, 6), and (4, 8).
   b. Draw a straight line through these points, and write its equation.
2. Repeat Exercise **1** for the points $(-4, -2), (-2, -1), (2, 1)$, and $(4, 2)$.
3. Repeat Exercise **1** for the points (3, 2), (6, 4), and (9, 6).
4. Repeat Exercise **1** for the points $(2, -1), (4, -2)$, and $(6, -3)$.

Sketch each line in the same coordinate plane. Write the slope of each line.

5. $y = x$ **6.** $y = 2x$ **7.** $y = 3x$ **8.** $y = \frac{1}{3}x$

Write the equation of each line through the origin with the given slope.

9. 1   **10.** 5   **11.** -1 **12.** $\frac{1}{10}$ **13.** -10 **14.** 123

Sketch the line through the origin and each given point. Then write the equation of the line.

15. $A(2, 2)$ **16.** $B(3, 6)$ **17.** $C(8, 4)$
18. $D(5, 2)$ **19.** $E(1, 6)$ **20.** $P(4, -4)$
21. $Q(4, -2)$ **22.** $R(-5, -5)$ **23.** $S(-5, -1)$
24. $T(8, 0)$

Graph each equation and write the slope of the straight line.

25. $y = 3x + 2$ **26.** $6 = 2x + 2y$
27. $y = 3x - 5$ **28.** $x - 3y = 6$
29. $y = 5 - 3x$ **30.** $y + x = \frac{2x + 3}{2}$

Through two points, only one straight line may be drawn. In other words, two points determine a straight line. Draw the straight line through each pair of points and write the slope of the line.

31. $(0, 0), (1, 3)$ **32.** $(1, 3), (4, 4)$
33. $(5, 7), (6, 9)$ **34.** $(6, 10), (2, 3)$
35. $(4, 0), (0, 6)$ **36.** $(-1, -2), (-4, -3)$

Without drawing a graph, write the slope of the straight line which passes through each pair of points.

37. $(0, 0), (1, -2)$ **38.** $(0, 0), (1, 2)$
39. $(2, 3), (4, 5)$ **40.** $(-1, 2), (2, -1)$
41. $(-5, 0), (0, -5)$ **42.** $(100, 200), (300, 700)$

8-9
Equations
of Lines

For most students, the opening statement should be a summary statement. However, be prepared to explain it further.

OBJECTIVE:
To write an equation for a line given adequate information about its slope and/or its elements.

All equations of straight lines are equivalent to equations of one of the following forms.

1. $y = mx + c$
2. $x = c$

An equation which is equivalent to $x = c$ has a graph which is a straight line parallel to the y-axis. It does not have a slope.

If an equation is equivalent to $y = mx + c$ then it has slope m and passes through the point $(0, c)$. This point is called the **y-intercept.** When an equation is given in the form $y = mx + c$, it is said to be in the **slope-intercept form.**

EXAMPLE

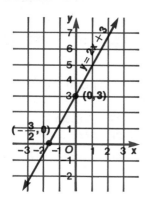

Graph $y = 2x + 3$.

The y-intercept is $(0, 3)$. The x-coordinate of the x-intercept is found by letting $y = 0$ and solving for x. In this example, the x-intercept is $\left(-\dfrac{3}{2}, 0\right)$. Since two points determine a straight line, knowing these or any two points is sufficient to graph the line.

If the slope of a line and one point of the line are known, it is possible to write the equation of the line.

EXAMPLE

Focus on the fraction $\dfrac{y - 14}{x - 4}$ and ask why it is important that (x, y) is a point *other than* $(4, 14)$.

Write an equation for the line which has slope 3 and contains the point $(4, 14)$.

Let (x, y) represent the coordinates of another point of the line. Since the slope may be written as the difference of the y-coordinates divided by the difference of the x-coordinates, the following is true. Remember $m = 3$.

$$\frac{y - 14}{x - 4} = 3 \Leftrightarrow y - 14 = 3(x - 4)$$

In general, if you know the slope, m, of a line and the coordinates, (a, b), of a point of the line, then the equation $y - b = m(x - a)$ describes the line. When an equation is given in the form $y - b = m(x - a)$, it is said to be in the **point-slope form.**

If necessary, use Exercises 1-4 as class discussion for slow students.

EXERCISES

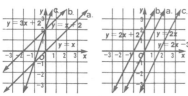
1. Sketch these lines in the same coordinate plane.
   a. $y = x$ **b.** $y = x + 2$ **c.** $y = 3x + 2$
2. Repeat Exercise **1** for these equations.
   a. $y = 2x$ **b.** $y = 2x + 2$ **c.** $y = 2x - 3$
3. Repeat Exercise **1** for these equations.
   a. $y = \dfrac{1}{2}x$ **b.** $y = \dfrac{1}{2}x + 4$ **c.** $y = \dfrac{1}{2}x - 4$
4. Repeat Exercise **1** for these equations.
   a. $y - 1 = 2(x - 1)$ **b.** $y - 1 = 4(x - 1)$
   c. $y - 3 = 2(x + 2)$

5. $m = -1$, Answers will vary.
6. $m = -1$ 7. $m = -2$
8. $m = -3$

For Exercises 10-15 encourage students to first write equations in the form $y = mx + c$. Then they may graph directly.

9. (5) See section notes in T.G.
   (6) See section notes in T.G.
   (7) See section notes in T.G.
   (8) See section notes in T.G.
10. See section notes in T.G.
11. See section notes in T.G.
12. See section notes in T.G.
13. See section notes in T.G.
14. See section notes in T.G.
15. See section notes in T.G.
16. $y = 7x + 5$
17. $y = \frac{1}{3}x + 1$
18. $y = -3x - 3$ 19. $y = 2$
20. $y - 3 = 4(x - 2)$
21. $y = 3$ 22. $y = -5(x - 5)$
23. $y = \frac{1}{3}x$

Exercises 25-34 are early experiences in solving systems of open sentences.

24. Point-slope form:
$y - b = m(x - a)$:
$y - b = mx - ma$:
$y = mx - ma + b$. Let
$c = ma + b$ (which are given real numbers); then $y = mx + c$: slope-intercept form
25. See section notes in T.G.
$A \cap B = \left\{ \left(\frac{-8}{5}, \frac{11}{5} \right) \right\}$,

26. See section notes in T.G.
27. See section notes in T.G.
28. See section notes in T.G.
29. See section notes in T.G.
30. See section notes in T.G.
31. $P \cap Q = \{(x, y) \mid y > x + 3\}$
32. See section notes in T.G.
33. $P \cap S = \emptyset$
34. See section notes in T.G.
35. Yes. Answers will vary.

Write the slope of each line. Also name a point on each line.

5. $y = -x$

6. $y - 2 = -(x + 3)$

7. $y = -2x - 4$

8. $y + 1 = -3(x + 1)$

9. Sketch each line in Exercises **5–8.**

Sketch each line in a separate coordinate plane.

10. $y = x + 6$

11. $y = 2x - 4$

12. $2y - 2 = 3x - 6$

13. $x + y = 3$

14. $2x + 5y = 10$

15. $3y - 4 - x = 3$

Write the equation for each line.

16. The line has a slope of 7 and contains the point (0, 5).

17. The line has a slope of $\frac{1}{3}$ and contains the point (0, 1).

18. The line has a slope of -3 and contains the point (0, -3).

19. The line has a slope of 0 and contains the point (0, 2).

20. The line has a slope of 4 and passes through (2, 3).

21. The line has a slope of 0 and passes through (3, 3).

22. The line has a slope of -5 and passes through (5, 0).

23. The line has a slope of $\frac{1}{3}$ and passes through (0, 0).

24. Show that the point-slope form and the slope-intercept form of an equation are equivalent.

25. In the same coordinate plane, show $A = \{(x, y) \mid y = 3x + 7\}$ and $B = \left\{ (x, y) \mid y = \frac{1}{2}x + 3 \right\}$. What is $A \cap B$?

26. a. Graph $y = \frac{1}{2}x - 3$ and $y = -x + 1$ in the same coordinate plane.

b. On the graph of Part **a**, shade $A \cap B$ where $A = \left\{ (x, y) \mid y > \frac{1}{2}x - 3 \right\}$ and $B = \{(x, y) \mid y > -x + 1\}$.

Shade each region in a separate coordinate plane.

27. $P = \{(x, y) \mid y > x\}$

28. $Q = \{(x, y) \mid y > 3 + x\}$

29. $R = \{(x, y) \mid y < -x\}$

30. $S = \{(x, y) \mid y < x - 1\}$

Combine your answers to Exercises **27–30** to show or describe each set.

31. $P \cap Q$ **32.** $P \cap R$ **33.** $P \cap S$ **34.** $R \cap S$

35. Are the points $(0, c)$ and $(1, m + c)$ on the graph of $y = mx + c$? Would it be easier to plot these points or the x- and y-intercepts to graph the line?

Chapter Summary

1. A mapping or relation from set A to set B is a set of ordered pairs with each first component from set A and each second component from set B.
2. Mappings may be described by the listing method, in set-builder notation, in an arrow diagram, or in a graph.
3. If the ordered pair (a, b) belongs to a mapping, then b is the image of a. The element a maps to b, $a \rightarrow b$.
4. A function from set A to set B maps each element of A to exactly one element of B.
5. A one-to-one (1-1) correspondence between set A and set B is a function from A to B for which each element of B is an image of exactly one element of A.
6. Graphs of mappings may be described by arrow symbolism or by an equation in which y represents the image of x.
7. Functions may be described in functional notation where $f(x)$ may be thought of as the value of the image of x.
8. To graph a function on R, graph enough ordered pairs which belong to the function to see a pattern. Connect these points with a smooth line.
9. The set of numbers used as replacements for a variable in a function is called the domain of the function.
10. Once a function and its domain are given, the range of the function is the set of images of the values in the domain.
11. The equation $y = mx + c$ is the slope-intercept form for a straight line. The real number m describes the slope or steepness of the line. The y-intercept, $(0, c)$, is the point where the line crosses the y-axis.
12. The equation $y - b = m(x - a)$ is the point-slope form for a straight line. The line has slope m and passes through point (a, b).
13. All equations of straight lines are equivalent to either $y = mx + c$ or $x = c$. Lines described by $x = c$ have no slope.

REVIEW EXERCISES   8-1

1. See section notes in T.G.

1. A = {red, green, amber} and B = {stop, go}
Draw an arrow diagram to show the mapping, *on a traffic signal means,* from A to B.

2.

P is greater than Q

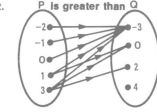

3. $\{(-1, -1), (0, 0), (1, 1),$
$(2, 2), (4, 4)\}$
4. $\{(0, 0), (-1, 1), (1, 1), (2, 4)\}$
5. $\{(-1, 1), (0, 2), (2, 4)\}$
6. a. $\{(2, 0), (2, 2), (2, 4), (2, 6),$
$(3, 0), (3, 3), (3, 6), (4, 0), (4, 4),$
$(6, 0)\ (6, 6)\}$
b.

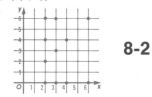

8-2

7. a. Monday and Fridays
b. Wednesday and Saturday
c. None
8. $f(x) = x^2 + 1,$
$x \rightarrow x^2 + 1,$
$y = x^2 + 1$
9. $g(x) = 2x - 1,$
$x \rightarrow 2x - 1,$
$y = 2x - 1$
10. $h(x) = \frac{1}{2}x^2,$
$x \rightarrow \frac{1}{2}x^2,\ y = \frac{1}{2}x^2,$
11. $a = 3, b = -2$
12. $f(2) = 12$ **13.** $f(-1) = -3$
14. $f(0) = -2$ **15.** $f\left(\frac{1}{2}\right) = 0$
16. $f\left(\frac{-1}{2}\right) = -3$
17. Not a function **18.** Function
19. Function **20.** Not a function

2. $P = \{-2, -1, 0, 1, 3\}$ and $Q = \{-3, 0, 2, 4\}$.
Draw an arrow diagram to show the mapping, *is greater than,* from P to Q.

$X = \{-1, 0, 1, 2, 4\}$. Describe each mapping on X by a set of ordered pairs.
3. *is equal to*
4. *has a square of*
5. *is two more than*

6. A mapping *R* on the set $T = \{0, 2, 3, 4, 6\}$ is described by the open sentence *x exactly divides y.*
   a. Describe *R* as a set of ordered pairs.
   b. Graph *R*.

7. Janet, Sheena, Freda, and Margaret like to play tennis together but cannot all be free to play on every evening. Janet is unable to play on Tuesdays, Wednesdays, and Saturdays. Sheena is free to play on Wednesdays, Thursdays, and Saturdays. Freda has to stay at home on Mondays and Thursdays. Margaret can play on Mondays, Tuesdays, and Fridays. None of them play on Sundays.
   a. On what evenings can Janet and Margaret play?
   b. When can Freda and Sheena play?
   c. On what evenings can Janet, Freda, and Margaret play together?

Redefine each function on R using each of the three ways of describing a function.
8. *f* maps each real number *x* to its square plus 1.
9. *g* maps each real number *x* to its double less 1.
10. *h* maps each real number *x* to half its square.

11. A function *f* on R is defined by $f(x) = ax + b$ where *a* and *b* are integers. Given that $f(3) = 7$ and $f(1) = 1$, find *a* and *b*.

$f(x) = 2x^2 + 3x - 2, x \in R$. Find each value.

12. $f(2)$ **13.** $f(-1)$ **14.** $f(0)$ **15.** $f\left(\frac{1}{2}\right)$ **16.** $f\left(-\frac{1}{2}\right)$

Which of the following mappings are functions?
17. $\{(0, 0), (2, 1), (4, 2), (6, 3), (2, -1), (4, -2)\ (6, -3)\}$
18. $\{(0, 0), (2, 1), (4, 2), (6, 3), (8, 2), (10, 1), (12, 0)\}$
19. $\{(1, a), (2, a), (3, a), (4, a), (5, a)\}$
20. $\{(a, 1), (a, 2), (a, 3), (a, 4), (a, 5)\}$

8-2, 8-3

b.

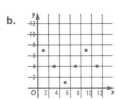

21. State whether each arrow diagram describes a mapping, a function, or a one-to-one correspondence.

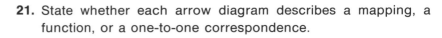

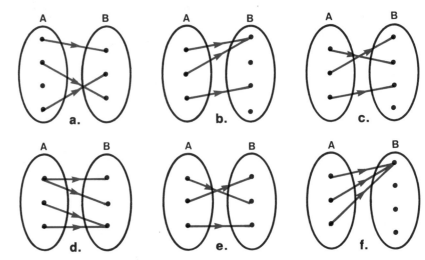

22. Describe the function $x \rightarrow x + 4$ on Z as a set of ordered pairs.

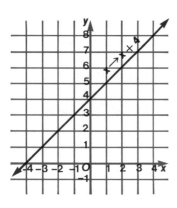

23. A one-to-one correspondence is set up from {fractions} to {points in the coordinate plane} such that to each fraction $\dfrac{y}{x}$ there corresponds the point (x, y), and to each point (x, y) there corresponds the fraction $\dfrac{y}{x}$. The variables are on the set of natural numbers.

Draw a graph to show the set of points which corresponds to each set of fractions.

a. $\left\{\dfrac{1}{2}, \dfrac{2}{4}, \dfrac{3}{6}, \dfrac{4}{8}, \dfrac{5}{10}, \dfrac{6}{12}\right\}$

b. $\left\{\dfrac{7}{1}, \dfrac{4}{3}, \dfrac{1}{5}, \dfrac{4}{7}, \dfrac{7}{9}, \dfrac{4}{11}\right\}$

8-5

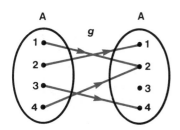

A g A

24. The arrow diagram defines a function g from A to A.
  a. Write the image of 2 under g.
  b. What elements of the domain have 2 as their image?
  c. Write the range of g.
  d. List the ordered pairs of g, and graph g.

25. Repeat Exercise **24** for the function h defined in this arrow diagram.

A h A

26. A function f is defined by $f(x) = x^4$ and the domain of f is $\{x \mid x < 0,\ x \in R\}$. Find the range of the function.

27. A function $g = \{(-3, -3),\ (-2, -1,),\ (-1, 1),\ (0, 3),\ (1, 5),\ (2, 7),\ (3, 9)\}$. List the domain and range of g.

The domain of each function is given. State the range.

28. $f(x) = x^2 + 2x$
  The domain of f is $\{x \mid x \le 1,\ x \in R\}$

29. $g(x) = \dfrac{2}{x}$
  The domain of g is $\{x \mid x \ne 0,\ -1 \le x \le 1,\ x \in R\}$

30. $h(x) = -x + |x|$
  The domain of h is R.

The range of each function is given. State a domain which would give the indicated range.

31. $f(x) = \dfrac{1}{x}$
  The range of f is $\{f(x) \mid f(x) < 0,\ f(x) \in R\}$.

32. $g(x) = \dfrac{1}{x^2}$
  The range of g is $\left\{1, \dfrac{1}{4}, \dfrac{1}{9}, \dfrac{1}{16}, \dfrac{1}{25}, \dfrac{1}{36}, \ldots\right\}$.

33. $h(x) = x^3 + 1$
  The range of h is $\{h(x) \mid h(x) > 0,\ h(x) \in R\}$.

8-6

Graph each set of points in a separate coordinate plane.

34. $\{(x, y) \mid y = 3\}$
35. $\{(x, y) \mid y > 4\}$
36. $\{(x, y) \mid y = 6\}$
37. $\{(x, y) \mid 1 \le y < 5\}$
38. $\{(x, y) \mid 0 < x < 3\}$
39. $\{(x, y) \mid x \ge -2\}$
40. $\{(x, y) \mid x = 2,\ y = 3\}$
41. $\{(x, y) \mid -1 < x < 0\}$

---

24. **a.** 1 **b.** 1, 4 **c.** 1, 2, 4
d. (1, 2), (2, 1), (3, 4), (4, 2)

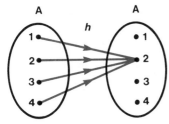

25. **a.** 2 **b.** 1, 2, 3, 4 **c.** 2
d. (1, 2), (2, 2), (3, 2), (4, 2)
See section notes in T.G.
26. $\{f(x) \mid f(x) > 0, f(x) \in R\}$
27. domain $\{-3, -2, -1,$
0, 1, 2, 3$\}$, range
$\{-3, -1, 1, 3, 5, 7, 9\}$
28. $\{f(x) \mid 0 \le f(x), f(x) \in R\}$
29. $\{g(x) \le -2 \text{ or } g(x) \ge 2,$
$g(x) \in R\}$
30. $\{h(x) \mid h(x) \ge 0, h(x) \in R\}$
31. $\{x \mid x < 0, x \in R\}$
32. $\{x \mid x \in N\}$
33. $\{x \mid x > -1, x \in R\}$
34. See section notes in T.G.
35. See section notes in T.G.
36. See section notes in T.G.
37. See section notes in T.G.
38. See section notes in T.G.
39. See section notes in T.G.
40. See section notes in T.G.
41. See section notes in T.G.

42. a. $\{(x, y) \mid 2 < y < 5\}$
b. $\{(x, y) \mid -2 \le x \le 5\}$
c. $\{(x, y) \mid -4 \le x \le 3,$
$2 \le y \le 6\}$

43.

$X \cap Y = \{(2, 1)\}$

44.

8-7, 8-8

45.   **46.**

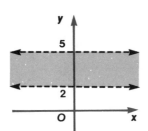

47. a

b. $A \cap B = \{(x, y) \mid 3 \le x \le 5,$
$-1 \le y \le 2\}$

$A \cap B$ = a rectangle bounded by
$x = 3$, $x = 5$, $y = -1$, and $y = 2$.

8-9

48. See section notes in T.G.
49. See section notes in T.G.
50. See section notes in T.G.
51. See section notes in T.G.
52. See section notes in T.G.
53. See section notes in T.G.
54. See section notes in T.G.
55. See section notes in T.G.
56. See section notes in T.G.
57. See section notes in T.G.
58. See section notes in T.G.
59. See section notes in T.G.
60. See section notes in T.G.
61. See section notes in T.G.
62. See section notes in T.G.
63. See section notes in T.G.
64. See section notes in T.G.

42. Use set notation to define the set of points in each shaded region.

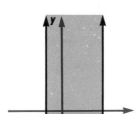

a.   **b.**   **c.**

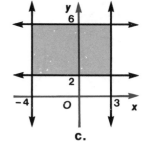

43. On the same diagram, draw the sets of points, $X = \{(x, y) \mid x = 2\}$, and $Y = \{(x, y) \mid y = 1\}$. Describe the set $X \cap Y$.

44. Graph these equations in the same coordinate plane.
   a. $y = 3x$ **b.** $y = 3x + 3$ **c.** $y = 3x - 2$

45. Repeat Exercise **44** for these equations.

   a. $y = \dfrac{1}{2}x$ **b.** $y = \dfrac{1}{2}x + 3$ **c.** $y = \dfrac{1}{2}x - 2$

46. Plot the points $A(0, 4)$, $B(1, 3)$, $C(2, 2)$, and $D(4, 0)$. Draw the straight line through these points. State which of the following equations correspond to the points on this line.
   a. $y = 4 - x$ **b.** $x + y = 4$ **c.** $y = x + 4$

47. a. Sketch the following sets of points on the same coordinate plane.
   $A = \{(x, y) \mid 3 \le x \le 5\}$ $B = \{(x, y) \mid -1 \le y \le 2\}$
   b. Describe in set notation and in words $A \cap B$.

48. Show on a coordinate plane the set $A \cap B$ where $A = \{(x, y) \mid y > x + 2\}$ and $B = \{(x, y) \mid y < x + 5\}$.

Graph each line.
49. $y = x + 1$ **50.** $y = x + 3$
51. $y = -x + 1$ **52.** $y = -x - 1$
53. $\{(x, y) \mid y = x\}$ **54.** $\{(x, y) \mid y = 3x\}$
55. $\{(x, y) \mid 2y = x\}$ **56.** $2x + 3y = 12$
57. $3x - y = 6$ **58.** $4x - 5y + 20 = 0$
59. $y - 4 = 2(x + 3)$ **60.** $y = 2(x - 1)$
61. $y - 2 = x$ **62.** $y - 2 = x + 2$
63. $y + 1 = 4(x + 1)$ **64.** $y - 1 = 2x - 2$

CHAPTER 9

ratio and proportion

9-1
Ratio

OBJECTIVE:

To describe the relation between two measurements as a ratio.

Stress this distinction. Have students name other examples and decide for each which is more appropriate to use: Ratio or difference. There may, of course, be valid disagreements.

EXAMPLES

Students with 5- or 10-speed bicycles may wish to discuss gear ratios further.

At the end of a baseball game, the scoreboard shows Hawks 8, Cardinals 2. The following statements compare the scores.

The Hawks defeated the Cardinals by six runs.
The Hawks outscored the Cardinals by a ratio of 4 to 1. $\left(\text{Notice that } \frac{8}{2} = \frac{4}{1}.\right)$

Two quantities may be compared either by looking at a difference or by looking at a **ratio.**

Often the ratio is the more appropriate means of comparison.

1. A batter recipe calls for 2 parts cornmeal to 1 part flour. The ratio of cornmeal to flour is 2 to 1. This may be written 2:1.
2. The gear ratio for a given set of gears is 3:1.

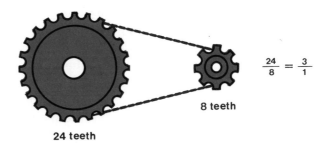

$$\frac{24}{8} = \frac{3}{1}$$

8 teeth

24 teeth

3. If you say that a soft maple tree grows twice as fast as a hard maple, you are saying that the ratio of soft maple growth to hard maple growth is 2:1.

Encourage students to read *x:y* as, "In the ratio *x* to *y*."

A *ratio* is a comparison of two quantities measured or counted by the same unit of measure.

To express a ratio in *simplest form* means that the fraction form of the ratio is in *lowest terms*. The ratio 64:32 in simplest form is 2:1 since $\frac{64}{32} = \frac{2}{1}$.

EXERCISES

1. 5:8 **2.** 9:5 **3.** 2:5

4. 3:5 **5.** 5:6 **6.** 12:5 **7.** $\frac{1}{1}$

In Exercises 5 and 7, stress that giving simplest form requires the same unit of measure. For example, 3 ft and 9 in. are not in ratio *3:9*, but rather *36:9*.

8. $\frac{1}{1}$

9.

Length of a dimension

10. 10 cm, $7\frac{1}{2}$ cm

11. 5:4, 5:4, 25:16

12. $\frac{15}{16}$, $\frac{16}{15}$, $\frac{15}{31}$

13. $\frac{4}{5}$ **14.** Pork and beans 23¢,

Grapefruit 7:6, Lunch meat 16:15, Peas $1.00

Express each ratio in simplest form. Remember that the two quantities must be measured by the same unit.

1. 25:40　　　**2.** $2\frac{1}{4}:1\frac{1}{4}$　　　**3.** 18¢:45¢

4. 600 m:1 km　**5.** 15 sq ft to 2 sq yd　**6.** 1 sq ft to 60 sq in.

7. 2 cm to 20 mm

8. What is the ratio of the lengths of two sides of a square?

9. On graph paper, draw a rectangle with length and width in the ratio 2:1. What have you not been told?

10. If in Exercise **9** the width is 5 cm, what is the length? If the length is 15 cm, what is the width?

11. Two squares have sides with lengths 15 mm and 12 mm. Find the ratio of the lengths of their sides. Find the ratio of their perimeters. Find the ratio of their areas.

12. A man earns $150 per week and his wife earns $160. What is the ratio of the man's wage to his wife's? What is the ratio of the wife's wage to her husband's? What is the ratio of the man's wage to the total household income?

13. A city has a population of 11,700. There are 5200 people under 21 years of age. Calculate the ratio of the number of people under 21 to the number of people over 21.

14. The same items are purchased from the same store on January 15 of one year and on January 15 of the next year. The table records this information for comparison. Give a numerical value for each letter in the table.

Item	Second Year Cost	First Year Cost	Ratio of Cost Increase or Decrease Second Year:First Year
Oranges	$1.25 per dozen	$1.00 per dozen	5:4
Pork and Beans	2 cans for 41¢	M¢ per can	41:46
Grapefruit	10¢ each	7 for 60¢	P:Q
Lunch meat	12 oz for $.96	1 lb for $1.20	R:S
Peas	3 cans for T¢	25¢ per can	4:3

Excursions in Mathematics:
Irrational Numbers

In the figure, *d* is the length of the diagonal of a square which is one unit on a side. The *exact* length of *d* is an irrational number.

1. Would it be possible to find two whole numbers, *n* and *m*, so that *n*:*m* = length of diagonal:length of side?
2. What would you say to someone who claimed to have found *n, m* ∈ W such that $\frac{d}{s} = \frac{n}{m}$? Begin by asking yourself whether *d* is an irrational number if $\frac{d}{s} = \frac{n}{m}$.

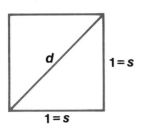

1. No 2. Answers will vary; Impossible

9-2
Rate

OBJECTIVES:
1. To solve rate problems using the *unitary method.*
2. To graph rate situations using an equation of form *y = mx.*
3. To identify the slope (*m*) as the rate per unit.

The word **rate** is used to give a relationship between quantities measured by different units of measure. When you say *50 miles per hour* you are relating distance and time; *50 miles per hour* is a rate of speed. If you say *100 bushels per acre* you might be relating quantity of corn to land area, which is a rate of crop yield.

A rate may give a relationship between quantities measured by the same unit of measure. For example, a recycling plant may find that for 5 tons of collected garbage, there are 2 tons of reusable material. The rate of usable material is $\frac{2}{5}$ ton per ton.

The word *per* often is used in giving rates.

EXAMPLES

1. The rent is 150 dollars *per* month.
2. The cost is 57 dollars *per* tire.
3. The speed is 88 feet *per* second.

255

Rates sometimes are given for several units. The price of apples might be 5 for 39¢. The rate per unit is $7\frac{4}{5}$¢ per apple $\left(\frac{39}{5} = 7\frac{4}{5}\right)$.

Many problems involving rates may be solved by first finding a rate per unit and then multiplying.

EXAMPLES

1. Five yards of fabric cost $4.25. Find the cost of 12 yards.

Let u be the unit cost.
$5u = 4.25 \Leftrightarrow u = .85$
Find the cost of 12 yards (units).
$$12u = c$$
$$12(.85) = c$$
$$10.20 = c$$
So, 12 yards will cost $10.20.

2. A woman on a business trip drives 200 km in $2\frac{1}{2}$ hr. How long does it take her to go 140 km?

Let u be the number of *minutes* needed to travel 1 km.

$$200\,u = 150 \Leftrightarrow u = \frac{3}{4}$$

Find t, the time it takes for 140 km.

$t = 140u$

$t = 140 \cdot \dfrac{3}{4}$

$t = 105$ or 1 hour, 45 minutes
It takes her 1 hr 45 min to travel 140 km.

EXERCISES

Find each rate in the given units.
1. 8 oranges cost 96¢; cents per orange
2. 20 candy bars cost $3.00; cents per bar
3. 273 units of electricity per week; units per day
4. 20 km in 4 hours; km per hour
5. 20 apples weigh 2 kg; apples per kg
6. 140 km takes $2\frac{1}{2}$ hours; km per hour
7. A man types 3600 words in 1 hour. What is his rate of typing in words per minute?
8. What is the rate per minute of a typist who types 3840 words in 1 hour?
9. A year's television rental is $130. What is the rate per week?
10. A year's rent for a house is $3120. What is the rate per week?

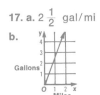

11. The cost of 6 meters of cloth is $6.72. What is the cost of 1 meter? What is the cost of 11 meters?

12. A car travels 456 km on 48 liters of gas. How far does it go on 30 liters?

13. A man earns $26 for an 8-hour day. How much does he earn at the same rate for a 40-hour week?

14. A factory makes 375,000 cars in a year. Find the rate of production per week and per day. The factory is closed for two weeks of the year. The workers have a 5-day week.

15. A car travels at 20 meters per second. How many meters does it travel per hour? How many kilometers does it travel per hour?

16. A machine which breaks up old roadbeds moves 2 miles in 3 hours.

  a. Give its rate of speed in miles per hour.

  b. Complete the following table for the machine.

Hours	1	3	4	5	0
Miles	?	2	?	?	?

  c. On a coordinate plane, label the *x*-axis *hours* and the *y*-axis *miles*. Plot the points from the table in Part **b** and draw the graph.

  d. How does the slope of the graph compare with your answer to Part **a**?

17. An airplane at cruising speed and altitude uses fuel at a rate of 5 gallons every two miles.

  a. Write the rate of fuel usage in gallons per mile.

  b. Draw a graph as in Exercise **16**. Label the *x*-axis *miles* and the *y*-axis *gallons*.

  c. How does the slope of the graph compare with your answer to Part **a**?

18. The table shows the amounts of materials for mixing concrete.

Concrete in Cubic Yards	Water in Gallons	Sand in Pounds	Rock or Gravel in Pounds	Cement in Pounds
1	25	1400	1600	560
2	50	2800	3200	1120
3	75	4200	4800	1680
4	100	5600	6400	2240

a. How many gallons of water are required to mix 6 cubic yards of concrete?

b. How many pounds of rock are required for $1\frac{1}{2}$ cubic yards of concrete?

c. To make $\frac{1}{2}$ cubic yard of concrete, how much of each ingredient is used?

d. Write the amount of each ingredient needed to make 7 cubic yards of concrete.

19. In recipe books, quantities are given for a certain number of servings. The amount of each ingredient can be graphed in the form $y = mx$. If the graphs for each ingredient are placed on the same coordinate plane, the recipe for any quantity or any number of servings can be read from the graph.

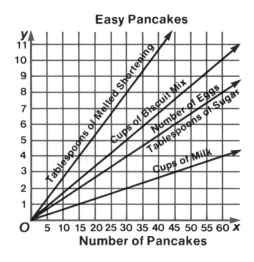

Easy Pancakes

Number of Pancakes

a. List the ingredients for making 30 pancakes.
b. List the ingredients for making 15 pancakes.
c. Why was the length of one unit drawn shorter on the *x*-axis than on the *y*-axis?

20. The list of ingredients is for hot chocolate.

Hot Chocolate
1 cup water
2 ounces unsweetened chocolate
1 pinch salt
4 tablespoons sugar
3 cups milk
Makes 6 servings

a. Place this list on a coordinate plane using the *x*-axis for the number of servings. (To make a convenient graph, make the units on the *y*-axis twice as long as the units on the *x*-axis.)

b. Read your graph to write the list of ingredients as it would be given for 18 servings.

9-3
Direct
Proportion

The following table and graph show the cost per ounce of a certain candy.

Candy in Ounces	Cost in Pennies
1	3
2	6
3	9
4	12
5	15
6	18

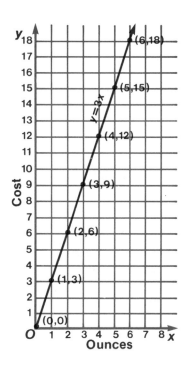

Rate: 3¢ per ounce   **Slope: 3**

When two quantities are related to give a graph with equation $y = mx$, the two quantities are directly proportional. In the table, the cost is directly proportional to the number of ounces.

Notice that for any two ordered pairs (*ounces, cost*), the ratio of the weights is the same as the ratio of the costs.

EXAMPLES

1. The points (1, 3) and (4, 12) are on the graph shown above.

$$4:1 = 12:3 \quad \text{or} \quad \frac{4}{1} = \frac{12}{3}$$

2. The points (2, 6) and (6, 18) are shown on the graph.

$$6:2 = 18:6 \quad \text{or} \quad \frac{6}{2} = \frac{18}{6}$$

This fact about equal ratios can be used to solve problems involving direct proportion.

EXAMPLES

1. If 27 cm³ of gold weighs 522 g, find the mass of 18 cm³.

If w is the mass of 18 cm³ of gold, then (522, 27) and (w, 18) will be points on the graph. Using equal ratios, the following equation may be written.

$$\frac{w}{522} = \frac{18}{27} \Leftrightarrow w = \frac{18}{27} \cdot \frac{522}{1}$$

$$\Leftrightarrow w = 348$$

The mass of gold is 348 grams.

2. A restaurant uses 6 gallons of cooking oil each week. How many gallons does it use in 31 days?

Days	Gallons
7	6
31	x

$$\frac{x}{6} = \frac{31}{7} \Leftrightarrow x = \frac{31}{7} \cdot \frac{6}{1}$$

$$\Leftrightarrow x = \frac{186}{7} \text{ or } 26\frac{4}{7}$$

Stress this example. Students should be able to use both methods.

The number of gallons the restaurant uses in 31 days is $26\frac{4}{7}$.

Notice that in the examples a rate per unit was not computed. It saved steps to use facts about ratios. This method may be called the **ratio method** of calculation. If you used the **unitary method** of calculation to solve the example about the cooking oil, the solution would be as follows.

EXAMPLE

In 7 days, 6 gallons are used. The rate is $\frac{6}{7}$ gallons per day. In 31 days, $31 \cdot \frac{6}{7}$ gallons are used. The number of gallons used in 31 days is $26\frac{4}{7}$.

EXERCISES

1. $3.96 2. 912 km

Solve each problem using the ratio method.

1. Handkerchiefs are priced at 3 for 99¢. Find the cost of 1 dozen.

2. A car travels 456 km on 40 liters of gasoline. How far does it go on a full tank of 80 liters?

3. If 72 books weigh 9 kg, how many books weigh 6 kg?

4. If 72 books weigh 9 kg, what is the mass of 80 books?

5. $45.65 is exchanged for £20.75. How much is $80 worth in pounds? The symbol £ is used for British pounds.

6. A hotel charge for 5 days is $111.75. What is the charge for 8 days?

7. On a house plan, 5 cm represents 8 m. What actual length is represented by 9.5 cm? What length on the plan represents 28 m?

8. Oranges cost $1.16 per dozen. Find the cost of 27 oranges.

9. A firm's weekly wages for 350 employees is $52,510. At the same average wage, what is the weekly wage for 250 employees?

10. A stack of 350 sheets of paper is 2.1 cm high. How high a stack is 500 sheets?

11. If 4 Swiss francs can be exchanged for $8, what are 104 Swiss francs worth in American money?

12. Suppose (3, 4) and (x, y) are two *different* points on a straight line, $x, y \in N$. Which of the following information is enough to determine which straight line contains the two points?

  a. $\frac{3}{x} = \frac{4}{y}$ **b.** $x - 3 = y - 3$ **c.** $\frac{3}{4} = \frac{x}{y}$ **d.** $\frac{3}{4} = \frac{y}{x}$ **e.** $3y = 4x$

13. Which of the equations listed in Exercise **12** are equivalent to $\frac{3}{x} = \frac{4}{y}$?

14. The graph gives the cost for different quantities of a book.

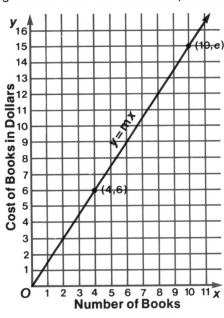

261

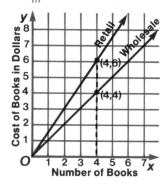

Cost of Books in Dollars — Number of Books

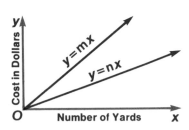

Cost in Dollars — Number of Yards

Ask which letter gives the shop
charge in the equation
$y = mx + c$.

a. How many books does m dollars buy?

b. Is it true that $4c = 6 \cdot 10$?

c. What numerical value for n makes $c = nm$ a true statement?

15. The graphs show both wholesale and retail costs for different quantities of a book.

a. Markup refers to the difference between retail and wholesale price. How much markup is on an order of 20 books?

b. How much markup is on an order of 8 books?

c. Do number of books and amount of markup vary in direct proportion?

16. The retail cost y of x yards of a certain material is given by $y = mx$.

The wholesale cost y' of the same material is given by $y' = nx$.

a. What is the markup on one yard of material?

b. Write an equation in which y is the amount of markup and x is the number of yards purchased.

c. If a dealer uses the formula, retail price = (wholesale price) $+ \frac{1}{2}$(wholesale price), what is $m:n$ in simplest form?

17. A mechanic charges $5.00 as a shop charge for every job. In addition, she charges $8.00 per hour for the time she works on an auto.

a. Do *time mechanic worked on car* and *amount of bill* vary in direct proportion?

b. Write an equation in which y is the amount of the bill and x is the number of hours the mechanic works on a car.

c. Another mechanic uses no shop charge but charges more per hour. Both mechanics charge the same amount for a 5-hour job. What does this other mechanic charge per hour?

18. On a trip of a miles, m gallons of gasoline were consumed. Find the average rate of gasoline consumption on the trip. Is it possible that not a single mile on the entire trip consumed exactly the average?

OBJECTIVE:

9-4

Solving Proportions

To solve a given open sentence in form $\frac{a}{b} = \frac{c}{d}$ by using form $ad = bc$.

When an equation is given by two equal fractions, an equivalent equation often can be written by *cross-multiplication*.

$$\frac{a}{b} = \frac{c}{d} \Leftrightarrow ad = bc$$

You may imagine an "x" which shows the terms which are multiplied.

$$\frac{a}{b} \times \frac{c}{d} \Leftrightarrow \boldsymbol{ad = bc}$$

For $b \neq 0$ and $d \neq 0$, the two equations easily are shown to be equivalent.

Multiply both sides by bd. $\quad \dfrac{a}{b} = \dfrac{c}{d} \Leftrightarrow bd \cdot \dfrac{a}{b} = bd \cdot \dfrac{c}{d}$

Simplify both sides. $\qquad\qquad\qquad \Leftrightarrow \quad ad = bc$

In solving proportions, cross-multiplication provides a quick way to obtain an equivalent equation which does not contain fractions.

EXAMPLES

Stress that there is nothing tricky about cross multiplication. It is just a matter of not recording a step in finding an equivalent equation.

1. $\dfrac{2x}{5} = \dfrac{3}{4} \Leftrightarrow 8x = 15$

$$\Leftrightarrow \quad x = \frac{15}{8}$$

2. $\dfrac{p}{x} = \dfrac{q}{r} \Leftrightarrow qx = pr$

$$\Leftrightarrow \quad x = \frac{pr}{q}$$

The terms of a proportion often are named as shown.

$$\frac{\textcircled{a} \times \textcircled{c}}{\textcircled{b} \times \textcircled{d}} \begin{array}{l} \leftarrow \boldsymbol{means} \\ \leftarrow \boldsymbol{extremes} \end{array}$$

Using these names for the terms, the cross-multiplication rule is: *In a proportion, the product of the means equals the product of the extremes.*

EXERCISES

1. $x = 12$ **2.** $x = 2$ **3.** $x = 2$

Solve each proportion for x. Use cross-multiplication as the first step.

1. $\dfrac{x}{4} = \dfrac{3}{1}$

2. $\dfrac{x}{6} = \dfrac{1}{3}$

3. $\dfrac{x}{4} = \dfrac{1}{2}$

4. $x = 6$ **5.** $x = \frac{9}{2}$ **6.** $x = \frac{5}{2}$

7. $x = 18$ **8.** $x = \frac{15}{4}$ **9.** $x = 8$

10. $x = 3$ **11.** $x = \frac{15}{4}$ **12.** $x = 9$

13. $x = 16$ **14.** $x = 4$ **15.** $x = \frac{3}{2}$

16. $x = -\frac{3}{2}$ **17.** $x = -\frac{1}{2}$

18. $x = \frac{1}{10}$ **19.** $x = \frac{11}{10}$ **20.** $x = \frac{3}{2}$

21. $x = 7.6$ **22.** $x = 1.44$

23. $x = 10$ **24.** $x = 7.5$ **25.** $x = \frac{a}{2}$

26. $x = \frac{3b}{a}$ **27.** $x = a^2$

28. $x = \frac{bd}{c}$ **29.** $x = \frac{1}{a+1}$

30. $x = \frac{a-b}{c}$ **31.** $x = \frac{a}{5}$

32. $x = \frac{3q}{p}$ **33.** $x = 7a$

34. $x = \frac{5b}{a}$ **35.** $x = \frac{pq}{1-q}$

36. $\frac{am}{n+m}$

In Exercises 25-36, remind students to think only of x as the variable. If this does not help, remind students that the task, as before, is to isolate x on one side of the equation.

4. $\dfrac{x}{4} = \dfrac{3}{2}$

5. $\dfrac{x}{3} = \dfrac{3}{2}$

6. $\dfrac{x}{5} = \dfrac{1}{2}$

7. $\dfrac{3}{x} = \dfrac{1}{6}$

8. $\dfrac{4}{5} = \dfrac{3}{x}$

9. $\dfrac{5x}{4} = 10$

10. $\dfrac{2x}{8} = \dfrac{3}{4}$

11. $\dfrac{5}{4x} = \dfrac{1}{3}$

12. $\dfrac{0.2x}{3} = \dfrac{3}{5}$

13. $\dfrac{x-1}{3} = \dfrac{5}{1}$

14. $\dfrac{x+2}{2} = \dfrac{3}{1}$

15. $\dfrac{2x-1}{2} = 1$

16. $\dfrac{2x+9}{2} = 3$

17. $\dfrac{4-x}{3} = \dfrac{3}{2}$

18. $\dfrac{2x+1}{2} = \dfrac{3}{5}$

19. $\dfrac{2x-3}{4} = -\dfrac{1}{5}$

20. $\dfrac{2-3x}{3} = -\dfrac{5}{6}$

21. $\dfrac{x}{5.7} = \dfrac{4}{3}$

22. $\dfrac{3}{x} = \dfrac{5}{2.4}$

23. $\dfrac{x}{8} = \dfrac{2.5}{2}$

24. $\dfrac{2x}{5} = \dfrac{5.4}{1.8}$

25. $\dfrac{x}{a} = \dfrac{1}{2}$

26. $\dfrac{x}{3} = \dfrac{b}{a}$

27. $\dfrac{a}{x} = \dfrac{1}{a}$

28. $\dfrac{b}{x} = \dfrac{c}{d}$

29. $\dfrac{1-x}{x} = \dfrac{a}{1}$

30. $\dfrac{a-b}{x} = c$

31. $\dfrac{a+x}{a-x} = \dfrac{3}{2}$

32. $\dfrac{px-q}{px+q} = \dfrac{1}{2}$

33. $\dfrac{x-a}{x+a} = \dfrac{3}{4}$

34. $\dfrac{ax+b}{ax-b} = \dfrac{3}{2}$

35. $\dfrac{x+p}{x} = \dfrac{1}{q}$

36. $\dfrac{x}{a-x} = \dfrac{m}{n}$

9-5
More About Proportion

EXAMPLES

OBJECTIVE:

To decide whether or not a given situation may be modeled by a direct proportion.

Some quantities do not vary in direct proportion. Study the following examples.

1. Henry VIII had 6 wives. How many wives did Henry IV have?

There is no connection between the number of the king and the number of his wives, so proportion does not apply.

2. A satellite is traveling in an orbit 1600 km above the earth. It takes 2 hours to circle the earth. At what height is a satellite traveling if it takes 3 hours to circle the earth?

You do not know whether the height is directly proportional to the number of hours, so you cannot answer the question. (In fact, the height is 4160 km not 2400 km as it would be if the quantities were directly proportional.)

In Example 3 deciding that the relationship is not a direct proportion requires naming (a, b) and (c, d) in the relation such that $\dfrac{a}{c} = \dfrac{b}{d}$

By this time, students should believe that this is the same as saying that no m exists such that $y = mx$ for each (x, y) in the relation.

3. The table and graph show the relationship between the length of a side and the area of a square.

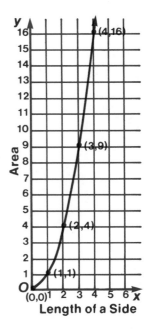

Length of a Side	Area
0	0
1	1
2	4
3	9
4	16

Since $\dfrac{4}{2} \neq \dfrac{9}{4}$, the length of a side and the area of a square are not directly proportional.

4. An electrician sells heavy cable at \$1 per foot for the first 5 feet and at 80¢ per foot for additional feet of wire over 5 feet.

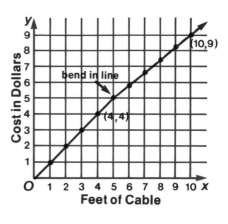

Feet of Cable	Cost in Dollars
1	1.00
2	2.00
3	3.00
4	4.00
5	5.00
6	5.80
7	6.60
8	7.40
9	8.20
10	9.00

Since $\dfrac{10}{4} \neq \dfrac{9}{4}$ the number of feet of cable and the cost in dollars are not directly proportional.

EXERCISES

Exercises 12 and 13 make good
group discussion. Exercise
13 may be a bit difficult.
If treated as a group discussion,
it offers an opportunity to
discuss the concept of
mechanical advantage. In
Exercises 13-16, the problem
of friction is avoided with
"balancing" instead of
"moving" loads. This may be
pointed out to students.

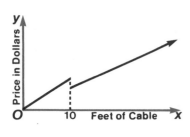

1. A flower catalog gives the following prices for daffodil bulbs. Is the cost in direct proportion to the number of bulbs?

Number of Bulbs	12	50	100
Cost in Dollars	.80	$3.11	$5.81

2. A television rental charge is 45¢ per week for a 50-cm screen and 50¢ per week for a 60-cm screen. Is the rental charge in direct proportion to the dimension of the screen?

3. The ticket for a 24-km journey costs 54 British pence. What will it cost for a 60-km journey if the cost is directly proportional to the distance?

4. An orchestra takes 35 minutes to play Beethoven's Fourth Symphony. How long does it take to play his Sixth Symphony?

5. A building 20 m high casts a shadow 9 m long. What length of shadow is cast at the same time by a tree 15 m high?

6. A shopkeeper buys 48 toys for $151.06. What does he pay for 120 of the same toys if there is no discount for a larger quantity?

7. A man with 3 children earns $10,000 per year. What does a man with 5 children earn?

8. At a school party, 7 cookies are provided for every 5 children. How many cookies are provided for 96 children?

9. A man who owns 1600 shares in a company receives an income of $249. Another man who owns shares in the same company receives $199.20. How many shares does he own?

10. An agent receives a commission of $147 on sales totaling $5880. At the same rate, what commission does he receive on sales of $26,040? What sales earn him a commission of $100.80?

11. In a bookstore, 100 books occupy 1.80 m of shelf. What length of shelf is required for 540 similar books? If shelves are 1.25 m long, how many shelves are needed for 540 books?

12. An electrical cable sells for 50¢ per foot. However, for orders of more than 10 feet, there is a 10% discount.

a. Do price and feet of cable vary in direct proportion?
b. What is the price per foot for 80 feet of cable?
c. Do price and feet of cable vary in direct proportion for all orders of more than 10 feet?
d. Which costs more, 10 feet of cable or 11 feet of cable?

13.

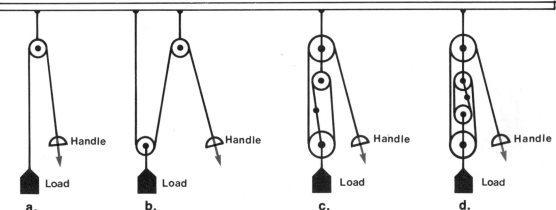

a.   b.   c.   d.

13. a. $\frac{1}{1}$, $\frac{2}{1}$, $\frac{3}{1}$, $\frac{4}{1}$ **b.** 1 ft, 2 ft, 3 ft, 4 ft **c.** 240, 120, 80, 60

Each pulley system is designed to lift a load by pulling on the rope in the direction shown by the arrow.

a. For each pulley arrangement, find $\dfrac{\text{distance handle moves}}{\text{distance load moves}}$.

b. For each arrangement, write the distance the handle moves in lifting the load one foot.

c. For each arrangement, how much force, in pounds, is needed at the handle to balance a load of 240 pounds?

OBJECTIVE:
To name (length on map, actual length) given a map (plan), a scale, and one coordinate of the ordered pair.

9-6
Scale

Maps of countries and plans of buildings, cars, and airplanes are based on direct proportion. The ratios of distances on the map and corresponding distances on the ground are equal.

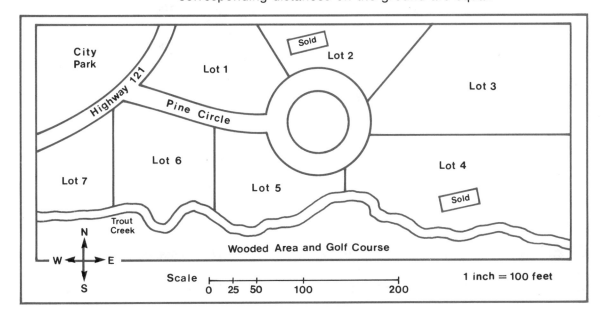

The map shows building lots for sale. Each inch on the map corresponds to 100 feet on the ground.

The ratio $\dfrac{\text{distance on the map}}{\text{corresponding distance on the ground}}$ often is called the **representative fraction (R.F.)** of the map.

On the map of building lots, R.F. $= \dfrac{1}{1200}$.

$$\frac{1 \text{ inch}}{100 \text{ feet}} = \frac{\frac{1}{12}}{100} = \frac{1}{1200}$$

An ant is shown magnified 10 times. In this case, the ratio of length on the picture to length on the ant is $10:1$. Therefore, R.F. $= 10$.

The representative fraction for a drawing may be used to calculate distances.

EXAMPLE

It is not serious if students forget the words *representative fraction*. It is serious if they forget how to use the concept involved here.

On a map with R.F. $1:10{,}000$, calculate the distance on the map which represents 1 km on the ground. Also, find the distance on the ground represented by 12.5 cm on the map.

$$\text{Distance on map} = \frac{1}{10{,}000} \text{ of distance on ground}$$

$$= \frac{1}{10{,}000} \cdot 1 \text{ km}$$

$$= \frac{1}{10{,}000} \cdot 1000 \text{ m}$$

$$= \frac{1}{10{,}000} \cdot 1000 \cdot 100 \text{ cm}$$

$$= 10 \text{ cm}$$

$$\text{Distance on ground} = 10{,}000 \cdot \text{distance on map}$$

$$= 10{,}000 \cdot 12.5 \text{ cm}$$

$$= 125{,}000 \text{ cm}$$

$$= 1250 \text{ m}$$

$$= 1.25 \text{ km}$$

EXERCISES

1. 1.54 cm 2. 63.20 cm 3. 26 cm

A plan has a scale of $1:100$. What distance on the plan represents each length?

1. 154 cm   **2.** 6320 cm   **3.** 26 cm

On a map with a scale of 1:1000, what actual distance is represented by each length on the map?

4. 12 cm   **5.** 1.34 cm   **6.** 0.285 cm

7. a. The scale of a plan is given. By measuring, find the distance represented by 1 cm on the plan.

1 cm   0   1   2   3   4   5 km

Allow students to use reference materials when making conversions with the metric system.

b. What is the R.F. of the plan?
c. What distance is represented by a line of length 3.65 cm on the plan?
d. What length on the plan represents an actual length of 27.8 m?

Stress the fact that R.F. is completely independent of which units of measure happen to be used.

8. a. What is the R.F. for a map with a scale of 1 cm to 2 km?
b. If two cities are 94 km apart, what is the distance between them on the map?
c. If the distance between two cities on the map is 27.4 cm, how far apart are they?

9. The R.F. of a map is $\dfrac{1}{50,000}$. Calculate the distance on the map which represents 42 km. How many km are represented by 11.8 cm?

10. The R.F. of a map is $\dfrac{1}{200,000}$. What is the actual distance between two cities which are 3.8 cm apart on the map? If two hills are 14.8 km apart, what is the distance between them on the map?

11. The scale of a building site plan is $\dfrac{1}{500}$.

a. A rectangular plot on the plan measures 6.8 cm by 3.7 cm. What are the actual measurements? What is the real area of the plot?
b. What area in m² does 1 cm² represent? Find the real area of a building which occupies 32 cm² on the plan.

12. The distance from Rome to Milan is 612 km.
a. How far apart would these cities appear on a map with R.F. of $\dfrac{1}{1,000,000}$?
b. How far apart would they appear on a map with R.F. of $\dfrac{1}{750,000}$?

13. a. 1:108 **b.** $2\frac{1}{4}$ ft **c.** The

bathtub would be $4\frac{1}{2}$ ft long.

That's short! **d.** 27 sq yd

13. A floor plan for a two-bedroom apartment is shown.

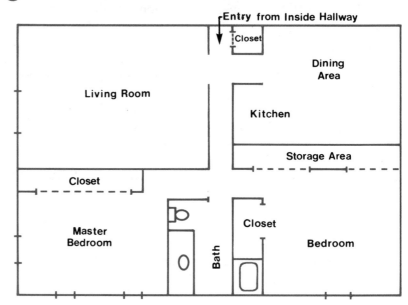

In real life it is often very important to be able to spot errors in maps (plans), as is required by part c of Exercise 13.

a. The living room is 18 feet long. If the length of the living room on the plan measures 2 inches, what is the R.F. for the plan?

b. About how many feet wide is the closet in the master bedroom?

c. Is the length of the bathtub drawn correctly? Explain your answer.

d. About how many square yards of carpeting would be needed to carpet the living room?

9-7
Inverse Proportion

OBJECTIVE:

To name the other coordinate given three coordinates of two ordered pairs in an inverse proportion.

The table and graph show the relationship between speed and time for trains from Minneapolis to Spokane.

Average Speed mph	Time in Hours
•	•
•	•
25	60
50	30
75	20
100	15
125	12
•	•
•	•

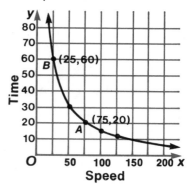

In this case, the ratio of any two speeds is the reciprocal of the ratio of the corresponding times. For example, look at points A and B on the graph. The ratio of the speed at A to the speed at B is $\frac{75}{25} = 3$. The ratio of the time at A to the time at B is $\frac{20}{60} = \frac{1}{3}$.

When two quantities vary in this way, they are **inversely proportional** to each other.

Whenever two quantities are directly proportional, the graph of the relationship has an equation of the form $y = mx$. Whenever two quantities are inversely proportional, the graph of the relationship has an equation of the form $y = \dfrac{m}{x}$, or $xy = m$.

The equation of the graph relating time to speed of trains is $y = \dfrac{1500}{x}$, or $xy = 1500$.

Calculations involving inverse proportion usually are done in one of two ways.

I. *Product Method of Calculation*
The first step in this method is to find the value for m in the equation $xy = m$, or $y = \dfrac{m}{x}$.

EXAMPLES

1. If a can of worms is divided among 15 birds, each bird gets 12 worms. How many worms does each bird get if the worms are divided among 20 birds?

   The total number of worms $= 15 \cdot 12 = 180$.

   If y is the number of worms each bird gets, and x is the number of birds, then $y = \dfrac{180}{x}$. So, if the worms are divided among 20 birds, each gets $\dfrac{180}{20}$ or 9 worms.

2. It takes 10 hours for 3 persons working together to paint a house. How many hours does it take 2 persons to paint the house? If x is the number of people, and y is the number of

hours, then $xy = 3 \cdot 10 = 30$. For 2 persons, $y = 2$; so $x \cdot 2 = 30$ and $x = 15$. Thus, it takes 15 hours for 2 persons to do the job.

Notice that sometimes unusual units are used. In Example **2**, for instance, the number 30 is the number of *worker-hours*.

EXAMPLES

Ask students to name other examples of unusual units.

1. If you use 2 kilowatts of electricity for 8 hours, you use 16 kilowatt-hours of electricity. A kilowatt-hour is the unit used to calculate electric bills.
2. Airlines measure service to the public in passenger-miles or seat-miles. An airplane which travels 200 miles with 50 passengers aboard is giving 10,000 seat-miles of service.

II. *Ratio Method of Calculation*
In using the ratio method, you do not first calculate m in the equation $y = \dfrac{m}{x}$. Instead, use the fact that the ratios of the two types of quantities are inversely proportional.

EXAMPLES

For pairs (a, b) and (c, d) in a relation, stress that $\dfrac{a}{c} = \dfrac{b}{d}$ for direct proportion and $\dfrac{a}{c} = \dfrac{d}{b}$ for inverse proportions.

1. If a can of worms is divided among 15 birds, each bird gets 12 worms. How many worms does each bird get if the worms are divided among 20 birds?

   If s is the number of worms each bird gets, then $\dfrac{15}{20} = \dfrac{s}{12}$. Solving for s, $s = 9$. Each bird gets 9 worms.
2. It takes 16 hours to make a trip by car at an average speed of 57 km per hour. Find the average speed the driver maintains to make the trip by car in 12 hours.

Number of Hours	Number of km Per Hour
16	57
12	x

$$\frac{x}{57} = \frac{16}{12} \Leftrightarrow x = \frac{16}{12} \cdot 57$$
$$\Leftrightarrow x = 76$$

The average speed required is 76 km/hr.

EXERCISES

1. Not inversely proportional
2. Inversely proportional
3. Not inversely proportional
4. Inversely proportional

Determine whether or not each pair of quantities is inversely proportional.
1. The number of ice cream cones you buy and their total cost.
2. The number of men on a job and the time it takes to finish the job.
3. A girl's age and her grade in mathematics.
4. The number of cattle in a field and the time taken to eat the available grass. Assume all cattle eat at the same rate.

5. The number of ice cream bars you can buy and the cost per bar, given that you have only a certain amount of money.

Solve each problem to which proportion applies.

6. A boy rides his bicycle a certain distance in 40 minutes. His average speed is 15 km per hour. If he reduces his time to 30 minutes, what is his average speed?

7. How many days does it take 20 people to do a job which 25 people can do in 32 days? Assume that all people work at the same rate.

8. A car takes 12 hours for a trip at an average speed of 50 km/h. What average speed is necessary to make the trip in 10 hours?

9. A teacher has enough money to order 48 paperback books at $1.25 each. She decides instead to order books with hard covers at $3.25 each. How many can she buy for the same total cost?

10. A contractor estimates that he can do a certain job in 9 months with 280 men. He is asked instead to do the work in 7 months. How many more men must he hire? Assume that all men work at the same rate.

11. A camp director estimates that she has enough food for 6 meals for 150 girls. Thirty more girls arrive than are expected. How many meals can the director supply to each girl? Assume that all girls eat the same amount per meal.

Read Exercise 12 and ask which "math book assumption" is being made which might not be true of real cattle.

12. A farmer has enough grain to feed 50 cattle for 10 weeks. He sells 10 of the cattle. How much longer does the grain last?

13. One train makes a trip in 5 hours, traveling at a speed of 56 km per hour. A second train makes the same trip in 4 hours. What is its speed?

14. A woman walks for $6\frac{1}{2}$ hours at 6 km per hour. If she walks at $6\frac{1}{2}$ km per hour, how long does she walk to cover the same distance?

15. It is known that for a given mass of gas, the volume is inversely proportional to the pressure. When the volume is 60 cm³, the pressure is 1.5 atmospheres.
  a. Find the volumes for pressures of 1, 2, and 0.8 atmospheres.
  b. Find the pressures for volumes of 90, 48, and 200 cm³.

16. It is known that for a given voltage, the current in a circuit is inversely proportional to the resistance in the circuit. When the current is 2 amperes, the resistance is 3 ohms.
  a. Find the resistances for currents of 5, $1\frac{1}{2}$, and 0.2 amperes.
  b. Find the currents for resistances of 5, 2, and 12 ohms.

MATHEMATICS
AND
APPLICATIONS

Today many archaeologists use processes and techniques which require a knowledge of statistics and computers. In the past, archaeologists examined a limited number of objects collected at a village site. They then made deductions about the nature of the people. Examination of arrowheads and pottery remains could be used, for example, to infer the types of tools used by the people, the foods they ate, the trade routes they used, and so on.

The modern archaeologist tries to describe the total ecology of a village. The large store of information he gathers allows a more complete description of a primitive culture.

An example of the new archaeology can be found at Kampsville, Illinois, north of St. Louis. A large archaeological team, headed by Dr. Stuart Struever of Northwestern University, is excavating the Koster village site. It was occupied by 15 different Indian cultures over a period of 7200 years.

D. R. Baston

The team digs a portion of the site each day. Materials are sorted, washed, and rushed to laboratories for analyses. Remains of cultures of different eras are found on different levels. Many different kinds of materials are found, but each gives particular clues about the ecology of an era.

For example, pollen grains are practically indestructible. Analysis of pollen found at different levels, or horizons, makes it possible to compare the plant life around a village site. Snails are quite sensitive to temperature and environment. By comparing the different types of snail shells at a village site, the archaeologist can determine whether the village was in a forest or grassland and what the average temperature extremes were.

These are only two of the many types of information which a modern archaeologist adds to the findings and interpretations of the old archaeology.

D. R. Baston

THE NEW ARCHAEOLOGY

George D. Olson

his findings using statistics. For this reason, people learning to be archaeologists today learn statistical techniques. The stress on describing the total ecology at the Koster site provides so much information needing analysis that a statistician-computer expert works with the team at the site.

D. R. Baston

These new types of information require a different type of analysis. The traditional archaeologist could look at an arrowhead, for example, and conclude the culture had achieved a particular skill level. Today's archaeologist notes the level of skill attained, but he also wants to know the environment within which the skill was used.

Many of the environmental measures are present to some degree in all eras. Ragweed pollen might be present in each culture's environment. The archaeologist must determine when there is enough of it to say that ragweed was a significant factor.

To describe a *culture,* an archaeologist exhibits the artifacts he has found. To describe the *environment,* or ecology, the archaeologist must analyze

D. R. Baston

OBJECTIVE:

To read and construct graphs having different unit lengths for the two axes.

EXAMPLE

There may be some students who think of slope without relating it to how axes are indexed. Be prepared to help them by having them compare the two graphs for $y = 30x$.

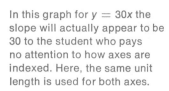

In this graph for $y = 30x$ the slope will actually appear to be 30 to the student who pays no attention to how axes are indexed. Here, the same unit length is used for both axes.

When graphs are drawn to picture relationships between types of quantities, it often is convenient to use different unit lengths on the two axes.

An economy car gets 30 miles per gallon of fuel on highway driving. Graph the relationship between gallons used and miles traveled.

Gallons	0	1	2	3	4	5	6
Miles	0	30	60	90	120	150	180

If a unit is the same length on both the *x*- and *y*-axes, the graph is too difficult to draw and read.

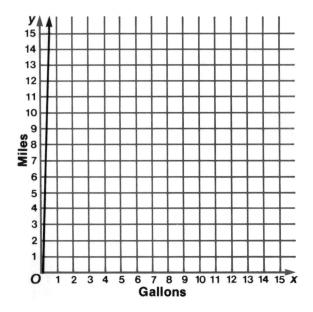

By using very short units on the *y*-axis and longer units on the *x*-axis, you have a more readable graph.

Here, too, $y = 30x$! However, the slope *appears* to be 1 if no attention is given to how axes are indexed. Stress to students that in fact the slope is 30. Stress that $\frac{x_2 - x_1}{y_2 - y_1}$ always defines slope while appearances may not.

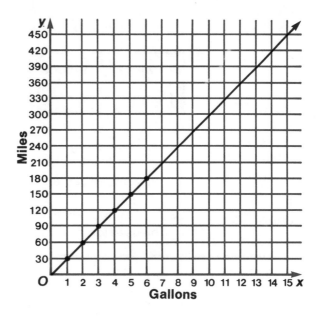

EXERCISES

1. A graph is shown for converting Austrian schillings into British pence, and vice versa.

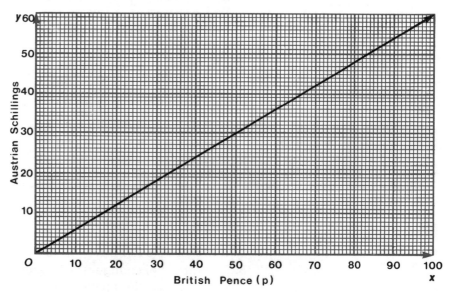

a. Read from the graph the number of British pence, p, that can be obtained for 12, 30, 45, and 56 Austrian schillings.
b. Read from the graph the number of Austrian schillings that can be obtained for 25p, 35p, 72p, and 90p.

2. Assume that a car travels 15 miles for every gallon of gas. Copy and complete this table.

Number of Gallons	1	2	3	4	5	6	7	8
Number of Miles	15	?	?	?	?	?	?	?

a. Draw the graph and find the amount of gas used for trips of 100 mi, 85 mi, and 50 mi.

b. How far can the car travel on 2.5 gal, 5.5 gal, and 6.8 gal of gas?

3. A manufacturer of weed killer recommends that 1 kg of chemical be used for every 50 m² of ground. Copy and complete this table.

Area of Ground in m²	50	100	150	200	250	300
Mass of Chemical in kg	1	?	?	?	?	?

a. Draw a graph and find the approximate mass of chemical to cover 80 m², 120 m², 220 m², and 275 m² of ground.

b. How much ground can be covered by 1.5 kg, 2.5 kg, and 4.5 kg of chemical?

4. The distance from the earth to the moon is about 384,000 km. A rocket traveling at an average speed of 9600 km/h takes $\frac{384,000}{9600}$ hours, or 40 hours, to travel this distance. Copy and complete this table by calculating each time of travel.

Speed of Rocket in km/h	9600	12,800	16,000	19,200	25,600	32,000
Time of Travel in Hours	40	?	?	?	?	?

The graph connecting these points is not a straight line. Why not? Draw a smooth graph. From the graph, estimate the time a rocket takes to travel at 10,000 km/h. At 30,000 km/h.

5. The rate of exchange is 5.5 Danish kroner to $1. Draw a graph which shows the relation between kroner and dollars.

a. Find the number of dollars that can be obtained for 10, 15, and 18 kroner.

b. Find the number of kroner that can be obtained for 27¢, 54¢, and 72¢.

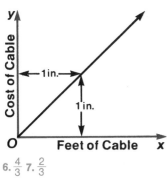

Cost of Cable / Feet of Cable

6. $\frac{4}{3}$ 7. $\frac{2}{3}$

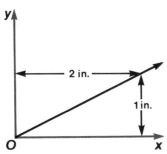

6. On the graph, the unit on the *y*-axis is one dollar. The unit on the *x*-axis is one foot. The graph shows the cost of cable. One foot of cable costs 75¢.

If unit lengths were marked on both axes, what number would be used for $\dfrac{\text{length representing a unit along } y\text{-axis}}{\text{length representing a unit along } x\text{-axis}}$?

7. To show the cost of the same type of cable as in Exercise **6,** what number would be needed for

$$\dfrac{\text{length representing a unit along } y\text{-axis}}{\text{length representing a unit along } x\text{-axis}}?$$

9-9
Average Speed

OBJECTIVE:
To construct and/or read a graph which models a trip made at average speed ($d = rt$).

Point out that days are never that calm and motors never run that smoothly. These offer more examples of what were called "math book assumptions."

Suppose a boat is going from Escanaba, Michigan to St. Joseph, Michigan. If it takes 10 hours to go 250 miles, then its average speed is 25 mph. Imagine that the day is very calm and the throttle of the motor is not touched once during the day. Then, perhaps the boat is traveling exactly 25 mph during the entire 10 hours. A graph relating distance to time for this trip is shown.

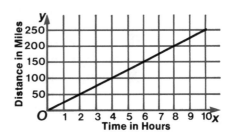

Suppose that another boat stops for fishing between the fourth and seventh hours. Then it is driven twice as fast after fishing. Its graph looks quite different.

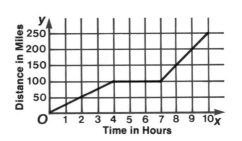

Notice that from 4 to 6 along the *x*-axis, the *y*-value does not change. At 5 hours into the trip, 100 miles have been covered; (5, 100) is a point on the graph. At 6 hours into the trip, still only 100 miles have been covered; (6, 100) is a point on the graph. Between 7 and 10 hours, the slope is twice what it was between 0 and 4. As you remember, the slope is greater as the rate increases.

Considering the entire trip, the average speed for both boats is the same. Both boats covered 250 miles in 10 hours for an average speed of 25 miles per hour.

The relation between time and distance for a heavy truck making a 60-mile trip is shown in the graph. The solid line shows the actual relation between time and distance. The broken line shows the trip as it would be had it been made in the same time at a constant speed.

DISCUSSION QUESTIONS

1. During the trip, the truck driver takes a 15-minute coffee break. How long has he been on the road when he takes the break?
2. During which quarter-hour is the truck moving at the slowest rate? (Do not count the coffee break.)
3. Look at each quarter-hour of the trip. Make up road conditions which could explain the rate of speed.
4. What would the graph look like if the driver backs up for 15 minutes and then goes on again?
5. During which 15-minute period does the truck go faster than its average speed? During which 15-minute period does it go slower than its average speed?

EXERCISES

On the same coordinate plane, draw distance-time graphs to show a 40-km trip made by each person.

1. A person walking at an average speed of 8 km/h (On the graph

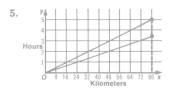

5.

First girl — $3\frac{1}{3}$ hr

Second girl — 5 hr $26\frac{2}{3}$ km

Exercise 6 makes a good discussion exercise. To solve the problem easily by graphing, index the x-axis by hour increments, beginning with 9:00 A.M.

6.

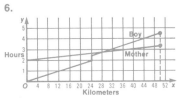

He arrives at 1:40 PM. Mother arrives at 12:15 PM. She overtakes him at 11:39 AM, after she has traveled $25\frac{5}{7}$ miles.

paper, show that in 1 hour he goes 8 km, in 2 hours 16 km, and so on, and draw a straight line.)

2. A person cycling at 20 km/h

3. A truck driver traveling at 40 km/h

4. A motorist driving at 80 km/h

5. Draw a graph to show the progress of two girls who leave at the same time from Luton to cycle to Reading, 80 km away. One cycles at 24 km/h and the other at 16 km/h. From the graph, find when each girl reaches Reading. How far ahead is the first girl when she reaches Reading?

6. A boy leaves Jackson at 9 A.M. to cycle to Monroe, 50 km away. He travels at a speed of 12 km/h. After cycling for 2 hours, he stops for $\frac{1}{2}$ hour for a picnic and then goes on as before. At 11 A.M. his mother leaves Jackson to go to Monroe in her car traveling at 40 km/h. Draw a graph and find when each reaches Monroe. When and where does the mother overtake the boy?

The black line in the figure shows the progress of a truck which leaves Toledo at 8 A.M. and travels toward Cleveland, a distance of 130 km. The broken line illustrates the journey of a car from Cleveland to Toledo on the same road. Use the graph to do Exercises **7–12.**

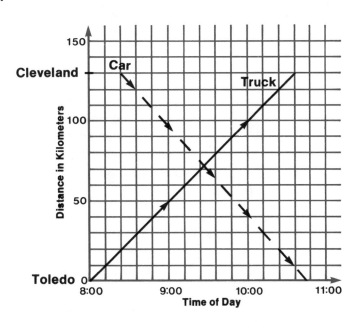

7. How far does the truck go the first hour? How far does it go the second hour? What is the truck's average speed?
8. When does the truck reach Cleveland?
9. When does the car leave Cleveland?
10. How far does the car go the first hour? What is the car's average speed?
11. When does the car reach Toledo?
12. When and where do the truck and the car pass each other?

13. The graph shows the distance a truck covers on a two-hour trip in heavy traffic.

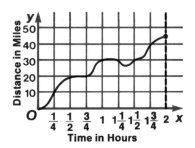

a. For about how long to the nearest half hour is traffic at a standstill?
b. How long after the trip begins does the truck head in the wrong direction to clear the way for emergency equipment?
c. Which half-hour section of the trip shows the greatest average speed of the truck?

14. The truck in Exercise **13** travels 45 miles in two hours. A second truck makes the same trip in the same time. The second truck begins the trip at 2:00 A.M. There are no traffic problems, but the truck has an engine problem. Draw a graph on a coordinate system similar to that in Exercise **13** for the second truck. The second truck maintains the same speed for the entire trip.

Excursions in Mathematics:
Area Under a Curve

The graph shows the speeds at which a truck travels during a four-hour trip.

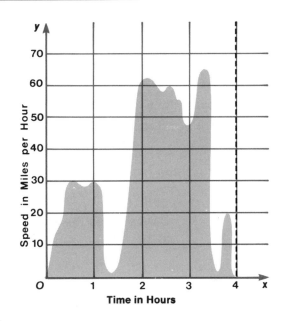

Imagine that as a unit of area measurement you use a rectangle which measures (length of unit along x-axis) · (length of unit along y-axis).

The distance

If you knew how many of these units were needed to cover the shaded area in the graph, what would you know about the trip?

If you are having difficulty, first think about what the shaded area means in this figure.

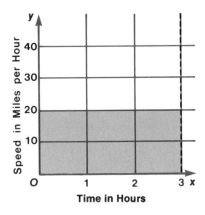

In this trip, the driver goes exactly 20 mph for 3 hours.

Suggested Activities

1. What is the speed of light? What is the distance between the sun and the earth? Use these facts to find how long it takes for light to travel from the sun to the earth.

2. Find the distance that a ray of light travels in a year. (This is one of the astronomical units of distance, the light-year.)

3. What is the circumference of the earth at the equator? What is the speed of radio waves? Find the time it takes a radio wave to travel once around the earth at the equator.

Excursions in Mathematics:
Slope of a Curve

What does the slope of the curve represent? What is the slope at 1?

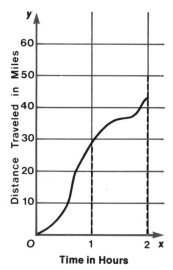

If you are having difficulty, first look at this figure which shows a trip taken at constant speed. Ask yourself what m represents in this graph.

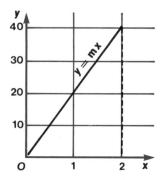

Chapter Summary

1. A ratio is a comparison of two quantities measured or counted by the same unit of measure.
2. A rate is used to give a relationship between quantities measured by different units of measure.
3. Two types of quantities are directly proportional when they are related to give a graph with equation $y = mx$.
4. Problems involving direct proportion may be solved by the ratio method of calculation or by the unitary method of calculation.
5. In a proportion, the product of the means equals the product of the extremes.
6. The scale of a map often is given by the representative fraction. The representative fraction, R.F., is the ratio of the distance on the map to the corresponding distance on the ground.
7. Two types of quantities are inversely proportional when they are related to give a graph with equation $y = \dfrac{m}{x}$, or $xy = m$.
8. Problems involving inverse proportion may be solved by the product method of calculation or by the ratio method of calculation.

REVIEW EXERCISES

9-1

Express each ratio in simplest form. Remember that the quantities must be measured by the same unit.

1. 3:8 2. 4:1 3. 7:24 4. 5:6, 5:6
5. 10.5¢/apple 6. $151.50
7. 55 wds/min 8. 99¢

1. 75¢ : $2.00   **2.** 1.2 kg : 300 g   **3.** 35 min : 2 hr

4. Two squares have sides of lengths 20 cm and 24 cm. Find the ratio of the length of the side of the smaller square to the length of the side of the larger square. Find the ratio of the perimeter of the smaller square to the larger square.

9-2

5. Find the rate in cents per apple if 14 apples cost $1.47.
6. A man earns $30.30 for an 8-hour day. How much does he earn at the same rate for a 40-hour week?
7. What is the rate in words per minute of a typist who types 3300 words in 1 hour?

9-3

Solve each problem which involves proportion. If proportion does not apply, write *cannot solve*.

8. Soap costs 66¢ for 8 cakes. What is the cost for 12 cakes?

9. A sum of money is invested at 6%. It yields an annual interest of $111. If the interest rate decreases, the annual interest drops to $101.75. What is the new interest rate?

10. Typing paper costs 75¢ for 100 sheets. What is the cost of 180 sheets?

11. Typing paper costs 75¢ for 100 sheets. How many sheets do you buy for 60¢?

12. It takes 5 days for 24 workers to pick a berry crop. How many workers, working at the same rate, can pick the crop in 3 days?

13. The cost of 100 shares in a company is $48.
    a. What is the cost of 175 shares?
    b. If you invest $120 in the company, how many shares can you buy?

14. To insure a house for $14,000, a man pays an annual premium of $33.60. What premium does his next-door neighbor pay at the same rate to insure her house for $16,500?

15. Potatoes to serve 4 people are boiled for 20 minutes. How long should they be boiled for 6 people?

16. A vertical post $1\frac{1}{2}$ m high casts a shadow 72 cm long.
    a. Find the length of the shadow cast by a tree 10 m high.
    b. Find the height (to the nearest tenth m) of a flagpole which casts a shadow 10 m long.

17. An 11-person hockey team scores 8 goals in one game. How many goals does it score if the team is made up of 7 persons?

18. A chicken farmer estimates that she has enough grain to feed her 2000 hens for two weeks. If she buys 800 more hens, how long can she feed her hens?

19. One portion of ice cream for each of 54 students costs $4.32. Ice cream worth $5.20 is ordered. How many students get a second helping?

20. If £5 buys 90 Danish kroner, how many kroner do you get for £8? How many £, British pounds, do you get for 72 Danish kroner?

9-4

Solve each proportion for x. Use cross-multiplication as the first step.

21. $\dfrac{x}{6} = \dfrac{2}{3}$

22. $\dfrac{2}{x - 3} = 1$

23. $\dfrac{2}{5x - 1} = \dfrac{2}{3x + 5}$

24. $\dfrac{x + 1}{x - 1} = \dfrac{3}{2}$

25. $\dfrac{5}{2x - 1} = \dfrac{8}{3x + 1}$

26. $\dfrac{2x - y}{3y + 2x} = \dfrac{4}{7}$

9-5

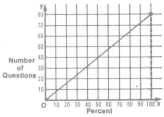
Solve each problem which involves direct proportion. If direct proportion does not apply, write *cannot solve.*

27. Out of each $1 of revenue from taxes, a city spends 36 cents on education and 28 cents on housing. If the total amount spent on housing is $504,000, how much is spent on education?

28. Miguel stands with both feet on a scale. His mass registers at 60 kg.
    a. What does the scale read if he stands with one foot on it and the other foot on the floor?
    b. What does the scale read if he stands with one foot on it and holds the other foot in the air?

29. A record played at 45 rpm takes 13 minutes. If the record is played at $33\frac{1}{3}$ rpm, how long does it take?

30. Wall-to-wall carpeting for a room 4 m by 3.5 m costs $144. How much does the same kind of carpeting cost for a room 3.5 m by 3 m?

9-6

31. **a.** What is the R.F. of a map with a scale of 5 cm to 1 km?
    b. Two cities are 12.5 cm apart on this map. What is the actual distance between them?
    c. The length of a road is 9 km. What is its length on the map?

32. The R.F. of a map is 1:200,000.
    a. If two cities are 64 km apart, how far apart are they on the map?
    b. If two cities are 4.3 cm apart on the map, what is the actual distance between them?

9-7

33. The wavelength of a radio transmission is inversely proportional to the frequency. A radio station has a wavelength of 1500 m and a frequency of 200 kilocycles per second.
    a. Find the frequency of Radio 20 which has a wavelength of 400 m.
    b. Find the wavelength of Radio 4, which has a frequency of 809 kilocycles per second, to the nearest meter.

34. Draw a graph to convert examination scores to percentages. Use 1 cm to represent 10 correct questions on the *x*-axis. Use 1 cm to represent 10% on the *y*-axis.
    a. Find the percentages equivalent to scores of 60, 36, and 55.
    b. Find scores out of 80 corresponding to 50%, 72%, and 43%.
    c. Check your answers to Parts **a** and **b** arithmetically.

9-8

35. Examination scores may be read as percentages from the graph. The original scores are shown on the horizontal axis and the

percentages on the vertical axis.

a. Write the percentages equivalent to scores of 140, 100, 62, and 35.

b. Write the scores out of 140 equivalent to 20%, 50%, 76%, and 91%.

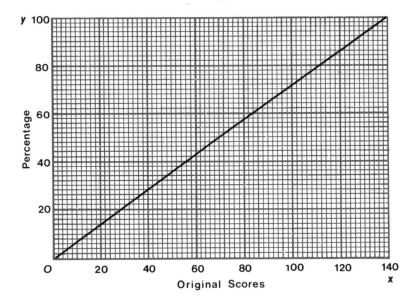

9-9

36. On a flight from London to Cairo, a plane leaves London at 10:30 P.M. It arrives in Cairo at 7:00 the next morning. The distance from London to Cairo via Rome, where the plane stops for 1 hour, is 3870 km. Find the average speed of the plane while it is in the air.

37. A train leaves Basle at noon. It is scheduled to reach Stuttgart, 259 km away, at 3:30 P.M. What is the average speed of the train?

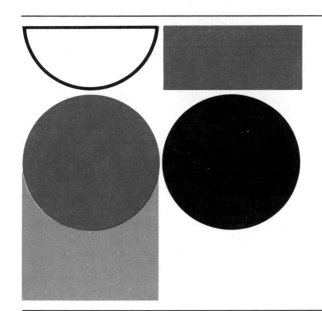

CHAPTER 10

systems of open sentences

10-1
Graphing Solution Sets

OBJECTIVE:

To draw the graph of a given linear open sentence.

You already have studied the solution sets of equations and inequations. Consider $x + 2 = 5$, $x \in N$. The result of replacing x by 3 is the true statement $3 + 2 = 5$. False statements result from all other replacements for x. The solution set of $x + 2 = 5$ is $\{3\}$ as shown on the number line.

The solution set of $x + 2 \leq 5$, $x \in N$, is $\{1, 2, 3\}$.

An open sentence may have two variables, as in $2x + y \leq 6$, x, $y \in W$. Since there are two variables, replacements for x and y must be made in pairs.

x	y	$2x + y \leq 6$	True or False
0	6	$2 \cdot 0 + 6 \leq 6$	T
1	6	$2 \cdot 1 + 6 \leq 6$	F
0	0	$2 \cdot 0 + 0 \leq 6$	T

x	y	2x + y ≤ 6	True or False
2	2	$2 \cdot 2 + 2 \leq 6$	T
3	3	$2 \cdot 3 + 3 \leq 6$	F
3	0	$2 \cdot 3 + 0 \leq 6$	T
4	0	$2 \cdot 4 + 0 \leq 6$	F

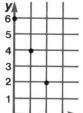

The replacements for x and y are written as ordered pairs. Replacements which make the sentence true include (0, 6), (0, 0), (2, 2), and (3, 0).

The solution set of an open sentence with two variables can be shown by a graph. The graph of the solution set of $2x + y \leq 6$, x, $y \in$ W, is shown.

EXAMPLES

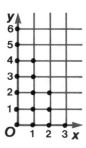

1. Find the solution set of $2x + y = 6$, x, $y \in$ W. Show the solution set on a graph.
   The solution set is {(0, 6), (1, 4), (2, 2), (3, 0)}.

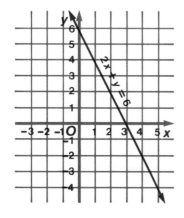

2. Show on a graph the solution set of $2x + y = 6$, x, $y \in$ R.
   Since x, $y \in$ R, there are infinitely many ordered pairs in the solution set. All these ordered pairs lie on the line through the points (0, 6), (1, 4), (2, 2), and (3, 0). The straight line is the graph of the solution set of $2x + y = 6$.

3. Show on a graph the solution set of $2x + y \leq 6$, x, $y \in$ R.
   The solution set of an inequation graphs as a region of the coordinate plane. In this example, the points of the line $2x + y = 6$ also belong to the solution set. Therefore, a solid line is drawn to show the graph of $2x + y = 6$, which is the *boundary* of the solution set. All points of a region on one side of this line and the points on the

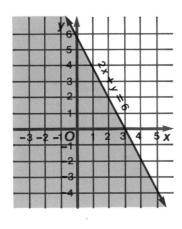

line belong to the solution set. By testing a few points, you can decide which region to shade, the region above or the region below the line.

Suppose you have an open sentence and some ordered pairs. You wish to test each ordered pair to see if it belongs to the solution set of the open sentence. You may plot each ordered pair using a dot if it does belong and a circle if it does not belong to the solution set. For example, test (1, 1), (3, 1), (0, 2), (2, 0), and (2, 2) to see if they belong to the solution set of $x + 3y \geq 6$, $x, y \in$ W.

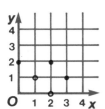

Ordered Pair	$x + 3y \geq 6$	True or False
(1, 1)	$1 + 3 \cdot 1 \geq 6$	F
(3, 1)	$3 + 3 \cdot 1 \geq 6$	T
(0, 2)	$0 + 3 \cdot 2 \geq 6$	T
(2, 0)	$2 + 3 \cdot 0 \geq 6$	F
(2, 2)	$2 + 3 \cdot 2 \geq 6$	T

EXERCISES

1.

2.

3. See section notes in T.G.
4. See section notes in T.G.
5. See section notes in T.G.

Test each ordered pair to see if it belongs to the solution set of the open sentence. Plot each ordered pair. Use a dot if it belongs and a circle if it does not.

1. $x + y = 4$, $x, y \in$ W; (0, 4), (1, 3), (2, 2), (3, 1), (4, 0), (1, 1), (3, 3)

2. $2x + y = 4$, $x, y \in$ W; (0, 4), (0, 1), (2, 0), (2, 3), (1, 2)

3. $x + y \leq 2$, $x, y \in$ W; (0, 0), (0, 1), (0, 2), (0, 3), (3, 0), (2, 0), (1, 1), (1, 0)

4. $2x - y = 2$, $x, y \in$ R; (0, −2), (0, 2), (2, 2), (2, 1), (3, 4), (3, 2), $\left(\frac{1}{2}, -1\right)$

291

Find pairs of replacements for x and y which make each sentence true. Draw a graph to show the set of points which have these pairs as coordinates.

5. $x + y = 6$, $x, y \in W$
6. $x + y = 6$, $x, y \in R$
7. $x - y = 0$, $x, y \in W$
8. $x - y = 0$, $x, y \in R$
9. $2x + y = 8$, $x, y \in W$
10. $2x + y = 8$, $x, y \in R$
11. $y = 2$, $y \in Z$
12. $y = 2$, $y \in R$
13. $x = 4$, $x \in Z$
14. $x = 4$, $x \in R$
15. $x + 2y \geq 4$, $x, y \in R$
16. $y \geq x$, $x, y \in R$

OBJECTIVE:

To express a linear open sentence expressed in one form in the required equivalent form.

10-2
Forms of Linear Equations

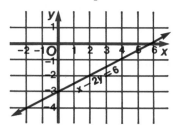

Stress that allowing $a = 0$ or $b = 0$ makes it possible to express *every* linear equation with these forms.

The graph of $x - 2y = 6$ is a straight line when $x, y \in R$.

$$x - 2y = 6 \Leftrightarrow -2y = -x + 6$$
$$\Leftrightarrow \quad y = \frac{1}{2}x - 3$$

The slope is $\frac{1}{2}$. The y-intercept is $(0, -3)$. Because its graph is a straight line, $x - 2y = 6$ is called a **linear equation.**

In Chapter 8, you learned that every linear equation is equivalent to $y = mx + c$ or $x = c$. The form in which an equation is written often depends on what is to be done with it. An equation may be graphed easily when written as $y = mx + c$. The slope of the line is m. The y-intercept is $(0, c)$. For the work in this chapter, it often will be convenient to write linear equations in one of two other equivalent forms. Every linear equation can be expressed in one or the other of these forms.

1. $ax + by + c = 0$ x-term + y-term + constant = zero
2. $ax + by = c$ x-term + y-term = constant

EXAMPLES

Ask what kind of line results if $a \neq 0$ and $b = 0$? if $a = 0$ and $b \neq 0$?

1. $x - 2y + 6 = 0$
     $ax + by + c = 0$
2. $x - 3y = 2$
     $ax + by = c$
3. $0 \cdot x + 2y - 3 = 0$
     $ax + by + c = 0$ where $a = 0$

The graph of a linear equation in any form may be drawn by finding the y-intercept and the x-intercept.

EXAMPLES

1. Graph $x - 2y + 6 = 0$, $x, y \in R$.
Find the value of x when $y = 0$.

$$x - 2y + 6 = 0$$
$$x - 2 \cdot 0 + 6 = 0 \Leftrightarrow x + 6 = 0$$
$$\Leftrightarrow \quad x = -6$$

When $y = 0$, x must be -6. Therefore, $(-6, 0)$ is the x-intercept.
Find the value of y when $x = 0$.

$$x - 2y + 6 = 0$$
$$0 - 2y + 6 = 0 \Leftrightarrow -2y = -6$$
$$\Leftrightarrow \quad y = 3$$

When $x = 0$, y must be 3. Therefore, $(0, 3)$ is the y-intercept.
Since two points determine a straight line, the graph can now be drawn.

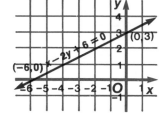

2. Graph $x + 2y \geq 4$, $x, y \in R$.
To graph the inequation, first graph the boundary line, $x + 2y = 4$.

$$0 + 2y = 4 \Leftrightarrow 2y = 4 \qquad x + 2 \cdot 0 = 4 \Leftrightarrow x + 0 = 4$$
$$\Leftrightarrow \quad y = 2 \qquad\qquad\qquad x = 4$$

The y-intercept is $(0, 2)$.   The x-intercept is $(4, 0)$.

The solution set of $x + 2y = 4$ is shown by the straight line through the points $(0, 2)$ and $(4, 0)$.

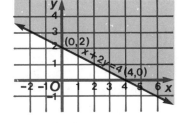

All points of the solution set of $x + 2y > 4$ lie in one of the regions bounded by this line. Test $(0, 0)$. Since $(0, 0)$ is not a solution, the region required is not the one containing the origin. The solution set of $x + 2y \geq 4$ is the union of the two sets graphed as the line and the shaded region.

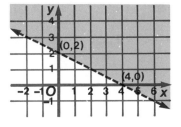

The boundary line is not included in the graph of the solution set of $x + 2y > 4$. A broken line in the graph is used to show that solutions of $x + 2y = 4$ are not included.

An inequation whose graph has a straight line as its boundary is called a **linear inequation.**

EXERCISES

1. $2x + y - 4 = 0$, $2x + y = 4$, $y = 2x - 4$ **2.** $2x - y - 1 = 0$, $2x - y = 1$, $y = 2x - 1$
3. $x + 3y - 6 = 0$, $x + 3y = 6$, $y = -\frac{1}{3}x + 2$ **4.** $x + 2y - 3 = 0$, $x + 2y = 3$, $y = -\frac{x}{2} + \frac{3}{2}$
5. $x - y - 5 = 0$, $x - y = 5$, $y = x - 5$ **6.** $2x - y + 1 = 0$, $2x - y = -1$, $y = 2x + 1$
7. $2x - 3y - 6 = 0$, $2x - 3y = 6$, $y = \frac{2}{3}x - 2$
8. $3x + 2y + 6 = 0$, $3x + 2y = -6$, $y = -\frac{3}{2}x - 3$
9. $3x - 4y - 12 = 0$, $3x - 4y = 12$, $y = \frac{3}{4}x - 3$
10. $x - 2y + 2 = 0$, $x - 2y = -2$, $y = \frac{1}{2}x + 1$
11. $x + 2 = 0$, $x = -2$, $x = -2$
12. $y - 3 = 0$, $y = 3$, $y = 3$
13. Answers will vary.
14.
15.

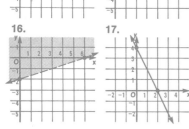

16.
17.

18. See section notes in T.G.
19. See section notes in T.G.
20. See section notes in T.G.
21. See section notes in T.G.
22. See section notes in T.G.
23. See section notes in T.G.
24. See section notes in T.G.
25. See section notes in T.G.

Express each equation in each of the following three linear forms.

a. $ax + by + c = 0$
b. $ax + by = c$
c. $y = mx + c$ or $x = c$

1. $2x + y - 4 = 0$ **2.** $2x - y - 1 = 0$ **3.** $x + 3y - 6 = 0$
4. $x + 2y = 3$ **5.** $x - y = 5$ **6.** $2x - y = -1$
7. $2x - 3y - 6 = 0$ **8.** $3x + 2y + 6 = 0$ **9.** $y = \frac{3}{4}x - 3$
10. $y = \frac{1}{2}x + 1$ **11.** $x = -2$ **12.** $y = 3$

13. In Exercises **1–12** the letter c is used for the constant term in each form of a linear equation. What can you say about the actual values of each c in each form in Exercises **1–12**?

Graph each equation or inequation. The variables are on R.

14. $x - 3y = 6$ **15.** $x - 3y \leq 6$ **16.** $x - 3y < 6$
17. $2x + y = 4$ **18.** $2x + y \geq 4$ **19.** $2x + y > 4$
20. $2x - 3y - 6 = 0$ **21.** $2x - 3y - 6 \geq 0$ **22.** $2x - 3y - 6 < 0$
23. $x \geq -2$ **24.** $y < 3$ **25.** $x \leq 0$

Excursions in Mathematics: More on Slope and Intercepts

Consider two equivalent forms of a linear equation.

$$-3x + 4y + 8 = 0 \qquad ax + by + c_1 = 0$$

$$y = \frac{3}{4}x - 2 \qquad y = mx + c_2$$

The constants in the two equations at the left are not the same. Therefore, in general forms, they will be shown as c_1 and c_2. The first equation may be written in the slope-intercept form.

$$-3x + 4y + 8 = 0 \Leftrightarrow 4y = 3x - 8$$

$$\Leftrightarrow y = \frac{3}{4}x - 2$$

$$ax + by + c_1 = 0 \Leftrightarrow by = -ax - c_1$$

$$\Leftrightarrow y = -\frac{a}{b}x - \frac{c_1}{b}$$

You can see now that $m = -\frac{a}{b}$ and $c_2 = -\frac{c_1}{b}$.

EXAMPLES

1. Write $-3x + 4y + 8 = 0$ in slope-intercept form. Use the general equation.

$$a = -3, b = 4, c_1 = 8$$

$$y = -\frac{a}{b}x - \frac{c_1}{b}$$

$$y = -\frac{-3}{4}x - \frac{8}{4} \Leftrightarrow y = \frac{3}{4}x - 2$$

2. Write $2x - 5y + 15 = 0$ in slope-intercept form.

$$y = \frac{-2}{-5}x - \frac{15}{-5} \Leftrightarrow y = \frac{2}{5}x + 3$$

EXERCISES

Write each equation in slope-intercept form. Use the formulas for m and c_2.

1. $x + 2y - 5 = 0$ **2.** $-2x + 2y + 9 = 0$

3. $4x - 3y + 12 = 0$ **4.** $3x - 5y + 6 = 0$

5. $x - 4y - 7 = 0$ **6.** $-x + 3y - 5 = 0$

7. $2y - 2x + 7 = 0$ **8.** $2x + y - \frac{3}{2} = 0$

9. $\frac{1}{2}y - \frac{2}{3}x + \frac{1}{4} = 0$ **10.** $2 - 3y + x = 0$

OBJECTIVE:

To indicate the solution set of a system of two or more linear inequations by graphing.

10-3

Systems of Equations and Inequations

Is it possible for a solution to satisfy two or more equations at the same time? Can you find a set of replacements which is a solution set for *both* $x - y = 2$ *and* $x + y = 4$?

When $x = 3$ and $y = 1$, both $x - y = 2$ and $x + y = 4$ are true statements.

$$
\begin{array}{ll}
x - y = 2 & x + y = 4 \\
3 - 1 \overset{?}{=} 2 & 3 + 1 \overset{?}{=} 4 \\
2 = 2 & 4 = 4
\end{array}
$$

Ask: If A and B are the solution sets of open sentence I and open sentence II, what is the solution set of the system? (A ∩ B)

Thus, $(3, 1)$ satisfies both equations. No other point in the plane will be a solution for both equations. The solution set for $x - y = 2$ *and* $x + y = 4$ is $\{(3, 1)\}$.

When two or more equations or inequations are considered at the same time, the equations or inequations are called a **system.**

The solution set for a system of equations or inequations is the set of replacements which satisfy *all* equations or inequations in the system.

Two or more equations or inequations may be graphed in the same coordinate plane. The intersection of these graphs is the solution set for the system of equations or inequations.

For the remainder of this book, unless otherwise stated, the variables are assumed to be on R.

EXAMPLES

1. Show graphically the solution set of the system $y < x$ and $x + 2y \leq 4$.

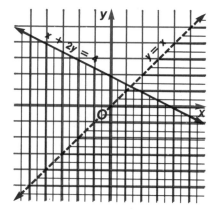

The solution set for $y < x$ is shaded by horizontal lines.

The solution set for $x + 2y \leq 4$ is shaded by vertical lines.

The solution set for the system, $y < x$ and $x + 2y \leq 4$, is shaded by both vertical and horizontal lines. This checkered area includes the boundary where the line is solid. It does not include the boundary where the line is broken.

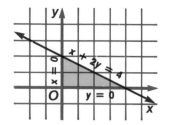

2. Shade the solution set of the system $x \geq 0$ and $y \geq 0$ and $x + 2y \leq 4$.

In this example, the intersection of three sets must be found.

$$\{(x, y)|x \geq 0\} \cap \{(x, y)|y \geq 0\} \cap \{(x, y)|x + 2y \leq 4\}$$

EXERCISES

Graph the solution set of each system of inequations in Exercises 1–6.

1. $x \geq 0$ *and* $y \geq 0$ *and* $x + y \leq 5$
2. $x \geq 0$ *and* $y \geq 0$ *and* $2x + y \leq 6$
3. $x > 0$ *and* $y > 0$ *and* $x + y < 8$
4. $x > 0$ *and* $y > 0$ *and* $2x + 3y < 12$
5. $x \leq 0$ *and* $y \leq 0$ *and* $x + y \geq -6$
6. $x > 0$ *and* $y < 0$ *and* $x + 2y > 8$

7. Explain why the solution set of $x \geq 3$ *and* $x < 2$ is empty.
8. Show the solution set of $-2 \leq x$ *and* $x \leq 2$. The notation $-2 \leq x \leq 2$ may be used for this system of inequations.
9. How many inequations are there in the system $-2 \leq x \leq 2$ *and* $-4 \leq y \leq 4$? Show its solution set.

On graph paper, shade or color each solution set lightly. Show clearly the intersection of the solution sets. Notice that commas sometimes replace *and* in systems of equations and inequations.

10. $y \geq 2, x + y \leq 6$
11. $x \geq 0, y \leq x$
12. $y \leq 0, y \leq x$
13. $y \leq 6, y \geq x, y \geq -x$
14. $x < 10, y < x, y > -x$
15. $y \geq 0, y \leq x, x + y \leq 5$
16. $x \geq 0, y \geq 0, y \leq 5, y \leq 8 - x$
17. $x + y \leq 2, y \geq x - 4$
18. $y > 2x - 1, x + 2y \geq 6, y \leq 5$

10-4
Solving Systems – Graphing

The two straight lines graphed in the same coordinate plane show the solution sets of the equations $x + y = 5$ and $x - y = 1$. The solution set of the system is the intersection of the two solution sets. This intersection is given by the coordinates of the point where the two lines intersect. Since this point is $A(3, 2)$, the solution set of the system is $\{(3, 2)\}$.

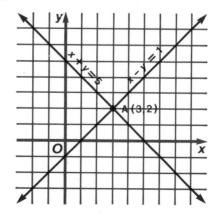

To use the **graphical method** for solving a system of equations, first graph the equations. Then inspect the graph to find the intersection of the lines. This intersection is the solution set for the system.

EXAMPLE

Solve $x + 3 = y$ and $x + y = 1$ graphically.

$$x + 3 = y \Leftrightarrow y = x + 3$$
$$x + y = 1 \Leftrightarrow y = -x + 1$$

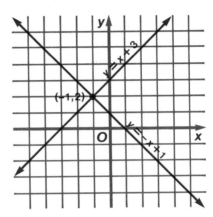

The lines intersect at $(-1, 2)$. The solution for the system $x + 3 = y$ and $x + y = 1$ is $(-1, 2)$. Check this solution by replacing x with -1 and y with 2 in both equations of the system.

1. See section notes in T.G.
2. See section notes in T.G.
3. See section notes in T.G.
4. See section notes in T.G.
5. See section notes in T.G.

EXERCISES

6. See section notes in T.G.
7. See section notes in T.G.
8. See section notes in T.G.
9. See section notes in T.G.
10. See section notes in T.G.

Exercise 11 may be treated as a discussion exercise after students have done Exercises 7-10.

11. $y = x + 5, y = x - 5$
$y = \frac{3}{2}x - \frac{5}{2}, y = \frac{3}{2}x + \frac{5}{2}$
$y = -\frac{3}{4}x + \frac{1}{2}, y = -\frac{3}{4}x + 2$
$y = -\frac{1}{2}x + \frac{5}{2}, y = -\frac{1}{2}x - 1$

Their graphs are parallel. Solution set is the empty set.
12. See section notes in T.G.
$\{(x, y) \mid y = 4 + 3x, x \in R\}$

Find graphically the solution set of each system of equations.

1. $x = 3$ and $y = 4$
2. $x = 0$ and $y = -2$
3. $x + y = 7$ and $y = 3$
4. $x + y = 6$ and $x = -3$
5. $x + y = 8$ and $y = x$
6. $y = x + 2$ and $y = 4 - x$
7. $y = x + 5$ and $y = x - 5$
8. $3x - 2y = 5$ and $2y = 5 + 3x$
9. $3x + 4y = 2$ and $2y = 4 - \frac{3}{2}x$
10. $x + 2y = 5$ and $2y = -x - 2$
11. Write each equation in Exercises **7-10** in the form $y = mx + c$. When the equations in a system have the same value for m and different values for c, how do their graphs compare? What is the solution set of such a system?

Find graphically the solution set of each system of equations.
12. $y = 4 + 3x$ and $6x - 2y = -8$

13. $5x - y = 3$ and $2y = 10x - 6$

14. $x + y = 2$ and $2y = 4 - 2x$

15. $\frac{1}{3}x + \frac{1}{3}y = 2$ and $y = 6 - x$

16. Write each equation in Exercises **12–15** in the form $y = mx + c$. When the equations in a system have the same values for m and c, how do their graphs compare? What is the solution set of such a system?

Using graph paper with small subdivisions (10 marks to represent one unit), find the solution set for each system. Round the solutions to one decimal place.

17. $y = x$ and $x + y = 1$

18. $x + y = 2$ and $2x - y = 2$

19. $3x + 2y = 6$ and $x - y = 1$

20. $2x + y + 2 = 0$ and $y = x + 2$

21. $x - y = 1$ and $3x + 4y = 12$

22. $x + 3y = 3$ and $x + y = 0$

23. $x - y = -4$ and $x + 2y = 4$

24. $3x - 2y + 6 = 0$ and $3x - 2y = 0$

25. $x + 3y = 9$ and $x + y = 5$ and $2x - y = 4$

26. $x + y = 2$ and $3x - 2y = 11$ and $2x - y = 7$

10-5
Solving Systems
– Elimination

OBJECTIVE:

To solve a system of two linear equations in two variables by using the elimination method.

As you may have decided in the previous exercises, solving systems of equations by graphing may be inaccurate. Errors may be made in drawing the lines or in reading the graphs. Fortunately, there are more accurate means of solving systems of equations.

In solving the system $3x - 2y = 8$ and $8x + 2y = 14$, you may think in this way.

See T.G. on the type of reasoning required here.

1. If the same number is added to both sides of an equation, the resulting equation is equivalent to the first. You may add 14 to both sides of the first equation.

$$\begin{array}{r} 3x - 2y = 8 \\ 14 = 14 \\ \hline 3x - 2y + 14 = 22 \Leftrightarrow 3x - 2y = 8 \end{array}$$

For this system, there are two ways to write 14. The second equation of the system says that $8x + 2y = 14$. Here is a clever way to add 14 to both sides of the first equation.

$$3x - 2y = 8$$
$$\underline{8x + 2y = 14}$$
$$11x = 22 \Leftrightarrow 3x - 2y = 8$$

2. The value of x may now be found by solving $11x = 22$, $x = 2$.
3. If $x = 2$, then $3x - 2y = 8$ becomes $3 \cdot 2 - 2y = 8$. Solving this equation gives the value for y, $y = -1$.
4. The solution for the system is $x = 2$, $y = -1$. The solution set is $\{(2, -1)\}$.
5. Check the solution by substituting for x and y in both of the original equations.

Notice that when the same number was added to both sides of $3x - 2y = 8$, the variable y was *eliminated*. This happened because $-2y$ and $2y$ are additive inverses.

If the equations in the system $3x - 2y = 8$ *and* $4x + y = 7$ are combined as in the previous problem, no variable is eliminated.

$$3x - 2y = 8$$
$$\underline{4x + y = 7}$$
$$7x - y = 15$$

The equation $7x - y = 15$ still contains two variables.

Remember that you may use another rule to find equivalent equations. If both sides of an equation are multiplied by the same number, an equation equivalent to the first equation results. The solution set for $2(4x + y) = 2 \cdot 7$ is the same as the solution set for $4x + y = 7$. Therefore, the solution set for the system $3x - 2y = 8$ *and* $4x + y = 7$ is the same as the solution set for the system $3x - 2y = 8$ *and* $8x + 2y = 14$. Using this equivalent system, the variable y may be eliminated.

Stress repeatedly in the examples that equivalent open sentences have the same solution set (and the same graph). Therefore, any open sentence in a system may be replaced by an equivalent open sentence.

EXAMPLES

Stress the goal of replacing equations by equivalent equations. It is to find a system of one of the following types:

$$\left\{ \begin{array}{l} ax + by = c \\ px + (-b)y = d \end{array} \right\}$$

or

$$\left\{ \begin{array}{l} ax + by = c \\ (-a)x + gy = d \end{array} \right\}$$

1. Solve the system $3x - 2y = 8$ *and* $4x + y = 7$.

$$3x - 2y = 8 \Leftrightarrow \qquad\qquad 3x - 2y = 8$$
$$4x + y = 7 \Leftrightarrow 2(4x + y) = 2 \cdot 7 \Leftrightarrow \underline{8x + 2y = 14}$$
$$11x = 22$$
$$x = 2$$

Substitute for x in $3x - 2y = 8$.

$$3x - 2y = 8$$
$$3 \cdot 2 - 2y = 8 \Leftrightarrow 6 - 2y = 8$$
$$\Leftrightarrow - 2y = 2$$
$$\Leftrightarrow y = -1$$

The solution set for the system is $\{(2, -1)\}$.

Check:
$$3x - 2y = 8$$
$$3 \cdot 2 - 2(-1) \overset{?}{=} 8$$
$$6 + 2 \quad \overset{?}{=} 8$$
$$8 = 8$$

$$8x + 2y = 14$$
$$8 \cdot 2 + 2(-1) \overset{?}{=} 14$$
$$16 + (-2) \overset{?}{=} 14$$
$$14 = 14$$

2. Solve the system $\frac{2}{7}x + \frac{3}{7}y = 1$ *and* $\frac{1}{4}x - \frac{1}{6}y = \frac{1}{3}$.

When one or both of the equations in a system contain fractions, it is usually best to find equivalent equations without fractions.

$$\frac{2}{7}x + \frac{3}{7}y = 1 \Leftrightarrow 7\left(\frac{2}{7}x + \frac{3}{7}y\right) = 7 \cdot 1 \Leftrightarrow 2x + 3y = 7$$

$$\frac{1}{4}x - \frac{1}{6}y = \frac{1}{3} \Leftrightarrow 12\left(\frac{1}{4}x - \frac{1}{6}y\right) = 12 \cdot \frac{1}{3} \Leftrightarrow 3x - 2y = 4$$

Now solve the system $2x + 3y = 7$ *and* $3x - 2y = 4$.
In order to eliminate a variable, equivalent equations must be found for both equations in this system.

a.
$$2x + 3y = 7 \Leftrightarrow 2(2x + 3y) = 2 \cdot 7 \Leftrightarrow \quad 4x + 6y = 14$$
$$3x - 2y = 4 \Leftrightarrow 3(3x - 2y) = 3 \cdot 4 \Leftrightarrow \quad 9x - 6y = 12$$
$$\overline{ 13x \qquad = 26}$$
$$x = 2$$

Substitute for x in $2x + 3y = 7$.

$$2x + 3y = 7$$
$$2 \cdot 2 + 3y = 7 \Leftrightarrow y = 1$$

The solution for the system is $(2, 1)$.

$$2x + 3y = 7$$
$$2 \cdot 2 + 3 \cdot 1 \overset{?}{=} 7$$
$$4 + 3 \quad \overset{?}{=} 7$$
$$7 = 7$$

$$3x - 2y = 4$$
$$3 \cdot 2 - 2 \cdot 1 \overset{?}{=} 4$$
$$6 - 2 \quad \overset{?}{=} 4$$
$$4 = 4$$

Stress that the students may choose which variable to eliminate.

b. You could eliminate x instead of y in the previous system.

$$2x + 3y = 7 \Leftrightarrow \quad 3(2x + 3y) = \quad 3 \cdot 7 \Leftrightarrow \quad 6x + 9y = 21$$
$$3x - 2y = 4 \Leftrightarrow -2(3x - 2y) = -2 \cdot 4 \Leftrightarrow -6x + 4y = -8$$
$$\overline{ 13y = 13}$$
$$y = 1$$

Substitute for y in $2x + 3y = 7$.

$$2x + 3y = 7$$
$$2x + 3 \cdot 1 = 7 \Leftrightarrow x = 2$$

The solution for the system is $(2, 1)$.

The **elimination method** allows you to use the two equations in two variables to find equations in one variable.

DISCUSSION QUESTIONS

The system $2x + 3y = 13$ *and* $6x - 5y = -3$ was solved by four different students. Each student's work is shown here.

Student 1

$$2x+3y=13 \Leftrightarrow 5(2x+3y)=5 \cdot 13 \Leftrightarrow 10x+15y=65$$
$$6x-5y=-3 \Leftrightarrow -3(6x-5y)=3 \cdot (-3) \Leftrightarrow 18x-15y=-9$$
$$\overline{28x = 56}$$
$$x = 2$$

$$2x+3y = 13$$
$$2 \cdot 2 +3y = 13 \Leftrightarrow 3y = 9$$
$$\Leftrightarrow y = 3$$

Solution : $(2,3)$

Student 2

$$2x+3y=13 \Leftrightarrow -3(2x+3y)=-3 \cdot 13 \Leftrightarrow -6x-9y=-39$$
$$6x-5y = -3 \qquad\qquad \Leftrightarrow 6x-5y=-3$$
$$\overline{-14y=-42}$$
$$y = 3$$

$$6x-5y = -3$$
$$6x-5 \cdot 3 = -3 \Leftrightarrow 6x=12$$
$$\Leftrightarrow x = 2$$

Solution: $(2,3)$

Student 3

$$2x+3y = 13 \Leftrightarrow 12x+18y = 78$$
$$6x-5y=-3 \Leftrightarrow -12x+10y = 6$$
$$\overline{28y=84}$$
$$y = 3$$

$$6x - 5y = -3$$
$$6x-5 \cdot 3 = -3 \Leftrightarrow 6x=12$$
$$\Leftrightarrow x = 2$$

Solution: $(2,3)$

Student 4

$$2x+3y=13 \Leftrightarrow 2x+3y = 13$$
$$6x-5y=-3 \Leftrightarrow \frac{18}{5}x-3y = -\frac{9}{5}$$
$$\overline{\frac{28}{5}x = \frac{56}{5}}$$
$$x = 2$$

$$6x-5y = -3$$
$$12 -5y = -3 \Leftrightarrow 15=5y$$
$$\Leftrightarrow 3 = y$$

Solution: $(2,3)$

1. Which students chose to eliminate x? Which students chose to eliminate y?

2. What numbers were used by Student 3 to multiply both sides of each equation?

3. What numbers were used by Student 4 to multiply both sides of each equation?

4. Student 4 does not object to working with fractions. Student 4 wishes to eliminate x by multiplying both sides of the first equation by some number. What number should he use for the following system?

$$7x - y = 10$$
$$3x + 5y = -18$$

You wish to eliminate y in each system without using fractions. What is the smallest possible whole number that could appear in each □?

5. $3x - 4y = 10 \Leftrightarrow \bigcirc x - \square y = \triangle$
   $5x + 6y = 13 \Leftrightarrow \bigcirc x + \square y = \triangle$

6. $37x + 20y = 98 \Leftrightarrow \bigcirc x + \square y = \triangle$
   $68x + 25y = 77 \Leftrightarrow -\bigcirc x - \square y = -\triangle$

7. $2x + 64y = 2 \Leftrightarrow \bigcirc x + \square y = \triangle$
   $3x + 32y = 5 \Leftrightarrow -\bigcirc x - \square y = -\triangle$

8. $A, B, C, D, E, F \in W$
   $Ax + By = C \Leftrightarrow \bigcirc x + \square y = \triangle$
   $Dx + Ey = F \Leftrightarrow -\bigcirc x - \square y = -\triangle$

EXERCISES

 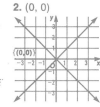
Solve each system of equations by graphing and elimination.

1. $x + y = 8$
   $x - y = 2$

2. $x + y = 0$
   $x - y = 0$

3. $2x + y = 7$
   $3x - 2y = 7$

4. $3x - 2y = 7$
   $4x - 3y = 9$

Solve each system of equations by elimination.

5. $x + y = 12$
   $x - y = 4$

6. $x + y = 6$
   $x - y = 0$

7. $x + y = 5$
   $x - y = 2$

8. $x + 2y = 3$
   $-x + 3y = 2$

9. $2x - y = 4$
   $-2x - 3y = -4$

10. $-3x + 4y = 7$
   $3x + y = -2$

11. $2x + 3y = 5$
   $x + y = 2$

12. $2x + 5y = 16$
   $x - y = 1$

13. $2x - y = 5$
   $x - 2y = 4$

14. $3x + 4y = -7$
   $2x + y = -3$

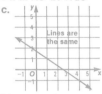
15. $x + y = 0$
$4x + 3y = 3$

16. $2x - 5y = 1$
$4x - 3y = 9$

17. $2x + 4y = 7$
$4x - 3y = 3$

18. $4x - 5y = 22$
$7x + 3y = 15$

19. $2y - 3x = 0$
$x - y + 2 = 0$

20. $2x + 3y - 8 = 0$
$3x + 2y - 17 = 0$

21. $7x + 4y - 1 = 0$
$5x + 2y + 1 = 0$

22. $2x - 7y + 3 = 0$
$3x - 7y + 1 = 0$

23. $5x = 8y$
$4x - 3y + 17 = 0$

24. $x + y = 2$
$2x - y = 2$

25. $2x - 3y = 5$

$\frac{1}{2}x - y = 1$

26. $2x - y = 7$

$\frac{3}{4}x - \frac{1}{2}y = 3$

27. $x + \frac{1}{2}y = 4$

$\frac{1}{3}x - y = -1$

28. $\frac{1}{3}x + 5 = \frac{2}{3}y$

$\frac{1}{2}x + \frac{1}{3}y = \frac{1}{2}$

29. $\frac{1}{2}x + \frac{1}{5}y = 1$

$\frac{1}{3}x - \frac{1}{5}y = 4$

30. $\frac{2x + y}{3} = 5$

$\frac{3x - y}{5} = 1$

31. $5x + 3y = 2x + 7y = 29$

32. $\frac{2x - 3y}{4} = \frac{3x - 2y}{5} = 7\frac{1}{2}$

33. Try to solve the system $2x + 3y = 5$ and $4x + 6y = 6$ by the elimination method.
  a. Is it possible to eliminate only one of the variables?
  b. Do you get a true or a false statement when eliminating a variable?
  c. Graph the two equations in the same coordinate plane. Do you now see why you could not eliminate only one variable?
  d. Write the solution set of this system.

34. Repeat Exercise **33,** using the system $2x + 3y = 5$ and $4x + 6y = 10$.

If the solution set for a system of equations is ø, the system is said to be *inconsistent*. Find the solution set for each system. When the solution set is ø, write *inconsistent system*.

35. $2x + 4y + 5 = 0$
$x + 2y + 5 = 0$

36. $2x + 4y + 10 = 0$
$x + 2y + 5 = 0$

37. $3(x - y + 4) = 9$
$x = y$

38. $2(x + y) = 6 - y$
$x + y = 0$

39. $3(x - y + 3) = 9$
$x = y$

40. $2(x + 3) = 6 - 2y$
$3x + y = 0$

A method for solving a system of equations $y = mx + c$ and $y = nx + d$ is shown in this flow chart.

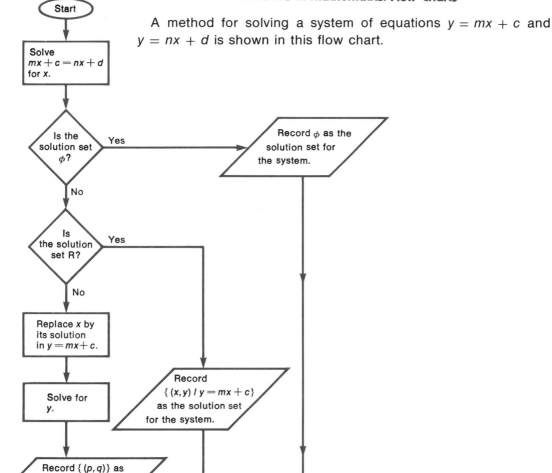

1. Which method of solving systems of equations is used in this flow chart?

2. Use this flow chart to solve each system of equations.

a. $y = 2x + 6$ and $y = \dfrac{1}{2}x + \dfrac{3}{2}$

b. $y = 3x + 2$ and $y = 4x - 1$

c. $y = 5x + 7$ and $y = 5x - 2$

3. Construct a flow chart to find the number of solutions (0, 1, or many) for $y = mx + c$ and $y = nx + d$.

1. Answers will vary.
2. a. $(-3, 0)$ **b.** $(3, 11)$ **c.** ϕ
3. Answers will vary.

OBJECTIVE:
To solve a system of two linear equations in two variables by using the substitution method.

Solving Systems – Substitution

To substitute means to *put in place of*. The **method of substitution** is an easy way to solve a system of equations if one of the terms in x or y has a coefficient of 1.

EXAMPLE

Solve: $3x - 2y = 8$
$\qquad 4x + y = 7$

The second equation is equivalent to $y = 7 - 4x$. You now have another way to give the value for y, as $7 - 4x$. The expression $7 - 4x$ may be substituted for y in the first equation.

$$3x - 2(7 - 4x) = 8$$
$$3x - 14 + 8x = 8 \Leftrightarrow 11x = 22$$
$$\Leftrightarrow \quad x = 2$$

Substitute for x in the first equation.

$$3x - 2y = 8$$
$$6 - 2y = 8 \Leftrightarrow -2y = 2$$
$$\Leftrightarrow \quad y = -1$$

The solution set is $\{(2, -1)\}$.

The substitution method may be used when none of the coefficients is 1. In such cases, however, you usually will have to work with fractions.

EXAMPLE

Solve: $2x + 3y = 7$
$\qquad 3x - 2y = 4$

Remind students that it would be acceptable to find x in terms of y. The first equation could be used to obtain $x = \dfrac{7}{2} - \dfrac{3}{2}y$.

Find y in terms of x from the first equation.

$$2x + 3y = 7 \Leftrightarrow 3y = 7 - 2x$$
$$\Leftrightarrow \quad y = \frac{7}{3} - \frac{2}{3}x$$

Substitute for y in the second equation.

$$3x - 2y = 4$$
$$3x - 2\left(\frac{7}{3} - \frac{2}{3}x\right) = 4 \Leftrightarrow 3x - \frac{14}{3} + \frac{4}{3}x = 4$$
$$\Leftrightarrow 9x - 14 + 4x = 12$$
$$\Leftrightarrow \qquad\qquad 13x = 26$$
$$\Leftrightarrow \qquad\qquad\quad x = 2$$

Substitute for x in the first equation.

$$2x + 3y = 7$$
$$2 \cdot 2 + 3y = 7 \Leftrightarrow 3y = 3$$
$$\Leftrightarrow y = 1$$

The solution is (3, 1).

Unless you enjoy working with fractions, you probably have decided to use the elimination method to solve a system of equations when none of the coefficients is 1.

EXERCISES

1. (2, 3) 2. (3, 0) 3. (0, 0)
4. (2, 4) 5. (5, 5) 6. (2, 4)
7. (12, 4) 8. $(-6, -3)$ 9. (2, 1)
10. (7, 3) 11. $(-1, 2)$ 12. (10, 5)
13. (2, 3) 14. (5, -2)
15. $(-1, -2)$ 16. (3, 4)
17. $(-2, -2)$ 18. $\frac{3}{2}$, -3

19. $-\frac{1}{3}$, $-\frac{2}{3}$, 20. (3, 2)

21. $\frac{1}{2}$, 2 22. (1, -2)

23. (12, -50) 24. (4, 3)
25. (5, 0) 26. (3, -1)

Remind students to make the computation as easy as possible when choosing which variable in which equation to isolate.

Solve each system of equations by graphing, by elimination, and by substitution. Compare the results from the three methods.

1. $y = x + 1$
$2x - 3y = -5$

2. $x = 3 - 2y$
$2x - 2y = 6$

3. $x - y = 0$
$2x + 2y = 0$

4. $-3x + 2y = 2$
$2x + 3y = 16$

Solve each system of equations by substitution.

5. $y = x$
$2x - y = 5$

6. $y = 2x$
$6x - y = 8$

7. $x = 3y$
$2x - 3y = 12$

8. $x = 2y$
$3x - 10y = 12$

9. $x = y + 1$
$x + 5y = 7$

10. $x = y + 4$
$x + 3y = 16$

11. $y = x + 3$
$2x + 3y = 4$

12. $y = x - 5$
$x + 2y = 20$

13. $y = 2x - 1$
$3y - 2x = 5$

14. $x = 2y + 9$
$x + 5y + 5 = 0$

15. $u = 2v + 3$
$5u - 2v + 1 = 0$

16. $q = 2p - 2$
$5p - 4q + 1 = 0$

17. $a - 2b = 2$
$3b - 5a = 4$

18. $y + 2x = 0$
$4x + y = 3$

19. $2x + y = 0$
$7x + 5y = 1$

20. $x - 2y + 1 = 0$
$2x + 3y = 12$

21. $6u - v = 1$
$4u - 3v + 4 = 0$

22. $a + b + 1 = 0$
$9a + 8b + 7 = 0$

23. $5p + q = 10$
$14p + 3q = 18$

24. $s - 8t + 20 = 0$
$5s - 7t + 1 = 0$

25. $x - y = 5$

$\frac{1}{5}x + y = 1$

26. $\frac{2}{3}x + y = 1$

$x + y = 2$

MATHEMATICS AND APPLICATIONS

CREDIT CARDS

Today, credit cards are common replacements for cash and checks. However, in order for the cards to be useful, a credit card company must be certain that the purchases are billed to the proper person. A one-to-one correspondence is set up between people's names and credit-card numbers. Then a company is able to use its computer to detect an incorrectly written number.

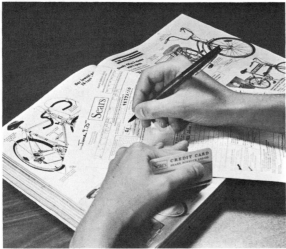

Don Parsisson

Suppose you use your father's credit card to order a 10-speed bike from a catalog. His credit card number is 97873-10. By mistake, you write 98773-10 on the order form. The company could detect your error with a system similar to the following one.

Credit Card No: 97873-10

Divide 3 by 1; the remainder is	0
Divide 7 by 2; the remainder is	1
Divide 8 by 3; the remainder is	2
Divide 7 by 4; the remainder is	3
Divide 9 by 5; the remainder is	4
Sum of the remainders is	10
Divide 10 by 11; the remainder is	10

The remainder 10, used as the numeral after the dash in the credit-card number, serves as a check.

Bruce Charlton

Using the same process as the computer, examine the incorrect credit-card number. Do you get the same "check digit"?

Is there anything special about dividing by 11? Could you divide by 7 with the same result? Can you construct an error which this method will not detect?

A Line Through Two Points

OBJECTIVE:

To find the equation of the line containing two given points by solving a system in variables m and c.

Exactly one straight line may be drawn through any two different points. When the two points have the same value for y, the equation may be written in the form $y = c$. The equation of the straight line through the points (2, 3) and (5, 3) is $y = 3$. When two points have the same value for x, the equation may be written in the form $x = c$. The equation of the straight line through $(-3, -2)$ and $(-3, 4)$ is $x = -3$. When neither the values for x nor the values for y are the same, the equation of the straight line may be written in the form $y = mx + c$ where m is not zero.

EXAMPLES

Insist that students use the methods outlined here, even if they find the desired equation by other means.

1. Find the equation of the straight line through (1, 5) and (3, 11). Use $y = mx + c$ to write two equations.

$$5 = m \cdot 1 + c \qquad \text{because (1, 5) is on the line}$$
$$11 = m \cdot 3 + c \qquad \text{because (3, 11) is on the line}$$

Values for m and c are needed to make $y = mx + c$ true for (1, 5) and (3, 11). These values of m and c can be found by treating m and c as variables and solving the system.

$$5 = m \cdot 1 + c \Leftrightarrow c = 5 - m$$

Substitute for c in $11 = 3m + c$.

$$11 = 3m + (5 - m) \Leftrightarrow 11 = 2m + 5$$
$$\Leftrightarrow \quad 6 = 2m$$
$$\Leftrightarrow \quad 3 = m$$

Substitute 3 for m in $5 = m + c$.

$$5 = 3 + c \Leftrightarrow c = 2$$

The equation of the line through (1, 5) and (3, 11) is $y = 3x + 2$.

2. Find the slope-intercept form of the equation of the line through (5, 2) and (2, 0). Then write the equation in the form $ax + by = c$ where a, b, c, $\in Z$ and $a > 0$.

$$y = mx + c$$
$$2 = m \cdot 5 + c$$
$$0 = m \cdot 2 + c \Leftrightarrow c = -2m$$

Substitute for c in the first equation.

$$2 = 5m + c$$
$$2 = 5m - 2m \Leftrightarrow 2 = 3m$$
$$\Leftrightarrow \frac{2}{3} = m$$

Substitute $\frac{2}{3}$ for m in $c = -2m$.

$$c = -2 \cdot \frac{2}{3} \Leftrightarrow c = \frac{-4}{3}$$

The equation is $y = \frac{2}{3}x - \frac{4}{3}$.

Now find the equivalent equation in the form $ax + by = c$ with $a > 0$.

$$y = \frac{2}{3}x - \frac{4}{3} \Leftrightarrow 3y = 2x - 4$$
$$\Leftrightarrow -2x + 3y = -4$$
$$\Leftrightarrow (-1)(-2x + 3y) = (-1)(-4)$$
$$\Leftrightarrow 2x - 3y = 4$$

An equivalent form of $y = \frac{2}{3}x - \frac{4}{3}$ is $2x - 3y = 4$.

EXERCISES

1. $x = 1$ 2. $y = 2x + 2$
3. $y = 10x - 10$ 4. $y = 3x - 2$
5. $y = x - 5$ 6. $y = -2$
7. $y = \frac{1}{2}x + 3$ 8. $y = x$
9. $2x - 3y = 3$ 10. $x + 2y = 3$
11. $5x - 2y = 0$ 12. $3x - 2y$
$= -5$ 13. $2x - 5y = 0$
14. $5x + 2y = 10$

Write the equation of the line through each pair of points. Use one of the forms $y = mx + c$, or $x = c$.

1. $(1, -3)$ and $(1, 5)$ **2.** $(2, 6)$ and $(3, 8)$
3. $(1, 0)$ and $(2, 10)$ **4.** $(-1, -5)$ and $(1, 1)$
5. $(1, -4)$ and $(5, 0)$ **6.** $(5, -2)$ and $(-2, -2)$
7. $(2, 4)$ and $(4, 5)$ **8.** $(0, 0)$ and $(1, 1)$

Write the equation of the line through each pair of points. Use the form $ax + by = c$ where $a > 0$.

9. $(3, 1)$ and $(6, 3)$ **10.** $(5, -1)$ and $(-1, 2)$
11. $(0, 0)$ and $(2, 5)$ **12.** $(3, 7)$ and $(-1, 1)$
13. $(0, 0)$ and $\left(\frac{1}{2}, \frac{1}{5}\right)$ **14.** $\left(1, \frac{5}{2}\right)$ and $(2, 0)$

Excursions in Mathematics: Formula for Slope

1. $m = \frac{b_2 - b_1}{a_2 - a_1}$

1. Solve the following system for m, $a_1 \neq a_2$ and $b_1 \neq b_2$.

$$b_1 = ma_1 + c$$
$$b_2 = ma_2 + c$$

3. $b_2 - b_1 = m(a_2 - a_1)$

4. a. $y = x + 1$ **b.** $y = \frac{3}{5}x + \frac{7}{5}$

c. $y = -\frac{3}{2}x - \frac{13}{2}$ **d.** $y = -x$
$+ 4$ **e.** $y = \frac{3}{2}x$ **f.** $y = \frac{3}{2}x$

g.

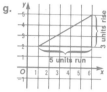

$\frac{b_2 - b_1}{a_2 - a_1} = \frac{5 - 2}{6 - 1} = \frac{3}{5} = \frac{\text{rise}}{\text{run}}$

5. b. and **d.** **e.** (2) $x = c$

2. If (a_1, b_1) and (a_2, b_2) are two points, m is the slope of the line through them. When the system of equations for these two points is solved, the formula for the slope of the line through the points results.

$$m = \frac{b_2 - b_1}{a_2 - a_1}$$

3. Multiply both sides of the equation for m by $(a_2 - a_1)$. The result of this multiplication is written in the point-slope form of an equation, $y - y_1 = m(x - x_1)$, where $y = b_2$ and $x = a_2$.

4. Use the formula to find the slope of the line through each pair of points. Write the equation of each line.

a. (1, 2) and (5, 6) **b.** (1, 2) and (6, 5)
c. (−3, −2) and (−1, −5) **d.** (3, 1) and (1, 3)
e. (0, 0) and (2, 3) **f.** (−2, −3) and (0, 0)
g. Plot the points $(a_1, b_1) = (1, 2)$ and $(a_2, b_2) = (6, 5)$. Show that $\frac{b_2 - b_1}{a_2 - a_1}$ is $\frac{\text{rise}}{\text{run}}$ for the line through these two points.

5. For which pairs of points may the formula for finding the slope not be used?

a. (3, 5) and (2, 6) **b.** (5, 1) and (5, 2)
c. (1, 3) and (2, 3) **d.** (4, 4) and (4, 3)
e. When the formula may not be used, which equation describes the line through the two points?

(1) $y = c$ **(2)** $x = c$ **(3)** $y = mx + c$

10-8
Applications

PROBLEM 1

Many problems contain two or more unknown quantities. Often, problems with two unknown quantities can be solved by using two equations in two variables.

A rectangle is to be drawn with perimeter 75 cm. The length is to be 13 cm more than the width. What is the length to be?

The two unknown quantities in this problem are length and width. If you use x to denote the length and y to denote the width, two equations can be written. You know from the problem that $x = y + 13$. The perimeter of a rectangle is twice the length added to twice the width. With this knowledge you may write the second equation, $2x + 2y = 75$. You now have a system of equations.

$$x = y + 13$$
$$2x + 2y = 75$$

Solve by substitution.

$$2x + 2y = 75$$

$$2(y + 13) + 2y = 75 \Leftrightarrow 2y + 26 + 2y = 75$$

$$\Leftrightarrow \qquad 4y = 49$$

$$\Leftrightarrow \qquad y = 12\frac{1}{4}$$

$$x = 12\frac{1}{4} + 13 = 25\frac{1}{4}$$

The length is to be $25\frac{1}{4}$ cm.

PROBLEM 2

Mary buys 5 pints of red paint and 3 pints of blue paint for $14.50. John buys 2 pints of red paint and 4 pints of blue paint for $10.00. The paint is purchased for stage props for a class play. The class treasurer wants to record the price per pint for each color. How much per pint is the red paint? The blue paint?

Let r represent the price per pint of red paint. Let b represent the price per pint of blue paint. Then two equations may be written.

Problems 2 and 3 will convince most students that using two variables is very convenient for some problems.

$$5r + 3b = 14.50 \qquad \text{Mary's expenditure}$$
$$2r + 4b = 10.00 \qquad \text{John's expenditure}$$

Solve this system of equations for r and b.

$$5r + 3b = 14.50 \Leftrightarrow \quad 20r + 12b = \quad 58.00$$
$$2r + 4b = 10.00 \Leftrightarrow -6r - 12b = -30.00$$
$$\overline{\qquad\qquad 14r \qquad\quad = \quad 28.00}$$
$$r = \quad 2.00$$

$$5r + 3b = 14.50$$
$$5 \cdot 2.00 + 3b = 14.50 \Leftrightarrow 10.00 + 3b = 14.50$$
$$\Leftrightarrow \qquad 3b = \quad 4.50$$
$$\Leftrightarrow \qquad b = \quad 1.50$$

The red paint is $2.00 per pint.
The blue paint is $1.50 per pint.

PROBLEM 3

A motorboat is going downstream with the current. It covers 2 miles in 15 minutes. The return trip upstream takes $\frac{1}{2}$ hour. Find the boat's speed in still water.

Use the distance-rate-time formula, $d = rt$, for this problem. Let s be the speed of the boat in still water. Let c be the rate of the current.

	d miles	r mph	t hours
Downstream	2	$(s + c)$	$\frac{1}{4}$
Upstream	2	$(s - c)$	$\frac{1}{2}$

When the motorboat is going downstream, it goes faster because of the current. When the motorboat is going upstream, it goes slower because of the current.

Solve these two equations for s and c. The equations are written using the formula $d = rt$.

$$2 = (s + c)\frac{1}{4} \Leftrightarrow 2 = \frac{1}{4}s + \frac{1}{4}c \Leftrightarrow 8 = s + c$$

$$2 = (s - c)\frac{1}{2} \Leftrightarrow 2 = \frac{1}{2}s - \frac{1}{2}c \Leftrightarrow \underline{4 = s - c}$$

$$12 = 2s$$
$$6 = s$$

The speed of the boat in still water is 6 mph.

EXERCISES

1. $x = 74$, $y = 38$ 2. $x = \frac{75}{2}$, $y = \frac{51}{2}$ 3. $w = 33$, $l = 51$

4. $w = \frac{7}{2}$, $l = \frac{61}{2}$ 5. Red = $.30 Blue = $.40 6. Expensive = $1.00, Inexpensive = $.40

7. $m = 4$, $c = -6$, $a = 5$

Solve each problem by using a system of equations.

1. The sum of two whole numbers is 112. Their difference is 36. Find the numbers.
2. The sum of two rational numbers is 63. Their difference is 12. Find the numbers.
3. The sum of the length and the width of a rectangle is 84 cm. The length is 18 cm more than the width. Find the length and the width.
4. The perimeter of a rectangle is 68 cm. The length is 27 cm more than the width. Find the length and width.
5. Six red pens and four blue pens cost $3.40. Three red pens and ten blue pens cost $4.90. Find the price of each pen.
6. Twelve expensive flower bulbs and eight inexpensive bulbs cost $15.20. Nine of the expensive ones and four of the inexpensive ones cost $10.60. Find the price of each bulb.
7. A straight line has equation $y = mx + c$. Two points on the line are (2, 2) and (3, 6). Write two equations and solve them for m and c. If $(a, 14)$ lies on the line, find a.

8. Repeat Exercise **7** if the points $(-1, -2)$ and $(3, 10)$ lie on the line. Does $(-2, -7)$ lie on this line?

9. The straight line with equation $px + qy = 1$ passes through $(3, -2)$ and $(-5, 4)$. Find p and q.

10. Find a and b if $ax + by = 29$ when $x = 3$ and $y = 5$, and $ax + by = 13$ when $x = 7$ and $y = -2$.

11. For the series $3 + 9 + 15 + 21 + \ldots$, the nth term is of the form $nd + k$, where d and k are constants. Using the first and second terms of the series, write two equations in d and k. Solve for d and k. Use your results to calculate the 100th term of the series.

12. The speed V meters per second of a train t seconds after the brakes are applied is given by $V = at + b$, where a and b are numbers. When $t = 0$, $V = 16$; when $t = 8$, $V = 10$. Find a and b.

13. Find t at the moment when the train in Exercise **12** stops.

14. The height h meters above the ground reached by a projectile after t seconds is given by the formula $h = at + bt^2$. Find the constants a and b, given that $h = 19$ when $t = 1$, and $h = 28$ when $t = 2$.

15. Chin takes 48 minutes to row 3 miles downstream. When he returns, he takes 90 minutes. What is the river's current?

16. A canoeist paddles 12 miles downstream in 80 minutes. He makes the return trip in 6 hours. At the same rate, how fast does he go in still water?

17. Rita is three times as old as her sister. Four years from now she will be twice as old as her sister. What is Rita's age now?

18. Jerry is 2 years less than twice as old as Tom. In 5 years, Jerry's age will be $1\frac{1}{2}$ times Tom's age. Find their ages now.

19. Two women together have $1000. One woman's share equals the sum of $40 and twice the other woman's share. How much does each woman have?

20. A man has $3700 invested, part at 4% and part at 3%. The total annual income from the investment is $123. Find the amount invested at each rate. (Hint: Interest = principal · rate · time)

21. Divide 100 into two parts such that the larger part is 16 less than 3 times the smaller.

22. One woman earns an hourly rate of pay that is 15¢ more than the rate of another. The sum of the earnings of the two women for 8 hours work each is $38.00. What is the hourly rate of pay for each woman?

23. Two cars start toward each other from cities 208 miles apart. They meet after each has traveled 2 hours. The difference of their speeds is 8 miles per hour. What is the average rate of each car?

24. A motorist travels *x* km in *t* hours. His average speed is 68 km per hour. Write an equation in *x* and *t*. If he reduces his time by 10 minutes, his average speed is 72 km per hour. Write another equation in *x* and *t*. Find the time taken for the trip and the distance traveled.

25. Ammon is six years older than Thelma. Four years ago Ammon was twice as old as Thelma was at that time. Find the present age of each.

26. The ratio of two positive integers *x* and *y* is 5:3. Their difference is 56. Find the two integers.

27. If $2x + y = a + 3b$ and $x - 2y = 3a - b$, find *x* and *y* in terms of *a* and *b*.

28. A concert draws 480 people. Front seats cost $3 each. Back seats cost $2 each. The total receipts are $1162. How many front seats and how many back seats are purchased?

29. Machine A of a firm turns out 30 components per hour. The firm installs a new machine B. It turns out 40 components of the same kind per hour. Six hundred of these components are produced on a day when the total hours of machine operation is 18. How many hours are A and B operated? (Suppose that A and B are operated for *x* hours and *y* hours, respectively.)

30. A solution of hydrochloric acid in water is 30% acid by volume. How much acid is added to 500 cubic centimeters of the solution to increase the amount of acid to 40%? How much pure water is added to the resulting solution to decrease the amount of acid to 35%?

Chapter Summary

1. The solution set of an open sentence can be shown by a graph.
2. A linear equation can be written in each of these forms.
   a. $ax + by + c = 0$ **b.** $ax + by = c$ **c.** $y = mx + c$ or $x = c$
3. The graph of a linear equation is a straight line. Such a graph may be drawn in two ways.
   a. Find the coordinates of the *x*-intercept and the *y*-intercept.
   b. Write the equation in the form $y = mx + c$ which gives the slope *m* and the *y*-intercept $(0, c)$.

4. The graph of a linear equation divides the coordinate plane into two regions. Each region is the graph of the solution set of an inequation.
5. An inequation whose graph has a straight line as its boundary is called a linear inequation.
6. The solution set for a system of equations or inequations is the set of replacements which satisfy all equations or inequations in the system.
7. The solution set of a system of inequations is given best by a graph.
8. The solution set of a system of equations can be found in three ways.
   a. Graph the solution sets to find the point of intersection. This gives only approximate solutions.
   b. Eliminate one of the variables by the use of equivalent equations.
   c. Substitute if one of the terms in x or y has a coefficient of 1.
9. Some practical problems may be solved by writing a system of equations or inequations.

REVIEW EXERCISES 10-1

1. See section notes in T.G.
2. See section notes in T.G.
3. See section notes in T.G.
4. See section notes in T.G.
5. See section notes in T.G.
6. See section notes in T.G.

Show the solution set for each equation or inequation as a graph in a coordinate plane.

1. $2x + y = 7$
2. $x + 2y \leq 4$
3. $0 \leq x \leq 5$
4. $x + y < 12$
5. $y \leq 3x - 15$
6. $-2 \leq y \leq 2$

The figure shows the graph of the line with equation $2x + y = 8$.
7. Write the coordinates of the points A and B.
8. Which regions are given by $\{(x, y)|2x + y \geq 8\}$?
9. Use set notation to define the region AOB.
10. Write an inequation whose solution set is shown by the shaded region in the coordinate plane.

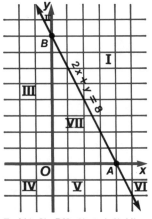

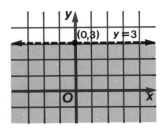

7. $A(4, 0)$, $B(0, 8)$ 8. I, II, VI
9. $\{(x, y) \mid y \leq -2x + 8, y \geq 0,$
$x \geq 0\}$ 10. $y < 3$

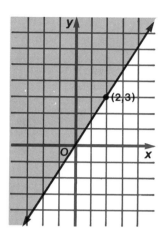

11. Write an inequation whose solution set is shown by the shaded region on the coordinate plane.

10-2

Write each equation in the two forms $ax + by + c = 0$ and $y = mx + c$.

12. $5x - 2y = 6$

13. $\frac{1}{2}x + \frac{1}{3}y = \frac{1}{4}$

14. $2x + y = 3$

15. $2x - 3y = 9$

10-3

11. $y \geq \frac{3}{2}x$ 12. $5x - 2y - 6 = 0$,
$y = \frac{5}{2}x - 3$ 13. $6x + 4y - 3$
$= 0, y = -\frac{3}{2}x + \frac{3}{4}$ 14. $2x + y -$
$3 = 0, y = -2x + 3$ 15. $2x -$
$3y - 9 = 0, y = \frac{2}{3}x - 3$

Show the solution set for each system as a graph.

16. $x \geq 0, y \geq 0, x + y \leq 10$

17. $x > 0, y > 0, 2x + 5y < 20$

18. $x \geq 0, y \geq 0, x \leq 8, y \leq 3$

19. $x < 0, y < 0, x + 2y > -20$

20. $y \leq 8, y \geq x, 2x + y \geq 4$

21. $x \geq 0, y \geq 0, 2x + y \leq 10, x + 2y \leq 10$

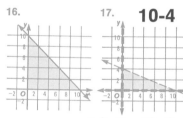

10-4

Graphically solve each system of equations.

22. $x = 7, 4x - 3y = 36$

23. $x - y = 5, 2x + 5y - 10 = 0$

24. $x + y = 4, 2x - y + 1 = 0$

25. $x - y + 2 = 0, 3x - y + 2 = 0$

10-5, 10-6

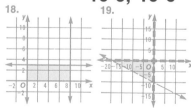

Solve each system of equations.

26. $x - y = 2$
$2x + 3y = 4$

27. $x + y + 1 = 0$
$x - 5y + 7 = 0$

28. $2x + 5y = 14$
$3x - 2y = -17$

29. $x + y = 0$
$2x + 3y = 6$

30. $\frac{1}{4}x + \frac{1}{3}y = \frac{5}{4}$

$\frac{2}{3}x - \frac{1}{5}y = \frac{1}{15}$

31. $x + 2y = 8$

$\frac{3}{4}x + \frac{1}{2}y = 4$

32. $3x = 4y$

$\frac{1}{2}x + \frac{1}{3}y = 1$

33. $\frac{1}{4}x + \frac{1}{6}y = 1$

$4x - y = 5$

20. See section notes in T.G.
21. See section notes in T.G.
22. See section notes in T.G.
23. See section notes in T.G.
24. See section notes in T.G.
25. See section notes in T.G.
26. $(2, 0)$ **27.** $(-2, 1)$ **28.** $(-3, 4)$
29. $(-6, 6)$ **30.** $(1, 3)$ **31.** $(4, 2)$
32. $\frac{4}{3}, 1$ **33.** $(2, 3)$

34. $\frac{1}{4}(x - 1) + y = 8$

$\frac{1}{6}(y - 1) + x = 6$

35. $\frac{x}{2} + \frac{y}{2} = 1$

$\frac{2x + 4y}{5} - \frac{x - y}{3} = -2$

10-7

Write the equation of the line through each pair of points. Write each equation in both of the following forms.

    a. $y = mx + c$ or $x = c$
    b. $ax + by = c$

36. (3, 1) and (−1, 2)

37. (0, 4) and (−2, −4)

38. (−1, −2) and (−1, 3)

39. (2, 6) and $\left(\frac{1}{3}, -1 \right)$

10-8

40. When $x = 2$ and also when $x = -1$, $x^2 + ax + b = 0$. Write and solve two equations in a and b.

41. $S = \{(x, y) \mid 2x + 3y = 0\}$ and $T = \{(x, y) \mid 4x - y = 7\}$. Find $S \cap T$.

42. Points (1, 2) and (−1, −4) lie on the straight line with equation $y = mx + c$. By substituting the coordinates of the points into this equation, write two equations in m and c. Solve these equations for m and c.

43. Scores which range from 24 to 88 are scaled so as to range from 20 to 100. An original score x becomes a scaled score y where $y = px + q$, and p and q are constants. Find p and q.

44. What is the scaled score for an original score of 60 in Exercise **43?**

45. If $5x - y = 8$ and $5y - x = 20$, find the value of $x^2 + y^2$.

46. For the series $8 + 12 + 16 + 20 + \ldots$ the notation $S_1 = 8$, $S_2 = 8 + 12$, $S_3 = 8 + 12 + 16$, $\ldots$ can be used to denote the sum of terms. If $S_n = an^2 + bn$, substitute $n = 1$ and $n = 2$ to obtain two equations which you can solve to find a and b. Find the sum of the series to 100 terms.

CHAPTER 11

using square roots

11-1
Squares and Square Roots from a Graph

OBJECTIVE:

To use the graph of $y = x^2$ to read squares and square roots of numbers.

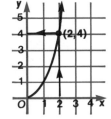

The graph of the function $y = x^2$, $x \in R$, is shown.

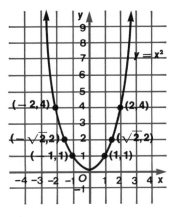

If x is replaced by r or by $-r$, $r \in R$, the value of y that results for each is the same. This occurs because $r^2 = (-r)^2$.

A carefully drawn graph of $y = x^2$ can be used to find squares of numbers. Only Quadrant **I** of the graph, where $x \geq 0$, is needed.

To find the square of 2, read the value of y which corresponds to $x = 2$ on the graph. To find the square of -2, remember that $(-2)^2 = 2^2$. Therefore, $(-2)^2 = 2^2 = 4$.

A **square root** of a number b is a number a such that $a^2 = b$. The **principal square root** of a number is its nonnegative square root.

The radical symbol $\sqrt{}$ is used to mean *principal square root of*.

EXAMPLES

1. $\sqrt{16} = 4$ because $4^2 = 16$ and $4 \geq 0$

2. $\sqrt{100} = 10$ because $10^2 = 100$ and $10 \geq 0$

3. $\sqrt{x^4} = x^2$ because $x^2 \cdot x^2 = x \cdot x \cdot x \cdot x = x^4$ and $x^2 \geq 0$

4. $\sqrt{x^2} = |x|$ because $|x| \cdot |x| = x^2$ and $|x| \geq 0$

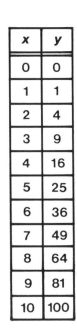

The graph of $y = x^2$ also can be used to find square roots of numbers. Begin with the value of y. Find the corresponding value of x.

To find the square root of 4, first locate 4 on the y-axis. Then find its corresponding value on the x-axis. Following the arrows on the graph, you can see that $\sqrt{4} = 2$.

The following graph is drawn with a 1:10 ratio for unit length on the y-axis to unit length on the x-axis. This graph can be used to find the squares of numbers between 0 and 10.

x	y
0	0
1	1
2	4
3	9
4	16
5	25
6	36
7	49
8	64
9	81
10	100

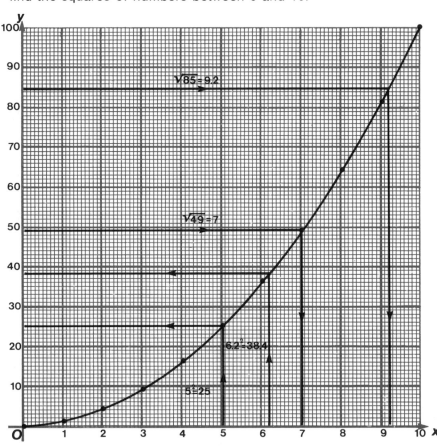

1. Find the square of 5, that is, 5^2.

Locate 5 on the *x*-axis. Find the corresponding value for *y* on the graph. $5^2 = 25$

2. Find $(6.2)^2$.

Locate 6.2 on the *x*-axis. Find its corresponding value on the *y*-axis. $(6.2)^2 = 38.4$ to one decimal place.

The principal square root of a number between 0 and 100 may be found on the graph by reading from the *y*-axis to the *x*-axis.

EXAMPLES

1. Find $\sqrt{49}$. Locate 49 on the *y*-axis. Follow the arrow to the graph and then down to the *x*-axis. The corresponding *x*-value is 7. Therefore, $\sqrt{49} = 7$.

2. Find $\sqrt{85}$. Find 85 on the *y*-axis. Following the arrows to the *x*-axis, you see that $\sqrt{85}$ is approximately 9.2.

EXERCISES

1. 64.0 2. 81.0 3. 20.3 4. 5.3
5. 50.4 6. 42.3 7. 49.0 8. 100.0
9. 10.9 10. 31.4 11. 67.2 12. 90.3
13. 4.5 14. 3.3 15. 9.4 16. 9.5
17. 8.0 18. 9.0 19. 8.7 20. 8.9
21. 3.9 22. 4.0 23. 4.1 24. 7.4
25. 4.4 cm 26. 7.3 m 27. 8.6 mm
28. 9.8 m 29. 5.3 cm 30. 8.9 mm

As an additional exercise, students may be asked to construct the graph for $y = \sqrt{x}$ for $0 \le x \le 100$ and to compare it to the one on page 320.

Use the graph in this section to write the square of each number to one decimal place.

1. 8	**2.** 9	**3.** 4.5
4. 2.3	**5.** 7.1	**6.** 6.5
7. 7	**8.** 10	**9.** 3.3
10. 5.6	**11.** 8.2	**12.** 9.5

Use the graph to write each square root to one decimal place.

13. $\sqrt{20}$	**14.** $\sqrt{11}$	**15.** $\sqrt{87}$
16. $\sqrt{90}$	**17.** $\sqrt{64}$	**18.** $\sqrt{81}$
19. $\sqrt{75}$	**20.** $\sqrt{80}$	**21.** $\sqrt{15}$
22. $\sqrt{16}$	**23.** $\sqrt{17}$	**24.** $\sqrt{55}$

Use the graph to find the approximate length to one decimal place of the side of each square with the given area.

25. 19 cm²	**26.** 54 m²	**27.** 74 mm²
28. 96 m²	**29.** 28 cm²	**30.** 80 mm²

11-2

OBJECTIVE:
To find m^2 for $m \in W$ using a table of squares for n where $1 \le n < 10$.

Tables of Squares

The table on pages 520–521 gives the squares of numbers from 1.00 to 9.99.

To find 5.57^2, use the part of the table shown.

	0	1	2	3	4	5	6	7	8	9
5.5	30.25	30.36	30.47	30.58	30.69	30.80	30.91	31.02	31.14	31.25

Find the first two digits of 5.57 in the left column of the table and the third digit at the top of the table. Read across from 5.5 until you come to the number below 7. $5.57^2 = 31.02$ to two decimal places.

Similarly, $5.5^2 = 30.25$ and $5.59^2 = 31.25$ to two decimal places. Remember that $5.5 = 5.50$, so you think of 0 as the third digit. Notice that the table in this book gives squares rounded to two decimal places.

Use the table on pages 520–521 to read the square of each number to two decimal places.

1. 2.5   **2.** 3.5   **3.** 4.5
4. 4.51   **5.** 4.52   **6.** 4.59
7. 7.0   **8.** 7.01   **9.** 7.10
10. 9.2   **11.** 9.29   **12.** 6.99
13. 2.02   **14.** 5.47   **15.** 8.76

Table 1 can also be used to find the square of a number less than 1 or greater than 10.

1. Use the table to find 45.6^2. The table gives the square of a number between 1 and 10 only.

$$45.6 = 4.56 \cdot 10 \qquad 4.56 \text{ is between 1 and 10.}$$
$$45.6^2 = (4.56 \cdot 10)^2$$
$$= (4.56 \cdot 10) \cdot (4.56 \cdot 10)$$
$$= 4.56^2 \cdot 10^2$$
$$= 20.79 \cdot 100 \qquad \text{From the table}$$
$$45.6^2 = 2079$$

2. $139^2 = (1.39 \cdot 100)^2$
$139^2 = 1.39^2 \cdot 100^2$
$139^2 = 1.93 \cdot 10000 \qquad$ From the table
$139^2 = 19300$

3. $0.78^2 = \left(\dfrac{7.8}{10}\right)^2$

$0.78^2 = \dfrac{60.84}{100} \qquad$ From the table

$0.78^2 = 0.6084$

EXERCISES

Use the table and the method of this section to find the square of each number to the accuracy the table permits.

1. 23.5	**2.** 37.1	**3.** 89.2
4. 10.1	**5.** 456	**6.** 209
7. 500	**8.** 905	**9.** 0.29
10. 0.87	**11.** 0.56	**12.** 0.33

Find each square to the accuracy the table permits.

13. 12.9^2	**14.** 152^2	**15.** 0.78^2
16. 0.789^2	**17.** 30.7^2	**18.** 123.8^2
19. 653.2^2	**20.** 0.206^2	

Use the graph or the table to find the square of each number to the accuracy the table permits.

21. 5	**22.** 15	**23.** 25
24. 50	**25.** 500	**26.** 8.5
27. 0.5	**28.** 12.5	**29.** 17
30. 71	**31.** 0.39	**32.** 0.246
33. 128	**34.** 271.9	**35.** 15.8

Find the area of each square to the accuracy the table permits with a side of the following length.

36. 3.5 cm	**37.** 16 mm	**38.** 1.06 m
39. 37.1 cm		

Find the value of each expression to the accuracy the table permits.

40. $3^2 + 13^2$	**41.** $2.3^2 + 1.7^2$	**42.** $8.4^2 - 1.6^2$

11-3
Simplifying Radicals

OBJECTIVE:
To simplify a radical expression not containing radicals in a denominator.

EXPLORATORY EXERCISES

1. Fill in each blank.

a. $\sqrt{36} =$ ___?___   **b.** $\sqrt{9} =$ ___?___

c. $\sqrt{4} =$ ___?___   **d.** $\sqrt{9} \cdot \sqrt{4} =$ ___?___

e. $\sqrt{36} = \sqrt{9} \cdot$ ___?___   **f.** $\sqrt{144} =$ ___?___

g. $\sqrt{16} =$ ___?___   **h.** $\sqrt{9} =$ ___?___

i. $\sqrt{16} \cdot \sqrt{9} =$ ___?___   **j.** $\sqrt{144} = \sqrt{16} \cdot$ ___?___

These are intended to be class or group work.

2. What conclusion about $\sqrt{ab}$, $a \geq 0$, $b \geq 0$, can you draw from Exploratory Exercise 1?

3. Fill in each blank.

a. $\sqrt{9} = \underline{\quad?\quad}$

b. $\sqrt{36} = \underline{\quad?\quad}$

c. $\sqrt{4} = \underline{\quad?\quad}$

d. $\dfrac{\sqrt{36}}{\sqrt{4}} = \underline{\quad?\quad}$

e. $\sqrt{9} = \dfrac{\sqrt{36}}{\underline{\quad?\quad}}$

f. $\sqrt{16} = \underline{\quad?\quad}$

g. $\sqrt{64} = \underline{\quad?\quad}$

h. $\sqrt{4} = \underline{\quad?\quad}$

i. $\dfrac{\sqrt{64}}{\sqrt{4}} = \underline{\quad?\quad}$

j. $\sqrt{16} = \dfrac{?}{\sqrt{4}}$

4. What conclusion about $\sqrt{\dfrac{a}{b}}$, $a \geq 0$, $b \geq 0$ can you draw from Exploratory Exercise **3**?

The preceding problems are examples of two properties of square roots.

**If $n, m \in R$ and $n > 0$, $m > 0$, the following statements
are true.**

1. The Multiplication Property of Square Roots

$$\sqrt{n \cdot m} = \sqrt{n} \cdot \sqrt{m}$$

2. The Division Property of Square Roots

$$\sqrt{\frac{n}{m}} = \frac{\sqrt{n}}{\sqrt{m}} \qquad \text{when } m \neq 0$$

These properties may be used to simplify square roots which are not perfect squares. To combine radicals by addition or subtraction, use the Distributive Property to combine like terms.

EXAMPLES

1. $\sqrt{50} = \sqrt{25 \cdot 2}$
$= \sqrt{25} \cdot \sqrt{2}$
$= 5\sqrt{2}$

2. $\sqrt{75a^2x} = \sqrt{25 \cdot 3 \cdot a^2 \cdot x}$
$= \sqrt{25a^2} \cdot \sqrt{3x}$
$= 5a\sqrt{3x} \qquad \text{when } a \geq 0$

3. $\sqrt{27} + \sqrt{12} = \sqrt{9 \cdot 3} + \sqrt{4 \cdot 3}$

Use the $\qquad = 3\sqrt{3} + 2\sqrt{3}$
Multiplication
Property for
Square Roots.

Use the $\qquad = (3 + 2)\sqrt{3}$
Distributive
Property.

$\qquad\qquad = 5\sqrt{3}$

4. $\sqrt{75} + \sqrt{12} - \sqrt{40} = 5\sqrt{3} + 2\sqrt{3} - 2\sqrt{10}$
$\qquad\qquad\qquad\qquad = 7\sqrt{3} - 2\sqrt{10}$

When a number is not a perfect square, its square root should be written in **simplest radical form.** The square root is in simplest radical form if no factor of the number is a perfect square.

EXAMPLES

1. The simplest radical form of $\sqrt{80}$ is $4\sqrt{5}$.

$$\sqrt{80} = \sqrt{16 \cdot 5} = \sqrt{16} \cdot \sqrt{5} = 4\sqrt{5}$$

2. The simplest radical form of $\sqrt{63b}$ is $3\sqrt{7b}$.

$$\sqrt{63b} = \sqrt{9 \cdot 7b} = \sqrt{9} \cdot \sqrt{7b} = 3\sqrt{7b}$$

EXERCISES

It is acceptable if slow students are assigned only numerical exercises.

1. $2\sqrt{2}$ **2.** $3\sqrt{3}$ **3.** $2\sqrt{6}$
4. $2\sqrt{x}$ **5.** $5a\sqrt{3a}$ **6.** $\sqrt{5}$
7. $6\sqrt{3}$ **8.** $2x\sqrt{x} + 2$ **9.** $3\sqrt{2}$
10. 10 **11.** $\sqrt{2}$ **12.** $6\sqrt{2} - 5$
13. $4 - 3\sqrt{2}$ **14.** $11\sqrt{10} - 10$
15. $(b + 1)\sqrt{b}$ **16.** $(5a - 2)$
$\sqrt{3a}$ **17.** $2a + 2\sqrt{a}$
18. $(4 + b)\sqrt{b} + 1$ **19.** $6\sqrt{3}$
20. 5 **21.** $35\sqrt{6}$ **22.** $4\sqrt{2}$

Write each square root in simplest radical form. All variables represent nonnegative real numbers.

1. $\sqrt{8}$ **2.** $\sqrt{27}$ **3.** $\sqrt{24}$

4. $\sqrt{4x}$ **5.** $\sqrt{75a^3}$ **6.** $\dfrac{1}{3}\sqrt{45}$

7. $\sqrt{108}$ **8.** $\sqrt{4x^3 + 8x^2}$

Perform each operation. Write your answer in simplest radical form. The variables a and b are greater than zero.

9. $\sqrt{8} + \sqrt{2}$ **10.** $\sqrt{25} + 5$

11. $\sqrt{32} - \sqrt{8} - \sqrt{2}$ **12.** $\sqrt{50} - \sqrt{25} + \sqrt{2}$

13. $\sqrt{16} - \sqrt{8} - \sqrt{2}$ **14.** $\sqrt{1000} - \sqrt{100} + \sqrt{10}$

15. $\sqrt{b^3} + \sqrt{b}$ **16.** $\sqrt{75a^3} - 2\sqrt{3a}$

17. $\sqrt{4a^2} + \sqrt{4a}$ **18.** $\sqrt{16b + 16} + \sqrt{b^3 + b^2}$

19. $\sqrt{18} \cdot \sqrt{6}$ **20.** $(\sqrt{5})^2$

21. $5\sqrt{3} \cdot 7\sqrt{2}$ **22.** $\sqrt{18} + \sqrt{72} - \sqrt{50}$

23. $7\sqrt{2}$ **24.** $2a\sqrt{b}$ **25.** $4\sqrt{5}$
26. 4 **27. a.** $\sqrt{25} = 5 \neq \sqrt{9} + \sqrt{16} = 7$ **b.** $\sqrt{9} = 3 \neq \sqrt{25} - \sqrt{16} = 1$ **28.** ab **29.** a^3 **30.** abc
31. a^3b^3c **32.** $b(b^2 + a^2)$
33. $\sqrt{b} - \sqrt{a}$ **34.** No
35.

One solution.
36. $\{x \mid 0 \leq x \leq 9, x \in R\}$

Use Exercises 33-36 to challenge able students if slow students need more time on other exercises.

23. $\sqrt{50} + \sqrt{8}$ **24.** $\sqrt{a^2b} - 2a\sqrt{b} + \sqrt{9a^2b}$

25. $2\sqrt{20} - \dfrac{3}{4}\sqrt{80} + \sqrt{45}$ **26.** $\sqrt{48} \div \sqrt{3}$

27. Use $a = 9$, $b = 16$, and $c = 25$ to show that each sentence is *false*.

  a. $\sqrt{a + b} = \sqrt{a} + \sqrt{b}$
  b. $\sqrt{c - b} = \sqrt{c} - \sqrt{b}$

Assume $a = \sqrt{2}$, $b = \sqrt{3}$, and $c = \sqrt{5}$. Rewrite each expression as a product using only a, b, and c as factors.

28. $\sqrt{6}$ **29.** $2\sqrt{2}$

30. $\sqrt{30}$ **31.** $6\sqrt{30}$

32. $\sqrt{27} + \sqrt{12}$

33. If $0 < a < b < c$ and $b - a = c - b$, which is larger: $\sqrt{b} - \sqrt{a}$ or $\sqrt{c} - \sqrt{b}$?

34. Is it possible that if $b - a > 1000$ then $0 < \sqrt{b} - \sqrt{a} < 1$?

35. Graph the function $f(x) = \sqrt{x}$ where $x \in \{x \mid x \geq 0, x \in R\}$. How many solutions are there for $\sqrt{x + 9} - \sqrt{x} = 1$, where $x \geq 0$?

36. If x is a variable on $\{x \mid x \geq 0, x \in R\}$, what is the solution set for $\sqrt{x + 7} - \sqrt{x} \geq 1$?

11-4
Reducing Fractions Containing Radicals

OBJECTIVE:

To simplify a radical expression containing radicals in a denominator.

EXAMPLES

Sometimes the denominator of a fraction contains a square root. If the fraction is to be in simplest radical form, the denominator must contain no radicals. Remember that you may obtain an equivalent fraction by multiplying numerator and denominator by a nonzero number. This gives you a way to write a fraction in simplest radical form. If $\sqrt{a}$ is a factor of the denominator, simply multiply both numerator and denominator by $\sqrt{a}$.

$$\begin{aligned}
\mathbf{1.}\quad \frac{14}{\sqrt{7}} &= \frac{14\sqrt{7}}{\sqrt{7} \cdot \sqrt{7}} \\
&= \frac{14\sqrt{7}}{\sqrt{49}} \\
&= \frac{14\sqrt{7}}{7} \\
&= 2\sqrt{7}
\end{aligned}$$

Remind students that this is a specialized use of $\sqrt{m}\ \sqrt{n} = \sqrt{mn}$.

Here $\sqrt{n}\ \sqrt{n} = \sqrt{n^2} = n$.

2. $\dfrac{10}{\sqrt{20}} + 3\sqrt{5} = \dfrac{10}{2\sqrt{5}} + 3\sqrt{5}$

$\qquad\qquad\quad = \dfrac{10\sqrt{5}}{2\sqrt{5}\cdot\sqrt{5}} + 3\sqrt{5}$

$\qquad\qquad\quad = \dfrac{10\sqrt{5}}{2\cdot 5} + 3\sqrt{5}$

$\qquad\qquad\quad = \dfrac{10\sqrt{5}}{10} + 3\sqrt{5}$

$\qquad\qquad\quad = \sqrt{5} + 3\sqrt{5}$

$\qquad\qquad\quad = 4\sqrt{5}$

3. $\sqrt{\dfrac{2}{3}} = \dfrac{\sqrt{2}}{\sqrt{3}} = \dfrac{\sqrt{2}\cdot\sqrt{3}}{\sqrt{3}\cdot\sqrt{3}} = \dfrac{\sqrt{6}}{\sqrt{9}} = \dfrac{\sqrt{6}}{3}$

Stress the fact that Example 4 would be nonsense for $x \le 0$.

4. $\dfrac{3\sqrt{x} - 2}{\sqrt{2x}} = \dfrac{(3\sqrt{x} - 2)\cdot\sqrt{2x}}{\sqrt{2x}\cdot\sqrt{2x}}$

$\qquad\qquad = \dfrac{3\sqrt{x}\ \sqrt{2x} - 2\sqrt{2x}}{2x}$

$\qquad\qquad = \dfrac{3\sqrt{2x^2} - 2\sqrt{2x}}{2x}$

$\qquad\qquad = \dfrac{3x\sqrt{2} - 2\sqrt{2x}}{2x} \qquad$ if $x > 0$

EXERCISES

Ask students which would *always* exist as a real number, $\sqrt{x^2}$ or $(\sqrt{x})^2$ for $x \in$ R.

1. $\frac{5}{2}\sqrt{2}$ 2. $5\sqrt{3}$ 3. $\frac{1}{2}\sqrt{3a}$

4. $\frac{1}{b}\sqrt{ab}$ 5. 12 6. 2 7. $\frac{\sqrt{2}}{4}$

8. $2\sqrt{5}$ 9. $2\frac{\sqrt{5}}{a}$ 10. $\frac{a\sqrt{b}}{b^2}$

11. $7x$

Perform each operation. Write all radicals in simplest radical form. The variables are greater than zero.

1. $\sqrt{\dfrac{1}{2}} + \sqrt{8}$

2. $2\sqrt{\dfrac{3}{4}} + \sqrt{48}$

3. $\sqrt{\dfrac{a}{3}} + \sqrt{\dfrac{a}{12}}$

4. $\dfrac{a\sqrt{b}}{b\sqrt{a}}$

5. $(2\sqrt{3})^2$

6. $\sqrt{\dfrac{2}{3}}\ \sqrt{\dfrac{9}{5}}\ \sqrt{\dfrac{10}{3}}$

7. $\dfrac{\sqrt{6}}{2\sqrt{12}}$

8. $\dfrac{2\sqrt{15}}{\sqrt{3}}$

9. $\dfrac{10}{a\sqrt{5}}$

10. $\dfrac{a}{\sqrt{b^3}}$

11. $(\sqrt{7x})^2$

Solve each equation. The variables are on the set of positive real numbers.

It is not essential that slow students work Exercises 12-20.

12. $x = 5$ 13. $x = 1$ 14. $x = \frac{8}{3}$

15. $x = \sqrt{2}$ 16. $x = \sqrt{\frac{2}{2}}$

17. $x = \sqrt{5}$ 18. $x = \sqrt{3}$

19. $x = 2499$ 20. $x = \frac{2}{9}$

12. $\dfrac{5}{\sqrt{x}} = \sqrt{x}$ **13.** $\sqrt{4x} = 3 - \sqrt{x}$

14. $\dfrac{\sqrt{x^3}}{\sqrt{x}} = 16 - 5x$ **15.** $5x = 7\sqrt{2} - \sqrt{8}$

16. $\sqrt{2}x = \dfrac{\sqrt{8} - \sqrt{2}}{\sqrt{2}}$ **17.** $\dfrac{\sqrt{2x^2}}{\sqrt{2}} = \sqrt{5}$

18. $7\sqrt{x} = \dfrac{10\sqrt{3} - \sqrt{27}}{\sqrt{x}}$ **19.** $\sqrt{4x + 4} = 100$

20. $\sqrt{2x} + 3 = 5 - \sqrt{8x}$

11-5
Square Root Tables

OBJECTIVE:
To find $\sqrt{n}$, $n \geq 0$, $n \in Q$, and n given by a decimal expansion by using tables.

The table on pages 522–523 gives square roots for numbers from 1.00 to 9.99.

The table on pages 524–525 gives square roots for numbers from 10.0 to 99.9.

These tables are read in the same way as the table for squares of numbers.

EXAMPLES

Use Tables 2 and 3 to find each square root.

1. $\sqrt{6} = 2.45$ **2.** $\sqrt{60} = 7.75$

3. $\sqrt{4.23} = 2.06$ **4.** $\sqrt{42.3} = 6.50$

5. $\sqrt{90} = 9.49$ **6.** $\sqrt{92.8} = 9.63$

DISCUSSION QUESTIONS

The purpose of these questions is to make sure students can read tables.

1. 2.24 2. 2.24 3. 2.26 4. 2.28
5. 2.61 6. 1.00 7. 3.16 8. 5.53
9. 6.00 10. 1.41 11. 1.95
12. 7.07 cm 13. 1.32 m 14. 3.74
15. 1.72

Use the tables of square roots to find the square root of each number.

1. 5	**2.** 5.01	**3.** 5.10
4. 5.18	**5.** 6.8	**6.** 1.01
7. 10	**8.** 30.6	**9.** 36.0
10. 2	**11.** 3.81	

Calculate the length of the sides of each square with the area given.

12. 50 cm²   **13.** 1.75 m²

Find the value of each expression.

14. $\sqrt{(1^2 + 2^2 + 3^2)}$ **15.** $\sqrt{(2.1^2 - 1.2^2)}$

The tables may be used to find the square root of a number less than 1 or greater than 100.

Use tables to find $\sqrt{123}$.

The tables give square roots of numbers from 1 to 100 only, so $\sqrt{123}$ cannot be found directly. From the tables, however, you can see that $\sqrt{1.23} = 1.11$ and $\sqrt{12.3} = 3.51$. You can use either of these square roots to compute $\sqrt{123}$.

$$\sqrt{123} = \sqrt{1.23 \cdot 100} \qquad \sqrt{123} = \sqrt{12.3 \cdot 10}$$
$$= \sqrt{1.23} \cdot \sqrt{100} \qquad = \sqrt{12.3} \cdot \sqrt{10}$$
$$= 1.11 \cdot 10 \qquad\qquad = (3.51)(3.16)$$
$$= 11.1 \qquad\qquad\qquad = 11.09$$
$$\qquad\qquad\qquad\qquad = 11.1$$

Since 100 has an exact square root and 10 does not, the first of these two methods is easier.

To find the square root of a number between 100 and 10,000, first express the number as a multiple of 100.

EXAMPLES

1. $\sqrt{6020} = \sqrt{60.2 \cdot 100} = 7.76 \cdot 10 = 77.6$
2. $\sqrt{193.6} = \sqrt{1.94 \cdot 100} = 1.39 \cdot 10 = 13.9$

Since the tables list only three digit numbers, 193.6 must be rounded to 194. The answer 13.9 is fairly close to $\sqrt{193.6}$.

To find the square root of a number less than 1, use the Division Property of Square Roots.

EXAMPLES

1. $\sqrt{0.123} = \sqrt{\dfrac{12.3}{100}} = \dfrac{\sqrt{12.3}}{\sqrt{100}} = \dfrac{3.51}{10} = 0.351$

2. $\sqrt{0.0123} = \sqrt{\dfrac{1.23}{100}} = \dfrac{\sqrt{1.23}}{\sqrt{100}} = \dfrac{1.11}{10} = 0.111$

Remember that problems such as these have approximate answers since you are working with irrational numbers.

EXERCISES

Write each number as $a \cdot 100$ or $a \cdot \dfrac{1}{100}$ so that a is a number between 1 and 100.

1. 234	**2.** 200	**3.** 2135
4. 0.52	**5.** 0.5	**6.** 0.145
7. 0.06	**8.** 0.025	**9.** 0.7777

10. 11.6 **11.** 20.2 **12.** 22.4
13. 23.8 **14.** 35.0 **15.** 93.8
16. 16.7 **17.** 0.6 **18.** 0.888
19. 0670 **20.** 0.212 **21.** 0.134
22. 20.8 **23.** 0.958 **24.** 61.0
25. 80.6 **26.** 1.53 **27.** 28.4
28. 6.08 **29.** 0.868 **30.** 48.0
31. 3.54 **32.** 0.988 **33.** 23.3
34. 116 **35.** 157 **36.** 351
37. 366 **38.** 0.0894 **39.** 0.0224
40. 0.0539

Use tables and the method of this section to find the square root of each number.

10. 135	**11.** 407	**12.** 500
13. 567.8	**14.** 1230	**15.** 8800
16. 278	**17.** 0.36	**18.** 0.789
19. 0.45	**20.** 0.045	**21.** 0.018
22. 432	**23.** 0.917	**24.** 3726

Find the value of each square root.

25. $\sqrt{6500}$	**26.** $\sqrt{2.34}$	**27.** $\sqrt{804}$
28. $\sqrt{36.92}$	**29.** $\sqrt{0.753}$	**30.** $\sqrt{2300}$
31. $\sqrt{12.5}$	**32.** $\sqrt{0.9753}$	**33.** $\sqrt{498}$

The previous methods can be extended to numbers greater than 10,000 or less than 0.01.

Samples   **1.** $\sqrt{19360} = \sqrt{1.94 \cdot 10000} = 1.39 \cdot 100 = 139$

2. $\sqrt{0.0039} = \sqrt{\dfrac{39}{10000}} = \dfrac{6.24}{100} = 0.0624$

Find the square root of each number.

34. 13,500	**35.** 24,600	**36.** 123,456
37. 134,000	**38.** 0.008	**39.** 0.0005
40. 0.0029		

Slow students may need help in Exercises 34-40 to reach the conclusion that the ideal powers of 10 are 1, 100, 1000, etc. Such powers of ten may be described as "those with an even number of zeros."

Excursions in Mathematics: An Iterative Method for Finding Square Roots

An *iterative method* is an approximation method in which a process is repeated many times. In order to use an iterative method for approximating square roots, the following property is needed.

For any positive real number *n*, $n \div \sqrt{n} = \sqrt{n}$.

EXAMPLES

1. $36 \div \sqrt{36} = \sqrt{36}$ *or* $36 \div 6 = 6$
2. $81 \div \sqrt{81} = \sqrt{81}$ *or* $81 \div 9 = 9$

In using the iterative method, the first step is to estimate the square root of the number.

To find the square root of 2.89, you might guess 1.6. To check if this guess is correct, divide 2.89 by 1.6.

$$1.6\overline{)2.8\,90}\;\;\overset{1.81}{}$$

The divisor 1.6 is not equal to the quotient 1.81. Therefore, the guess is not correct. The correct value of the square root lies between the divisor and the quotient.

The key idea in the iterative method is to use a first guess to find a better second estimate. This second estimate is the number half-way between the quotient and the divisor in the check. To find this new estimate, the sum of the quotient and the divisor is divided by 2.

$$\frac{1.6 + 1.81}{2} = \frac{3.41}{2} = 1.705$$

The new estimate, 1.705, is much closer than the previous estimate to the actual square root of 2.89.

EXAMPLE

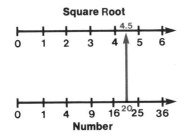

Square Root

Number

$$447\overline{)2000.000}\;\;\overset{4.474}{}$$
1788
2120
1788
3320
3129
1910

1. Calculate $\sqrt{20}$.

From the number line, the first estimate is 4.5.

If the quotient of 20 divided by 4.5 is 4.5, then the first estimate is correct. If the quotient is not 4.5 exactly, then $\sqrt{20}$ lies between 4.5 and the quotient.

$$\frac{20}{4.5} = \frac{200}{45} = \frac{40}{9} = 4.44$$

$\dfrac{20}{4.5} = 4.44$ Therefore, $\sqrt{20}$ lies between 4.5 and 4.44.

For a second estimate, take the average of 4.5 and 4.44.

$$\text{A second estimate} = \frac{4.5 + 4.44}{2} = 4.47$$

$\dfrac{20}{4.47} = 4.474$ Therefore, $\sqrt{20}$ lies between 4.47 and 4.474.

$$\text{A third estimate} = \frac{4.47 + 4.474}{2} = 4.472$$

Each of the estimates 4.5, 4.47, 4.472 is a better approximation for $\sqrt{20}$ than the previous one.

There is no limit to the number of times an estimate can be improved. If 4.472 is not accurate enough, you can make a fourth estimate.

A large amount of arithmetic work is necessary when an iterative method is used to find square roots. A hand calculator would speed this work.

EXERCISES

1. 2.45 **2.** 5.39 **3.** 9.38 **4.** 7.48
5. 6.32 **6.** 2.65 **7.** 9.49 **8.** 4.12
9. 4.47 **10.** 1.73 **11.** 3.85
12. 2.86 **13.** 8.68 **14.** 7.53
15. 1.26 **16.** 3.4641 **17.** 8.3066
18. 2.8284 **19.** 4.6476 **20.** 9.6644

Use the iterative method to find by a good first estimate and one division the square roots of each number rounded to two decimal places. Use a hand calculator if you have access to one.

1. 6   **2.** 29   **3.** 88
4. 56   **5.** 40   **6.** 7
7. 90   **8.** 17   **9.** 20
10. 3

Use the iterative method to find each square root rounded to two decimal places.

11. $\sqrt{14.8}$ **12.** $\sqrt{8.2}$ **13.** $\sqrt{75.4}$
14. $\sqrt{56.7}$ **15.** $\sqrt{1.59}$

Write the square root of each number to two decimal places using tables. By one division calculate the square root to four decimal places.

16. 12   **17.** 69   **18.** 8
19. 21.6   **20.** 93.4

11-6
Approximations

OBJECTIVE:

To determine the number of significant digits for certain decimal numbers.

Stress that usage dictates the degree of error which is acceptable in giving approximations.

The symbol $\doteq$ is used to mean *is approximately equal to*. Often the square root of a positive integer will be an irrational number. Remember that no ratio of integers or repeating decimal can be used to name an irrational number. In the case of an irrational number, the best you can do is to give an approximation for its value. The accuracy of the approximation will depend upon its use.

In solving problems, a rough ***estimate*** often is made as a first step to help you know what type answer to expect. The result of an estimate is also an ***approximation.***

EXAMPLE

Since 20 is between 16 and 25, $\sqrt{20}$ must be between $\sqrt{16}$ and $\sqrt{25}$. That is, $\sqrt{20}$ must be between 4 and 5. A rough estimate of $\sqrt{20}$ might be 4.5. You can check this estimate by squaring 4.5.

$$4.5^2 = 20.25$$

If you accept this much error, 4.5 is a good approximation for $\sqrt{20}$.

Measurement is usually approximate. Measures such as length, weight, time, and area are given by approximations.

Suppose you measure the length of a window with a steel tape. You find that it is 67.3 cm long. If a cloth tape measure is used, your measurement probably will be less accurate. You might find using a cloth tape that the window is about 67 cm long.

A convenient way to indicate the degree of approximation is by means of the number of digits used. You say that 67.3 cm has 3 **significant digits,** and that 67 has 2 significant digits.

EXAMPLES

1. 2.3 cm has 2 significant digits.
2. 1234 m has 4 significant digits.

A zero is a significant digit except when it is used simply to indicate the position of the decimal point.

EXAMPLES

Numerals like 3200 were omitted in the examples, since working with them requires using scientific notation. This topic is treated in *Algebra 2*.

1. 504 cm: 3 significant digits
2. 5.04 m: This is the same length, expressed in a different unit. Therefore, it has 3 significant digits.
3. 2.40 m: The 0 indicates that the length has been measured to the nearest hundredth of a meter. Therefore, the 0 is significant. There are 3 significant digits.
4. 0.45: The 0 shows the position of the point. Therefore, it is not counted as a significant digit. There are 2 significant digits.
5. 0.0810: The first two 0's show the position of the decimal point and are not significant. The third 0 shows that the number is accurate to four decimal places and is significant. Therefore, 0.0810 has 3 significant digits.

EXERCISES

1. 2,3 **2.** 4,5 **3.** 9,10 **4.** 11,12
5. 3,4 **6.** 6,7 Answers will vary in Exercises 7-12. **7.** 6.5 → 42.25
8. 8.4 → 70.56 **9.** 9.7 → 94.09
10. 2.8 → 7.84 **11.** 2.2 → 4.84
12. 5.5 → 30.25 **13.** 2 **14.** 2
15. 3

Write two consecutive whole numbers between which each square root lies.

1. $\sqrt{5}$ **2.** $\sqrt{24}$ **3.** $\sqrt{87}$
4. $\sqrt{137}$ **5.** $\sqrt{13.7}$ **6.** $\sqrt{47}$

Estimate to one decimal place the square root of each number. Check your answer by squaring the estimate.

7. 42   **8.** 70   **9.** 94
10. 8   **11.** 5   **12.** 30

Give the number of significant digits in each number.

13. 2.2 cm   **14.** 13 years   **15.** 154 months

16. 8 kg

17. 6 cm²

18. 32.4 liters

19. 9.9 seconds

20. 1256 kg

21. 23

22. 2.03

23. 0.0003

24. 0.303

25. 1.555

26. 0.0404

27. 0.001

28. 10.03

29. 205

30. 2.050

Estimate to 2 significant digits each square root.

31. $\sqrt{12}$

32. $\sqrt{50}$

33. $\sqrt{3}$

34. $\sqrt{7}$

35. $\sqrt{90}$

36. $\sqrt{6}$

OBJECTIVE:

11-7

The Pythagorean Theorem

To determine the length of the third side given lengths for two sides of a right triangle.

You may think of a *right angle* as the angle formed by the corner of a square. A ***right triangle*** is a triangle which contains a right angle.

The longest side of a right triangle is the side opposite the right angle. This side is called the ***hypotenuse.***

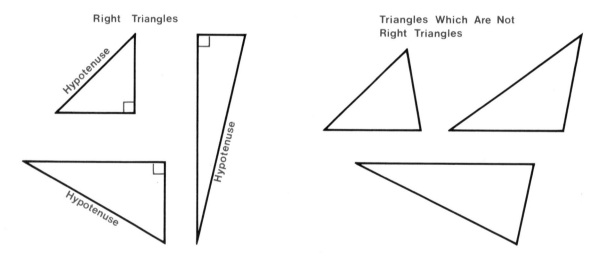

Right Triangles

Triangles Which Are Not Right Triangles

The lengths of the sides of a right triangle are related in a special way.

Students should memorize this fact.

If *c* is the length of the hypotenuse of a right triangle and *a* and *b* are the lengths of the other two sides, then $a^2 + b^2 = c^2$.

EXAMPLES

1.

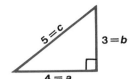

$$a^2 + b^2 = c^2$$
$$4^2 + 3^2 = 5^2$$
$$25 = 25$$

Encourage skeptics to check some right triangles by actually measuring lengths of sides.

2.

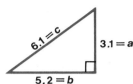

All lengths are rounded to 2 significant digits.

$$a^2 + b^2 = c^2$$
$$3.1^2 + 5.2^2 \doteq 6.1^2$$
$$37.0 \doteq 37.2$$

The difference is due to rounding.

The relationship $a^2 + b^2 = c^2$ for right triangles is called the **Pythagorean Theorem.** This theorem is named for Pythagoras, a Greek mathematician. Pythagoras lived in the sixth century B.C. and proved the theorem.

A proof using areas for the Pythagorean Theorem follows.

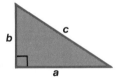

1. Use a right triangle with sides of lengths a, b, and c. A square with sides of length c is drawn on the hypotenuse of this triangle. A square with sides of length $a + b$ is completed around the first square.

Note that in this course the word "proof" means no more than "to present a fairly convincing case that something is so." The word will be defined more formally in *Geometry* and *Algebra 2*.

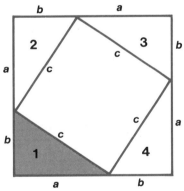

2. The area of the large square is found by multiplying the measures of two sides together.

$$(a + b) \cdot (a + b) = a(a + b) + b(a + b)$$
$$= a^2 + ab + ab + b^2$$
$$= a^2 + 2ab + b^2$$

The area of the smaller square is $c \cdot c$, or c^2. The area of each triangle is $\frac{1}{2}ab$. Therefore, the total area of the four triangles is $4 \cdot \frac{1}{2}ab$, or $2ab$.

Remind students that going from Step 3 to Step 4 is based on a procedure very familiar to them: The same number may be subtracted from both sides of an equation.

3. The sum of the total area of the four triangles and the area of the small square is equal to the area of the large square.

$$a^2 + 2ab + b^2 \quad = \quad 2ab \quad + \quad c^2$$
Area of large square   Area of 4 triangles   Area of small square

4. Subtract $2ab$ from both sides of the equation to obtain $a^2 + b^2 = c^2$.

The Pythagorean Theorem may be used to find the length of the third side of a right triangle if the lengths of two sides are known.

EXAMPLE

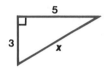

$$x^2 = 3^2 + 5^2$$
$$x^2 = 9 + 25$$
$$x^2 = 34$$
$$x = \sqrt{34}$$

From the table on page 524, $x \doteq 5.83$.

EXERCISES

1. $b^2 + c^2 = a^2$ 2. $d^2 + e^2 = f^2$
3. $p^2 + r^2 = q^2$ 4. $y^2 + z^2 = x^2$
5. $\sqrt{65} = 8.06$ 6. $\sqrt{149} = 12.2$

Use the Pythagorean Theorem to write an equation describing the lengths of the sides of each right triangle.

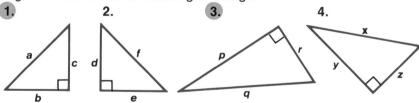

1.   2.   3.   4.

Calculate the length of the hypotenuse of each right triangle.

5.   6.

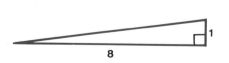

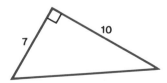

7. $\sqrt{17.80} = 4.22$ **8.** $\sqrt{5} = 2.24$
9. 5 **10.** 13 **11.** 17 **12.** 25
13. (1) $a^2 = c^2 - b^2$ **(2)** $b^2 =$
$c^2 - a^2$ **14.** 6 **15.** 9 **16.** $\sqrt{20}$
$= 4.47$ **17.** $\sqrt{39} = 6.24$
18. Yes **19.** No **20.** No **21.** Yes
22. No **23.** Yes **24.** Yes **25.** Yes

7. **8.**

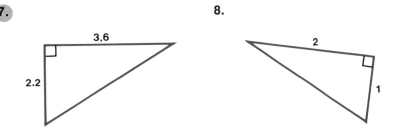

Suggest using the tables for these exercises.

Use the Pythagorean Theorem to find the value of x for each right triangle.

9. **10.** **11.** **12.**

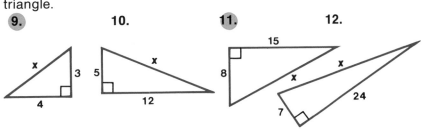

13. Change the Pythagorean Theorem into two equivalent forms.

(1) $a^2 = \underline{\quad ? \quad} - \underline{\quad ? \quad}$

(2) $b^2 = \underline{\quad ? \quad} - \underline{\quad ? \quad}$

Use the results of Exercise **13** to calculate x for each triangle.

14. **15.** **16.** **17.**

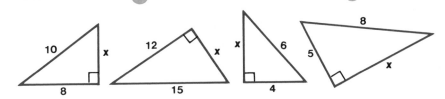

Ask how the triangles of Exercises 23 and 25 would compare in size. Also, ask if $a^2 + b^2 = c^2$ implies that $(ka)^2 + (kb)^2 = (kc)^2$.

If a triangle has sides of lengths a, b, and c and $a^2 + b^2 = c^2$, then it is a right triangle. For each set of three numbers, decide if a triangle with the given lengths of sides is a right triangle.

Samples **1.** $\{3, 4, 5\}$ **2.** $\{8, 10, 12\}$

$3^2 + 4^2 \overset{?}{=} 5^2$ $8^2 + 10^2 \overset{?}{=} 12^2$

$9 + 16 \overset{?}{=} 25$ $64 + 100 \overset{?}{=} 144$

$25 = 25$ $164 \neq 144$

Right triangle   Not a right triangle

18. $\{6, 8, 10\}$ **19.** $\{7, 9, 11\}$ **20.** $\{8, 11, 14\}$

21. $\{9, 12, 15\}$ **22.** $\{1, 10, 11\}$ **23.** $\{7, 24, 25\}$

24. $\{8, 15, 17\}$ **25.** $\{14, 48, 50\}$

11-8

To compute the distance between two given points in the plane.

The Distance Formula

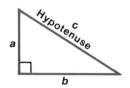

Suppose you know the lengths of two sides of a right triangle, and you know which side is the longest, the hypotenuse.

You can find the length of the remaining side by using one of the following formulas.

$$c = \sqrt{a^2 + b^2}$$
$$a = \sqrt{c^2 - b^2}$$
$$b = \sqrt{c^2 - a^2}$$

These formulas are derived from the Pythagorean Theorem.

EXAMPLE

Calculate the length of side b for this right triangle.

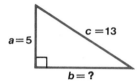

$$b = \sqrt{c^2 - a^2}$$
$$b = \sqrt{13^2 - 5^2}$$
$$= \sqrt{169 - 25}$$
$$= \sqrt{144}$$
$$b = 12$$

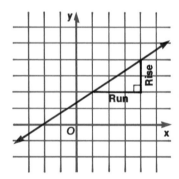

The slope of a straight line is given by $\frac{rise}{run}$. If this is shown on a graph, you see that a right triangle is drawn.

The distance between two points in a coordinate plane can be found by using this $\frac{rise}{run}$ triangle. The hypotenuse of this right triangle will be the distance between the two points. You can calculate the length of the hypotenuse using one of the formulas derived from the Pythagorean Theorem.

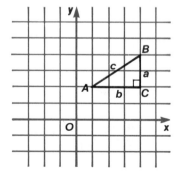

The distance between two points, A and B, may be calculated using a right triangle and the formula $c = \sqrt{a^2 + b^2}$.

The values for a and b are easy to find. The *rise*, the difference in the two values of y, is a and the *run*, the difference in the two values of x, is b.

EXAMPLE

It may be helpful to return to this after the examples below and have students find

$c = \sqrt{(2-10)^2 + (1-7)^2}$

Calculate the distance between (1, 2) and (7, 10).

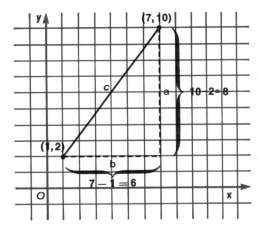

$c = \sqrt{(10-2)^2 + (7-1)^2}$

$c = \sqrt{8^2 + 6^2}$

$\quad = \sqrt{64 + 36}$

$\quad = \sqrt{100}$

$c = 10$

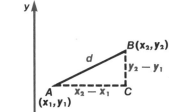

Suppose you have point A with coordinates (x_1, y_1) and point B with coordinates (x_2, y_2).

The distance between A and B is

$$d = \sqrt{(x_2 - x_1)^2 + (y_2 - y_1)^2}$$

This is called the *distance formula*.

The squares of both positive and negative numbers are positive. Therefore, either point may be called (x_1, y_1) and the other called (x_2, y_2). Study the examples to see that there is no difference.

EXAMPLES

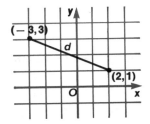

1. Calculate the distance between $(-3, 3)$ and $(2, 1)$.

a. $d = \sqrt{(-3 - 2)^2 + (3 - 1)^2}$

$\quad d = \sqrt{(-5)^2 + 2^2}$

$\quad\quad = \sqrt{25 + 4}$

$\quad\quad = \sqrt{29}$

$\quad d \doteq 5.39$

b. $d = \sqrt{(2 - (-3))^2 + (1 - 3)^2}$

$\quad d = \sqrt{5^2 + (-2)^2}$

$\quad\quad = \sqrt{25 + 4}$

$\quad\quad = \sqrt{29}$

$\quad d \doteq 5.39$

Stress this. → In calculation **a,** $(x_1, y_1) = (2, 1)$ and $(x_2, y_2) = (-3, 3)$. In calculation **b,** $(x_1, y_1) = (-3, 3)$ and $(x_2, y_2) = (2, 1)$. The two calculations are identical in the third row after squaring.

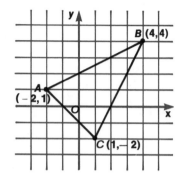

2. Calculate the lengths of the sides $\overline{AB}$ and $\overline{BC}$ of the triangle with vertices $A(-2, 1)$, $B(4, 4)$ and $C(1, -2)$ to show that the triangle is isosceles. An isosceles triangle is one which has two sides of the same length.

$$AB = \sqrt{(4 - (-2))^2 + (4 - 1)^2}$$
$$AB = \sqrt{6^2 + 3^2}$$
$$= \sqrt{36 + 9}$$
$$= \sqrt{45}$$
$$AB \doteq 6.71$$

Remind students of the meaning of $\doteq$.

$$BC = \sqrt{(1 - 4)^2 + (-2 - 4)^2}$$
$$BC = \sqrt{(-3)^2 + (-6)^2}$$
$$= \sqrt{9 + 36}$$
$$= \sqrt{45}$$
$$BC \doteq 6.71$$

Since $AB = BC$, the triangle is isosceles.

EXERCISES

Use the formulas derived from the Pythagorean Theorem to solve each problem. Write your answers with 2 significant digits.

1. The sides of a rectangle are 5 cm and 6 cm long. Calculate the length of a diagonal.

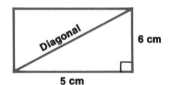

2. A rectangle is 10 cm long. Its diagonals each measure 12 cm. Calculate the width of the rectangle.

3. A ladder 10 m long has its base 3 m from the foot of a wall, as shown in the figure. How far up the wall does the ladder reach?

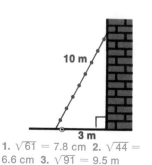

1. $\sqrt{61} = 7.8$ cm **2.** $\sqrt{44} = 6.6$ cm **3.** $\sqrt{91} = 9.5$ m

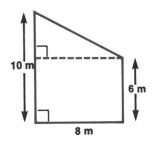

10 m

6 m

8 m

4. $\sqrt{80}$ = 8.9 m **5.** $\sqrt{72}$ = 8.5 km **6.** $\sqrt{100}$ = 10 cm
7. 170 km **8.** 130 ft **9.** 15 ft
10. 5 **11.** $\sqrt{5}$ **12.** 2 $\sqrt{5}$
13. $\sqrt{34}$ **14.** 5 **15.** 13 **16.** 13
17. 15 **18.** $AB = \sqrt{37}$, $AC = \sqrt{37}$, $BC = 5\sqrt{2}$

Suggest to slow students that they draw a picture of the chute in Exercise 9. Encourage them to use the picture to look for (or draw) a usable right triangle.

4. The figure shows the end view of a shed. Calculate the length of the sloping edge of the roof.

5. A ship sails 6 km north, then 6 km east. How far is it from its starting point?

6. In a right triangle, the sides containing the right angle are 6 cm and 8 cm long. Calculate the length of the hypotenuse.

7. A plane flies 120 km south, then 150 km east, then 200 km north. How far is the plane from its starting point?

8. On a baseball diamond, the distance from home plate to first base is 90 feet. The distance from home plate to third base is 90 feet. What is the distance across the infield from first base to third base?

9. A 25-foot chute is attached to a grain bin 30 feet above the ground. The end of the chute is lowered to 10 feet above the ground to fill a truck. How far from the building is the end of the chute?

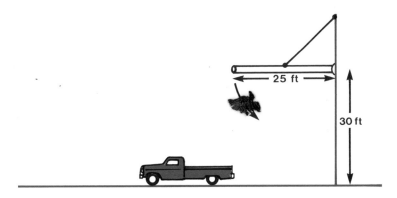

25 ft

30 ft

Use the distance formula to calculate the lengths of the line segments joining each pair of points. Write your answers in simplest radical form.

10. $A(1, 1)$ and $B(5, 4)$

11. $A(2, 1)$ and $B(4, 2)$

12. $A(-1, 1)$ and $B(3, 3)$

13. $A(2, -1)$ and $B(5, 4)$

Calculate the distance between each pair of points.

14. The origin and $P(3, 4)$

15. $O(0, 0)$ and $R(-5, -12)$

16. $S(-2, 5)$ and $T(3, -7)$

17. $U(4, -11)$ and $V(-5, 1)$

18. The vertices of a triangle are $A(4, 4)$, $B(-2, 3)$, and $C(3, -2)$. Use the distance formula to show that triangle ABC is an isosceles triangle.

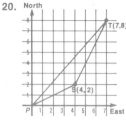
19. Which point is closer to (3, 4): (0, 4) or (5, 1)?

20. A ship S is situated 4 km east and 2 km north of a port P. Another ship T is situated 7 km east and 8 km north of P. Draw a diagram and calculate the distance between the ships to 2 significant digits. Hint: Think of coordinates with P as the origin and axes pointing east and north.

Excursions in Mathematics: A Distance Formula

1. A special distance formula may be derived to find the distance between two points on a line given by $y = mx$.

$$d = \sqrt{(x_2 - x_1)^2 + (y_2 - y_1)^2}$$
$$d = \sqrt{(x_2 - x_1)^2 + (mx_2 - mx_1)^2}$$
$$d = \sqrt{(x_2 - x_1)^2 + [m(x_2 - x_1)]^2}$$
$$d = \sqrt{(x_2 - x_1)^2 + m^2(x_2 - x_1)^2}$$

2. If a line has slope 3, what is the distance between the point with an x-value of 3 and the point with an x-value of 5?

$$d = \sqrt{(x_2 - x_1)^2 + m^2(x_2 - x_1)^2}$$
$$d = \sqrt{(5 - 3)^2 + 3^2(5 - 3)^2}$$
$$= \sqrt{4 + 9 \cdot 4}$$
$$= \sqrt{40}$$
$$d = 2\sqrt{10}$$

3. Use the new formula to calculate each of the following distances.

   a. If a line has slope 2, what is the distance between the point with an x-value of 3 and the point with an x-value of 5?

   b. Check your answer to Part **a** by calculating the distance between (1, 0) and (5, 8), points on the line $y = 2x - 2$.

   c. If a line has slope $\dfrac{1}{2}$, what is the distance between the point with an x-value of -1 and the point with an x-value of 3?

   d. Check your answer to Part **c** by calculating the distance between $(-1, 1)$ and (3, 3), points on the line $y = \dfrac{1}{2}x + \dfrac{3}{2}$.

4. Is the following the same special distance formula as the one given in this Excursion? Why or why not?

$$d = |x_2 - x_1| \cdot \sqrt{1 + m^2}$$

11-9
Subjects of Formulas

OBJECTIVE:
To change the subject of a
formula to that specified.

Remind students that most of the
work here simply requires them
to apply the procedures for
finding equivalent equations.

Formulas often are given with one letter standing alone on one side of the equal sign. In such cases, the letter standing alone may be called the **subject** of the formula. *Area is the subject of $A = lw$ and of $A = \pi r^2$.*

Sometimes it is convenient to change the subject of the formula. Suppose you encountered many problems in which the area of a circle was given and the radius was to be found. If the subject of the formula for area of a circle were r, your calculations would be much easier. To find such a formula, you could solve for r in $A = \pi r^2$.

$$A = \pi r^2 \Leftrightarrow \pi r^2 = A$$
$$\Leftrightarrow r^2 = \frac{A}{\pi}$$
$$\Leftrightarrow r = \sqrt{\frac{A}{\pi}}$$

The subject of the formula has been changed from A to r. To change the subject of a formula, you must solve a **literal equation.** This is an equation in which letters are used to represent numbers.

EXAMPLES

Note that "change the subject of
the formula to w" may be
interpreted as "isolate w."
Thinking this way will provide
security for some students.

1. A hardware store sets the retail price of a lawn mower by the following formula.

$$R = \frac{3}{2} W + 5 \qquad \text{where} \qquad \begin{array}{l} R = \text{retail price in dollars} \\ W = \text{wholesale price in dollars} \end{array}$$

a. Change the subject of the formula to W.

b. Use the formula from Part **a** to compute the wholesale price of a lawn mower which the store advertises for $110.

$$\textbf{a. } R = \frac{3}{2} W + 5 \Leftrightarrow \qquad 2R = 3W + 10$$
$$\Leftrightarrow 2R - 10 = 3W$$
$$\Leftrightarrow \frac{2R - 10}{3} = W$$
$$\Leftrightarrow \qquad W = \frac{2R - 10}{3}$$

$$\textbf{b. } W = \frac{2R - 10}{3}$$
$$W = \frac{2 \cdot 110 - 10}{3}$$
$$= \frac{220 - 10}{3}$$
$$W = 70 \qquad\qquad \text{The wholesale price is \$70.}$$

2. The formula $d = rt$ gives the distance d km covered by an object moving at an average speed of r km/h for t hours. Change the subject of the formula to r. Then calculate the average speed of: **a.** a car which travels 150 km in $2\frac{1}{2}$ hours;

b. a space probe which travels the 380,000 km between the earth and the moon in 3 days.

$$d = rt \Leftrightarrow \frac{d}{t} = r$$

$$\Leftrightarrow r = \frac{d}{t}$$

a. $r = \dfrac{d}{t}$

$$r = \frac{150}{2\frac{1}{2}}$$

$$r = 60$$

b. $r = \dfrac{d}{t}$

$$r = \frac{380,000}{3 \cdot 24}$$

$$r = 5280$$

The average speed of the car is 60 km/h. The average speed of the space probe is 5280 km/h.

3. A temperature in Fahrenheit degrees, F, can be changed to Celsius degrees, C, by the formula $C = \frac{5}{9}(F - 32)$. Make F the subject of this formula. Then calculate F when $C = 0$ and $C = 100$.

$$C = \frac{5}{9}(F - 32) \Leftrightarrow 9C = 5(F - 32)$$

$$\Leftrightarrow 9C = 5F - 160$$

$$\Leftrightarrow 5F = 9C + 160$$

$$\Leftrightarrow F = \frac{1}{5}(9C + 160)$$

$$F = \frac{1}{5}(9C + 160)$$

$$F = \frac{1}{5}(0 + 160)$$

$$F = 32$$

$$F = \frac{1}{5}(9C + 160)$$

$$F = \frac{1}{5}(900 + 160)$$

$$F = \frac{1}{5} \cdot 1060$$

$$F = 212$$

If $C = 0$, then $F = 32$. If $C = 100$, then $F = 212$.

When the subject of a formula is changed, the result may appear in different forms. These forms, however, are equivalent. For example, a formula for an electric current is $I = \dfrac{nE}{R + nr}$. Change the subject of the formula to n.

Do not insist that slow students study this example if previous examples seem to be about all they can manage.

$$I = \frac{nE}{R + nr} \Leftrightarrow I(R + nr) = nE$$

$$\Leftrightarrow IR + Inr = nE$$

$$\Leftrightarrow Inr - nE = -IR$$

$$\Leftrightarrow n(Ir - E) = -IR$$

$$\Leftrightarrow \qquad n = \frac{-IR}{Ir - E} \quad \text{or} \quad n = \frac{IR}{E - Ir}$$

The two equations for n are equivalent. If the numerator and denominator of the first form are multiplied by -1, the second form is obtained.

EXERCISES

1. $x = \dfrac{P}{4}$ 2. $I = \dfrac{A}{w}$ 3. $d = rt$;

$t = \dfrac{d}{r}$ 4. $V = RI; R = \dfrac{V}{I}$

5. $b = \dfrac{2A}{a}$ 6. $S = \sqrt{A}$ 7. $a = \dfrac{2A}{3b}$

8. $m = \dfrac{(y - c)}{x}$

1. The perimeter of a square is given by the formula $P = 4x$. Change the subject to x.
2. The area of a rectangle is given by the formula $A = lw$. Change the subject to l.
3. The speed of a train is given by $r = \dfrac{d}{t}$. Change the subject to d; to t.
4. Change the subject of the formula for current in a circuit, $I = \dfrac{V}{R}$; to V; to R.
5. Change the subject of the formula for the area of a triangle, $A = \dfrac{1}{2}\, ab$, to b.
6. The area of a square is given by $A = s^2$. Change the subject to s.
7. Change the subject of the formula for the area of a metal plate, $A = \dfrac{3}{2}\, ab$, to a.
8. The equation of a straight line can be written as $y = mx + c$. Change the subject to m.

9. $C = Id^2; d = \dfrac{C}{I}$ **10.** $r = \dfrac{D}{2}$

$(\pi + 1)$ **11. a.** $d = \dfrac{(n - 2a)}{3}$

b. $d = 6$ **12. a.** $I = \dfrac{2s - na}{n}$

b. $I = \dfrac{5}{2}$ **13.** $m = \sqrt{ab}$ **14.** $h =$

$\dfrac{3L + c}{8}$ **15.** $x = \dfrac{y - 1}{y + 1}$

16. a. $r = \dfrac{c}{2\pi}$, $r = .80$

b. $\pi = \dfrac{c}{d}$, $\pi = 3.14$

17. $\pi = \dfrac{A}{r^2}$, 3.14 **18.** $h = \dfrac{A}{2\pi r} - r$

19. a. Form may vary:

$s = c + \dfrac{cp}{100}$ **b.** Form may vary:

$p = \dfrac{100s}{p + 100}$ **20. a.** S = 64

b. 60, 62, 63, 63$\dfrac{1}{2}$, 63$\dfrac{3}{4}$, 63$\dfrac{7}{8}$

c. $r = \dfrac{s - a}{s}$; $r = \dfrac{1}{3}$

See T.G. on different uses which may be made of this section.

For slow students, Exercise 19 may be treated best as a discussion exercise.

9. The formula for the illumination given by a lamp is $I = \dfrac{C}{d^2}$. Change the subject to C; to d.

10. Change the subject of the formula for the distance around a track, $D = 2r(\pi + 1)$, to r.

11. A number n in a sequence is given by the formula $n = 2a + 3d$.
   a. Change the subject of the formula to d.
   b. Calculate d when $n = 30$ and $a = 6$.

12. The sum of the numbers in a series can be given by $S = \dfrac{1}{2}n(a + l)$.
   a. Change the subject of the formula to l.
   b. Calculate l when $S = 75$, $n = 20$, and $a = 5$.

13. Make m the subject of the formula $\dfrac{m}{a} = \dfrac{b}{m}$.

14. A formula for the length of an arc is $L = \dfrac{1}{3}(8h - c)$. Change the subject to h.

15. Change the subject of the formula $y = \dfrac{1 + x}{1 - x}$ to x.

16. The formula for the circumference of a circle is $C = 2\pi r$ or $C = \pi d$ where r is the radius and d is the diameter.
   a. Change the subject of $C = 2\pi r$ to r. Calculate r to 2 significant digits when $C = 5$ cm and $\pi = 3.14$.
   b. Change the subject of $C = \pi d$ to π. Calculate π to 3 significant digits when $C = 6.9$ cm and $d = 2.2$ cm.

17. The formula for the area of a circle is $A = \pi r^2$. Change the subject of the formula to π. Calculate π to 3 significant digits when $r = 14$ cm and $A = 615.44$ cm².

18. The area of a cylinder is $A = 2\pi r(r + h)$. Make h the subject.

19. The profit $p\%$ on a sale is given by $p = \dfrac{100(s - c)}{c}$, where s and c are the selling price and cost price, respectively.
   a. Express s in terms of p and c.
   b. Express c in terms of p and s.

20. The sum of a series such as $32 + 16 + 8 + 4 + \dots$ to an infinite number of terms is given by the formula $S = \dfrac{a}{1 - r}$.

S is the sum, a is the first term, and r is the ratio of any term to the preceding term.

a. Use the formula to find the sum of the given series.

b. By adding the terms, find the sum of 4 terms, and of 5, 6, 7, 8, 9, and 10 terms.

c. Make r the subject of the formula. Calculate r when $S = 121\frac{1}{2}$ and $a = 81$.

Suggested Activity

Find out more about the history and approximations for pi, π.

Chapter Summary

1. A square root of a number b is a number a such that $a^2 = b$. The principal square root of a number is its nonnegative square root. The radical symbol $\sqrt{}$ means *the principal square root of*.

2. Tables may be used to find the squares and square roots of some numbers.

3. If $n, m \in$ R and $n > 0, m > 0$, the following statements are true.

   a. $\sqrt{n \cdot m} = \sqrt{n} \cdot \sqrt{m}$

   b. $\sqrt{\dfrac{n}{m}} = \dfrac{\sqrt{n}}{\sqrt{m}}$

4. A square root is in simplest radical form if no factor of the expression is a perfect square and if there are no square roots in the denominator of a fraction.

5. The symbol $\doteq$ is used to mean *is approximately equal to*.

6. When solving a problem, a rough estimate will help you know what type answer to expect. The result of an estimate is an approximate number.

7. The Pythagorean Theorem relates the sides of a right triangle. If c is the length of the hypotenuse of a right triangle and a and b are the lengths of the other two sides, then $a^2 + b^2 = c^2$.

8. The distance between two points is given by the formula $d = \sqrt{(x_2 - x_1)^2 + (y_2 - y_1)^2}$.
9. The subject of a formula may be changed by solving a literal equation.

REVIEW EXERCISES

11-1

1. a. 9.6 b. .49 c. 2.2 d. 2.7
2. 5.29 3. 47.6 4. 34.3 5. 82.6

11-2

6. 25, 36, 49, 64, 81 7. 33.64 m²
8. 2.84 • 10¹; 807 9. 4.56 • 10²;
208,000 10. 3.4 • 10⁻¹; .116
11. 8.7 • 10⁻²; .00757 12. 6√2
13. $\frac{1}{7}\sqrt{14}$ 14. 12√14 15. 0 16. 3
17. 40 18. 2.5 19. 1.2 mm
20. 140 cm; Answers wi'l vary in Exercises 21-23. 21. 3.6 22. 1.7
23. 8.4 24. 13.1 25. 2.41
26. 0.259 27. 32.9 28. 104

11-1

1. Use the graph on page 320 to find each number to 2 significant digits.
   a. $(3.1)^2$ **b.** $(.7)^2$ **c.** $\sqrt{5}$ **d.** $\sqrt{7.2}$

11-2

Use tables to find the square of each number to 3 significant digits.
2. 2.3   3. 6.9   4. 5.86   5. 9.09

6. Write all the whole numbers between 20 and 90 which are perfect squares.
7. Find the area of a square with a side of length 5.8 m.

Write each number as $a \cdot 10^n$. Then use the tables to find the square of each number.
8. 28.4   9. 456   10. 0.34   11. 0.087

11-3

Write each expression in simplest radical form.
12. $\sqrt{72}$ 13. $\sqrt{\dfrac{2}{7}}$ 14. $2\sqrt{7} \cdot 3\sqrt{8}$
15. $\sqrt{7} + \sqrt{28} - \sqrt{63}$

11-4

Write the square root of each number.
16. 9   17. 1600   18. 6.25

19. Find the side of a square with area 1.44 mm².
20. Find the perimeter of a square whose area is 1225 cm².

Estimate each square root to 2 significant digits.
21. $\sqrt{13}$ 22. $\sqrt{3}$ 23. $\sqrt{70}$

Use tables to find the square root of each number to 3 significant digits.
24. 171   25. 5.79   26. 0.067
27. 1080   28. 10,800

11-5

29. $9 < \sqrt{91} < 10$
30. $5 < \sqrt{27} < 6$
31. $2 < \sqrt{4.9} < 3$ **32. a.** 26.5
b. 837 **c.** .265 **33.** $x = 10$

Write two consecutive whole numbers between which each square root lies.

Sample $3 < \sqrt{10} < 4$

29. $\sqrt{91}$ **30.** $\sqrt{27}$ **31.** $\sqrt{4.9}$

32. Given that $\sqrt{7} \doteq 2.65$ and that $\sqrt{70} \doteq 8.37$, find the approximate square root of each number.
  a. 700   **b.** 700,000   **c.** 0.07

11-6

34. $x = 26$ **35.** $x = \sqrt{111} = 10.5$
36. $x = 9$ **37.** $x = 7.81$
38. $x = 11.7$ **39.** $x = 10.5$
40. $x = 8.66$ **41.** 12.6 km
42. $\sqrt{125} \doteq 11.2$ **43.** $AB = 5 = DC$; $\overline{AD}$ is longer. **44. a.** $A = a \cdot b - 2c^2$ **b.** 750 cm²

Use the Pythagorean Theorem to calculate the value of x in each triangle.

33.   **34.**   **35.**   **36.**

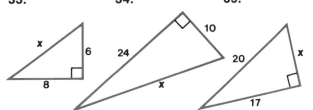
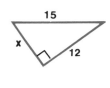

In each triangle, calculate x to 3 significant digits.

37.   **38.**   **39.**   **40.**

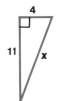
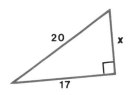
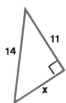

11-7

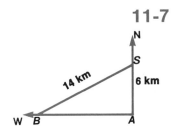

41. In the figure, A and B are coast guard observation posts. Post B is due west of A. From A a ship S is sighted due north and 6 km away. From B the ship is 14 km away. Calculate the distance between A and B.

42. If P is the point $(3, 4)$ and Q is $(8, -6)$, calculate the distance between P and Q.

43. A is the point $(1, 2)$, B is $(4, 6)$, C is $(-1, 2)$ and D is $(-5, -1)$. Use the distance formula to show that $AB = DC$. Which is longer, $\overline{BC}$ or $\overline{AD}$?

11-8

44. Two squares of side c cm are removed from a rectangular steel plate of length a cm and width b cm.
  a. Write a formula for the area, A cm², of the remainder of the plate.
  b. Calculate A when $a = 50$, $b = 40$, and $c = 25$.

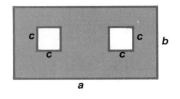

349

45. A rectangular field measures 150 m by 54 m. Find the length of the side of a square which has the same area.

46. Write the 5th, 8th, and 20th terms of a sequence of whole numbers which starts 1, 4, 9, 16, ... Which term of the sequence is one million?

47. If a rectangle is four times as long as it is wide, show in a drawing how it can be divided into four equal squares. If the area of the rectangle is 784 cm², find the lengths of its sides.

48. A rectangle is twice as long as it is wide. It has an area of 10 cm². Find its dimensions to 3 significant digits.

49. If $x = 3a + b$, $y = a - 3b$, and $P = 4x - 3y$, express P in terms of a and b. Find P given that $a = 3.4$ and $b = 0.8$.

50. The formula $Ft = m(v - u)$ occurs in mechanics. Change the subject to m; to v; to u.

51. From the formula $R = \dfrac{kL}{d^2}$, express d in terms of R, k, and L. Calculate d when $k = 7.5$, $L = 3$, and $R = 2.5$.

CHAPTER 12

polynomials

12-1 Simplifying Expressions

You already have studied and simplified expressions such as $7a - 12a$ and $15y - 4 - 5y + 7$. In this chapter, you will study and simplify more complex expressions.

EXAMPLES

OBJECTIVE:

To solve open sentences which are equivalent to a relation between two polynomials.

1. Simplify $3x^3 + 4x^2 + x^3 - 2x^2$.

Use the
Commutative Property
of Addition.

$$3x^3 + 4x^2 + x^3 - 2x^2 = 3x^3 + x^3 + 4x^2 - 2x^2$$

Use the Distributive Property.

$$= (3 + 1)x^3 + (4 - 2)x^2$$
$$= 4x^3 + 2x^2$$

2. Simplify $2(x^2 + 3) - x(5 + 2x) + 10x$.

The definition of *like terms* may need to be restated here.

Use the Distributive
   Property.

$$2(x^2 + 3) - x(5 + 2x) + 10x$$
$$= 2x^2 + 6 - 5x - 2x^2 + 10x$$

Rearrange terms.

$$= 2x^2 - 2x^2 - 5x + 10x + 6$$

Use the Distributive Property.

$$= (2 - 2)x^2 + (-5 + 10)x + 6$$
$$= 5x + 6$$

With practice, you may be able to omit some of the steps and not write the reason for each step.

Finding sums and differences of algebraic expressions often

involves simplifying expressions. You may treat subtraction as addition of additive inverses. The inverse of an expression is found by changing the sign of each term.

EXAMPLES

Some students may be helped by thinking of $-(7x^2 - 3xy + 8y^2)$ as $-1(7x^2 - 3xy + 8y^2)$.

1. Find the sum of $4x^2 - 3xy - 2y^2$ and $-7x^2 + 5xy - 8y^2$.

$4x^2 - 3xy - 2y^2 + (-7x^2 + 5xy - 8y^2)$
$$= 4x^2 - 7x^2 - 3xy + 5xy - 2y^2 - 8y^2$$
$$= -3x^2 + 2xy - 10y^2$$

2. Subtract $-7x^2 - 3xy + 8y^2$ from $4x^2 - 3xy - 2y^2$

$(4x^2 - 3xy - 2y^2) - (-7x^2 - 3xy + 8y^2)$
$$= 4x^2 - 3xy - 2y^2 + 7x^2 + 3xy - 8y^2$$
$$= 11x^2 - 10y^2$$

Many open sentences are easier to solve if the expressions on each side of the equal sign are simplified first.

EXAMPLES

For some students, a review of the procedures for finding equivalent open sentences may be needed.

1. $5(x - 4) + 3(1 - x) = 10 - x \Leftrightarrow 5x - 20 + 3 - 3x = 10 - x$
$$\Leftrightarrow \quad 2x - 17 = 10 - x$$
$$\Leftrightarrow \quad 2x + x = 10 + 17$$
$$\Leftrightarrow \quad 3x = 27$$
$$\Leftrightarrow \quad x = 9$$

The solution set is $\{9\}$.

2. $3x - 2(3x - 1) > 7 \Leftrightarrow 3x - 6x + 2 > 7$
$$\Leftrightarrow \quad -3x > 5$$
$$\Leftrightarrow \left(-\frac{1}{3}\right)(-3x) < \left(-\frac{1}{3}\right)(5)$$
$$\Leftrightarrow \quad x < -\frac{5}{3}$$

The solution set is $\left\{x \mid x < -\frac{5}{3}\right\}$.

EXERCISES

1. $10a$ **2.** $2a$ **3.** $-2a$ **4.** $-10a$
5. $9x^2$ **6.** $3x^2$ **7.** $6x^2$ **8.** 0
9. $4x^2 - 3xy$ **10.** $3a^2 - 5ab$
11. $5x - y$ **12.** $5a - b$
13. $6x^2 - 2$ **14.** $2xy$ **15.** $2pq$
16. $2x + 4y$

Simplify each expression.

1. $6a + 4a$ **2.** $6a - 4a$ **3.** $-6a + 4a$
4. $-6a - 4a$ **5.** $5x^2 + 4x^2$ **6.** $4x^2 - x^2$
7. $3x^2 + 3x^2$ **8.** $x^2 - x^2$
9. $x^2 - xy + 3x^2 - 2xy$ **10.** $4a^2 - 4ab - a^2 - ab$
11. $2(x + y) + 3(x - y)$ **12.** $3(a - b) + 2(a + b)$
13. $2(x^2 + 1) + 4(x^2 - 1)$ **14.** $xy + yx$
15. $3pq - qp$ **16.** $4x + 3y - 2x + y$

17. 0 18. $7x^2$ 19. $-y^2 + 6y$
20. $5i + 2k$ 21. $-a^2 - 3a - 2$
22. $-2bc$ 23. $\frac{2}{3} a^2 - 4$ 24. 0
25. $2a + 1$ 26. $2x^2 + 3x + 4$
27. $2x^2 - 3x$ 28. $-a - 2$
29. $-2b^2 + 8$ 30. $-2x$
31. $2a^2 - 4a + 7$ 32. $2x^2$
33. $2 + y^2$ 34. $x = -\frac{4}{3}$
35. $x > \frac{7}{9}$ 36. $x \leq 5$ 37. $x = \frac{1}{2}$
38. $x = \frac{7}{11}$ 39. $x \in R$ 40. $x \geq \frac{3}{4}$

See T.G. on a possible use of
Chapter 18 if the needs of slow
students tend to slow class
progress here.

17. $2a - 2b - 2a + 2b$
18. $5x^2 + x + 2x^2 - x$
19. $3y^2 - 4y^2 + 7y - y$
20. $7i - 2j + 3k - (2i + k - 2j)$
21. $a^2 - 2a - 5 - (2a^2 + a - 3)$
22. $a(b + c) - b(c + a) - c(a + b)$
23. $a^2 + \frac{1}{3}a - 2 - \left(\frac{1}{3}a^2 + \frac{1}{3}a + 2\right)$
24. $p(q - r) + q(r - p) + r(p - q)$

Add each pair of expressions.
25. $a + b + 2$ and $a - b - 1$
26. $x^2 + 2x + 1$ and $x^2 + x + 3$
27. $x^2 - x + 3$ and $x^2 - 2x - 3$
28. $a^2 + a + 1$ and $-a^2 - 2a - 3$
29. $b^2 + 2b + 4$ and $-3b^2 - 2b + 4$

Subtract the first expression from the second.
30. $x^2 + x + 1$ from $x^2 - x + 1$
31. $a^2 + 2a - 3$ from $3a^2 - 2a + 4$
32. $6(x^2 - 2)$ from $4(2x^2 - 3)$
33. $8(1 - 2y^2)$ from $5(2 - 3y^2)$

Solve each equation or inequation.
34. $3(x + 2) + 2(x - 1) = 8(x + 1)$
35. $4(x - 3) + 5(x + 1) > 0$
36. $8(x - 1) - 2(x + 5) \leq 12$
37. $4x - 2(1 - 3x) = 3$
38. $5(2x - 3) - 2(6x - 5) = 3(3x - 4)$
39. $2(5x - 1) - 3(2x - 1) \leq 1 + 4x$
40. $10(1 - x) \leq 5(2x - 1) + 3(3 - 4x)$

12-2
Classifying
Polynomials

OBJECTIVE:

To simplify a polynomial and
state its degree.

EXAMPLES

When an expression is stated in simplest form, it should contain
no two like terms.

Expression	Simplified Expression
$3x^2 - 5xy + 6y - 2x^2 - 6y$	$x^2 - 5xy$
$8x^3 - (6x^2 + 8x - 3x + 8x^2 - 5x - 14x^2)$	$8x^3$
$x + y + w + z - w$	$x + y + z$

There are special names for some expressions. The name depends on the number of terms in the expression. An expression such as $8x^3$ which has only one term is called a ***monomial.*** An expression such as $x^2 - 5xy$ which has two terms is called a ***binomial.*** An expression such as $x + y + z$ which has three terms is called a ***trinomial.*** Of course, this naming process could go on forever. To avoid creating and learning different names for other expressions, the word ***polynomial*** is used to mean an expression with two or more terms. It is acceptable to use the word polynomial to refer to a monomial.

In this book the word polynomial is reserved for expressions in which each term is a product of *only* numbers and variables.

EXAMPLES

1. $3x + y$ is a polynomial.

2. $3\sqrt{x} + y$ is not a polynomial.

3. $x + 4$ is a polynomial.

4. $\dfrac{3}{x + 4}$ is not a polynomial.

5. $8x^2 - 3xy + 5y^2$ is a polynomial.

6. $8x^2 - \dfrac{3}{xy} + 5y^2$ is not a polynomial.

If only one variable is used in a polynomial, then the polynomial is said to be a polynomial in that variable.

EXAMPLES

1. $5x^3$ is a monomial in x.

2. $3y^3 - 3y^2 + 2$ is a trinomial in y.

3. $x^2 + 1$ is a binomial in x.

4. $37w^{20}$ is a monomial in w.

A polynomial also may be classified by its degree. The ***degree of a monomial*** is the sum of the exponents of the variables. The ***degree of a polynomial*** is the greatest degree of its monomial terms. A term which has no variable is called a ***constant term.*** A nonzero constant term has degree zero. The number zero as a monomial has no degree.

EXAMPLES

1. $8x^3$ is a monomial of degree 3.

2. $4xy^3$ is a monomial of degree 1 + 3 or 4.

3. $4y^2 + 2y + 6$ is a trinomial of degree 2. In other words, it is a second-degree trinomial.

4. $5x^3y^2 + 2x^2y^2 + y$ is a trinomial of degree 3 + 2 or 5.

Emphasize this. → Remember, before classifying a polynomial, be sure it is written in simplest form. That is, be sure there are no two like terms in the polynomial. If a polynomial is in simplest form, it may be classified by its number of terms and degree.

EXAMPLES

In this section the word *equivalent* means *names the same number as.*

Classify each expression, written in its simplest form, according to the number of terms it has and its degree. Be as specific as possible.

1. $x^5 + 4x(1 + x) + x(2 - x^4) = x^5 + 4x + 4x^2 + 2x - x^5$
$$= 4x^2 + 6x$$
The original expression is equivalent to a binomial of degree two. You may also say it is a quadratic binomial.

2. $2x(x^2 - 4y) + y^2 - 2y(y - 5x) = 2x^3 - 8xy + y^2 - 2y^2 + 10xy$
$$= 2x^3 + 2xy - y^2$$
The original expression is equivalent to a third-degree trinomial. You may also say it is a cubic trinomial.

3. $x^6 - 4(x^5 + x^3) + 2x^3 - 3x^4 = x^6 - 4x^5 - 4x^3 + 2x^3 - 3x^4$
$$= x^6 - 4x^5 - 3x^4 - 2x^3$$
The original expression is equivalent to a polynomial of degree six.

A major function of this exercise set is to further development of manipulative skills.

EXERCISES

1. trinomial of degree 2
2. binomial of degree 1
3. binomial of degree 1
4. trinomial of degree 3
5. trinomial of degree 3
6. polynomial of degree 4
7. polynomial of degree 3
8. monomial of degree 0
9. polynomial of degree 3
10. monomial of no degree
11. polynomial of degree 4
12. trinomial of degree 3
13. trinomial of degree 3
14. trinomial of degree 4
15. trinomial of degree 2
16. trinomial of degree 3
17. trinomial of degree 5
18. binomial of degree 3
19. polynomial of degree 3
20. trinomial of degree 7
21. trinomial of degree 4
22. trinomial of degree 3
23. polynomial of degree 5
24. polynomal of degree 5
25. polynomial of degree 3

When possible, simplify each expression. Then classify each expression according to the number of terms it has and its degree.

1. $z^2 + z + 1$
2. $2x + 3$
3. $5 + 2x + 6(x + 1)$
4. $x^2 - 14x^2y + 6y^2$
5. $3y^2(y + 1) - 3y$
6. $y^2 - 4 + y(y^2 - 4) - 2y^2(y^2 - 4)$
7. $-20y^3 + 3x - y^2 - 14x^2y + 20x^3$
8. $24(x - 3) - 12(2x - 3)$
9. $7a^2(a + 1) - 5a(a + 1) - 2(a + 1)$
10. $3x^2 - 3(x - x) - 3x^2$
11. $x^2 - 1 + 5y(x^2 - 1) + 4y^2(x^2 - 1)$
12. $y^3 - 4 + y(4 - y^2) - 2y(4 - y^2)$
13. $15x^3 + 21x(x + 1) - 12(x - 1) - 3x(7x + 9)$
14. $4z(zx + y) - 3wxyz$
15. $(5x + 3)2 + (5x + 3)4x$
16. $5x(2 + 4x) + 3(2 + 4x)$
17. $x^4(y^2 - x) + 2xy - y^2(x^4 - y)$
18. $(a^2 + b)b^2 - (a + b^2)a^2$
19. $m(n^2 + m^2) - n(n^2 - m^2)$
20. $6x(4x^2yz^2 - xy^2z^2) + x^3y^3z$
21. $4p^2(5p - 4q) + (15pq)^2$
22. $7x[2(x^2 + 4) - x] - 5x(2x^2 - 3)$
23. $7x[(x^4 - 2) + 3x] - 4x(x^3 - 3)$
24. $5a(a^2x^2 + 2ax) - 2c(x^2 + 3)$
25. $(3x^2 - 2y^2) - 4(xy + x^2) + 2(xy^2 - 3x)$

26.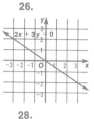

27.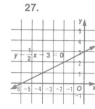

28.

29.

A polynomial of degree one may be called a *linear expression*. Each equation is a linear expression set equal to zero. Graph each equation.

26. $2x + 3y = 0$

27. $y - \dfrac{1}{2}x - 3 = 0$

28. $x - 5 = 0$

29. $y - 3x = 0$

30. $y + 8 = 0$

31. $y - 3x + 2 = 0$

32. Imagine you knew that an equation was found by setting a polynomial of degree one in two variables equal to zero. What could you know about the graph of the equation?

30.- 32. See section notes in T.G.

12-3
Multiplying Polynomials

OBJECTIVE:

To find the product of two polynomials by repeated usage of the Distributive Property.

Some students may be helped as follows. Name the sum $c + d$ by s where $s = c + d$. Then write $(a + b)(c + d)$ or $(a + d) s$
$= as + ds$
  $a(c + d) + b(c + d)$
    •
    •
    •
  $ac + ad + bc + bd$

To multiply two binomials, you should keep in mind that any expression represents a single number. To multiply $(a + b)$ by $(c + d)$ think of $(c + d)$ as a single number and use the Distributive Property.

$$(a + b)(c + d) = a(c + d) + b(c + d)$$

To complete the multiplication of these binomials, the Distributive Property is used again. This time, however, $(c + d)$ is thought of as the sum of two numbers.

Use the Distributive Property. Treat $(c + d)$ as one number.

$$(a + b)(c + d) = a(c + d) + b(c + d)$$

Use the Distributive Property. Treat $(c + d)$ as the sum of two numbers.

$$= ac + ad + bc + bd$$

The same product results if $(a + b)$ is treated as a single number in the first step.

Use the Distributive Property.

$$(a + b)(c + d) = (a + b)c + (a + b)d$$

Use the Distributive Property.

$$= ac + bc + ad + bd$$

Use the Commutative Property of Addition.

$$= ac + ad + bc + bd$$

This process may be used with polynomials of more than two terms. In these cases you will be using the Generalized Distributive Property. In the first step, think of one of the polynomials as a single number.

EXAMPLES

1. $(x^2 + x + 3)(x^2 + 2x + 5)$

Use the
Distributive Property.
Treat $(x^2 + 2x + 5)$
as a single number.

$= x^2(x^2 + 2x + 5) + x(x^2 + 2x + 5) + 3(x^2 + 2x + 5)$

Use the
Distributive Property.
Treat $(x^2 + 2x + 5)$
as a sum of numbers.

$= x^4 + 2x^3 + 5x^2 + x^3 + 2x^2 + 5x + 3x^2 + 6x + 15$

Group
like terms.

$= x^4 + 2x^3 + x^3 + 5x^2 + 2x^2 + 3x^2 + 5x + 6x + 15$

Simplify.

$= x^4 + 3x^3 + 10x^2 + 11x + 15$

2. $(x - 6xy - 5y^2)(-2xy + 3y^2)$

$= x(-2xy + 3y^2) - 6xy(-2xy + 3y^2) - 5y^2(-2xy + 3y^2)$

$= -2x^2y + 3xy^2 + 12x^2y^2 - 18xy^3 + 10xy^3 - 15y^4$

$= -2x^2y + 3xy^2 + 12x^2y^2 - 8xy^3 - 15y^4$

When polynomial factors are multiplied together, the polynomial product is called the ***expansion*** of the factors. The expression $ac + ad + bc + bd$ is called the expansion of $(a + b)(c + d)$.

EXAMPLES

1. The expression $x^3 - x^2 - x + 10$ is the expansion of $(x + 2)$ $(x^2 - 3x + 5)$.

$(x + 2)(x^2 - 3x + 5) = x(x^2 - 3x + 5) + 2(x^2 - 3x + 5)$
$= x^3 - 3x^2 + 5x + 2x^2 - 6x + 10$
$= x^3 - x^2 - x + 10$

2. Expand $(a + b + c)(x + y + z)$.

$(a + b + c)(x + y + z)$
$= a(x + y + z) + b(x + y + z) + c(x + y + z)$
$= ax + ay + az + bx + by + bz + cx + cy + cz$

EXERCISES

Expand each product. If possible, simplify the expansion.

1. $(x + y)(x + y)$
2. $(x - y)(x - y)$
3. $(x + y)(x - y)$
4. $(a + b)(a + b)$
5. $(a - b)(a - b)$
6. $(a + b)(a - b)$

7. $z^2 + 2z + 1$ **8.** $2a^2 + 7a + 3$
9. $4b^2 + 12b + 9$ **10.** $12c^2 +$
$23c + 10$ **11.** $x^2 + x - 2$
12. $x^2 - x - 12$ **13.** $x^2 +$
$3x - 10$ **14.** $a^3 - 3a^2 - 2a + 6$
15. $b^4 - 4b^3 - 4b + 16$ **16.** $c^5 -$
$c^3 - 5c^2 + 5$ **17.** $3d^4 - 5d^2 - 2$
18. $2e^5 - 5e^3 + 5e^2 - 20$
19. $8f^5 - 2f^4 + 12f - 3$
20. $a^4x^2 - b^4y^2$ **21.** $5r^4 + 13r^2 s^2$
$- 6s^4$ **22.** $3a^3 + 6a^2 b^2 +$
$4ab + 8b^3$ **23.** $x^3 - 3x^2y +$
$3xy^2 - y^3$ **24.** $27x^3 + 54x^2y +$
$36xy^2 + 8y^3$ **25.** $27x^3 - 54x^2y +$
$36xy^2 - 8y^3$ **26.** $x^4 + 4x^3 + 6x^2 +$
$4x + 1$ **27.** $a^4 - 4a^3b +$
$6a^2b^2 - 4ab^3 + b^4$ **28.** $sx +$
$sy + sz + tx + ty + tz + ux +$
$uy + uz$ **29.** $x^5 + x^2 + x + 1$
30. $x^5 - x^2 + x - 1$ **31.** $x^5 - y^5$
32. $x^5 + y^5$

7. $(z + 1)(z + 1)$
⑨. $(2b + 3)(2b + 3)$
11. $(x + 2)(x - 1)$
⑬. $(x - 2)(x + 5)$
15. $(b - 4)(b^3 - 4)$
⑰. $(d^2 - 2)(3d^2 + 1)$
19. $(2f^4 + 3)(4f - 1)$
㉑. $(r^2 + 3s^2)(5r^2 - 2s^2)$

8. $(a + 3)(2a + 1)$
10. $(3c + 2)(4c + 5)$
12. $(x + 3)(x - 4)$
14. $(a^2 - 2)(a - 3)$
16. $(c^2 - 1)(c^3 - 5)$
18. $(e^3 + 4)(2e^2 - 5)$
20. $(a^2x + b^2y)(a^2x - b^2y)$
22. $\left(\dfrac{1}{2}a^2 + \dfrac{2}{3}b\right)(6a + 12b^2)$

23. $(x - y)(x^2 - 2xy + y^2)$
㉕. $(3x - 2y)(9x^2 - 12xy + 4y^2)$
27. $(a^2 - 2ab + b^2)(a^2 - 2ab + b^2)$
28. $(s + t + u)(x + y + z)$
㉙. $(x^4 - x^3 + x^2 + 1)(x + 1)$
30. $(x^4 + x^3 + x^2 + 1)(x - 1)$
31. $(x^4 + x^3y + x^2y^2 + xy^3 + y^4)(x - y)$
32. $(x^4 - x^3y + x^2y^2 - xy^3 + y^4)(x + y)$

24. $(3x + 2y)(9x^2 + 12xy + 4y^2)$

26. $(x^2 + 2x + 1)(x^2 + 2x + 1)$

12-4
Multiplying
Binomials

EXAMPLE

OBJECTIVE:

To write directly in simplified
form the product of two binomials
$ax + by$ and $px + qy$.

The purpose behind asking
students to think of a rectangular
area is to facilitate transfer to
Exercises such as 7 and 8.

When multiplying binomial factors, it sometimes is convenient to
think of rectangular areas.

What is the area of a rectangle that measures $(x + 2)$ by $(x + 3)$?

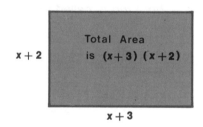

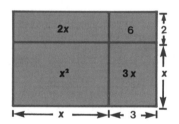

By comparing the two rectangles, you can see that the following
statement is true.

$$(x + 3)(x + 2) = x^2 + 3x + 2x + 6$$
$$= x^2 + 5x + 6$$

When two binomials are multiplied, there are four monomial terms
in the product before simplifying.

$$(a + b)(c + d) = ac + ad + bc + bd$$

With practice, you can do the multiplications mentally and record
the expansion directly.

EXAMPLES

It is assumed here that students understand multiplication of binomials. The goal in this section is to develop a skill.

The FOIL strategy is just one of several ways to aid this development. The teacher may feel free to dismiss the FOIL strategy and/or replace it.

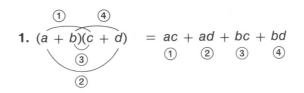

1. $(a + b)(c + d) = ac + ad + bc + bd$

2. $(2x - 5)(3x + 7) = 6x^2 + 14x - 15x - 35$
$$= 6x^2 - x - 35$$

Notice:

The first multiplication uses the	**F**irst term of each factor.
The second multiplication uses the	**O**utside terms of the factors.
The third multiplication uses the	**I**nside terms of the factors.
The fourth multiplication uses the	**L**ast term of each factor.

The word ***FOIL*** (**F**irst, **O**utside, **I**nside, **L**ast) may help you to remember the pattern for multiplying binomials. With still more practice, you may even begin simplifying each expansion as you multiply.

EXAMPLES

1. $(x + 5)(x - 3) = x^2 + 2x - 15$
① ② and ③ ④ combined

2. $(3x + 2)(2x - 3) = 6x^2 - 5x - 6$
F **O** and **I** **L** combined

EXERCISES

1. $x^2 + 4x + 3$ 2. $x^2 + 7x + 12$
3. $a^2 + 2a + 1$ 4. $4x^2 + 10x + 6$
5. $a^2 + 2ab + b^2$
6. $6x^2 + 19x + 15$

Draw an area diagram to illustrate each product. Then use the diagram to write the expansion of the factors. Simplify if possible.

1. $(x + 1)(x + 3)$ **2.** $(x + 3)(x + 4)$

3. $(a + 1)(a + 1)$ **4.** $(2x + 2)(2x + 3)$

5. $(a + b)(a + b)$ **6.** $(2x + 3)(3x + 5)$

7. 20 ft **8.** 30 ft **9.** 220 by 110
10. 90 **11. a.** $3x$, $2x - 6$,
$(x - 2)(x - 3)$, x^2
b. $(x - 2)(x - 3) = x^2 - 3x$
$-(2x - 6) = x^2 - 5x + 6$
12. $x^2 + 3x - 10$
13. $y^2 + 3y - 4$ **14.** $z^2 + z - 6$
15. $p^2 + p - 2$ **16.** $q^2 + q - 6$
17. $r^2 - 1$ **18.** $2s^2 + 3s - 2$
19. $4t^2 - 11t - 3$
20. $3u^2 + u - 4$ **21.** $4v^2 - 9$
22. $6w^2 - w - 1$
23. $20x^2 - 7x - 6$
24. $a^2 + 8a + 12$
25. $b^2 - 7b + 12$
26. $c^2 + 3c - 10$
27. $d^2 - 9d + 14$
28. $2x^2 - 7x - 4$
29. $2y^2 + y - 6$
30. $6z^2 + 16z + 8$
31. $6k^2 - 19k + 15$
32. $20m^2 + 2m - 6$

7. Jack has a square garden plot. He widens the plot by 5 feet and lengthens it by 10 feet. In this way, he gains an additional 350 square feet of garden. How long is his present garden? Hint: Draw a diagram for $(x + 5)(x + 10)$ and then write an equation.

8. Jack's neighbor also has a square garden plot. If she widens her plot by 5 feet and lengthens it by 10 feet, she gains an additional 500 square feet of garden. How long is her present garden?

9. A steel sheet is twice as long as it is wide. Strips are to be welded to the edges. If the length is increased by 1 inch and the width is increased by 3 inches, 773 square inches of sheet are added. What are the dimensions of the original sheet?

10. A square piece of canvas must be lengthened by 10 inches and then have 9 inches cut from the width. After this is done, the area will still be the same. How long is the original piece of canvas? Hint: Make x the length of the original piece and write the area for each piece.

11. a. Write an expression for the area of the shaded portion in each diagram.

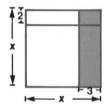 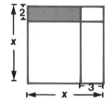 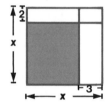 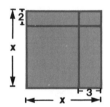

b. From the diagrams, you can see that $(x - 2)(x - 3)$ = area of Figure 4 − shaded area in Figure 1 − shaded area in Figure 2. Write this in equation form. Use the values you found for the figures.

Expand each product. First, try to write each answer directly. Do as much work mentally as possible. Then, if in doubt, you may check your work by writing out the steps using the Distributive Property.

12. $(x + 5)(x - 2)$ **13.** $(y + 4)(y - 1)$ **14.** $(z + 3)(z - 2)$
15. $(p - 1)(p + 2)$ **16.** $(q - 2)(q + 3)$ **17.** $(r + 1)(r - 1)$
18. $(s + 2)(2s - 1)$ **19.** $(t - 3)(4t + 1)$ **20.** $(u - 1)(3u + 4)$
21. $(2v + 3)(2v - 3)$ **22.** $(3w + 1)(2w - 1)$
23. $(4x - 3)(5x + 2)$ **24.** $(a + 6)(a + 2)$
25. $(b - 4)(b - 3)$ **26.** $(c + 5)(c - 2)$
27. $(d - 2)(d - 7)$ **28.** $(x + 4)(2x - 1)$
29. $(2y - 3)(y + 2)$ **30.** $(2z + 4)(3z + 2)$
31. $(3k - 5)(2k - 3)$ **32.** $(4m - 2)(5m + 3)$

33. $x^2 + 3xy + 2y^2$
34. $x^2 - 4xy + 3y^2$
35. $x^2 - 3xy + 10y^2$
36. $2a^2 + 5ab + 3b^2$
37. $2x^2 - 3xy + y^2$
38. $p^4 - q^4$ 39. $9m^2 - 4n^2$
40. $3s^2 + 7st - 6t^2$
41. $6u^2 - 16uv + 8v^2$
42. $15 + 11x + 2x^2$
43. $1 + 2y - 3y^2$ 44. $20 - 31x + 12x^2$

33. $(x + y)(x + 2y)$ **34.** $(x - y)(x - 3y)$
35. $(x + 2y)(x - 5y)$ **36.** $(a + b)(2a + 3b)$
37. $(x - y)(2x - y)$ **38.** $(p^2 + q^2)(p^2 - q^2)$
39. $(3m - 2n)(3m + 2n)$ **40.** $(s + 3t)(3s - 2t)$
41. $(2u - 4v)(3u - 2v)$ **42.** $(5 + 2x)(3 + x)$
43. $(1 - y)(1 + 3y)$ **44.** $(4 - 3x)(5 - 4x)$

12-5
Special Expansions

OBJECTIVE:
To write the product of $(a + b)^2$, $(a - b)^2$, $(a + b)(a - b)$ directly.

Study the following three expansions carefully.

$$(a + b)^2 = (a + b)(a + b)$$
$$= a^2 + 2ab + b^2$$

$$(a - b)^2 = (a - b)(a - b)$$
$$= a^2 - 2ab + b^2$$

$$(a + b)(a - b) = a^2 - ab + ab - b^2$$
$$= a^2 - b^2$$

Emphasize this. →

These three expansions are encountered often enough that you should learn them. It makes no difference what numerical or variable replacements are used for a and b. The patterns in the formulas will remain true.

EXAMPLES

1. $(x + 5)^2 = x^2 + 2 \cdot x \cdot 5 + 5^2 = x^2 + 10x + 25$
     $(a + b)^2 = a^2 + 2 \ \ a \ \ b + b^2$

2. $(2x - 3y)^2 = (2x)^2 - 2 \cdot 2x \cdot 3y + (3y)^2 = 4x^2 - 12xy + 9y^2$
     $(a - b)^2 \ = \ a^2 \ - \ 2 \ \ a \ \ b + \ b^2$

3. $(x + 3y)(x - 3y) = x^2 - 9y^2$
     $(a + b) \ (a - b) = a^2 - b^2$

These formulas also may be used when both a and b are replaced by numbers.

EXAMPLES

Ask students to find 99×99 by working with 100 and 1.

1. $(21)^2 = (20 + 1)^2 = 400 + 40 + 1 = 441$
     $(a + b)^2 = a^2 + 2ab + b^2$

2. $\left(\dfrac{1}{2} - \dfrac{\sqrt{5}}{10}\right)^2 = \dfrac{1}{4} - 2\left(\dfrac{1}{2}\right)\left(\dfrac{\sqrt{5}}{10}\right) + \dfrac{5}{100} = \dfrac{3}{10} - \dfrac{\sqrt{5}}{10}$
     $(a - b)^2 \ \ = a^2 - 2 \ \ a \ \ \ \ b \ \ + \ b^2$

3. $\left(\dfrac{1}{3} + \dfrac{\sqrt{7}}{6}\right)\left(\dfrac{1}{3} - \dfrac{\sqrt{7}}{6}\right) = \dfrac{1}{9} - \dfrac{7}{36} = -\dfrac{1}{12}$
     $(a + \ \ b) \ \ (a - \ \ b) \ \ = a^2 - b^2$

EXERCISES

1. $x^2 + 2xy + y^2$
2. $p^2 + 2pq + q^2$
3. $m^2 - 2mn + n^2$ 4. $u^2 - v^2$
5. $x^2 - 6x + 9$ 6. $x^2 - 25$

Expand each expression.

1. $(x + y)^2$ **2.** $(p + q)^2$ **3.** $(m - n)^2$
4. $(u + v)(u - v)$ **5.** $(x - 3)^2$ **6.** $(x + 5)(x - 5)$

7. $x^2 + 2x + 1$ 8. $x^2 - 100$
9. $a^2 - 4a + 4$ 10. $a^2 - 6a + 9$
11. $a^2 - 8a + 16$
12. $a^2 - 16a + 64$
13. $4x^2 + 4x + 1$
14. $9x^2 + 12x + 4$
15. $25x^2 + 30x + 9$
16. $100x^2 - 1$ 17. $4a^2 - 9$
18. $9a^2 - 1$ 19. $4a^2 - 20a + 25$
20. $25a^2 - 40a + 16$
21. $a^2 + 4ab + 4b^2$
22. $9x^2 - y^2$ 23. $16c^2 - 8cd + d^2$
24. $4m^2 - 9n^2$

25. $(x + 3)^2 = x^2 + 6x + 9$
26. $(y - 5)^2 = y^2 - 10y + 25$
27. $(a + 2)(a - 2) = a^2 - 4$
28. $(b - 1)^2 = b^2 - 2b + 1$
29. $(a + 2)^2 = a^2 + 4a + 4$
30. $(3y + 2x)(3y - 2x) = 9y^2$
$- 4x^2$ 31. $2x^2 + 12x + 20$
32. $2a^2 - 12a + 26$
33. $2x^2 - 18$
34. $12y$ 35. $-12b + 72$
36. $2ab - 2b^2$
37. $x^4 + 6x^2 + 9$
38. $y^4 - 4y^2 + 4$
39. $a^4 + 2a^2b^2 + b^4$
40. $x^4 - y^4$ 41. $a^2 + 2 + \frac{1^2}{a}$

42. $a^2 - 2 + \frac{1^2}{a}$ 43. $9x^2 - 6 + \frac{1}{x^2}$
44. $p^4 - 2p^2q^2 + q^4$
45. $x^4 - 2x^2y^2 + y^4$
46. 784   47. 1764
48. 9604   49. 961   50. 10,609
51. 3249   52. 899   53. 6396
54. 999,999   55. $11 + 6\sqrt{2}$
56. $\frac{109}{36} - \frac{1}{3}\sqrt{3}$
57. $\frac{3}{8} + \frac{1}{8}\sqrt{5}$

---

7. $(x + 1)^2$
8. $(x - 10)(x + 10)$
9. $(a - 2)^2$
10. $(a - 3)^2$
11. $(a - 4)^2$
12. $(a - 8)^2$
13. $(2x + 1)^2$
14. $(3x + 2)^2$
15. $(5x + 3)^2$
16. $(10x + 1)(10x - 1)$
17. $(2a + 3)(2a - 3)$
18. $(3a + 1)(3a - 1)$
19. $(2a - 5)^2$
20. $(5a - 4)^2$
21. $(a + 2b)^2$
22. $(3x + y)(3x - y)$
23. $(4c - d)^2$
24. $(2m + 3n)(2m - 3n)$

Replace each ___?___ to make a true equation.

25. $(x + \underline{\ \ ?\ \ })^2 = \underline{\ \ ?\ \ } + \underline{\ \ ?\ \ } + 9$
26. $(y - \underline{\ \ ?\ \ })^2 = \underline{\ \ ?\ \ } - \underline{\ \ ?\ \ } + 25$
27. $(a + \underline{\ \ ?\ \ })(a - \underline{\ \ ?\ \ }) = \underline{\ \ ?\ \ } - 4$
28. $(b - \underline{\ \ ?\ \ })^2 = \underline{\ \ ?\ \ } - 2b + \underline{\ \ ?\ \ }$
29. $(a + \underline{\ \ ?\ \ })^2 = \underline{\ \ ?\ \ } + 4a + \underline{\ \ ?\ \ }$
30. $(\underline{\ \ ?\ \ } + 2x)(\underline{\ \ ?\ \ } - 2x) = 9y^2 - \underline{\ \ ?\ \ }$

Simplify each expression.

31. $(x + 4)^2 + (x + 2)^2$
32. $(a - 5)^2 + (a - 1)^2$
33. $(x + 3)(x - 3) - (3 - x)(3 + x)$
34. $(y + 3)^2 - (y - 3)^2$
35. $(b - 6)^2 - (b + 6)(b - 6)$
36. $(a + b)(a - b) - (a - b)^2$

Expand each expression.

37. $(x^2 + 3)^2$
38. $(y^2 - 2)^2$
39. $(a^2 + b^2)^2$
40. $(x^2 + y^2)(x^2 - y^2)$
41. $\left(a + \dfrac{1}{a}\right)^2$
42. $\left(a - \dfrac{1}{a}\right)^2$
43. $\left(3x - \dfrac{1}{x}\right)^2$
44. $(p^2 - q^2)^2$
45. $(x - y)^2(x + y)^2$

Compute the value of each expression by using one of the special expansions. Hint: Remember that $47 = 50 - 3$, $62 = 60 + 2$, and so on.

46. $(28)^2$
47. $(42)^2$
48. $(98)^2$
49. $(31)^2$
50. $(103)^2$
51. $(57)^2$
52. $31 \cdot 29$
53. $82 \cdot 78$
54. $999 \cdot 1001$

Expand each expression. State each answer in simplest radical form.

55. $(3 + \sqrt{2})^2$
56. $\left(\dfrac{1}{6} - \sqrt{3}\right)^2$
57. $\left(\dfrac{1}{4} + \dfrac{\sqrt{5}}{4}\right)^2$

58. $\frac{50}{3} - \frac{8}{3}\sqrt{6}$

59. $-\frac{6}{25}$

60. $\frac{7}{16} - \frac{\sqrt{3}}{4}$

61. $\frac{7}{18} + \frac{\sqrt{10}}{9}$

62. $\frac{29}{25} - \frac{12\sqrt{5}}{25}$

63. $\frac{63}{64} - \frac{9\sqrt{6}}{32}$

64. 19.5, 2.45, 0.655, 10.1, -0.24, 0.004, 0.740, 0.0867, 0.295

58. $\left(4 - \dfrac{\sqrt{6}}{3}\right)^2$ **59.** $\left(\dfrac{1}{5} + \dfrac{\sqrt{7}}{5}\right)\left(\dfrac{1}{5} - \dfrac{\sqrt{7}}{5}\right)$ **60.** $\left(\dfrac{\sqrt{3}}{4} - \dfrac{1}{2}\right)^2$

61. $\left(-\dfrac{1}{3} - \dfrac{\sqrt{10}}{6}\right)^2$ **62.** $\left(\dfrac{-3}{5} + \dfrac{2\sqrt{5}}{5}\right)^2$ **63.** $\left(\dfrac{3}{8} - \dfrac{3\sqrt{6}}{8}\right)^2$

64. Use the square root table to express each answer in Exercises **55–63** as a decimal to the accuracy the table allows.

12-6
Solving Equations

Many equations with second-degree terms are equivalent to linear equations which you know how to solve.

EXAMPLES

OBJECTIVE:

To solve an equation of quadratic expressions which is equivalent to a linear equation.

1. Solve $2x^2 - (x - 3)^2 = (x + 2)(x - 1)$.

$$2x^2 - (x - 3)^2 = (x + 2)(x - 1)$$
$$\Leftrightarrow 2x^2 - (x^2 - 6x + 9) = x^2 + x - 2$$
$$\Leftrightarrow \qquad x^2 + 6x - 9 = x^2 + x - 2$$
$$\Leftrightarrow \qquad\qquad 6x - x = -2 + 9$$
$$\Leftrightarrow \qquad\qquad\qquad 5x = 7$$
$$\Leftrightarrow \qquad\qquad\qquad x = \frac{7}{5}$$

The solution set is $\left\{\dfrac{7}{5}\right\}$.

2. A sheet metal shop has an order for a rim. The rim must be 7 inches wide and have an area of 1034 square inches. What should be the radius of the inside hole?

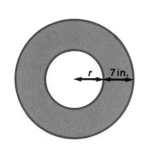

The area of the larger circle may be written two ways.

$$A_1 = \text{area of hole} + \text{area of rim}$$
$$= \quad \pi r^2 \quad + \quad 1034$$
$$A_2 = \text{area of larger circle}$$
$$= \quad \pi(r + 7)^2$$

Since $A_1 = A_2$ the following equation is true. Use $\pi = \dfrac{22}{7}$.

$$\pi r^2 + 1034 = \pi(r + 7)^2 \Leftrightarrow \pi r^2 + 1034 = \pi(r^2 + 14r + 49)$$
$$\Leftrightarrow \pi r^2 + 1034 = \pi r^2 + 14\pi r + 49\pi$$
$$\Leftrightarrow \qquad 1034 = 14\pi r + 49\pi$$
$$\Leftrightarrow \qquad 1034 = 44r + 154$$
$$\Leftrightarrow \qquad 880 = 44r$$
$$\Leftrightarrow \qquad 20 = r$$

Solution: The radius of the hole must be 20 inches.

Stress the fact that the equations in this section are carefully chosen to be equivalent to linear equations. Students should not believe that these are typical.

EXERCISES

1. $x = 2$ 2. $x = -1$

3. $x = -\frac{1}{2}$ 4. $x = 1$

5. $x = 0$ 6. $x = -1$

7. $x = -2$ 8. $x = -\frac{1}{5}$

9. $x = 0$ 10. $x = -\frac{4}{3}$

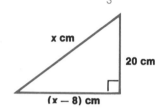

x cm

20 cm

(x − 8) cm

11. $x = \frac{1}{5}$ 12. $x = \frac{1}{2}$

13. $x = \frac{1}{2}$ 14. $x = -1$

15. 29, 20, 21 16. Square:

$\frac{15}{2}$ by $\frac{15}{2}$;

Rectangle: $\frac{9}{2}$ by $\frac{25}{2}$

17. $x = \frac{15}{2}$ 18. $x = -2$

19. $x = 5$ 20. $x = \frac{11}{2}$

21. $x = -\frac{1}{2}$ 22. $x = -\frac{2}{7}$

23. 65, 56, 33

24. - 26. See section notes in T.G.

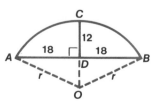

C

12

18   18

A   ID   B

r   r

O

Solve each equation.

1. $(x + 2)^2 = x^2 + 12$ 2. $(x - 3)^2 = x^2 + 15$

3. $(x + 5)(x + 3) = x^2 + 11$ 4. $(x - 4)(x - 2) = x^2 + 2$

5. $(x + 10)^2 = x^2 + 100$ 6. $(x - 1)^2 = x^2 + 3$

7. $(x + 4)^2 = (x + 3)(x + 6)$ 8. $(x + 1)(x + 2) = (x - 1)^2$

9. $(x - 12)^2 = x^2 + 144$ 10. $(2x + 4)^2 = 4x(x + 1)$

11. $(2x - 1)(x - 1) = 2x(x + 1)$ 12. $x(2x + 1) = (x - 1)(2x - 3)$

13. $(2x - 3)^2 = (2x + 1)^2$

14. $(x + 7)(x - 7) = (x + 9)(x - 5)$

15. Find the lengths of each side of the triangle. Use the Pythagorean Theorem.

16. The rectangle and square have the same area. Find the dimensions of each figure.

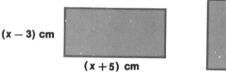

(x − 3) cm

(x + 5) cm

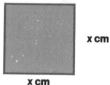

x cm

x cm

Solve each equation.

17. $x^2 - (x - 5)^2 = 50$ 18. $3 - (x + 2)^2 = 7 - x^2$

19. $x^2 - (x - 9)^2 = 9$ 20. $76 - (12 - x)^2 = 64 - x^2$

21. $2(x - 1)^2 - (x + 2)^2 = x^2 + 2$

22. $7 - (x - 2)(x - 3) = -(x + 1)^2$

23. The hypotenuse of a right triangle is $(5x + 5)$ cm long. The lengths of the other two sides are $(4x + 8)$ cm and $(3x - 3)$ cm. Find the length of each side.

24. A square metal plate 4 cm on a side is heated. Each side increases in length by t cm. Show this in a diagram. Write expressions for the original area, the new area, and the increase in area of the plate. If $t = 0.1$, calculate the increase in area.

25. A metal washer has an inner radius of r mm and a width of w mm. Write an expression for the outer radius. Show that the shaded area of the washer, A mm^2, is given by $A = \pi w(2r + w)$.

26. $\overset{\frown}{ACB}$ is an arc of a circle with its center at O. The length of chord $\overline{AB}$ is 36 meters. The greatest height of the arc above the chord $\overline{AB}$ is 12 meters. Let the radius of the circle be r meters.
    a. Express the length of $\overline{OD}$ in terms of r.
    b. Apply the Pythagorean Theorem on triangle OAD to form an equation in r.
    c. Solve this equation for r.

MATHEMATICS AND APPLICATIONS

population growth

Predicting how much food a country will need depends on knowing the rate of population growth. Predicting how many people a country will have depends on knowing today's population P, and the number of births B and deaths D this year. The rate of increase is $\dfrac{B - D}{P}$.

Suppose you live in Growth City, which has a population of 10,000 and a rate of increase of 3.5% per year. How long will it be before the city doubles in size?

Time	Population
Today	10,000
Year One	$10,000 + 3.5\% \cdot 10,000 = 10,350$
Year Two	$10,350 + 3.5\% \cdot 10,350 = 10,712$
Year Ten	14,101
Year Twenty	19,885

The rate of population increase in many under-developed countries is about 3.5%. Do you think these countries can double their food supply in 20 years?

If the rate of population increase for the world were about 2%, how many years would it take for the population to double?

The United States has taken a census every ten years since 1790. These figures are used to determine how many Congressional representatives each state is entitled to have. The Reverend Thomas Malthus used the 1790 census to make the first mathematical prediction of overpopulation. Believing that food production would follow a straight line on the graph, he conjectured that world population would exceed the world's ability to produce food.

Fortunately Malthus' prediction has not yet come true. Scientists are working to develop new sources of food and to improve farming practices. Solving food and population problems will require careful statistical analyses of accurate data.

WORLD POPULATION GROWTH

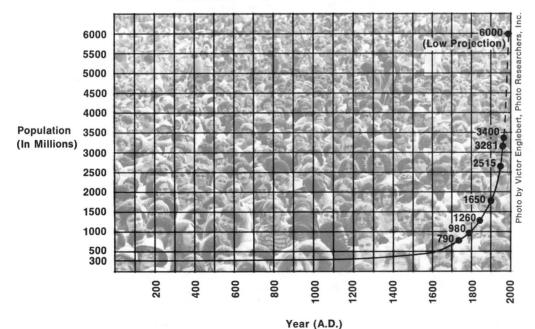

Population (In Millions)

Year (A.D.)

Photo by Victor Englebert, Photo Researchers, Inc.

12-7
Identities

The open sentence $2x = 6$ is true if $x = 3$ and false for any other replacement for x. However, the open sentence $y \cdot y^2 = y^3$ is a true sentence for *all* real number replacements for y. When an open sentence is true for all real number replacements, it is called an *identity*.

EXAMPLES

1. The sentence $(a + b)^2 = a^2 + 2ab + b^2$ is an identity.
2. The sentence $(a - b)^2 = a^2 - 2ab + b^2$ is an identity.

An identity may be defined as a general statement.

To show that an equation is an identity, you may show that its left side and right side can be expressed in exactly the same way. Once you have done this, you have shown that the original equation is equivalent to $0 = 0$, which is true for any replacements for the variables.

EXAMPLES

1. Show that $(p + q)^2 - 4pq = (p - q)^2$ is an identity.

$$(p + q)^2 - 4pq = (p - q)^2$$
$$\Leftrightarrow \quad (p + q)^2 - 4pq = p^2 - 2pq + q^2$$
$$\Leftrightarrow p^2 + 2pq + q^2 - 4pq = p^2 - 2pq + q^2$$
$$\Leftrightarrow \quad p^2 - 2pq + q^2 = p^2 - 2pq + q^2$$

Since the left side is the same as the right side, $(p + q)^2 - 4pq = (p - q)^2$ is an identity. If $p^2 - 2pq + q^2$ were subtracted from both sides of the equation in the last step, the result would be $0 = 0$.

2. A set of three natural numbers which satisfy the Pythagorean Theorem is called a *Pythagorean triple*. Show that $\{x^2 + y^2, x^2 - y^2, \text{ and } 2xy \mid x, y \in N \text{ and } x > y\}$ is always a Pythagorean triple.

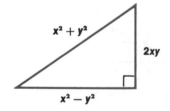

If the set is a Pythagorean triple, $(x^2 + y^2)^2 = (x^2 - y^2)^2 + (2xy)^2$ must be an identity.

$$(x^2 + y^2)^2 = (x^2 - y^2)^2 + (2xy)^2$$
$$\Leftrightarrow \quad (x^2 + y^2)^2 = x^4 - 2x^2y^2 + y^4 + 4x^2y^2$$
$$\Leftrightarrow \quad (x^2 + y^2)^2 = x^4 + 2x^2y^2 + y^4$$
$$\Leftrightarrow x^4 + 2x^2y^2 + y^4 = x^4 + 2x^2y^2 + y^4$$

This shows that $(x^2 + y^2)^2 = (x^2 - y^2)^2 + (2xy)^2$ is an identity.

EXERCISES

Exercises are to be assigned at the teacher's discretion.

Methods will vary.

Show that each equation is an identity.

1. $x(x - 1) = x^2 - x$

2. $4x(1 - x) = 4(x - x^2)$

3. $(a - b)^2 = (b - a)^2$

4. $(3m - n)^2 = (n - 3m)^2$

5. $(a + 2)^2 - 4a = a^2 + 4$

6. $(x - y)^2 + 2xy = x^2 + y^2$

7. $(a + b)(a - b) = a^2 - b^2$

8. $(x - 3)^2 + 12x = (x + 3)^2$

9. $(x + 1)^2 = (x + 3)(x - 1) + 4$

10. $(y - 3)^2 - (3 - y)^2 = 0$

11. $(1 + a^2)(1 + b^2) = (a + b)^2 + (ab - 1)^2$

12. $(ax + by)^2 + (bx - ay)^2 = (a^2 + b^2)(x^2 + y^2)$

13. Use $x^2 + y^2$, $x^2 - y^2$, and $2xy$, where $x > y$, as measures of the sides of a right triangle. Replace x and y by various pairs of natural numbers to obtain sets of Pythagorean triples.

14. Show that $x^2 + y^2$ is the hypotenuse, that is, the longest side of the right triangle in Exercise **13.** Hint: Show that $x^2 + y^2 > 2xy$ and $x^2 + y^2 > x^2 - y^2$. Remember, these relationships are true only when $x > y$.

Chapter Summary

1. An expression in simplest form contains the least possible number of terms connected by + or − signs.

2. If each term of an expression can be written in the form ax^n where $a \in Q$, x is a variable, and $n \in W$, then that expression is a polynomial in x.

3. A monomial is an expression with one term. A binomial is an expression with two terms. A trinomial is an expression with three terms.

4. The degree of a monomial is the sum of the exponents of the variables in the monomial. The degree of a polynomial is the greatest degree of its monomial terms.

5. Linear expressions have degree 1. Quadratic expressions have degree 2. Cubic expressions have degree 3.

6. Polynomials may be multiplied using the Distributive Property. The polynomial product is called the expansion of the factors.

7. Binomial factors may be multiplied mentally using the FOIL method.

8. $(a + b)^2 = a^2 + 2ab + b^2$
$(a - b)^2 = a^2 - 2ab + b^2$
$(a + b)(a - b) = a^2 - b^2$

9. Some second-degree equations may be solved by finding an equivalent linear equation.

10. An identity is an open sentence which is true for all real number replacements of the variables.

REVIEW EXERCISES 12-1, 12-2

Simplify each expression. Then classify it according to the number of terms it has and its degree.

1. $5x^2 - 3x^2$
2. $2y^2 - 6y^2$
3. $-z^2 - z^2$
4. $k^2 - k^2$
5. $2x + 3y - x - 3y$
6. $p^2 - 3q^2 - 3p^2 + 6q^2$
7. $3(x + y) + 2(x - y)$
8. $5(m^2 - n^2) - 3(m^2 + n^3)$
9. $4x^2 - 4x^3 - 2x^2 - 2x$
10. $a^3 - b^3 - a^3 - b^3$
11. $(x^2 - 2x - 3) + (2x^2 + 2x - 3)$
12. $(2y^2 + 3y - 4) - (y^2 - 3y - 4)$
13. $i + j - k - (2i - 3j + 5k)$
14. $k(2k - 1) - 2k(k + 2)$
15. $2(x^2 - x) + 3(x^2 + x^4) - (x^2 + 2x^4)$
16. $x(1 - 2x) - 2x(x^3 + 2) + (x^2 + x)$

Add.

17. $2x + 3y$ and $-6x + 12y$
18. $p - 3q - r$ and $5p + 3q + r$
19. $4c - 6d + 5e$ and $-2c - 3d - 7e$
20. $x^2 - x - 4$ and $3x^2 - x + 5$

Subtract.

21. $2x + 3y$ from $-6x + 12y$
22. $-7a - 8b$ from $3a - 9b$
23. $p - 3q - r$ from $5p + 3q + r$
24. $4c - 6d + 5e$ from $-2c - 3d - 2e$

Solve each equation or inequation if $x \in R$.

25. $5x - 2(x - 2) = 1$
26. $6 - (3 - 2x) > 7$
27. $3(x - 5) + 2(x - 1) = 3$
28. $4(1 + 2x) - 3(3x + 1) \leq 0$
29. $3(1 - x) - 2(x - 1) = 0$
30. $3x - 2(3x - 1) > 4$
31. $2x(x - 1) - x(4x + 1) = 2(1 - x^2)$
32. $x(x^2 - 3) - (x^3 + 2x) \leq 1$
33. $(x + 5)^2 = x^2 + 30$
34. $(x + 4)(x - 2) = x^2$
35. $(x + 4)(x + 7) = (x + 10)(x + 3)$
36. $(x - 3)(x + 3) = (x - 5)^2$

12-3

12-4, 12-5

12-6

37. $x(2x + 6) = 2(x^2 - 5)$
38. $(2x - 3)(4x + 1) = 2(2x - 1)^2$
39. $(2x + 3)(x - 2) = (2x - 1)(x - 1)$
40. $x(x - 9) + (x - 2)^2 = 2x(x - 6)$
41. $4x^2 - (2x - 7)^2 = 7$
42. $2(x + 3)^2 - (x - 1)^2 = x(x - 3)$

Expand each product and simplify if possible.

43. $(x + 1)(x + 2)$ **44.** $(x + 3)(2x + 1)$
45. $(2x + 3)(3x + 2)$ **46.** $(y - 2)(y - 4)$
47. $(y - 1)(2y - 1)$ **48.** $(2y - 3)(4y - 1)$
49. $(a + 3)(a - 2)$ **50.** $(b - 5)(b + 1)$
51. $(c + 6)(c^3 - 6c^2 + 5c)$ **52.** $(2x + 1)(3y^2 + 2xy + x^2)$
53. $(5y - 2)(y^4 - y^3 - 6y^2)$ **54.** $(4z - 3)(2z^2 + 7z + 4)$
55. $(a + b)(a^2 - 2ab + b^2)$ **56.** $(2a + b)(2a^2 + 4ab + 2b^2)$
57. $(5a - 2b)(3a - 2b)$ **58.** $(2 + x)(x + 2)$
59. $(1 - x)^2(4 - x)$ **60.** $(2 + 3x)(2 - 3x)$
61. $(y + 2)(3 - y)$ **62.** $(x + 4)^2(1 - x)^2$
63. $(z^2 - 3)(3 - z^2)$

Expand each product and simplify if possible. Then, classify each expression according to the number of terms it has and its degree.

64. $(a + 2)(b + 5)$ **65.** $(x - 1)(y - 4)$
66. $(x^2 + y^2)(x^2 - y^2)$ **67.** $(x + 3)(2x^2 - x - 3)$
68. $(5y - 2)(3y^2 - 4y + 5)$ **69.** $(a + b)^2 - (a^2 - b)^2$
70. $(p - q)^2 - (p + q)^2$ **71.** $(2x^3 + 3)^2 - (3x^3 + 2)^2$

72. $\left(x + \frac{1}{x}\right)^2 + \left(x - \frac{1}{x}\right)^2$

73. $(c + d)^2$ **74.** $(m + n)^2$ **75.** $(u^2 - v^2)^2$
76. $(x^4 - y^4)^2$ **77.** $(x^2 + 6)^2$ **78.** $(y - 3)^2$
79. $(2x^4 + 5)^2$ **80.** $(3y - 2)^2$

Expand each expression. State each answer in simplest radical form.

81. $(9 - \sqrt{8})^2$ **82.** $(6 + 2\sqrt{3})^2$ **83.** $\left(\frac{1}{4} + \frac{\sqrt{2}}{4}\right)^2$

84. $\left(-\frac{1}{2} + \frac{\sqrt{6}}{2}\right)^2$ **85.** $\left(\frac{2}{5} - \frac{3\sqrt{5}}{5}\right)^2$ **86.** $\left(-\frac{1}{6} - \frac{2\sqrt{7}}{3}\right)^2$

Prove that each equation is an identity.

87. $(x + 1)^2 - 1 = x(x + 2)$
88. $(a + b)^2 + (a - b)^2 = 2(a^2 + b^2)$
89. $(3k + 6)(3k - 6) = 9(k^2 - 4)$

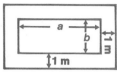
90. $a(b - c) + b(c - a) + c(a - b) = 0$

91. $(a + b)(a^2 - ab + b^2) = a^3 + b^3$

92. $(a^2 + b^2)^2 - (a^2 - b^2)^2 = 4a^2b^2$

93. $(x + y)(x + z) - x^2 = (y + z)(y + x) - y^2$

94. $(mq - sp)^2 - m(p - sq)^2 = (s^2 - m)(p^2 - mq^2)$

95. A rectangular lawn is *a* meters long and *b* meters wide. A concrete path 1 meter wide is laid around the outside of the lawn. Show this in a diagram. Write the length and breadth of the path. By subtracting the areas of two rectangles, find an expression for the area of the path.

96. In triangle *ABC*, the lengths of $\overline{AB}$, $\overline{BC}$, and $\overline{CA}$ are 13 cm, 14 cm, and 15 cm respectively. $\overline{AD}$ is the altitude from *A* to $\overline{BC}$ and is *h* cm long. $\overline{CD}$ is *x* cm long. Use the Pythagorean Theorem in triangles *ADC* and *ADB* to express h^2 in two ways. Obtain an equation in *x* and solve it. Then, calculate *h* and the area of triangle *ABC*.

CHAPTER 13

quadratic equations

13-1
Graphs of the Quadratic Function

An expression of the form $ax^2 + bx + c$, $a \neq 0$ is called a **quadratic expression** in x. Many of the products you expanded in Chapter 12 produced quadratic expressions.

EXAMPLES

OBJECTIVE:

To graph a given quadratic function.

1. $(2x + 3)(4x + 1) = \quad 8x^2 + 14x + \quad 3$
2. $(x + 1)(x - 3) \quad = \quad x^2 - \quad 2x - \quad 3$
3. $(2x - 5)(2x + 5) = \quad 4x^2 \qquad\quad - 25$
4. $(5x - 1)^2 \qquad = 25x^2 - 10x + \quad 1$

These definitions should be memorized.

A function $x \rightarrow ax^2 + bx + c$, $a \neq 0$, is called a **quadratic function.** Using functional notation, a quadratic function is one which can be expressed in the form $f(x) = ax^2 + bx + c$, $a \neq 0$.

See T.G. on using these exercises as discussion questions or group work.

EXERCISES

1. **2.**

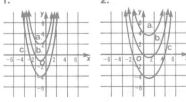

1. Graph each quadratic function in the same coordinate plane.
   a. $f(x) = x^2 + 2x + 3$ **b.** $f(x) = x^2 + 2x$
   c. $f(x) = x^2 + 2x - 3$
2. Graph each quadratic function in the same coordinate plane.
   a. $f(x) = \frac{1}{2} x^2 - x + 4$ **b.** $f(x) = \frac{1}{2} x^2 - x$

   c. $f(x) = \frac{1}{2} x^2 - x - 4$

3. The graphs "move up."
4. The graphs "move down."
5.   6.

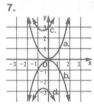

7.

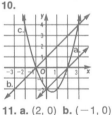

8. The graph opens upward.
9. The graph opens downward.

10.

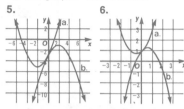

11. a. $(2, 0)$ b. $(-1, 0)$
c. Answers will vary.

Use the graphs in Exercises **1** and **2** to help you answer each question.

3. What happens to the graph of $f(x) = ax^2 + bx + c$, $a \neq 0$, if the value of c is increased but the values of a and b remain the same?

4. What happens to the graph of $f(x) = ax^2 + bx + c$, $a \neq 0$, if the value of c is decreased and the values of a and b remain the same?

5. Graph each quadratic function in the same coordinate plane.
  a. $f(x) = x^2 + x + 1$ **b.** $f(x) = -x^2 + x + 1$

6. Graph each quadratic function in the same coordinate plane.
  a. $f(x) = \dfrac{1}{2}x^2 + 2x - 3$ **b.** $f(x) = -\dfrac{1}{2}x^2 + 2x - 3$

7. Graph each quadratic function in the same coordinate plane.
  a. $f(x) = x^2$ **b.** $f(x) = -x^2$
  c. $f(x) = x^2 + x + 3$ **d.** $f(x) = -x^2 - x - 3$

Use Exercises **5–7** to help you answer each question.

8. Describe the graph of $f(x) = ax^2 + bx + c$ when a is positive.

9. Describe the graph of $f(x) = ax^2 + bx + c$ when a is negative.

10. Graph each function in the same coordinate plane.
  a. $g(x) = x - 2$ **b.** $h(x) = x + 1$ **c.** $f(x) = x^2 - x - 2$

11. Use the graph of Exercise **10** to answer each question.
  a. What point on the x-axis also is on the graphs of $g(x)$ and $f(x)$?
  b. What point on the x-axis also is on the graphs of $h(x)$ and $f(x)$?
  c. Since the product $(x - 2)(x + 1)$ equals $x^2 - x - 2$, you could write $f(x) = (x - 2)(x + 1)$. Explain how writing $f(x)$ as a product of factors makes it easy to find the values of x for which $f(x) = 0$.

OBJECTIVE:
To graph a given quadratic function and name its maximum or minimum point by inspection.

13-2

Axis of
Symmetry

If you study the graphs of quadratic functions that you have drawn, you may notice a common shape. This common shape is called a **parabola.**

EXAMPLES

1.

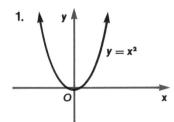

$y = x^2$

2.

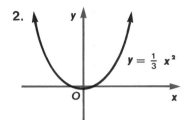

$y = \frac{1}{3} x^2$

3.

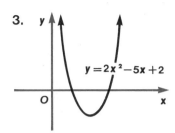

$y = 2x^2 - 5x + 2$

4.

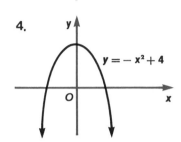

$y = -x^2 + 4$

5.

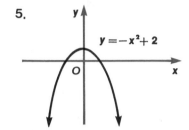

$y = -x^2 + 2$

6.

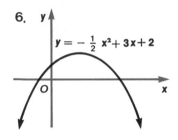

$y = -\frac{1}{2} x^2 + 3x + 2$

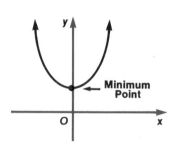

Minimum Point

Stress the cases $a > 0$ and $a < 0$.

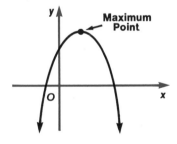

Maximum Point

The parabola may be turned upward as in the first three examples. The parabola may be turned downward as in the last three examples.

When the parabola is turned upward, there is a minimum point for the function. A ***minimum point*** of the parabola is the point whose y-coordinate is less than the y-coordinate of every other point on the graph. The graph of the quadratic function $f(x) = ax^2 + bx + c$ will have a minimum point if a is positive.

When the parabola is turned downward, there is a maximum point for the function. A ***maximum point*** of the parabola is the point whose y-coordinate is greater than the y-coordinate of every other point on the graph. The graph of the quadratic function $f(x) = ax^2 + bx + c$ will have a maximum point if a is negative.

If the graph of a quadratic function, as shown in the examples, is folded along a vertical line passing through the maximum or minimum point, the two halves of the graph exactly fit over each other.

EXAMPLE

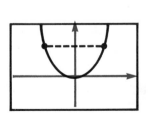
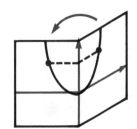

Whenever two halves of a graph fit exactly when it is folded along a line, the figure is *symmetric* about the line. The line is called the **axis of symmetry.** For a parabola, the axis of symmetry always passes through the maximum or minimum point.

By drawing and inspecting graphs, it sometimes is possible to determine the coordinates of the maximum or minimum point of a quadratic function.

EXAMPLE

Find the coordinates of the maximum or minimum point of $f(x) = 2x^2 - 8x - 3$.

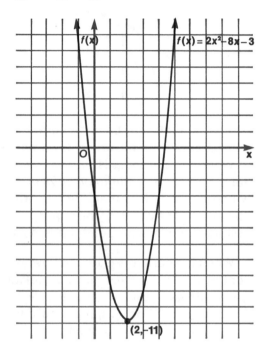

The minimum point is $(2, -11)$.

EXERCISES

1.

2.

3. See section notes in T.G.
4. See section notes in T.G.
5. See section notes in T.G.
6. a. $f(1) = f(3)$ **b.** $f(0) = f(4)$,
c. They are equal.

By drawing and inspecting a graph, determine the maximum or minimum point for each quadratic function. Write the coordinates of the point and sketch the axis of symmetry for the graph.

1. $f(x) = x^2 - 2x + 1$

2. $f(x) = \frac{1}{2}x^2 + 2x$

3. $f(x) = -x^2 - 6x + 5$

4. $f(x) = \frac{1}{5}x^2 + 3$

5. $f(x) = -3x^2 + 9x - 1$

6. The quadratic function $f(x) = 2x^2 - 8x + 1$ has a minimum value at $(2, -7)$.

7. a. $f(-2) = f(0)$
b. $f(-3) = f(1)$
c. $f(-1 - 3) = f(-1 + 3)$

If students appear ready, also ask in Exercise 7 if $f(-1 - w) = f(-1 + w)$ for any $w > 0$.

8. **9.**

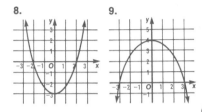

Consider assigning Exercises 12-20 to more able students while slow students spend more time with Exercises 1-11. If this is done, treat Exercises 17 and 19 as class discussion for the slow students.

10. **11.**

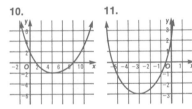

12. No **13.** Yes **14.** Yes **15.** Yes
16. Yes **17.** 0 **18.** 4 **19.** $x = 4$
20. $x = \dfrac{a + c}{2}$

a. How does $f(1)$ compare with $f(3)$?
b. How does $f(0)$ compare with $f(4)$?
c. How does $f(2 - 3)$ compare with $f(2 + 3)$?
7. The quadratic function $f(x) = -3x^2 - 6x + 5$ has a maximum value at $(-1, 8)$.
   a. How does $f(-2)$ compare with $f(0)$?
   b. How does $f(-3)$ compare with $f(1)$?
   c. How does $f(-1 - 3)$ compare with $f(-1 + 3)$?

Graph each quadratic function in a separate coordinate plane.
8. The graph of the function has a minimum point at $(0, -3)$ and also contains the points $(2, 0)$ and $(-2, 0)$.
9. The graph of the function has a maximum point at $(0, 4)$ and also contains the points $(-3, 0)$ and $(3, 0)$.
10. The graph of the function has a minimum point at $(4, -2)$ and also contains the points $(1, 0)$ and $(8, 0)$.
11. The graph of the function has a minimum point at $(-3, -3)$ and also contains the points $(-5, -1)$ and $(-1, -1)$.

State whether or not each function *can be* a quadratic function of the form $f(x) = ax^2 + bx + c$.
12. The graph of the function has a minimum point at $(0, 0)$ and also contains the points $(1, 3)$ and $(-1, 1)$.
13. The graph of the function has a maximum point at $(0, 0)$ and also contains the points $(-2, -3)$ and $(2, -3)$.
14. The graph of the function has a maximum point at $(3, 3)$ and also contains the points $(0, 0)$ and $(6, 0)$.
15. The graph of the function has a maximum point at $(-8, -10)$ and also contains the points $(0, -11)$ and $(-16, -11)$.
16. The graph of the function contains the points $(2, 0)$ and $(3, 0)$.

17. The graph of a quadratic function has a minimum point and contains the points $(2, 0)$ and $(-2, 0)$. What is the x-coordinate of the minimum point?
18. The graph of a quadratic function has a maximum point and contains the points $(2, 10)$ and $(6, 10)$. What is the x-coordinate of the maximum point?
19. The graph of a quadratic function contains points $(3, 8)$ and $(5, 8)$. What is the x-coordinate of the maximum or minimum point? In other words, what is the equation of the axis of symmetry?
20. If (a, b) and (c, b) are on the graph of a quadratic function, what is the x-coordinate of its maximum or minimum point? What is the equation of the axis of symmetry?

13-3

To name the maximum or minimum point of a given quadratic function without graphing.

Maximum and Minimum Points

If two points on the graph of a quadratic function have the same *y*-coordinate, then the *x*-coordinate of the maximum or minimum is halfway between the *x*-coordinates of these points. In other words, if (r, t) and (s, t) are on the graph of a quadratic function, then the *x*-coordinate of the maximum or minimum point is $\frac{r + s}{2}$.

EXAMPLE

Stress the fact that $f(p - w) = f(p + w)$. To see this, slow students may be very dependent on the following examples.

The points $(3, 3)$ and $(-1, 3)$ are on the graph of $f(x) = 2x^2 - 4x - 3$.

a. Since $a > 0$, $f(x)$ has a minimum point.

b. The *x*-coordinate of the minimum point is $\dfrac{3 + (-1)}{2} = \dfrac{2}{2} = 1$.

c. The *y*-coordinate of the minimum point is $f(1) = 2(1)^2 - 4(1) - 3 = -5$.
The function has a minimum point at $(1, -5)$.

Suppose that $f(x)$ is a quadratic function and p is the *x*-coordinate of its maximum or minimum point. Then, because of symmetry, $f(p - w) = f(p + w)$ for any number w.

EXAMPLES

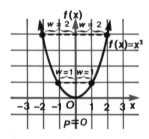

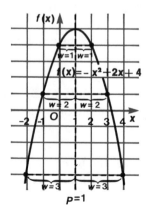

1. $f(x) = x^2$
$\quad p = 0$
When $w = 1$, $f(0 - 1) = f(0 + 1) = 1$
When $w = 2$, $f(0 - 2) = f(0 + 2) = 4$

2. $f(x) = -x^2 + 2x + 4$
$\quad p = 1$
When $w = 1$, $f(1 - 1) = f(1 + 1) = 4$
When $w = 2$, $f(1 - 2) = f(1 + 2) = 1$
When $w = 3$, $f(1 - 3) = f(1 + 3) = -4$

Some slow students may find
this derivation difficult while
more able students find it
fascinating. Allow adequate time
to discuss each step. Establish
the conclusion that it is correct
for specific examples. This
may be very important for slow
students.

If p is the x-coordinate of the maximum or minimum point, then the following is another way to write $f(p + w) = f(p - w)$.

$$a(p + w)^2 + b(p + w) + c = a(p - w)^2 + b(p - w) + c$$

You may treat this equation as a literal equation and solve it for p. To solve this literal equation, isolate p on one side of the equal sign. Assume that w is not zero.

$$a(p + w)^2 + b(p + w) + c = a(p - w)^2 + b(p - w) + c$$

Expand the first term.

$\Leftrightarrow a(p^2 + 2pw + w^2) + b(p + w) + c$
$= a(p^2 - 2pw + w^2) + b(p - w) + c$

Use the Distributive Property.

$\Leftrightarrow ap^2 + 2apw + aw^2 + bp + bw + c$
$= ap^2 - 2apw + aw^2 + bp - bw + c$

Subtract $ap^2 + aw^2 + bp + c$ from each side.

$\Leftrightarrow 2apw + bw = -2apw - bw$

Add $2apw$ to each side.

$\Leftrightarrow 4apw + bw = -bw$

Subtract bw from each side.

$\Leftrightarrow \qquad 4apw = -2bw$

Divide each side by $2w$ (remember $w \neq 0$).

$\Leftrightarrow \qquad 2ap = -b$

Divide each side by $2a$ (remember $a \neq 0$).

$\Leftrightarrow \qquad p = \dfrac{-b}{2a}$

This is a very important result because p is the x-coordinate of the maximum or minimum point for a quadratic function. You should learn this result.

This statement should be
memorized.

The x-coordinate of the maximum or minimum point of a quadratic function $f(x) = ax^2 + bx + c$ is $\dfrac{-b}{2a}$.

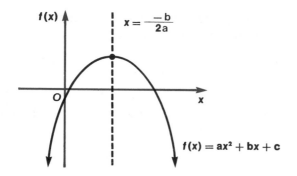

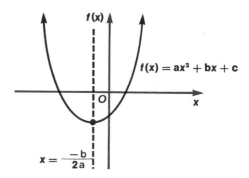

EXERCISES

1. $(-1, 0)$ **2.** $(0, 4)$ **3.** $\left(-\frac{1}{2}, 1\frac{1}{4}\right)$

4. $\left(-1, \frac{1}{2}\right)$ **5.** $(4, 32)$

6. $-\frac{3}{2}, -5\frac{3}{4}$ **7.** $(2, 4)$

8. $(1, 2)$ **9.** $(1, 1)$ **10.** $(1, 5)$
11. $(0, -4)$ **12.** $(0, 1)$ **13.** $(1, 3)$

14. $\left(-\frac{1}{2}, -\frac{3}{4}\right)$

For each quadratic function, find the coordinates of the maximum or minimum point by first finding the value of x halfway between the x-coordinates of the given points.

	Points on the Graph of the Function	The Function
1.	$(-2, 1)$ and $(0, 1)$	$f(x) = x^2 + 2x + 1$
2.	$(-3, -32)$ and $(3, -32)$	$f(x) = 4 - 4x^2$
3.	$(2, -5)$ and $(-3, -5)$	$f(x) = 1 - x - x^2$
4.	$\left(-5, \frac{17}{2}\right)$ and $\left(3, \frac{17}{2}\right)$	$f(x) = \frac{1}{2}x^2 + x + 1$
5.	$(-1, 7)$ and $(9, 7)$	$f(x) = 16 - x^2 + 8x$
6.	$\left(-4, -\frac{11}{3}\right)$ and $\left(1, -\frac{11}{3}\right)$	$f(x) = \frac{1}{3}x^2 + x - 5$

Find the coordinates of the maximum or minimum point of each quadratic function. Use the following three steps.

    a. From the value of a in $f(x) = ax^2 + bx + c$, decide if $f(x)$ has a maximum or minimum point.

    b. Find the x-coordinate of that point by computing $\frac{-b}{2a}$.

    c. Find the y-coordinate of that point by computing $f\left(\frac{-b}{2a}\right)$.

7. $f(x) = x^2 - 4x + 8$ **8.** $f(x) = x^2 - 2x + 3$
9. $f(x) = 2x^2 - 4x + 3$ **10.** $f(x) = -2x^2 + 4x + 3$
11. $f(x) = 4x^2 - 4$ **12.** $f(x) = 1 - x^2$
13. $f(x) = -3x^2 + 6x$ **14.** $f(x) = 3x^2 + 3x$

15. $(3, -19)$ **16.** $(3, -19)$
17. $(1, 9)$ **18.** $(-\frac{1}{2}, 1\frac{1}{4})$

Exercises 19 and 20 should be assigned to any student who remains in doubt about the axis of symmetry.

19.

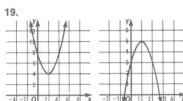

15. $f(x) = 2x^2 - 12x - 1$ **16.** $f(x) = -12x + 2x^2 - 1$
17. $f(x) = 5 - 4x^2 + 8x$ **18.** $f(x) = 1 - x - x^2$

19. Sketch graphs of the functions in Exercises **7, 10, 13,** and **18.** Check your answers to these exercises by inspecting the graphs.

20. Check the x-coordinates of the maximum or minimum points found in Exercises **1–6** by computing $\frac{-b}{2a}$ for each quadratic function.

21. A rain gutter is to be made by turning up the sides of a galvanized steel strip. The strip is 16 inches wide. Let x be the height of a side and f(x) be the cross-sectional area.

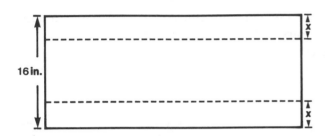

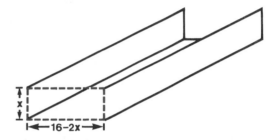

For Exercises 21-23, allow poor readers to work with better readers.

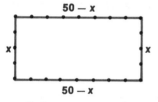

The cross-section is indicated in red. How high should the sides be to allow for the maximum flow of water? (Hint: Maximum flow will occur when the cross-sectional area is maximum.)

22. If you must make a rectangular pen and you only have 100 feet of fence, what should be the dimensions of the pen to give the maximum area? Let f(x) be the area of the rectangle.

23.

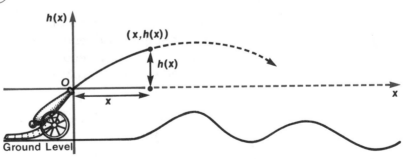

20. Check left to student.
21. $x = 4$ in.   **22.** 25 ft by 25 ft
23. a. 250 yd   **b.** 4000 yd

Imagine a coordinate plane with its origin at the muzzle of a gun. Projectiles from a gun should follow a path which is a parabola. Air resistance alters the path a little but not enough to be concerned about here.

a. The gun is set to fire projectiles according to the function $h(x) = x - \dfrac{x^2}{1000}$ where $h(x)$ is the height in yards the projectile is above the muzzle and x is the horizontal distance in yards the projectile is from the muzzle. What is the maximum height above the muzzle that the projectile may reach?

b. Another gun is set to fire projectiles according to the function $h(x) = 2x - \dfrac{x^2}{4000}$. What is the maximum height above the muzzle that these projectiles may reach?

Suggested Activity

As an after-school experiment, study what air resistance does to the path of each projectile thrown by hand.
  a. A baseball
  b. A steel ball bearing
  c. A basketball
  d. A balloon

Decide which path is most nearly a parabola. Then with classmates, discuss each of the following questions.

1. The lead balloon would follow a parabolic path more closely. 2. The lighter gravity on the moon would allow for larger parabolic paths using the same force.

1. How would the path of a balloon filled with lead compare with the path of a balloon filled with air?
2. Assume you can throw the projectiles while standing on the moon's surface. How would the paths on earth compare with the paths on the moon?

OBJECTIVE:

13-4   To name the number of solutions for $ax^2 + bx + c = 0$ by inspecting the graph for $f(x) = ax^2 + bx + c$.

Graphing Solutions

An equation which can be written as $ax^2 + bx + c = 0$, $a \neq 0$, is called a **quadratic equation.** The number of solutions in R that a particular quadratic equation may have depends on the particular quadratic equation involved.

EXAMPLES

Notice that the first three exercises correspond to the three examples.

1. $x^2 - 2x - 3 = 0$ is a quadratic equation. Its solution set is $\{-1, 3\}$.

$$\text{Check: } 3^2 - 2 \cdot 3 - 3 = 9 - 6 - 3 = 0$$
$$(-1)^2 - 2(-1) - 3 = 1 + 2 - 3 = 0$$

2. $x^2 - 8x + 16 = 0$ is a quadratic equation. Its solution set is $\{4\}$.

$$\text{Check: } 4^2 - 8 \cdot 4 + 16 = 16 - 32 + 16 = 0$$

3. $x^2 + 3x + 4 = 0$ is a quadratic equation. It has *no* real number solutions. Its solution set is $\varnothing$.

The following exercises present a method for finding the solution sets of quadratic equations.

EXERCISES

It may be best to use Exercises 1-12 as class discussion for slow students and very poor readers. In that case, Exercises 13-20 may serve as a check for remaining difficulties.

1.

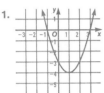

a. $(-1, 0)$, $(3, 0)$ **b.** $x = -1, 3$
c. $\{-1, 3\}$ **d.** Yes

2.

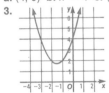

a. $(4, 0)$ **b.** $x = 4$ **c.** $\{4\}$ **d.** Yes

3.

a. None **b.** None **c.** $\varnothing$ **d.** Yes
4. 2 **5.** 1 **6.** 0 **7.** 1

 Draw the graph of $f(x) = x^2 - 2x - 3$.
   a. List any x-intercept of the graph.
   b. List any value of x for which $f(x) = 0$.
   c. What is the solution set of $x^2 - 2x - 3 = 0$?
   d. Compare the solution set in Part **c** to that in Example **1** in this section. Are they equal?

2. Draw the graph of $f(x) = x^2 - 8x + 16$.
   a. List any x-intercept of the graph.
   b. List any value of x for which $f(x) = 0$.
   c. What is the solution set of $x^2 - 8x + 16 = 0$?
   d. Compare the solution set in Part **c** to that in Example **2** in this section. Are they equal?

3. Draw the graph of $f(x) = x^2 + 3x + 4$.
   a. List any x-intercept of the graph.
   b. List any value of x for which $f(x) = 0$.
   c. What is the solution set of $x^2 + 3x + 4 = 0$?
   d. Compare the solution set in Part **c** to that in Example **3** in this section. Are they equal?

Every quadratic function $f(x) = ax^2 + bx + c$ is associated with a quadratic equation $ax^2 + bx + c = 0$. By inspecting the graph of each function, write the number of solutions there would be for the corresponding quadratic equation.

4.

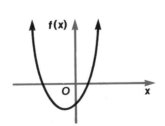

5.

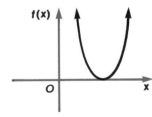

6.

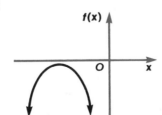

7.

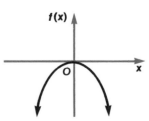

Repeat the following statement as often as required. "If $f(x) = ax^2 + bx + c$, then $ax^2 + bx + c = 0$ where the graph of f intersects the x-axis."

8. 2 **9.** 0 **10.** 2 **11.** 1

12. Answers may vary.; 2, 0

13.

c. $x = 2, -2$

14.

c. $x = 2, -2$

15. See section notes in T.G.
c. $x = 3$
16. See section notes in T.G.
b. $x = 2, 3$ **c.** $x = 2, 3$
17. See section notes in T.G.
b. Doesn't cross x-axis
c. No real solutions
18. See section notes in T.G.
b. $x = -1$ **c.** $x = -1$
19. See section notes in T.G.
b. $x = \frac{1}{2}, 3$ **c.** $x = \frac{1}{2}, 3$
20. See section notes in T.G.
b. Doesn't cross x-axis
c. No real solution

8.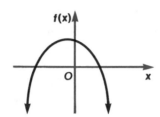

9.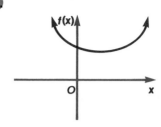

10.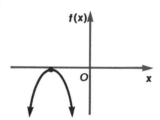

11.

12. a. What do you think is the maximum number of solutions in R that a quadratic equation may have?
b. What do you think is the least number of solutions in R that a quadratic equation may have?

Solve each equation by completing the following three steps.
a. Graph the quadratic function $f(x) = ax^2 + bx + c$.
b. Locate the x-intercepts of the graph.
c. Name the x-coordinates of the x-intercepts. That is, name values of x which make $ax^2 + bx + c = 0$.

13. $x^2 - 4 = 0$ **14.** $4 - x^2 = 0$
15. $x^2 - 6x + 9 = 0$ **16.** $x^2 - 5x + 6 = 0$
17. $x^2 + x + 1 = 0$ **18.** $x^2 + 2x + 1 = 0$
19. $2x^2 - 7x + 3 = 0$ **20.** $2x^2 - 4x + 3 = 0$

13-5
The Number of Solutions

OBJECTIVE:

To name the number of solutions of $ax^2 + bx + c = 0$ by computing $f(\frac{-b}{2a})$ and observing if $a < 0$ or $a > 0$.

This should be accepted by students as a summary statement.

In the last set of exercises, you used the *graphing method* to solve quadratic equations. The method may be outlined in three steps.

1. Draw the graph of the quadratic function, $f(x) = ax^2 + bx + c$.
2. Locate any x-intercepts of the graph.
3. The x-coordinate of each x-intercept found in Step **2** is a member of the solution set: $\{x \mid f(x) = 0\}$.

When looking for solutions to quadratic equations using the graphing method, you saw that there were three possible situations.

1. If the graph intersects the x-axis in two points, there are two solutions to the quadratic equation.
2. If the graph intersects the x-axis in one point, there is one solution in R to the quadratic equation.
3. If the graph does not intersect the x-axis, there are no solutions in R to the quadratic equation.

Using what you know about quadratic functions, you may decide how many solutions a particular quadratic equation has without graphing it. For $f(x) = ax^2 + bx + c, a \neq 0$, the value of a indicates whether the function has a maximum or minimum point. The coordinates of the point are $\left(\dfrac{-b}{2a}, f\left(\dfrac{-b}{2a} \right) \right)$.

EXAMPLES

1. How many solutions in R are there for $x^2 - 6x + 8 = 0$? Since $a > 0$, the graph has a minimum point.

$$\frac{-b}{2a} = \frac{6}{2 \cdot 1} = 3$$

$$f\left(\frac{-b}{2a} \right) = f(3)$$

$$= 3^2 - 6 \cdot 3 + 8$$

$$= -1$$

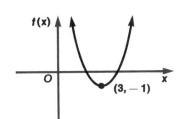

The minimum point, $(3, -1)$, is below the x-axis. This means that there are two solutions for $x^2 - 6x + 8 = 0$.

2. How many solutions in R are there for $-4 + 4x - x^2 = 0$? Since $a < 0$, the graph has a maximum point.

$$\frac{-b}{2a} = \frac{-4}{2(-1)} = 2$$

$$f\left(\frac{-b}{2a} \right) = f(2)$$

$$= -4 + 4(2) - (2)^2$$

$$= 0$$

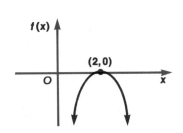

The maximum point, $(2, 0)$, is on the x-axis. This means that there is one solution for $-4 + 4x - x^2 = 0$.

3. How many solutions in R are there for $2x^2 + 4x + 5 = 0$? Since $a > 0$, the graph has a minimum point.

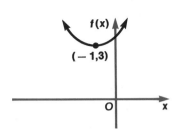

$$\frac{-b}{2a} = \frac{-4}{2 \cdot 2} = -1$$

$$f\left(\frac{-b}{2a}\right) = f(-1)$$

$$= 2(-1)^2 + 4(-1) + 5$$

$$= 3$$

The minimum point, $(-1, 3)$, is above the x-axis. This means that there are no solutions for $2x^2 + 4x + 5 = 0$.

EXERCISES

State the number of solutions that each quadratic equation has in R. Make your decision by locating maximum or minimum points.

1. $x^2 - 4x + 4 = 0$ **2.** $3x^2 - 6x + 4 = 0$

3. $x^2 - 4x = 0$ **4.** $-x^2 + 4x = 0$

5. $-x^2 + 6x - 9 = 0$ **6.** $-x^2 + 6x - 10 = 0$

7. $8 - 5x^2 = 0$ **8.** $-5x^2 - 1 = 0$

9. $-25 + 10x - x^2 = 0$ **10.** $2x^2 - 8 = 0$

11. $6x^2 - 2x = 1 - 2x$ (Hint: First write in the form $ax^2 + bx + c = 0$.)

12. $x^2 + x - 1 = x - 2$ **13.** $x^2 + x + 1 = x + 2$

For each set of conditions, how many solutions will $ax^2 + bx + c = 0$, $a \neq 0$, have in R? Remember that $f(x) = ax^2 + bx + c$.

14. $a > 0$ and $f\left(\frac{-b}{2a}\right) > 0$ **15.** $a > 0$ and $f\left(\frac{-b}{2a}\right) = 0$

16. $a > 0$ and $f\left(\frac{-b}{2a}\right) < 0$ **17.** $a < 0$ and $f\left(\frac{-b}{2a}\right) > 0$

18. $a < 0$ and $f\left(\frac{-b}{2a}\right) = 0$ **19.** $a < 0$ and $f\left(\frac{-b}{2a}\right) < 0$

20. Exercises **14–19** show six possible situations. In which of these situations is $\frac{-b}{2a}$ a solution of $ax^2 + bx + c = 0$? If you do not know the answer, draw and inspect a graph for each of the six situations.

13-6 *Calculating Solutions*

If the graph of $f(x) = ax^2 + bx + c$, $a \neq 0$, intersects the x-axis at two points, there are two solutions to $ax^2 + bx + c = 0$. However, drawing and inspecting graphs is not a completely accurate method for solving quadratic equations. Sometimes you can only estimate the solution.

If there are two values of x for which $f(x) = 0$, then they must be the same distance from the axis of symmetry.

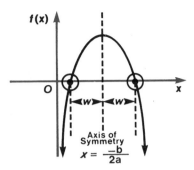

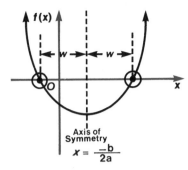

You know how to find the equation for the axis of symmetry. It is $x = \frac{-b}{2a}$. If w, the distance from the axis of symmetry to each x-intercept, is known, then the solutions of the quadratic equation may be computed. The two solutions are $\frac{-b}{2a} + w$ and $\frac{-b}{2a} - w$.

Since you do not know how to compute a value for w, it would be helpful if someone could give you the correct value of w each time you needed it. In this section a value for w will be provided for each equation you are asked to solve.

EXAMPLES

1. Solve $x^2 - 8x + 12 = 0$ if $w = 2$. The axis of symmetry of $f(x) = x^2 - 8x + 12$ is given by $x = \frac{-b}{2a}$.

$$x = \frac{-b}{2a}$$

$$x = \frac{-(-8)}{2 \cdot 1}$$

$$x = 4$$

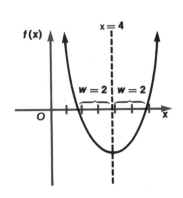

The solutions are $\frac{-b}{2a} + w$ and $\frac{-b}{2a} - w$.

$$\frac{-b}{2a} + w = 4 + 2 \qquad \frac{-b}{2a} - w = 4 - 2$$

$$\frac{-b}{2a} + w = 6 \qquad \frac{-b}{2a} - w = 2$$

The solution set is $\{6, 2\}$.

Check: $2^2 - 8(2) + 12 = 4 - 16 + 12 = 0$
$6^2 - 8(6) + 12 = 36 - 48 + 12 = 0$

385

2. Solve $3 - x - \frac{1}{4}x^2 = 0$ if $w = 4$.

$$x = \frac{-b}{2a}$$

$$x = \frac{-(-1)}{2\left(-\frac{1}{4}\right)}$$

$$x = \frac{1}{-\frac{1}{2}}$$

$$x = -2$$

The solutions are $\frac{-b}{2a} + w$ and $\frac{-b}{2a} - w$.

The solution set is $\{-6, 2\}$.

Check: $3 - (-6) - \frac{1}{4}(-6)^2 = 3 + 6 - 9 = 0$

$$3 - (2) - \frac{1}{4}(2)^2 = 3 - 2 - 1 = 0$$

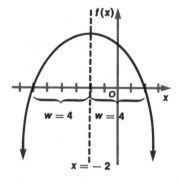

EXERCISES

1. $x = 1, 5$ **2.** $x = 1, -1$

3. $x = 2, 3$ **4.** $x = -\frac{1}{2}, -\frac{3}{2}$

5. $x = -7, 5$ **6.** $x = -\frac{1}{2}, \frac{3}{2}$

7. $x = 10, 20$ **8.** $x = 30, -28$

9. $x = -\frac{1}{3}, \frac{3}{2}$ **10.** $x = \frac{1}{4}, \frac{1}{3}$

11. Checks will vary.

Solve each quadratic equation without drawing a graph. Each equation has solutions in R. The distance between the axis of symmetry and an *x*-intercept, *w*, is provided for you.

1. $x^2 - 6x + 5 = 0$ $w = 2$

2. $x^2 - 1 = 0$ $w = 1$

3. $-2x^2 + 10x - 12 = 0$ $w = \frac{1}{2}$

4. $4x^2 + 8x + 3 = 0$ $w = \frac{1}{2}$

5. $x^2 + 2x - 35 = 0$ $w = 6$

6. $4x^2 - 4x - 3 = 0$ $w = 1$

7. $x^2 - 30x + 200 = 0$ $w = 5$

8. $x^2 - 2x - 840 = 0$ $w = 29$

9. $3 + 7x - 6x^2 = 0$ $w = \frac{11}{12}$

10. $12x^2 - 7x + 1 = 0$ $w = \frac{1}{24}$

11. Check each of your solutions in Exercises **1–10.**

12. Correct **13.** Incorrect
14. Correct **15.** Incorrect
16. Incorrect **17.** Incorrect
18.

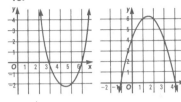

A *suggested* value for w is given for each quadratic equation. State whether each value of w is correct or incorrect.

12. $x^2 - 3x + 2 = 0$ $\qquad w = \dfrac{1}{2}$

13. $x^2 - 9x + 18 = 0$ $\qquad w = 1$
14. $4 - x^2 = 0$ $\qquad w = 2$
15. $4 + 3x - x^2 = 0$ $\qquad w = 2$
16. $x^2 + 4x - 5 = 0$ $\qquad w = 2$
17. $x^2 - 10x - 2000 = 0$ $\qquad w = 45$

18. For each incorrect value of w in Exercises **12–17**, carefully draw a graph and estimate the correct value of w.

OBJECTIVE:

To name the two real number solutions of $ax^2 + bx + c = 0$, $\sqrt{b^2 - 4ac}$

> 0 computing $\left(\dfrac{-b}{2a}\right) + \dfrac{\sqrt{b^2 - 4ac}}{|2a|}$ and $\left(\dfrac{-b}{2a}\right) - \dfrac{\sqrt{b^2 - 4ac}}{|2a|}$.

13-7
Finding Formulas for Solutions

Assume that $f(x) = ax^2 + bx + c$ is a quadratic function which intersects the x-axis at two points. You then know that for some $w > 0$, the two solutions of $f(x) = 0$ are $\dfrac{-b}{2a} + w$ and $\dfrac{-b}{2a} - w$. In other words, $f\left(\dfrac{-b}{2a} + w\right)$ and $f\left(\dfrac{-b}{2a} - w\right)$ both equal zero.

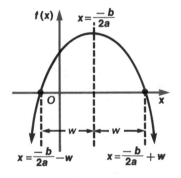

The equation $f\left(\dfrac{-b}{2a} + w\right) = 0$ may be written in the following form.

$$a\left(\dfrac{-b}{2a} + w\right)^2 + b\left(\dfrac{-b}{2a} + w\right) + c = 0$$

The equation $f\left(\dfrac{-b}{2a} - w\right) = 0$ may be written in the following form.

$$a\left(\dfrac{-b}{2a} - w\right)^2 + b\left(\dfrac{-b}{2a} - w\right) + c = 0$$

Remind students that in this section it is assumed that $f(x) = 0$ has two solutions.

These equations may be treated as literal equations and solved for w. Take ample time going from step to step as you study the solution of the first equation.

$$a\left(\frac{-b}{2a} + w\right)^2 + b\left(\frac{-b}{2a} + w\right) + c = 0$$

Some slow students may find this difficult while more able students find it fascinating.

Expand the first term.

$$\Leftrightarrow a\left(\frac{b^2}{4a^2} - \frac{bw}{a} + w^2\right)$$
$$+ b\left(\frac{-b}{2a} + w\right) + c = 0$$

Use the Distributive Property.

$$\Leftrightarrow \frac{b^2}{4a} - bw + aw^2$$
$$+ \frac{-b^2}{2a} + bw + c = 0$$

Simplify.

$$\Leftrightarrow \frac{b^2}{4a} - \frac{b^2}{2a} + aw^2 + c = 0$$

Combine $\frac{b^2}{4a}$ and $-\frac{b^2}{2a}$.

$$\Leftrightarrow \frac{-b^2}{4a} + aw^2 + c = 0$$

Subtract $\frac{-b^2}{4a} + c$ from each side.

$$\Leftrightarrow aw^2 = \frac{b^2}{4a} - c$$

Allow adequate time to discuss each step.

Divide each side by a (remember $a \neq 0$).

$$\Leftrightarrow w^2 = \frac{b^2}{4a^2} - \frac{c}{a}$$

Take the principal square root of each side (remember $w > 0$).

$$\Leftrightarrow w = \sqrt{\frac{b^2}{4a^2} - \frac{c}{a}}$$

Remind students that this is the w from the last section.

Multiply $\frac{c}{a}$ by $\frac{4a}{4a}$.

$$\Leftrightarrow w = \sqrt{\frac{b^2}{4a^2} - \frac{4ac}{4a^2}}$$

Combine the fractions.

$$\Leftrightarrow w = \sqrt{\frac{b^2 - 4ac}{4a^2}}$$

Use the Division Property of Square Roots.

$$\Leftrightarrow w = \frac{\sqrt{b^2 - 4ac}}{\sqrt{4a^2}}$$

Take the principal square root of $4a^2$.

$$\Leftrightarrow w = \frac{\sqrt{b^2 - 4ac}}{|2a|}$$

Notice that $\sqrt{4a^2}$ is written as $|2a|$ and not as $2a$. This is because a may be a positive or a negative number and $\sqrt{4a^2}$ means the positive square root of $4a^2$. If a were negative, $2a$ would not be the positive square root of $4a^2$. In order to be safe, the absolute value of $2a$ is given as the principal square root of $4a^2$ since $|2a|$ is positive.

Solving the other equation, $f\left(\dfrac{-b}{2a} - w\right) = 0$, for w should result in the same value of w. Again, take time going from step to step.

$$a\left(\frac{-b}{2a} - w\right)^2 + b\left(\frac{-b}{2a} - w\right) + c = 0$$

Logically, solving this second equation is redundant.

Since not many *Algebra 1* students are able logicians, they may find added security in seeing that both derivations yield the same result.

Expand the first term.

$$\Leftrightarrow a\left(\frac{b^2}{4a^2} + \frac{bw}{a} + w^2\right)$$
$$+ b\left(\frac{-b}{2a} - w\right) + c = 0$$

Use the Distributive Property.

$$\Leftrightarrow \frac{b^2}{4a} + bw + aw^2$$
$$- \frac{b^2}{2a} - bw + c = 0$$

Simplify.

$$\Leftrightarrow \frac{b^2}{4a} - \frac{b^2}{2a} + aw^2 + c = 0$$

Combine $\dfrac{b^2}{4a}$ and $-\dfrac{b^2}{2a}$.

$$\Leftrightarrow \frac{-b^2}{4a} + aw^2 + c = 0$$

Subtract $\dfrac{-b^2}{4a} + c$ from each side.

$$\Leftrightarrow aw^2 = \frac{b^2}{4a} - c$$

Divide each side by a (remember $a \neq 0$).

$$\Leftrightarrow w^2 = \frac{b^2}{4a^2} - \frac{c}{a}$$

Take the principal square root of each side (remember $w > 0$).

$$\Leftrightarrow w = \sqrt{\frac{b^2}{4a^2} - \frac{c}{a}}$$

Multiply $\dfrac{c}{a}$ by $\dfrac{4a}{4a}$.

$$\Leftrightarrow w = \sqrt{\frac{b^2}{4a^2} - \frac{4ac}{4a^2}}$$

Combine the fractions.

$$\Leftrightarrow w = \sqrt{\frac{b^2 - 4ac}{4a^2}}$$

Use the Division Property of Square Roots.

$$\Leftrightarrow w = \frac{\sqrt{b^2 - 4ac}}{\sqrt{4a^2}}$$

Do not demand memorization at this time. Allow students to refer to this result when working exercises.

Take the principal square root of $4a^2$.

$$\Leftrightarrow w = \frac{\sqrt{b^2 - 4ac}}{|2a|}$$

This is the same result as before. This means that when a quadratic equation has two solutions, you may find them by computing $\dfrac{-b}{2a} + \dfrac{\sqrt{b^2 - 4ac}}{|2a|}$ and $\dfrac{-b}{2a} - \dfrac{\sqrt{b^2 - 4ac}}{|2a|}$.

EXAMPLES

Remind students whenever necessary that $\dfrac{\sqrt{b^2 - 4ac}}{|\,2a\,|}$ is the "w" of Section 13-6.

1. Solve $x^2 + 2x - 3 = 0$.

$$\frac{-b}{2a} = \frac{-2}{2 \cdot 1} = -1$$

$$\frac{\sqrt{b^2 - 4ac}}{|2a|} = \frac{\sqrt{2^2 - 4 \cdot 1 \cdot (-3)}}{|2 \cdot 1|}$$

$$= \frac{\sqrt{16}}{2}$$

$$= 2$$

The solutions are $-1 + 2 = 1$ and $-1 - 2 = -3$.
The solution set is $\{-3, 1\}$.

Check: $(-3)^2 + 2(-3) - 3 = 9 - 6 - 3 = 0$
$(1)^2 + 2 \cdot 1 - 3 = 1 + 2 - 3 = 0$

2. Solve $-3x^2 + 7x - 2 = 0$.

$$\frac{-b}{2a} = \frac{-7}{2(-3)} = \frac{-7}{-6} = \frac{7}{6}$$

$$\frac{\sqrt{b^2 - 4ac}}{|2a|} = \frac{\sqrt{7^2 - 4(-3)(-2)}}{|2(-3)|}$$

$$= \frac{\sqrt{25}}{6}$$

$$= \frac{5}{6}$$

The solutions are $\dfrac{7}{6} + \dfrac{5}{6} = \dfrac{12}{6} = 2$ and $\dfrac{7}{6} - \dfrac{5}{6} = \dfrac{2}{6} = \dfrac{1}{3}$.

The solution set is $\left\{\dfrac{1}{3}, 2\right\}$.

Check: $(-3)(2)^2 + 7(2) - 2 = -12 + 14 - 2 = 0$
$(-3)\left(\dfrac{1}{3}\right)^2 + 7\left(\dfrac{1}{3}\right) - 2 = -\dfrac{1}{3} + \dfrac{7}{3} - 2 = 0$

EXERCISES

1. $x = 1, 3$ 2. $x = 4, -4$
3. $x = 4, 5$ 4. $x = \frac{3}{2}, \frac{1}{2}$
5. $x = -5, 4$
6. $x = 3, -1$ 7. $x = 3, -1$
8. $x = 3, -1$

Solve each quadratic equation by computing $\dfrac{-b}{2a} + \dfrac{\sqrt{b^2 - 4ac}}{|2a|}$

and $\dfrac{-b}{2a} - \dfrac{\sqrt{b^2 - 4ac}}{|2a|}$. Be sure to check each solution.

1. $x^2 - 4x + 3 = 0$ **2.** $16 - x^2 = 0$
3. $x^2 - 9x + 20 = 0$ **4.** $4x^2 - 8x + 3 = 0$
5. $x^2 + x - 20 = 0$ **6.** $-x^2 + 2x + 3 = 0$
7. $-2x^2 + 4x + 6 = 0$ **8.** $-3x^2 + 6x + 9 = 0$

9. $x = 4, 2$ **10.** $x = -4, 2$
11. $x = 2, -2$ **12.** $x = -10, 5$
13. $x = -\frac{2}{3}, \frac{1}{3}$ **14.** $x = \frac{1}{2}, -5$

15. 10 in. **16.** 20 ft **17.** $\frac{7}{2}$ in.

18. 6 ft

Solve each equation for x by finding an equivalent equation which allows you to compute $\dfrac{-b}{2a} + \dfrac{\sqrt{b^2 - 4ac}}{|2a|}$ and $\dfrac{-b}{2a} - \dfrac{\sqrt{b^2 - 4ac}}{|2a|}$.

Sample Solve $3x^2 + 3 = 2x^2 + 4x$.

$$3x^2 + 3 = 2x^2 + 4x \Leftrightarrow 3x^2 - 2x^2 - 4x + 3 = 0$$
$$\Leftrightarrow \qquad x^2 - 4x + 3 = 0$$

Now you may use the formulas.

9. $10 - 6x = 2 - x^2$ **10.** $7x^2 - x = 8 + 6x^2 - 3x$
11. $4 = x^2$ **12.** $x(x + 5) = 50$
13. $3x(3x + 1) = 2$ **14.** $2x(x + 5) = x + 5$

The following exercises may be solved by writing an appropriate quadratic equation and then solving it. When you have two values which solve the equation, you may have to ignore one of them. For example, the side of a rectangle cannot be -6 units in length. This solution should be ignored.

15. A rectangular metal plate is widened by 3 inches and lengthened by 1 inch to make it square. The original sheet had an area of 63 square inches. How long is a side of the enlarged sheet?

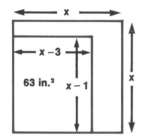

16. A square lot is widened by 1 foot and lengthened by 3 feet. The area of the enlarged lot is 483 square feet. How long was a side of the original lot?

17. Maggie has a rectangular metal sheet which measures 12 inches by 14 inches. She wants to cut out corners and fold the edges to make a box. When she is finished, she wants the bottom of the box to have an area of 63 square inches. How long is the side of one of the corners she should cut out of the sheet?

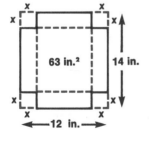

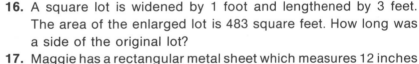

18. A ramp 10 feet in length is situated so that its rise is two feet longer than its run. How many feet long is the run? Use the Pythagorean Theorem.

The Quadratic Formula

OBJECTIVE:
To solve the equation
$ax^2 + bx + c = 0$ by using
the quadratic formula.

You have seen that a quadratic equation, $ax^2 + bx + c = 0$, may have two solutions.

$$x = \frac{-b}{2a} + \frac{\sqrt{b^2 - 4ac}}{|2a|} \qquad x = \frac{-b}{2a} - \frac{\sqrt{b^2 - 4ac}}{|2a|}$$

If a is positive, then $|2a| = 2a$ and the solutions may be simplified.

$$x = \frac{-b}{2a} + \frac{\sqrt{b^2 - 4ac}}{|2a|} \Leftrightarrow x = \frac{-b}{2a} + \frac{\sqrt{b^2 - 4ac}}{2a}$$

$$\Leftrightarrow x = \frac{-b + \sqrt{b^2 - 4ac}}{2a}$$

$$x = \frac{-b}{2a} - \frac{\sqrt{b^2 - 4ac}}{|2a|} \Leftrightarrow x = \frac{-b}{2a} - \frac{\sqrt{b^2 - 4ac}}{2a}$$

$$\Leftrightarrow x = \frac{-b - \sqrt{b^2 - 4ac}}{2a}$$

The material on this page is more difficult in appearance than it is, in fact, mathematically. It may be helpful to begin with an examination of less cluttered expressions such as the following. If $v < 0$, then

$$\frac{s}{v} + \frac{t}{|v|} = \frac{s}{v} + \frac{t}{-v}$$

$$= \frac{s}{v} - \frac{t}{v}$$

$$= \frac{s - t}{v}$$

If a is negative, then $|2a| = -2a$.

$$x = \frac{-b}{2a} + \frac{\sqrt{b^2 - 4ac}}{|2a|} \Leftrightarrow x = \frac{-b}{2a} + \frac{\sqrt{b^2 - 4ac}}{-2a}$$

$$\Leftrightarrow x = \frac{-b}{2a} - \frac{\sqrt{b^2 - 4ac}}{2a}$$

$$\Leftrightarrow x = \frac{-b - \sqrt{b^2 - 4ac}}{2a}$$

$$x = \frac{-b}{2a} - \frac{\sqrt{b^2 - 4ac}}{|2a|} \Leftrightarrow x = \frac{-b}{2a} - \frac{\sqrt{b^2 - 4ac}}{-2a}$$

$$\Leftrightarrow x = \frac{-b}{2a} + \frac{\sqrt{b^2 - 4ac}}{2a}$$

$$\Leftrightarrow x = \frac{-b + \sqrt{b^2 - 4ac}}{2a}$$

As you can see, it makes no difference whether a is positive or negative. The expressions used to find the solutions are the same in either case.

If there are solutions to a quadratic equation $ax^2 + bx + c = 0$, then the solutions may be found by computing the following values for x.

$$x = \frac{-b + \sqrt{b^2 - 4ac}}{2a} \qquad x = \frac{-b - \sqrt{b^2 - 4ac}}{2a}$$

Often, these two equations are combined into one equation using the symbol $\pm$. The symbol $\pm$ is read *plus or minus*.

The equation $x = \dfrac{-b \pm \sqrt{b^2 - 4ac}}{2a}$ is called the *quadratic formula.*

You have been using the quadratic formula, but not in its condensed form. It is a very important formula.

EXAMPLES

1. Solve $x^2 - 12x + 32 = 0$.

$$x = \frac{-b \pm \sqrt{b^2 - 4ac}}{2a}$$

$$x = \frac{-(-12) \pm \sqrt{(-12)^2 - 4 \cdot 1 \cdot 32}}{2 \cdot 1}$$

$$= \frac{12 \pm \sqrt{16}}{2}$$

$$= \frac{12 \pm 4}{2}$$

$$= \frac{12 + 4}{2} \qquad \text{or} \qquad \frac{12 - 4}{2}$$

$$x = 8 \text{ or } 4$$

Solution set is $\{4, 8\}$.

Check: $4^2 - 12 \cdot 4 + 32 = 16 - 48 + 32 = 0$
$8^2 - 12 \cdot 8 + 32 = 64 - 96 + 32 = 0$

2. Solve $6x^2 = 3x^2 + 8x - 2$.

The equation is not in the form for using the quadratic formula.

$$6x^2 = 3x^2 + 8x - 2 \Leftrightarrow 3x^2 - 8x + 2 = 0$$

$$x = \frac{-b \pm \sqrt{b^2 - 4ac}}{2a}$$

$$x = \frac{-(-8) \pm \sqrt{(-8)^2 - 4 \cdot 3 \cdot 2}}{2 \cdot 3}$$

$$= \frac{8 \pm \sqrt{40}}{6}$$

$$= \frac{8 \pm 2\sqrt{10}}{6}$$

$$x = \frac{4}{3} + \frac{\sqrt{10}}{3} \quad \text{or} \quad \frac{4}{3} - \frac{\sqrt{10}}{3}$$

The equation has two irrational solutions. The solution set is
$\left\{ \frac{4}{3} + \frac{\sqrt{10}}{3}, \frac{4}{3} - \frac{\sqrt{10}}{3} \right\}$.

Check: $3\left(\frac{4}{3} + \frac{\sqrt{10}}{3}\right)^2 - 8\left(\frac{4}{3} + \frac{\sqrt{10}}{3}\right) + 2$

$$= 3\left[\frac{16}{9} + 2\left(\frac{4}{3}\right)\left(\frac{\sqrt{10}}{3}\right) + \frac{10}{9}\right] - 8\left(\frac{4}{3} + \frac{\sqrt{10}}{3}\right) + 2$$

$$= \frac{16}{3} + \frac{8\sqrt{10}}{3} + \frac{10}{3} - \frac{32}{3} - \frac{8\sqrt{10}}{3} + 2$$

$$= 0$$

$$3\left(\frac{4}{3} - \frac{\sqrt{10}}{3}\right)^2 - 8\left(\frac{4}{3} - \frac{\sqrt{10}}{3}\right) + 2$$

$$= 3\left[\frac{16}{9} - 2\left(\frac{4}{3}\right)\left(\frac{\sqrt{10}}{3}\right) + \frac{10}{9}\right] - 8\left(\frac{4}{3} - \frac{10}{3}\right) + 2$$

$$= \frac{16}{3} - \frac{8\sqrt{10}}{3} + \frac{10}{3} - \frac{32}{3} + \frac{8\sqrt{10}}{3} + 2$$

$$= 0$$

Assure students that it would not be "wrong" to give solutions as $\frac{8 + \sqrt{40}}{6}$ and $\frac{8 - \sqrt{40}}{6}$. Stress, however, that it is conventional to express radicals in simple form.

Point out that it would be acceptable to list the solutions $\frac{4 + \sqrt{10}}{3}$ and $\frac{4 - \sqrt{10}}{3}$ using the form $\frac{4 \pm \sqrt{10}}{3}$.

EXERCISES

1. $x = 5, 7$ **2.** $x = -\frac{5}{2}, \frac{3}{2}$

3. $x = 3 \pm 2\sqrt{3}$

4. $x = \frac{7 \pm \sqrt{21}}{14}$

Solve each equation by using the quadratic formula.

1. $x^2 - 12x + 35 = 0$

2. $4x^2 + 4x = 15$

3. $x(x + 9) = 3(x + 1)$

4. $x(7x - 7) = -1$

5.

a. 1 **b.** $x = 2$ **c.** $b^2 - 4ac = 0$

6.

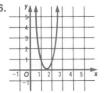

a. 1 **b.** $x = \dfrac{3}{2}$ **c.** $b^2 - 4ac = 0$

7.

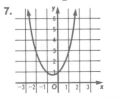

a. None **b.** $\dfrac{-1 \pm \sqrt{-3}}{2}$

c. $b^2 - 4ac = -3$ **d.** No

8.

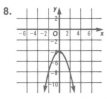

a. None **b.** $\dfrac{\pm \sqrt{-16}}{2}$

c. $b^2 - 4ac = -16$ **d.** No
9. See section notes in T.G.
a. 2 **b.** $x = 2, -2$
c. $b^2 - 4ac = 16$ **10.** 2 **11.** 1
12. 0 **13.** 0, 1 **14.** 0, 1
15. -300, 0 **16.** -300, 0
17. 500, 2 **18.** 500, 2 **19.** 800, 2
20. 800, 2

5. Draw the graph of $f(x) = x^2 - 4x + 4$.
  a. How many solutions are there for $x^2 - 4x + 4 = 0$?
  b. Solve $x^2 - 4x - 4 = 0$ by using the quadratic formula.
  c. Compute the value of $b^2 - 4ac$.
6. Draw the graph of $f(x) = 9 - 12x + 4x^2$.
  a. How many solutions are there for $9 - 12x + 4x^2 = 0$?
  b. Solve $9 - 12x + 4x^2$ by using the quadratic formula.
  c. Compute the value of $b^2 - 4ac$.
7. Draw the graph of $f(x) = x^2 + x + 1$.
  a. How many solutions are there for $x^2 + x + 1 = 0$?
  b. Solve $x^2 + x + 1 = 0$ by using the quadratic formula.
  c. Compute the value of $b^2 - 4ac$.
  d. Is there a real number equal to $\sqrt{b^2 - 4ac}$?
8. Draw the graph of $f(x) = -x^2 - 4$.
  a. How many solutions are there for $-x^2 - 4 = 0$?
  b. Solve $-x^2 - 4 = 0$ by using the quadratic formula.
  c. Compute the value of $b^2 - 4ac$.
  d. Is there a real number equal to $\sqrt{b^2 - 4ac}$?
9. Draw the graph of $f(x) = 4 - x^2$.
  a. How many solutions are there for $4 - x^2 = 0$?
  b. Solve $4 - x^2 = 0$ by using the quadratic formula.
  c. Compute the value of $b^2 - 4ac$.

Study your answers to Parts **a** and **c** of Exercises **5–9**. Then answer each question.
10. If $b^2 - 4ac > 0$, how many solutions in R do you think $ax^2 + bx + c = 0$, $a \neq 0$, has?
11. If $b^2 - 4ac = 0$, how many solutions in R do you think $ax^2 + bx + c = 0$, $a \neq 0$, has?
12. If $b^2 - 4ac < 0$, how many solutions in R do you think $ax^2 + bx + c = 0$, $a \neq 0$, has?

Compute the value of $b^2 - 4ac$. State the number of solutions in R that each quadratic equation has. You need not find the solutions, just state how many there are.
13. $25x^2 + 20x + 4 = 0$ **14.** $25x^2 - 20x + 4 = 0$
15. $25x^2 + 10x + 4 = 0$ **16.** $25x^2 - 10x + 4 = 0$
17. $25x^2 + 30x + 4 = 0$ **18.** $25x^2 - 30x + 4 = 0$
19. $25x^2 + 20x - 4 = 0$ **20.** $25x^2 - 20x - 4 = 0$

Solve each equation by using the quadratic formula. State each irrational solution in two forms. First, state the solution in simplest

21. $x = \dfrac{3 \pm \sqrt{15}}{6} \doteq 1.15, -0.15$

22. $x = \pm\dfrac{\sqrt{85}}{5} \doteq \pm 1.84$

23. $x = \dfrac{-1 \pm \sqrt{2}}{2} \doteq 0.207,$ -1.21 **24.** $x = \dfrac{-1 \pm 3\sqrt{5}}{2}$ $\doteq 2.85, -3.85$ **25.** $x = \dfrac{-6 \pm \sqrt{6}}{3} \doteq -1.84, -2.816$

26. $x = \dfrac{-7 \pm \sqrt{17}}{8} \doteq -0.360,$ -1.390 **27.** $x = 1 \pm \sqrt{2}$ $\doteq 2.414, 0.414$ **28.** $x = \dfrac{1 \pm \sqrt{3}}{2}$ $\doteq 1.366, -0.366$

29. $x = \dfrac{-5 \pm \sqrt{37}}{6} \doteq 0.180,$ -1.85 **30.** $x = -2 \pm \sqrt{7}$ $\doteq 0.646, -4.646$

radical form. Second, find the square root in the square root table and give the solution to the accuracy the table permits.

21. $6x^2 - 6x - 1 = 0$ **22.** $5x^2 = 17$

23. $6x^2 = 2x(2x - 1) + 1$ **24.** $x^2 = 11 - x$

25. $0 = -3x^2 - 12x - 10$ **26.** $7x = -(2 + 4x^2)$

27. $x(x - 2) = 1$ **28.** $2(x^2 - x) - 1 = 0$

29. $3x^2 = -5\left(x - \dfrac{1}{5}\right)$ **30.** $-3 = -x(x + 4)$

Excursions in Mathematics: Completing the Square

You have studied the special expansion of the form $(x + r)^2 = x^2 + 2rx + r^2$. The expression $x^2 + 2rx + r^2$ is called a perfect square trinomial. A quadratic equation such as $x^2 + 4x + 3 = 0$ may be solved by rewriting the equation so that the variable expression is a perfect square trinomial. To do this, follow these steps.

1. Rewrite the equation so that the variables are on one side of the equal sign and the constant term is on the other side.

$$x^2 + 4x + 3 = 0 \Leftrightarrow x^2 + 4x = -3$$

2. Add the square of one-half of the coefficient of x to each side of the equation.

$$x^2 + 4x = -3 \Leftrightarrow x^2 + 4x + 4 = -3 + 4$$
$$\Leftrightarrow x^2 + 4x + 4 = 1$$

3. Factor the quadratic expression.

$$x^2 + 4x + 4 = 1 \Leftrightarrow (x + 2)^2 = 1$$

4. Find the square root of each side of the equation. In this procedure, use the principal square root of the constant term *and* its negative.

$$(x + 2)^2 = 1 \Leftrightarrow (x + 2) = \pm\sqrt{1}$$
$$\Leftrightarrow (x + 2) = +1 \text{ or } (x + 2) = -1$$
$$\Leftrightarrow x = -1 \text{ or } x = -3$$

The solution set is $\{-1, -3\}$.
Check: $(-1)^2 + 4(-1) + 3 = 1 - 4 + 3 = 0$
$(-3)^2 + 4(-3) + 3 = 9 - 12 + 3 = 0$

This method is called completing the square.

EXERCISES

1. $x = 5, -3$ **2.** $x = 6, -8$

3. $x = 2, 5$ **4.** $x = \frac{1}{2}, 3$

5. $x = 1 \pm \sqrt{3}$

6. $x = 6 \pm 2\sqrt{3}$ **7.** No

8. $x = \frac{-b \pm \sqrt{b^2 - 4ac}}{2a}$

Even very able students may need a hint for Exercises 7 and 8. Suggest dividing both sides by a as a first step.

Solve each equation by completing the square.

1. $x^2 - 2x - 15 = 0$

2. $x^2 + 2x = 48$

3. $x^2 - 7x + 10 = 0$

4. $x^2 - \frac{7}{2}x + \frac{3}{2} = 0$

5. $x^2 - 2x - 2 = 0$

6. $x^2 - 12x + 24 = 0$

7. Can you use this method on a quadratic equation whose coefficient of x^2 is not 1?

8. Complete the square to solve $ax^2 + bx + c = 0$, $a \neq 0$. You should recognize the solution immediately.

13-9
The
Discriminant

OBJECTIVE:

To determine the number of real number solutions for $ax^2 + bx + c = 0$ by inspecting $b^2 - 4ac$.

The discussion here is not intended as "proof" of statements involving the discriminant. See T.G. regarding this.

For a quadratic equation $ax^2 + bx + c = 0$, $b^2 - 4ac$ is called the **discriminant**. The discriminant may be used to determine the number of solutions in R that a quadratic equation has. The three possibilities, that is, two, one, or no solutions, are discussed individually.

Possibility I

There are two solutions for $ax^2 + bx + c = 0$ if the graph of $f(x) = ax^2 + bx + c$ intersects the x-axis in two points.

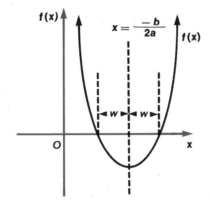 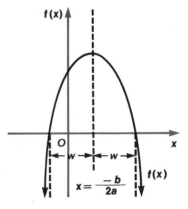

The two solutions are given by $\frac{-b}{2a} + w$ and $\frac{-b}{2a} - w$. You may remember showing that $w = \frac{\sqrt{b^2 - 4ac}}{|2a|}$. This expression for w will be positive if you can find the principal square root of $b^2 - 4ac$. Therefore, the discriminant, $b^2 - 4ac$, must be positive when there are two solutions.

Students should be guided to think as follows: "If I believe the quadratic formula always applies, what does this say about the discriminatnt $b^2 - 4ac$?"

Possibility II

There is one solution for $ax^2 + bx + c = 0$ if the graph of $f(x) = ax^2 + bx + c$ intersects the x-axis in one point.

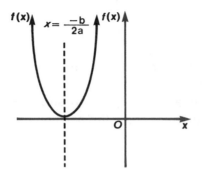 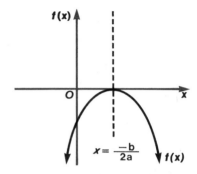

In this case, $w = 0$ because the x-intercept is on the axis of symmetry. Since $w = 0 = \dfrac{\sqrt{b^2 - 4ac}}{|2a|}$, you know that the numerator $\sqrt{b^2 - 4ac}$ must equal zero. This means that the discriminant, $b^2 - 4ac$, is 0 when there is one solution in R.

Possibility III

There are no real solutions for $ax^2 + bx + c = 0$ if the graph of $f(x) = ax^2 + bx + c$ does not intersect the x-axis.

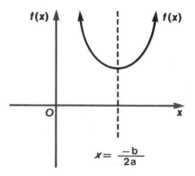 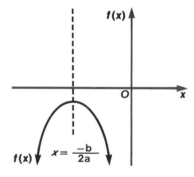

It would be disappointing if the quadratic formula produced real number solutions in this case. The only way not to have $\dfrac{\sqrt{b^2 - 4ac}}{|2a|}$ represent a real number is to have $b^2 - 4ac$ be negative. A negative number does not have a real number square root. So the discriminant, $b^2 - 4ac$, is negative when there is no real number solution.

You may use the discriminant to decide the number of solutions a quadratic equation has in R.

I. If $b^2 - 4ac > 0$, then $ax^2 + bx + c = 0$ has *two* real number solutions.

II. If $b^2 - 4ac = 0$, then $ax^2 + bx + c = 0$ has *one* real number solution.

III. If $b^2 - 4ac < 0$, then $ax^2 + bx + c = 0$ has *no* real number solutions.

EXERCISES

Use the quadratic formula to solve each equation. You may save time by following the steps in the flow chart.

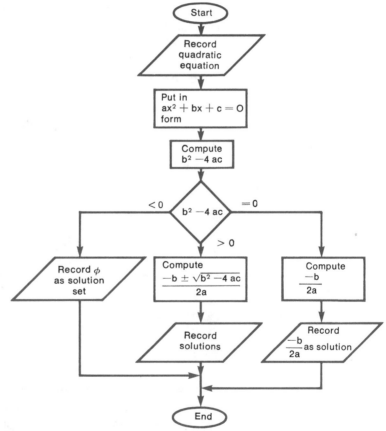

1. No real solutions 2. $x = \frac{5}{2}$

3. $x = -1, \frac{3}{2}$ 4. No real solutions

5. No real solutions 6. $z = 2, -2$

7. $x = -1, -\frac{1}{5}$

8. $x = \frac{-1 \pm \sqrt{21}}{2}$

9. No real solution

10. $x = \frac{7 \pm \sqrt{13}}{6}$

11. No real solutions

12. $\frac{23 \pm \sqrt{489}}{20}$

1. $2x^2 - 4x + 4 = 0$
3. $2x^2 - x - 3 = 0$
5. $z^2 + 4 = 0$
7. $5x^2 + 6x + 1 = 0$
9. $5 + 4x^2 = 3x$
11. $x^2 + 2 = 0$

2. $4x^2 - 20x + 25 = 0$
4. $z^2 + 11 = 0$
6. $z^2 - 4 = 0$
8. $x^2 + x - 5 = 0$
10. $3x^2 - 7x + 3 = 0$
12. $10x^2 = 23x - 1$

Exercises 13 and 14 show students what multiplying both sides of a quadratic equation by a constant does to the corresponding quadratic function.

13. a.

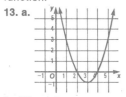

b. All points are common.
14. a. $x = 2, 4$ **b.** $x = 2, 4$
c. $x = 2, 4$ **d.** Yes
15. a.

b. $(2, 0), (-4, 0)$
16. a. $x = 2, -4$ **b.** $x = 2, -4$
c. Yes **17.** No real solution

You may need to stress for slow students that the procedure of dividing or multiplying both sides of an equation by the same number still applies.

18. $x = \frac{1}{2}$ **19.** No real solution

20. $x = \frac{5 \pm \sqrt{21}}{2}$

21. No real solution
22. No real solution
23. $x = 1, 2$ **24.** No real solution

25. $x = \pm \sqrt{2}$ **26.** $x = \frac{1}{2}, \frac{1}{7}$

27. $x = \frac{1 \pm \sqrt{5}}{2}$

28. $x = \pm \frac{2\sqrt{15}}{5}$

29. 21 rows **30.** 25 ft by 24 ft
31. 12 in. by 16 in.

---

13. a. Graph $g(x) = 2x^2 - 12x + 16$, $f(x) = x^2 - 6x + 8$, and $h(x) = \frac{1}{2} x^2 - 3x + 4$ in the same coordinate plane.

  b. What points do all the graphs have in common?

14. Use the quadratic formula to solve each equation.

  a. $2x^2 - 12x + 16 = 0$

  b. $x^2 - 6x + 8 = 0$

  c. $\frac{1}{2} x^2 - 3x + 4 = 0$

  d. Are these three equations equivalent?

15. a. Graph $g(x) = x^2 + 2x - 8$, and $f(x) = -x^2 - 2x + 8$ in the same coordinate plane.

  b. What points do the two graphs have in common?

16. Use the quadratic formula to solve each equation.

  a. $x^2 + 2x - 8 = 0$

  b. $-x^2 - 2x + 8 = 0$

  c. Are these two equations equivalent?

Use the quadratic formula to solve each equation. Use equivalent equations to make the computation easier. State irrational solutions in simplest radical form.

Sample $4x^2 - 12x + 8 = 0 \Leftrightarrow x^2 - 3x + 2 = 0$

17. $6x^2 - 24x + 30 = 0$

18. $20x^2 - 20x + 5 = 0$

19. $8x^2 = 8x - 8$

20. $3x^2 - 15x + 3 = 0$

21. $45x^2 + 15x + 30 = 0$

22. $\frac{1}{4} x^2 + \frac{x}{4} + \frac{5}{4} = 0$

23. $15x^2 + 30 = 45x$

24. $\frac{1}{6} x^2 = \frac{1}{3} x - \frac{1}{2}$

25. $12x^2 - 24 = 0$

26. $2x^2 = \frac{9x - 1}{7}$

27. $x^2 = x + 1$

28. $\frac{x}{3} (x + 3) = \frac{4}{5} + x$

Write an appropriate quadratic equation for each exercise and solve it. If a solution is meaningless, ignore it.

29. An auditorium seats 231 people. It has 10 more rows of seats than there are seats per row. How many rows of seats are there?

30. The area of a rectangular plot is 600 square feet. Its perimeter is 98 feet. What are the dimensions of the plot?

31. The lengths of sides of a rectangle are in the ratio $3:4$. The area of the rectangle is 192 square inches. What are the dimensions of the rectangle?

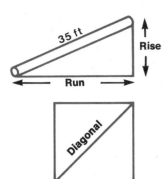

Rise

Run

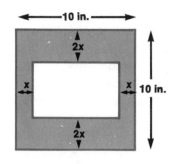

Diagonal

Side

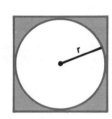

←——10 in.——→

2x

x x 10 in.

2x

32. Two consecutive odd integers are squared. The sum of the squares is 202. What are the two integers? (Hint: If the smaller of the two is x, then the larger must be $x + 2$.)

33. The product of two consecutive even integers is 1368. What are the two integers?

34. A 35-foot chute is positioned so that the rise is 7 feet less than the run. What is the rise? (Use the Pythagorean Theorem.)

35. The diagonal of a square is 6 feet longer than the length of one of its sides. How long is a side of the square?

36. When the street is widened, Mr. Jacobs loses 10 feet from the depth of his square lot. This leaves him 3000 square feet. Before the street was widened, how long was a side of his square lot?

37. The outside dimensions of a picture frame are 10 inches by 10 inches. The frame is twice as wide at the top and the bottom than at the sides. The picture area is 48 square inches. How wide is the frame at the sides?

32. -11 and -9, and 9 and 11
33. 36 and 38, -38 and -36
34. 21 ft 35. $6 + 6\sqrt{2}$ 36. 60 ft
37. 1 in. 38. $r = 1$ ft
39. $x = 20$ ft 40. 10

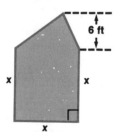

r

38. If the shaded area is $\dfrac{6}{7}$ square feet, what is the radius of the circle? Use $\pi = \dfrac{22}{7}$.

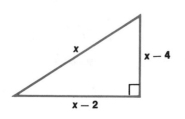

6 ft

x x

x

39. What is the value of x if the area of the entire region is 460 square feet?

x

x − 4

x − 2

40. The measurements of the sides of a right triangle are x, $x - 4$, and $x - 2$ feet. How long is the hypotenuse?

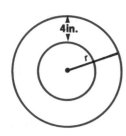

41. Four inches are cut from the edge of a disk. The remaining area is $84\frac{6}{7}$ square inches. What is the radius of the uncut part of the disk? Use $\pi = \frac{22}{7}$.

42. Lafe wishes to build a box by cutting 4 inch squares from the corners of a rectangular sheet and then folding the sides. He wants the box to contain 240 cubic inches. He also wants the box to be 4 inches longer than it is wide. How wide a sheet should he begin with?

43. Two trucks make the same run of 660 miles. The average speed of the second truck is 5 mph less than the speed of the first truck. It takes the second truck one hour longer to make the run than it takes the first truck. What is the average speed of the first truck? (Hint: Let x = average speed of the first truck.)

44. Two cars begin a 100-mile trip at the same time. The faster car averages 10 mph more than the slower car and arrives at the end of the trip 20 minutes sooner. What is the average speed for each car?

41. 9 in. 42. 14 in. 43. 60 mph
44. 2 hr at 50 mph, 1 hr 40 min at 60 mph

Chapter Summary

1. A trinomial of the form $ax^2 + bx + c$, $a \neq 0$, is called a quadratic expression.
2. Graphs of quadratic functions are in the shape of a parabola.
3. A minimum point is the point whose y-coordinate is less than or equal to the y-coordinate of every other point on the graph. The graph of $f(x) = ax^2 + bx + c$ will have a minimum point if $a > 0$.
4. A maximum point is the point whose y-coordinate is greater than or equal to the y-coordinate of every other point on the graph. The graph of $f(x) = ax^2 + bx + c$ will have a maximum point if $a < 0$.
5. The x-coordinate of the maximum or minimum point of a quadratic function $f(x) = ax^2 + bx + c$ is $\frac{-b}{2a}$. The point lies on the axis of symmetry of the parabola, $x = \frac{-b}{2a}$.

6. **I.** Assume that the graph of a quadratic function $f(x) = ax^2 + bx + c$ intersects the x-axis in two points. There are two solutions in R to the corresponding quadratic equation $ax^2 + bx + c = 0$. The solutions are the x-coordinates of the x-intercepts.

II. Assume that the graph of a quadratic function $f(x) = ax^2 + bx + c$ intersects the x-axis in one point. There is one solution in R to the corresponding quadratic equation $ax^2 + bx + c = 0$. The solution is the x-coordinate of the x-intercept.

III. Assume that the graph of a quadratic function $f(x) = ax^2 + bx + c$ does not intersect the x-axis. There are no solutions in R to the corresponding quadratic equation $ax^2 + bx + c = 0$.

7. If there are solutions in R to a quadratic equation $ax^2 + bx + c = 0$, then the solutions may be found by using the quadratic formula.

$$x = \frac{-b \pm \sqrt{b^2 - 4ac}}{2a}$$

8. The expression $b^2 - 4ac$ is called the discriminant of the quadratic equation $ax^2 + bx + c = 0$.

I. If $b^2 - 4ac > 0$, then $ax^2 + bx + c = 0$ has two solutions in R.

II. If $b^2 - 4ac = 0$, then $ax^2 + bx + c = 0$ has one solution in R.

III. If $b^2 - 4ac < 0$, then $ax^2 + bx + c = 0$ has no solutions in R.

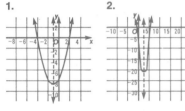

1.
2.
3.
4.

REVIEW EXERCISES

13-1, 13-2

5. min., $(\frac{1}{2}, -6\frac{1}{4})$

6. max., $(1, -6)$

7. max., $(13, 338)$

13-3

8. min., $(2, 12)$ 9. $x = 2, -1$
10. $x = 3, 6$ 11. $x = -9, 2$
12. $x = -5$

Graph each quadratic function. Sketch the axis of symmetry of each function.

1. $f(x) = x^2 + 2x - 8$ **2.** $f(x) = 3x^2 - 14x - 5$
3. $f(x) = x^2 + 5x + 4$ **4.** $f(x) = x^2 + 2x - 5$

State whether the graph of each function has a maximum or minimum point. State the coordinates of the point.

5. $f(x) = x^2 - x - 6$ **6.** $f(x) = -x^2 + 2x - 7$
7. $f(x) = -x^2 + 26x + 169$ **8.** $f(x) = x^2 - 4x + 16$

13-4, 13-5

Solve each equation by using the graphing method. Simplify each equation if necessary.

9. $x^2 - x - 2 = 0$ **10.** $x^2 - 5x = 4x - 18$
11. $x^2 + 7x = 18$ **12.** $x^2 + 10x + 25 = 0$

13. $x(5 + x) = -6$

14. $0 = -2x^2 - 5x + 3$

15. $2x^2 = 5x + 7$

16. $4x^2 + 121 = 12x$

13-7

17. Given that $\frac{1}{2}$ is a solution of $4x^2 + 2hx - 7 = 0$, find h.

18. Which of the following statements are true?
$f(x) = x^2 - 6x + 12$ cannot be
   a. negative.
   b. positive.
   c. greater than 3.
   d. less than 3.
   e. zero.

19. The perimeter of a rectangular plot of ground is 42 m. Its area is 80 m². Find the length and width of the plot. Hint: Let x be the width. Then $42 - 2x$ represents the sum of the other two sides.

20. The hypotenuse of a right triangle is 50 cm in length. The longer of the other two sides is 10 cm longer than the shorter side. Find the length of each side.

21. The sum S of the first n natural numbers is given by the formula $S = 1 + 2 + 3 + 4 + \cdots + n = \frac{1}{2}n(n + 1)$. How many consecutive natural numbers starting at 1 must be added together to give 3828?

22. The sum of two numbers is 20. If one of them is x, write an expression for the other. Find x **(a)** so that the product of the two numbers is a maximum, **(b)** so that the sum of the squares of the two numbers is a minimum.

13-8 Use the quadratic formula to solve each equation. If possible, find equivalent equations to simplify computation. Express irrational answers in simplest radical form.

23. $x^2 - 4x + 3 = 0$

24. $x(2x - 8) = -7$

25. $2x^2 = x + 3$

26. $5x^2 - 20x - 30 = 0$

27. $2x(x + 6) + 18 = 0$

28. $12x^2 = 48x - 36$

29. $\frac{x^2}{3} + 5x + \frac{1}{3} = 0$

30. $\frac{-5x^2 - 2x}{x} = -3x^2$

31. $6x\left(x + \frac{3}{2}\right) = -12$

32. $0 = 9x^2 + 6x + 1$

33. $\frac{-15}{y} = -y + 2$

34. $1.2(x^2 + 1) = -6x$

35. For each equation in Exercises **23–34** with irrational solutions, find decimal approximations for the solutions. State each answer to the accuracy the table permits.

13-9   By calculating the value of the discriminant, state the number of solutions each equation has in R. If necessary, use equivalent equations to make computation of the discriminant easier.

36. $x^2 + 2x - 3 = 0$ **37.** $16x^2 - 8x + 1 = 0$

38. $2x^2 - 16x + 30 = 0$ **39.** $-\dfrac{1}{2}x^2 = 5x - 6$

40. $4x^2 - x = -1$ **41.** $24x\left(x + \dfrac{3}{2}\right) = -6$

42. $(6x - 1)(x - 1) = 6$ **43.** $-\dfrac{2}{3}x^2 = 2(3 - 2x)$

44. $18 = 9x(4 - 3x)$ **45.** $-9x = -\dfrac{27}{5}x^2 - \dfrac{9}{5}$

Excursions in Mathematics: Parabolas

You have studied parabolas in the plane. Suppose that a portion of a parabola near its maximum or minimum point is rotated on its axis of symmetry. The outline of a dish-shaped object would be traced.

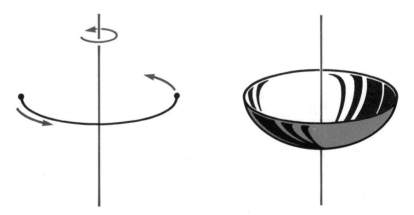

You probably have seen searchlights at a circus or store opening. To make the light stay in a narrow beam, the reflector should be in the shape pictured above. Such a reflector is called a *parabolic reflector*. Flashlights use the same principle but often use an approximation of a parabolic reflector.

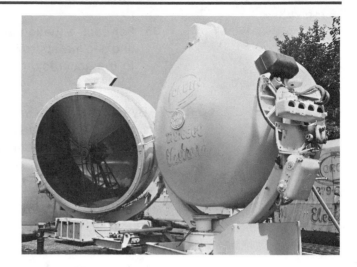

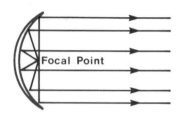

What makes the parabolic reflector special is that if the light source is placed at a special point, called the *focal point,* the light is reflected in parallel rays.

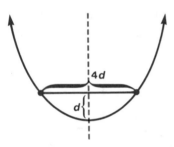

The focal point of a parabola is located on the axis of symmetry. If a horizontal line segment with its endpoints on the parabola is drawn through the focal point, its length is four times the distance from the focal point to the maximum or minimum point.

1. (0, 2) **2.** (0, 3) **3.** (0, 6)
4. $(0, \frac{1}{4})$ **5.** (0, 0)

By drawing and inspecting the graph of each equation, state the coordinates of each focal point.

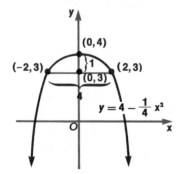

Sample   Find the focal point for $y = 4 - \frac{1}{4}x^2$.

The coordinates of the focal point are (0, 3).

1. $y = \frac{1}{8}x^2$ **2.** $12y = x^2$ **3.** $y = 1 - \frac{1}{8}x^2$

4. $y = x^2$ **5.** $4y = x^2 - 1$

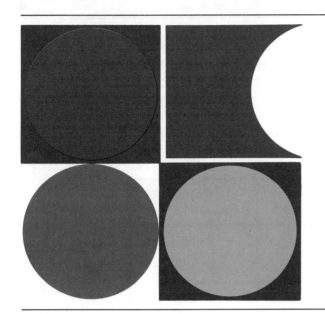

CHAPTER 14

factoring quadratic expressions

OBJECTIVE:
To factor a polynomial of degree two given a clue as to polynomial's type.

Prime Factors

To *factor* a number or expression means to write the number or expression as a product. This product is called a *factorization* of the number or expression.

EXAMPLES

Encourage students to check these examples by multiplying the factors.

Number or Expression	Factorization
12	$3 \cdot 4$
$x^2 + 10x$	$x(x + 10)$
$x^2 - x - 12$	$(x + 3)(x - 4)$
$2x^3 - 2x$	$2x(x - 1)(x + 1)$
32	$2 \cdot 2 \cdot 2 \cdot 2 \cdot 2$
32	$4 \cdot 8$
$x^3 - 4x$	$x(x^2 - 4)$
$x^3 - 4x$	$x(x - 2)(x + 2)$

From your work with whole numbers, you know that some are

prime and some are composite. A **prime number** is a whole number which cannot be factored as a product of two numbers between 1 and itself. The set of prime numbers is {2, 3, 5, 7, 11, 13, 17, 19, 23, 29, . . .}. A whole number which can be expressed as the product of two numbers between 1 and itself is called a **composite number.** A composite number can be factored into a product of prime numbers.

EXAMPLES

This is just to set the stage. The term *prime* for polynomials will be defined in Section 14-4, after enough experience to establish readiness.

Number	Prime Factorization
12	$2 \cdot 2 \cdot 3$
32	$2 \cdot 2 \cdot 2 \cdot 2 \cdot 2$
28	$2 \cdot 2 \cdot 7$
13,650	$2 \cdot 3 \cdot 5 \cdot 5 \cdot 7 \cdot 13$

In this algebra text, you also have factored some algebraic expressions. You have factored these expressions by removing common factors from the terms of a polynomial.

EXAMPLES

1. $3x^2y + 6xy^2 = 3 \cdot x \cdot y(x + 2y)$
   The common term removed is $3xy$.
2. $15abc - 5a^2b^2 - 10ab^2 = 5ab(3c - ab - 2b)$
   The common term removed is $5ab$.

When you remove a common term, you are factoring a polynomial as a monomial times a polynomial.

In Chapter 12 you expanded products by multiplying polynomials. You may think of factoring as beginning with an expansion and finding factors which would give that expansion. Keep the special products studied in Chapter 12 in mind as you factor polynomials.

$$a^2 - b^2 = (a + b)(a - b)$$
$$a^2 + 2ab + b^2 = (a + b)(a + b)$$
$$a^2 - 2ab + b^2 = (a - b)(a - b)$$
$$ac + ad + bc + bd = (a + b)(c + d)$$

EXAMPLES

1. $x^2 + 4x + 4 = (x + 2)(x + 2)$
2. $2x^2 + 5x - 12 = (2x - 3)(x + 4)$

DISCUSSION QUESTIONS

If students seem confident, these may be assigned as individual work. They are review exercises.

1. 30 **2.** 64 **3.** $5a + 10$
4. $7x^2 + 21x - 35$ **5.** $2a^2 + 8a$
6. $\frac{1}{2}ha + \frac{1}{2}hb$ **7.** $-12ax - 20bx$
8. $\pi r^3 + \pi r$ **9.** $-\frac{a}{6} + \frac{b}{8} - \frac{c}{10}$
10. $2 \cdot 2 \cdot 2 \cdot 2 \cdot 3 \cdot 3$
11. $2 \cdot 2 \cdot 2 \cdot 5 \cdot 5$ **12.** $2 \cdot 3 \cdot 3 \cdot 3 \cdot 3$
13. $x \cdot x \cdot (x - 3)$
14. $2 \cdot (a \cdot b \cdot b - 3)$
15. $2 \cdot x \cdot (2 \cdot x + 1)$
16. $2 \cdot 2 \cdot x \cdot (5 \cdot x - 2 \cdot y)$
17. $3 \cdot x \cdot x \cdot y \cdot y \cdot (2 \cdot y - 3 \cdot x)$
18. $\frac{1}{10} \cdot a \cdot b \cdot (2 \cdot a - b \cdot b)$

Find each product.

1. $2 \cdot 3 \cdot 5$

2. $2 \cdot 2 \cdot 2 \cdot 2 \cdot 2 \cdot 2$

3. $5(a + 2)$

4. $7(x^2 + 3x - 5)$

5. $2a(a + 4)$

6. $\frac{1}{2}h(a + b)$

7. $-4x(3a + 5b)$

8. $\pi r(r^2 + 1)$

9. $-\frac{1}{2}\left(\frac{a}{3} - \frac{b}{4} + \frac{c}{5}\right)$

Write each expression in factored form.

10. 144   **11.** 200   **12.** 162

13. $x^3 - 3x^2$ **14.** $4ab^2 - 6$ **15.** $4x^2 + 2x$

16. $20x^2 - 8xy$ **17.** $6x^2y^3 - 9x^3y^2$ **18.** $\frac{1}{5}a^2b - \frac{1}{10}ab^3$

EXERCISES

Exercises are presented here in related groups: 1-6 with 7-15; 16-21 with 22-30; and 31-36 with 37-48.

1. $x^2 - 1$ **2.** $9x^2 - 4$
3. $w^2 - p^2$ **4.** $25 - w^4$
5. $100 - 36z^2$ **6.** $a^2 - b^2$
7. $(w + 1)(w - 1)$
8. $(4 + x)(4 - x)$
9. $(2x + 3)(2x - 3)$
10. $(3w^2 + 5)(3w^2 - 5)$
11. $(x + y)(x - y)$
12. $(w^3 + w^4)(w^3 - w^4)$
13. $(2xy^2 + 5)(2xy^2 - 5)$
14. $(3x + 4y)(3x - 4y)$
15. $(\frac{2}{3}x + \frac{1}{4}y)(\frac{2}{3}x - \frac{1}{4}y)$
16. $x^2 + 2x + 1$
17. $9x^2 - 12x + 4$
18. $w^2 + 2wp + p^2$
19. $w^2 - 2wp + p^2$
20. $4x^2 + 4xy^2 + y^4$
21. $a^2 + 2ab + b^2$
22. $(x + 3)(x + 3)$
23. $(x - 3)(x - 3)$
24. $(y + 4)(y + 4)$
25. $(r + s)(r + s)$
26. $(w - 5)(w - 5)$
27.-36. See section notes in T.G.

Expand each product.

1. $(x + 1)(x - 1)$

2. $(3x + 2)(3x - 2)$

3. $(w + p)(w - p)$

4. $(5 - w^2)(5 + w^2)$

5. $(10 - 6z)(10 + 6z)$

6. $(a - b)(a + b)$

Each expression is written as $a^2 - b^2$. Factor each expression as a product $(a + b)(a - b)$.

7. $w^2 - 1$ **8.** $16 - x^2$ **9.** $4x^2 - 9$

10. $9w^4 - 25$ **11.** $x^2 - y^2$ **12.** $w^6 - w^8$

13. $4x^2y^4 - 25$ **14.** $9x^2 - 16y^2$ **15.** $\frac{4}{9}x^2 - \frac{1}{16}y^2$

Expand each product.

16. $(x + 1)(x + 1)$ **17.** $(3x - 2)(3x - 2)$
18. $(w + p)(w + p)$ **19.** $(w - p)^2$
20. $(2x + y^2)(2x + y^2)$ **21.** $(a + b)^2$

Factor each expression as a product.

22. $x^2 + 6x + 9$ **23.** $x^2 - 6x + 9$ **24.** $y^2 + 8y + 16$
25. $r^2 + 2rs + s^2$ **26.** $w^2 - 10w + 25$ **27.** $9d^2 + 6d + 1$
28. $h^2 - 26h + 169$ **29.** $x^2 - 4x + 4$ **30.** $2x + 4ax + 2a^2x$

Expand each product.

31. $(x + 2)(x + 1)$ **32.** $(y - 2)(y + 3)$ **33.** $(x - 5)(x + 10)$
34. $(x - 10)(x + 5)$ **35.** $(d + 7)(d + 1)$ **36.** $(x + c)(x + d)$

37. $(x + 2)(x + 3)$
38. $(x - 2)(x - 3)$
39. $(x - 3)(x + 2)$
40. $(x + 3)(x - 2)$
41. $(x + 5)(x - 4)$
42. $(x - 4)(x + 2)$
43. $(x + 1)(x + 2)$
44. $(x + 3)(x + 5)$
45. $(x + 1)(x + 12)$
46. $(x - 3)(x - 4)$
47. $(x + 7)(x + 3)$
48. $(x + 1)(x + 8)$

Factor each expression as a product $(x + a)(x + b)$, where a, $b \in Z$.

37. $x^2 + 5x + 6$ 38. $x^2 - 5x + 6$ 39. $x^2 - x - 6$

40. $x^2 + x - 6$ 41. $x^2 + x - 20$ 42. $x^2 - 2x - 8$

43. $x^2 + 3x + 2$ 44. $x^2 + 8x + 15$ 45. $x^2 + 13x + 12$

46. $x^2 - 7x + 12$ 47. $x^2 + 10x + 21$ 48. $x^2 + 9x + 8$

14-2
Reducing Fractions

OBJECTIVE:

To reduce (simplify) algebraic fractions involving factoring of the types covered in Section 14-1.

A fraction may be reduced by first finding the factors of the numerator and the denominator. Then both numerator and denominator may be divided by any common factor.

EXAMPLES

The concept of reducing or simplifying fractions has already been established. The new material in this section requires work with expressions like those of Section 14-1.

1. $\dfrac{36}{27} = \dfrac{2 \cdot 2 \cdot 3 \cdot 3}{3 \cdot 3 \cdot 3}$

    $= \dfrac{2 \cdot 2}{3}$

    $= \dfrac{4}{3}$

2. $\dfrac{55}{168} = \dfrac{5 \cdot 11}{2 \cdot 2 \cdot 2 \cdot 3 \cdot 7}$

This fraction cannot be reduced. There are no common factors in the numerator and denominator.

Algebraic fractions may be reduced in the same way. Restrictions must be placed on the variables in the denominator of an algebraic fraction. The values for the variables which would make the denominator zero are excluded.

EXAMPLES

Stress the fact that denominators may not be zero.

1. $\dfrac{x^2 + 2xy + y^2}{x^2 - y^2} = \dfrac{(x + y)(x + y)}{(x + y)(x - y)}$

              $= \dfrac{x + y}{x - y}$ if $x \neq y, -y$

2. $\dfrac{2x - 6}{x^2 + x - 12} = \dfrac{2(x - 3)}{(x + 4)(x - 3)}$

              $= \dfrac{2}{x + 4}$ if $x \neq -3, 4$

EXERCISES

1. $\frac{1}{3}$ 2. $\frac{4}{3}$ 3. 2   4. $\frac{13}{35}$ 5. $\frac{110}{273}$

6. $\frac{7}{15}$ 7. $\frac{1}{a-b}$ 8. $\frac{1}{2a+3b}$

9. $\frac{3}{p-1}$ 10. $\frac{4}{3}$ 11. $\frac{y+2}{4}$

12. $\frac{1}{x+1}$ 13. $\frac{a}{x-5}$

14. $\frac{1}{3(a+3)}$ 15. $\frac{x+2}{x+4}$

16. $\frac{a+b}{a-b}$ 17. $\frac{1}{x-3}$

18. $\frac{w+z}{w+2z}$ 19. $\frac{(x-2)(x+2)}{(x-3)(x+3)}$

20. $\frac{(x+2)(x+1)}{(x-2)(x-1)}$

Encourage students to check the types of factors covered in Section 14-1 in case of difficulty. Remind them *always* to begin by removing the common term.

Write each fraction in lowest terms. First factor the numerator and the denominator. Then divide the numerator and the denominator by the common factors. Assume that all denominators are nonzero.

1. $\frac{4}{12}$ **2.** $\frac{16}{12}$ **3.** $\frac{26}{13}$

4. $\frac{26}{70}$ **5.** $\frac{110}{273}$ **6.** $\frac{21}{45}$

7. $\frac{a+b}{a^2-b^2}$ **8.** $\frac{3}{6a+9b}$ **9.** $\frac{3p-3}{p^2-2p+1}$

10. $\frac{4x+20}{3x+15}$ **11.** $\frac{y^2-y-6}{4y-12}$ **12.** $\frac{x+2}{x^2+3x+2}$

13. $\frac{ax+5a}{x^2-25}$ **14.** $\frac{a-3}{3a^2-27}$ **15.** $\frac{x^2-x-6}{x^2+x-12}$

16. $\frac{a^2-b^2}{a^2-2ab+b^2}$ **17.** $\frac{x+3}{x^2-9}$ **18.** $\frac{w^2+2wz+z^2}{w^2+3wz+2z^2}$

19. $\frac{x^2-4}{x^2-9}$ **20.** $\frac{x^2+3x+2}{x^2-3x+2}$

OBJECTIVE:

14-3

To remove the common term of a polynomial so that "new" coefficients in the polynomial are relatively prime integers.

Relatively Prime Coefficients

Relatively prime may be a concept new to students.

Two integers which have only 1 or -1 as common factors are *relatively prime.*

EXAMPLES

Integers	Factorization	Relatively Prime ?
4 and 9	$4 = 2 \cdot 2$ and $9 = 3 \cdot 3$	Yes
6 and -15	$6 = \boldsymbol{3} \cdot 2$ and $15 = \boldsymbol{3} \cdot (-5)$	No
-27 and 16	$-27 = 3 \cdot 3 \cdot (-3)$ and $16 = 2 \cdot 2 \cdot 2 \cdot 2$	Yes
27 and 15	$27 = \boldsymbol{3} \cdot 3 \cdot 3$ and $15 = \boldsymbol{3} \cdot 5$	No

More than two integers are relatively prime if there is no factor common to all except 1 or -1.

EXAMPLES

Integers	Factorization		Relatively Prime ?
4, 9, −6, and 12	$4 = 2 \cdot 2$ $-6 = 2 \cdot (-3)$	$9 = 3 \cdot 3$ $12 = 2 \cdot 2 \cdot 3$	Yes
4, −6, 12, and −16	$4 = \mathbf{2} \cdot 2$ $12 = \mathbf{2} \cdot 2 \cdot 3$	$-6 = -3 \cdot \mathbf{2}$ $-16 = \mathbf{2} \cdot 2 \cdot 2 \cdot (-2)$	No
7, −21, and 42	$7 = 1 \cdot \mathbf{7}$ $42 = 2 \cdot 3 \cdot \mathbf{7}$	$21 = -3 \cdot \mathbf{7}$	No
7, 9, and −14	$7 = 1 \cdot 7$ $-14 = 2 \cdot (-7)$	$9 = 3 \cdot 3$	Yes

It often is easier to factor an expression if common terms are factored first. The Distributive Property may be used to do this.

EXAMPLE

Factor $5x^3yz^2 - 20x^2yz^2 + 15xyz^2$.

Notice that each term has $5xyz^2$ as a factor. Use the Distributive Property to remove this common term from the expression.

$$5x^3yz^2 - 20x^2yz^2 + 15xyz^2 = 5xyz^2(x^2 - 4x + 3)$$

For polynomials with coefficients in Z, ask if removing *all* common factors guarantees that the resulting polynomial will have relatively prime coefficients.

The polynomial $x^2 - 4x + 3$ can be factored as $(x - 3)(x - 1)$. If these steps are combined, you will have the expression factored as follows.

$$5x^3yz^2 - 20x^2yz^2 + 15xyz^2 = 5xyz^2(x^2 - 4x + 3)$$
$$= 5xyz^2(x - 3)(x - 1)$$

When a polynomial has rational numbers as coefficients, begin factoring by using the Distributive Property so that the polynomial is in the following form.

(rational number) · (polynomial with integers as coefficients)

When doing this, try to find a rational number so that the coefficients of the polynomial are relatively prime.

EXAMPLE

Factor $\frac{2}{3}x^2 - \frac{8}{3}x + 2$.

Remind slow students that $2 = \frac{6}{3}$. See T.G. for a step- by-step procedure which slow students may find helpful.

Use the Distributive Property to factor out $\frac{1}{3}$.

$$\frac{2}{3}x^2 - \frac{8}{3}x + 2 = \frac{1}{3}(2x^2 - 8x + 6)$$

Use the Distributive Property again to make the coefficients relatively prime.

$$= \frac{2}{3}(x^2 - 4x + 3)$$

Factor $x^2 - 4x + 3$.

$$= \frac{2}{3}(x - 3)(x - 1)$$

In each of the examples, the coefficients of the polynomial are made relatively prime. Then the common term is factored out of the polynomial.

EXAMPLES

Suggest to students that they may combine steps to remove the common term.

1. Factor $2x^4 + \frac{7}{3}x^3 - \frac{1}{3}x^2$.

$$2x^4 + \frac{7}{3}x^3 - \frac{1}{3}x^2 = \frac{6}{3}x^4 + \frac{7}{3}x^3 - \frac{1}{3}x^2$$

$$= \frac{1}{3}(6x^4 + 7x^3 - x^2)$$

$$= \frac{1}{3}x^2(6x^2 + 7x - 1)$$

2. Factor $\frac{4}{3}x^4y + 2x^3y - \frac{5}{6}x^2y - xy$.

$$\frac{4}{3}x^4y + 2x^3y - \frac{5}{6}x^2y - xy = \frac{8}{6}x^4y + \frac{12}{6}x^3y - \frac{5}{6}x^2y - \frac{6}{6}xy$$

$$= \frac{1}{6}(8x^4y + 12x^3y - 5x^2y - 6xy)$$

$$= \frac{1}{6}xy(8x^3 + 12x^2 - 5x - 6)$$

EXERCISES

1. RP **2.** 4 **3.** 7 **4.** RP **5.** 2 **6.** 4 **7.** 3 **8.** 3

Write *RP* if each set of integers is relatively prime. If the set is not relatively prime, name the largest whole number which is a factor of each integer.

1. $\{3, 4, 5\}$ **2.** $\{12, -16, 24\}$

3. $\{-63, 7, -49\}$ **4.** $\{39, 13, -26, 3\}$

5. $\{2, 4, 6, 8, \ldots\}$ **6.** $\{-12, -24, 48, 64\}$

7. $\{-6, -9, -12, -24\}$ **8.** $\{-6, -9, -12, -18\}$

9. $3(2x^2 - x + 3)$

10. $\frac{1}{3}(x^2 - 2x + 3)$

11. $\frac{5}{3}(9a^3 - a^2b - 6b^3)$

12. $\frac{1}{12}(8x - 3y + xy)$

It may be helpful for students to do some of these in class.

13. $\frac{1}{3}(9x^5y + 1)$

14. $\frac{1}{4}(2x^3 - x^2 - 3x + 4)$

15. $\frac{1}{2}(8 + 16x^2y^2 - x^4y^4)$

16. $\frac{1}{4}(2x^3 - 8xy + 3y^3)$

17. $3(10x^4 - 21x^2 - 10)$

18. $\frac{1}{7}(10x^4 - 21x^2 - 10)$

19. $xy^2(x^2 - 2x + 1)$

20. $ab\ (a^2 - b^2)$

21. $\frac{1}{2}x^3(2x^2 - 3x - 1)$

22. $\frac{1}{6}x^2yz\ (2x^2 - 3x - 1)$

23. $\frac{1}{8}(5x - 4xw + 3xw^2 - 2xw^3 + w^4)$ 24. $3s^2w\ (5 - 4w + 3w^2 - 2w^3 + w^4)$

25. $\frac{x^2y^2z}{2}\ (x^2 - 2xy + y^2)$

26. $7a^3b^3c^2\ (2a^2 + 5ab - 3b^2)$

Allow students to combine steps in removing the common term.

Make the coefficients of each polynomial relatively prime integers by factoring out a rational number.

Sample $\frac{2}{5}x^2 + xy - 2y^2 = \frac{2}{5}x^2 - \frac{5}{5}xy - \frac{10}{5}y^2$

$$= \frac{1}{5}(2x^2 + 5xy - 10y^2)$$

9. $6x^2 - 3x + 9$

10. $\frac{1}{3}x^2 - \frac{2}{3}x + 1$

11. $15a^3 - \frac{5}{3}a^2b - 10b^3$

12. $\frac{2}{3}x - \frac{1}{4}y + \frac{1}{12}xy$

13. $3x^5y + \frac{1}{3}$

14. $\frac{1}{2}x^3 - \frac{1}{4}x^2 - \frac{3}{4}x + 1$

15. $4 + 8x^2y^2 - \frac{1}{2}x^4y^4$

16. $\frac{1}{2}x^3 - 2xy + \frac{3}{4}y^3$

17. $30x^4 - 63x^2 - 30$

18. $\frac{10}{7}x^4 - 3x^2 - \frac{10}{7}$

If necessary, make the coefficients of each polynomial relatively prime. Then, factor out any common variable term of the expression.

19. $x^3y^2 - 2x^2y^2 + xy^2$

20. $a^3b - ab^3$

21. $x^5 - \frac{3}{2}x^4 - \frac{1}{2}x^3$

22. $\frac{1}{3}x^4yz - \frac{1}{2}x^3yz - \frac{1}{6}x^2yz$

23. $\frac{5}{8}x - \frac{1}{2}xw + \frac{3}{8}xw^2 - \frac{1}{4}xw^3 + \frac{w^4}{8}$

24. $15s^2w - 12s^2w^2 + 9s^2w^3 - 6s^2w^4 + 3s^2w^5$

25. $\frac{x^2y^2z}{2} - x^3y^3z + \frac{x^2y^4z}{2}$

26. $14a^5b^3c^2 + 35a^4b^4c^2 - 21a^3b^5c^2$

For Exercises 27-32, remind students to keep in mind the procedures learned in Section 14-1.

Make the coefficients relatively prime for each expression and remove the common term. Then try to further factor the polynomial factor into a product of two binomials.

Samples 1. $5x^3 + 20x^2 + 15x = 5x(x^2 + 4x + 3)$
$$= 5x\ (x + 3)(x + 1)$$

2. $2s^2w^2 - 2s^2w + \frac{s^2}{2} = s^2\left(2w^2 - 2w + \frac{1}{2}\right)$
$$= \frac{1}{2}s^2(4w^2 - 4w + 1)$$
$$= \frac{1}{2}s^2(2w - 1)(2w - 1)$$

27. $3x(x+1)(x+1)$
28. $b(a+5)(a-4)$
29. $\frac{1}{2}(x-3)(x+2)$
30. $3w^2(3w+1)(2w-1)$
31. $\frac{z^3}{3}(w+3)(w+3)$
32. $7a^2b^2(a+b)(a+2b)$

27. $3x^3 + 6x^2 + 3x$

29. $\frac{x^2}{2} - \frac{x}{2} - 3$

31. $\frac{w^2z^3}{3} + 2wz^3 + 3z^3$

28. $a^2b + ab - 20b$

30. $18w^4 - 3w^3 - 3w^2$

32. $7a^4b^2 + 21a^3b^3 + 14a^2b^4$

14-4
Prime Polynomials

OBJECTIVE:

To classify a simple quadratic expression as reducible, irreducible, not prime, or prime.

Some students may need to be reminded of the definition of *degree*.

The definitions in this section are for polynomials which have rational numbers as coefficients. A polynomial is **completely factored** when it is written as a product of factors such that the following statements are true.

> **1.** None of the polynomial factors can be factored further as a product of polynomials with lower degree.
> **2.** The coefficients of the terms of the polynomial factors are relatively prime integers.

EXAMPLES

Stress that the original polynomial had degree 3, but that the factors have lower degree.

1. $x^2y^3 - 2xy^3 - 15y^3 = y^3(x^2 - 2x - 15)$
$$= y^3(x-5)(x+3)$$

2. $w^3 + \frac{w^2}{6} - \frac{5w}{2} = w\left(w^2 + \frac{w}{6} - \frac{5}{2}\right)$
$$= \frac{1}{6}w(6w^2 + w - 15)$$
$$= \frac{1}{6}w(3w + 5)(2w - 3)$$

A polynomial which cannot be factored into polynomials of lower degree is called **irreducible.** An irreducible polynomial which has relatively prime integers as coefficients is called **prime.** With these definitions, you may say that a polynomial is **completely factored** when it is expressed as a product of primes.

EXAMPLES

Give adequate time to discussion of these examples.

Polynomial	Is it Irreducible?	Is it Prime?	Further Factorization
$x^2 + x + 2$	Yes	Yes	
$x^2 - 3x - 10$	No	No	$(x-5)(x+2)$
$3x^3 + 3$	Yes	No	$3(x^2 + 1)$

Polynomial	Is it Irreducible?	Is it Prime?	Further Factorization
$2x + 4$	Yes	No	$2(x + 2)$
$3x^2 + 6xy + 3y^2$	No	No	$3(x + y)(x + y)$
$3x^2 + 5xy + 3y^2$	Yes	Yes	

You may wonder how to determine if a polynomial is irreducible. For many polynomials, the decision is difficult. With practice, the task becomes easier. For certain types of polynomials there are tests which may be used. You will find it helpful now to keep in mind the special products that you have already studied. One such product is $(x + n)(x + m) = x^2 + (n + m)x + nm$.

EXAMPLE

Stress this. Use more examples if necessary.

Expand the product $(x + 3)(x + 5)$.

$$(x + 3)(x + 5) = x^2 + 5x + 3x + 15$$
$$= x^2 + (5 + 3)x + 15$$
$$= x^2 + 8x + 15$$
$$ax^2 + bx + c$$

Notice that $3 + 5 = b$ and $3 \cdot 5 = c$.

EXERCISES

1. $x^2 + x - 30$ **2.** $x^2 - x - 30$
3. $x^2 + 3x - 18$ **4.** $x^2 - 3x - 18$
5. $x^2 + 8x + 12$ **6.** $x^2 - 8x + 12$
7. $x^2 + 4x - 12$ **8.** $x^2 - 4x - 12$
9. $x^2 + 6x + 9$ **10.** $x^2 - 6x + 9$
11. $x^2 - 9$ **12.** $(x + 7)(x - 6)$
13. $(x - 7)(x + 6)$
14. $(x + 7)(x - 4)$
15. $(x - 7)(x + 4)$
16. $(x + 3)(x + 5)$
17. $(x - 3)(x - 5)$

For Exercises 12-22, suggest that students first write $(x \quad)$ $(x \quad)$ and then examine different ways factors of the constant term could have resulted in $x^2 + bx + c$.
18. $(x + 5)(x - 3)$
19. $(x - 5)(x + 3)$
20. $(x + 4)(x + 4)$
21. $(x - 4)(x - 4)$
22. - 24. See section notes in T.G.

Expand each product.

1. $(x - 5)(x + 6)$ **2.** $(x + 5)(x - 6)$ **3.** $(x - 3)(x + 6)$
4. $(x + 3)(x - 6)$ **5.** $(x + 2)(x + 6)$ **6.** $(x - 2)(x - 6)$
7. $(x - 2)(x + 6)$ **8.** $(x + 2)(x - 6)$ **9.** $(x + 3)(x + 3)$
10. $(x - 3)(x - 3)$ **11.** $(x + 3)(x - 3)$

Factor each polynomial completely. None of the polynomials are prime. If you have difficulty, study the expansions in Exercises **1–11** and look for patterns.

12. $x^2 + x - 42$ **13.** $x^2 - x - 42$ **14.** $x^2 + 3x - 28$
15. $x^2 - 3x - 28$ **16.** $x^2 + 8x + 15$ **17.** $x^2 - 8x + 15$
18. $x^2 + 2x - 15$ **19.** $x^2 - 2x - 15$ **20.** $x^2 + 8x + 16$
21. $x^2 - 8x + 16$ **22.** $x^2 - 16$

Factor each polynomial completely. Begin by removing common terms and making the coefficients relatively prime integers.

23. $3x^3 + 3x^2 - 18x$ **24.** $\dfrac{w^2}{3} - \dfrac{w^2}{3} - 2w$

25. $2b^3(a + 10)(a - 7)$

26. $\frac{s}{3}(w - 10)(w + 7)$

27. $a^2b^2(c + 3)(c + 5)$

28. $100(x^3 - 8x^2 + 15)$

29. $2x^2(x + 5)(x - 3)$

30. $\frac{x^2}{2}(x - 5)(x + 3)$

31. $\frac{1}{5}(x + 5)(x + 5)$

32. $4a^2c^3(b - 5)(b - 5)$

33. $3x^2z^2(y + 5)(y - 5)$

34. NP, R **35.** P **36.** NP, R

37. NP, I **38.** NP, R **39.** NP, I

40. NP, I

Consider allowing slow students to work with others on Exercises 34-40.

25. $2a^2b^3 + 6ab^3 - 140b^3$

26. $\frac{sw^2}{3} - sw - \frac{70s}{3}$

27. $a^2b^2c^2 + 8a^2b^2c + 15a^2b^2$

28. $100x^3 - 800x^2 + 1500x$

29. $2x^4 + 4x^3 - 30x^2$

30. $\frac{x^4}{2} - x^3 - \frac{15}{2}x^2$

31. $\frac{x^2}{5} + 2x + 5$

32. $4a^2b^2c^3 - 40a^2bc^3 - 100a^2c^3$

33. $3x^2y^2z^2 - 75x^2z^2$

Write P(prime) or NP(not prime) for each polynomial. For each polynomial that is not prime, write I(irreducible) or R(reducible).

34. $x^2 - 4x + 4$ **35.** $x^2 - 3x + 4$ **36.** $x^2 - 5x + 4$

37. $3x^2 - 6x + 12$ **38.** $2x^2 - x - 15$ **39.** $4x^2 - 2x + 30$

40. $6x^2 + 17x + 12$

14-5

Factoring Quadratic Expressions

OBJECTIVE:

To factor $ax^2 + bx + c$ where $a, b, c \in Z$, and $\sqrt{b^2 - 4ac} \in W$.

Expressions of the form $ax^2 + bx + c$, $a \neq 0$, may be called **quadratic expressions** in x. Look closely at the following multiplications of $(px + m)(qx + n)$ where $p, q, m, n \in Z$.

EXAMPLES

Stress the origin of the coefficient of the linear term in these examples.

1. $(3x - 2)(x + 5) = 3x^2 + 13x - 10$

The coefficient of x^2 was determined by multiplication ①. The constant term was determined by multiplication ④. The coefficient of x was determined by the sum of multiplications ② and ③.

2. $(5x - 2)(3x - 7) = 15x^2 - 41x + 14$

You may think of factoring a quadratic expression as "filling in the blanks." To factor $6x^2 - 7x - 5$, you must fill in the blanks to make a true sentence.

$$6x^2 - 7x - 5 = (\_\,x\,\_\,\_)(\_\,x\,\_\,\_)$$

Trying to factor this expression may seem like a guessing game.

There are several ways to find $6x^2$ as a product of two factors. One way is to multiply $6x \cdot 1x$. Try 6 and 1 as coefficients for x.

$$(6x \_\_)(1x \_\_) = 6x^2 - 7x - 5$$

Different pairs of factors for -5 are $-1 \cdot 5$, $5 \cdot (-1)$, $1 \cdot (-5)$, and $-5 \cdot 1$. Check these possible factors.

$$(6x - 1)(1x + 5) = 6x^2 + 29x - 5$$
$$(6x + 5)(1x - 1) = 6x^2 - 1x - 5$$
$$(6x + 1)(1x - 5) = 6x^2 - 29x - 5$$
$$(6x - 5)(1x + 1) = 6x^2 + 1x - 5$$

None of these polynomials is $6x^2 - 7x - 5$. When you multiply you need -7 as the coefficient of x.

Think of another way to find $6x^2$ as a product. Try $3x$ and $2x$.

$$(3x \_\_)(2x \_\_) = 6x^2 - 7x - 5$$

Try the factors of -5 with these factors for $6x^2$.

$$(3x - 1)(2x + 5) = 6x^2 + 13x - 5$$
$$(3x + 5)(2x - 1) = 6x^2 + 7x - 5$$
$$(3x + 1)(2x - 5) = 6x^2 - 13x - 5$$
$$(3x - 5)(2x + 1) = 6x^2 - 7x - 5$$

At last a factorization is found.

$$6x^2 - 7x - 5 = (3x - 5)(2x + 1)$$

You tried eight different ways to fill in the blanks before you found the factors of $6x^2 - 7x - 5$. As you gain experience, you will find it much easier to find the factors of a quadratic expression.

EXERCISES

1. $(x + 7)(x - 8)$
2. $(x - 7)(x + 8)$
3. $(2x - 3)(5x - 1)$
4. $(-3x + 2)(x + 2)$
5. $(-3x + 5)(2x + 7)$
6. $(+3x + 5)(-2x + 7)$
7. $7x$ **8.** $-7x$

Place signs in the factors of each quadratic expression to make a true sentence.

1. $x^2 - x - 56 = (x \underline{\quad ? \quad} 7)(x \underline{\quad ? \quad} 8)$
2. $x^2 + x - 56 = (x \underline{\quad ? \quad} 7)(x \underline{\quad ? \quad} 8)$
3. $10x^2 - 17x + 3 = (2x \underline{\quad ? \quad} 3)(5x \underline{\quad ? \quad} 1)$
4. $-3x^2 - 4x + 4 = (-3x \underline{\quad ? \quad} 2)(x \underline{\quad ? \quad} 2)$
5. $-6x^2 - 11x + 35 = (-3x \underline{\quad ? \quad} 5)(2x \underline{\quad ? \quad} 7)$
6. $-6x^2 + 11x + 35 = (3x \underline{\quad ? \quad} 5)(-2x \underline{\quad ? \quad} 7)$

Write the value for b which makes each sentence true.

7. $12x^2 + bx - 10 = (3x - 2)(4x + 5)$
8. $12x^2 + bx - 10 = (3x + 2)(4x - 5)$

9. $12x^2 + 23x + 10 = (3x + b)(4x + 5)$
10. $12x^2 − 23x + 10 = (3x − 2)(bx − 5)$
11. $36x^2 + 60x + 25 = (6x + 5)(6x + b)$
12. $36x^2 + bx − 25 = (6x + 5)(6x − 5)$
13. $15x^2 − 31x + 14 = (−3x + 2)(bx + 7)$
14. $15x^2 + 31x + 14 = (3x + b)(5x + 7)$

Factor each polynomial as a product $(px + m)(qx + n)$ where p, q, m, and $n \in Z$.

15. $4x^2 − 4x − 3$ **16.** $5x^2 + 12x + 4$ **17.** $6x^2 + 5x + 1$
18. $3x^2 + 8x + 5$ **19.** $x^2 + 10x + 16$ **20.** $9x^2 − 12x + 4$
21. $7x^2 + 34x − 5$ **22.** $9x^2 + 16x − 4$

Write *NF* (not factorable) for each polynomial which cannot be written as a product $(px + m)(qx + n)$ where p, q, m, and $n \in Z$. Factor the polynomial when possible.

23. $2x^2 + 4x + 3$ **24.** $2x^2 + 5x + 3$ **25.** $2x^2 + 7x + 3$
26. $2x^2 + 3x + 3$ **27.** $x^2 + x + 1$ **28.** $x^2 + 2x + 1$
29. $9x^2 − 9x − 4$ **30.** $9x^2 − 9x + 6$

Exercises 23-30 serve the same purpose as Exercises 34-40 of the previous section. They set the stage for Section 14-6.

14-6
More Factoring

OBJECTIVE:

To determine if $ax^2 + bx + c$, where $a, b, c \in Z$, is irreducible by examining $b^2 − 4ac$.

Suppose that $ax^2 + bx + c$ is a quadratic expression where a, b, and c are integers. How can you tell if the expression is irreducible? If you know the expression is irreducible, you should not spend time trying to factor it.

You really wish to know if integers p, q, m, and n can be found to make the following sentence true.

$$(px + m)(qx + n) = ax^2 + bx + c$$

Suppose that you have found such integers.

$$ax^2 + bx + c = (px + m)(qx + n)$$
$$= pqx^2 + pnx + qmx + mn$$
$$= pqx^2 + (pn + qm)x + mn$$

Then the following must be true.

$$a = pq \qquad b = pn + qm \qquad c = mn$$

EXAMPLES

1. $12x^2 + 29x + 14 = (3x + 2)(4x + 7)$
$\|\|\|\|\|\|\|$
$abcpmqn$
$a = 12 = 3 \cdot 4 = pq$
$b = 29 = 3 \cdot 7 + 4 \cdot 2 = pn + qm$
$c = 14 = 2 \cdot 7 = mn$

2. $-6x^2 + 28x - 30 = (3x - 5)(-2x + 6)$

$$\underset{a}{\|} \quad \underset{b}{\|} \quad \underset{c}{\|} \quad \underset{p}{\|} \quad \underset{m}{\|} \quad \underset{q}{\|} \quad \underset{n}{\|}$$

$$a = -6 = 3 \cdot (-2) = p \cdot q$$
$$b = 28 = 3 \cdot 6 + -2 \cdot (-5) = pn + qm$$
$$c = -30 = -5 \cdot 6 = mn$$

You could check more examples, but in each case the following is true.

If $ax^2 + bx + c = (px + m)(qx + n)$, then
$$a = pq$$
$$b = pn + qm$$
$$c = mn$$

When you worked with quadratic equations and the quadratic formula, you found that the discriminant was very important. You now will see how $b^2 - 4ac$ behaves when a quadratic expression can be factored into $(px + m)(qx + n)$.

$$\begin{aligned} b^2 - 4ac &= (pn + qm)^2 - 4 \cdot pq \cdot mn \\ &= p^2n^2 + 2pnqm + q^2m^2 - 4pqmn \\ &= p^2n^2 - 2pnqm + q^2m^2 \\ &= (pn - qm)^2 \end{aligned}$$

Since p, n, q, and m are all integers, $pn - qm$ must be an integer. If an integer is squared, the result is a perfect square. This perfect square is an element of $\{0, 1, 4, 9, 16, 25, 36, \ldots\}$.

Since $b^2 - 4ac = (pn - qm)^2$, $b^2 - 4ac$ is a perfect square.

EXAMPLES

1. The expression $x^2 - x - 12$ can be factored.

$$a = 1, b = -1, c = -12$$
$$\begin{aligned} b^2 - 4ac &= (-1)^2 - 4 \cdot 1 \cdot (-12) \\ &= 1 + 48 \\ &= 49 \\ &= 7^2 \end{aligned}$$

2. You have seen that $12x^2 + 29x + 14$ can be factored.

$$a = 12, b = 29, c = 14$$

Notice that it is assumed that students accept that if $a_1x^2 + b_1x + c_1 = a_2x^2 + b_2x + c_2$ then $a_1 = a_2$, $b_1 = b_2$, and $c_1 = c_2$.

See T.G. concerning this assumption.

Here it is simply stated that
$\sqrt{b^2 - 4ac} \in W$ implies
$ax^2 + bx + c$ can be factored.
See T.G.

$$b^2 - 4ac = 29^2 - 4 \cdot 12 \cdot 14$$
$$= 841 - 672$$
$$= 169$$
$$= 13^2$$

3. The quadratic expression $-6x^2 + 28x - 30$ can be factored.

$$a = -6,\ b = 28,\ c = 30$$
$$b^2 - 4ac = 28^2 - 4 \cdot (-6) \cdot (-30)$$
$$= 784 - 720$$
$$= 64$$
$$= 8^2$$

Assume a, b, and c are integers. If $ax^2 + bx + c$ is reducible, then $b^2 - 4ac$ is a perfect square.

The following statements are also true. If $b^2 - 4ac$ is a perfect square, then $ax^2 + bx + c$ is reducible. If $b^2 - 4ac$ is not a perfect square, the expression is irreducible. The following test may be used to decide if a quadratic expression is factorable.

Ask students if it would have
been helpful to know this for
Exercises 34-40 of Section 14-4
and for Exercises 23-30 of
Section 14-5.

If a, b, and c are integers, then $ax^2 + bx + c$ can be factored into $(px + m)(qx + n)$ where p, q, m, and n are integers *if and only if* $b^2 - 4ac$ is a perfect square.

EXERCISES

1. $2(x + 2)(x - 1)$ **2.** NF
3. NF **4.** $(x - 1)(x + 1)$
5. $(2x - 3)(2x - 3)$
6. $(3x - 4)(4x + 3)$ **7.** NF
8. $(x + 2)(x - 1)$ **9.** NF
10. $(2x + 1)(-x + 1)$
11. $4s(w - 2)(w + 2)$

Suggest that (sw) be thought of
as the variable for Exercise 11.

12. $\frac{1}{3}(q - 2)(q - 4)$
13. $500a^2(x + 7)(x - 2)$
14. $\frac{a}{6}(2x + 3)(x - 5)$

Factor each quadratic expression for which $b^2 - 4ac$ is a perfect square.

1. $2x^2 + 2x - 4$ **2.** $3x^2 + 2x - 4$ **3.** $x^2 + 1$
4. $x^2 - 1$ **5.** $4x^2 - 12x + 9$ **6.** $12x^2 - 7x - 12$
7. $12x^2 - 7x + 12$ **8.** $x^2 + x - 2$ **9.** $x^2 + x + 2$
10. $-2x^2 + x + 1$

Give a complete factorization for each expression.

11. $4sw^2 - 16s$ **12.** $\frac{q^2}{3} - 2q + \frac{8}{3}$

13. $500a^2x^2 + 2500a^2x - 7000a^2$ **14.** $\frac{ax^2}{3} - \frac{7ax}{6} - \frac{5a}{2}$

15. $\frac{1}{4}(4x + 1)(4x + 1)$

16. $(x + y)(x + y)$

17. $5x^2y^2(x + y)(x + y)$

18. $(6x - 5)(x + 2)$

19. $\frac{1}{6}(3x + 1)(2x + 1)$

20. $(7x + 4)(5x - 11)$

15. $4x^2 + 2x + \frac{1}{4}$

17. $5x^4y^2 + 10x^3y^3 + 5x^2y^4$

19. $x^2 + \frac{5}{6}x + \frac{1}{6}$

16. $x^2 + 2xy + y^2$

18. $6x^2 + 7x - 10$

20. $35x^2 - 57x - 44$

14-7
More Reducing

OBJECTIVE:

To express a product or quotient of rational expressions in reduced (simplified) form.

Complicated algebraic fractions may be reduced by first factoring. After the numerator and the denominator have been factored into prime factors, divide them by any common factors. When the numerator and denominator are relatively prime, the fraction is in lowest terms.

EXAMPLES

Stress the fact that the denominators may not be zero.

1. $\dfrac{12x^3y^2 + 20x^2y^2 - 8xy^2}{2x^4y - 8x^2y} = \dfrac{4xy^2(3x^2 + 5x - 2)}{2x^2y(x^2 - 4)}$

$$= \dfrac{2 \cdot 2 \cdot x \cdot y \cdot y \cdot (x + 2)(3x - 1)}{2 \cdot x \cdot x \cdot y \cdot (x + 2)(x - 2)}$$

$$= \dfrac{2y(3x - 1)}{x(x - 2)}$$

$$= \dfrac{6xy - 2y}{x^2 - 2x} \quad \text{if } \begin{cases} x \neq -2, 2, 0 \\ y \neq 0 \end{cases}$$

2. $\dfrac{(x^2 - 9)(x^2 + x - 6)}{(x^2 + 6x + 9)(x - 2)} = \dfrac{(x + 3)(x - 3)(x + 3)(x - 2)}{(x + 3)(x + 3)(x - 2)}$

$$= \dfrac{x - 3}{1}$$

$$= x - 3 \quad \text{if } x \neq -3, 2$$

When multiplying or dividing algebraic fractions, your work may be made easier if as a first step numerators and denominators are factored.

EXAMPLES

1. Factor. $\dfrac{x^2 - 9}{x^2 + x} \cdot \dfrac{x^2 - 1}{x - 3} = \dfrac{(x - 3)(x + 3)}{x(x + 1)} \cdot \dfrac{(x - 1)(x + 1)}{(x - 3)}$

Write the product. $= \dfrac{(x - 3)(x + 3)(x - 1)(x + 1)}{x(x + 1)(x - 3)}$

Reduce. $= \dfrac{(x + 3)(x - 1)}{x}$

$$= \dfrac{x^2 + 2x - 3}{x} \quad \text{if } x \neq 0, 3, -1$$

2. Use the definition of division.

$$\frac{a^2 - 1}{6a^3b^5} \div \frac{a + 1}{3a^3b^3} = \frac{a^2 - 1}{6a^3b^5} \cdot \frac{3a^3b^3}{a + 1}$$

Factor.

$$= \frac{(a + 1)(a - 1)}{6a^3b^5} \cdot \frac{3a^3b^3}{a + 1}$$

$$= \frac{(a + 1)(a - 1) \cdot 3a^3b^3}{6a^3b^5(a + 1)}$$

Reduce.

$$= \frac{a - 1}{2b^2} \quad \text{if} \begin{cases} a \neq 0, 1 \\ b \neq 0 \end{cases}$$

EXERCISES

Watch closely for abuses of canceling by students.

1. $\frac{x - 4}{x + 4}$ 2. $\frac{x - 2}{x + 3}$ 3. $\frac{2x - 1}{2x}$

4. 1 5. $\frac{x^2 + x + 1}{x + 2}$ 6. $\frac{2x + 1}{2x + 3}$

7. $3x$ 8. $\frac{2x^2 + x + 3}{(x - 1)(x + 1)}$ 9. $\frac{2x - 1}{2x + 1}$

10. $\frac{4x^2 + 7x - 2}{4x^2 - 4x - 3}$ 11. $\frac{2yx^3}{5ab^2}$

12. $\frac{y(x + y)}{x}$ 13. $\frac{(a - b)^2}{2b(a + b)}$

14. $m + n$ 15. $\frac{7a}{3}$ 16. 1

17. $\frac{ax}{2(x + y)}$ 18. $\frac{2(y + 3)}{27x}$

19. $\frac{4(a - 5)}{3(3a - 5)}$ 20. $\frac{(a - b)(a + b)^2}{a^3 b^3}$

Reduce each fraction to lowest terms. Assume that all denominators are nonzero.

1. $\frac{x^2 - 16}{x^2 + 8x + 16}$

2. $\frac{x^2 + x - 6}{x^2 + 6x + 9}$

3. $\frac{4x^2 - 4x + 1}{4x^2 - 2x}$

4. $\frac{(x^2 + x - 6)(x^2 + 3x - 4)}{(x^2 + 7x + 12)(x^2 - 3x + 2)}$

5. $\frac{(x - 1)(x^2 + x + 1)}{x^2 + x - 2}$

6. $\frac{2x^4 - 7x^3 - 4x^2}{2x^4 - 5x^3 - 12x^2}$

7. $\frac{3x(7x - 1)(4x + 5)}{28x^2 + 31x - 5}$

8. $\frac{(2x^2 + x + 3)(2x + 3)}{(2x^2 + x - 3)(x + 1)}$

9. $\frac{2x^2 + 5x - 3}{2x^2 + 7x + 3}$

10. $\frac{4x^2 + 7x - 2}{4x^2 - 4x - 3}$

Perform the indicated operation. Be sure that your answer is in lowest terms. Assume that all denominators are nonzero.

11. $\frac{14ab^2}{25x^2y} \cdot \frac{15x^5y^2}{21a^2b^4}$

12. $\frac{x^2 - y^2}{x} \div \frac{(x - y)}{y}$

13. $\frac{5a^2 - 5ab}{(a + b)^2} \div \frac{10ab}{a^2 - b^2}$

14. $\frac{m^2n}{mn + m^2} \cdot \frac{m^2 + 2mn + n^2}{mn}$

15. $\frac{x^2 - y^2}{15a} \cdot \frac{35a^2}{(x + y)(x - y)}$

16. $\frac{a^2 + a - 2}{a^2 - 4} \div \frac{a - 1}{a - 2}$

17. $\frac{5x^2 + 5xy - 10y^2}{x^2 - y^2} \cdot \frac{ax}{10x + 20y}$

18. $\frac{2x + 14}{3y - 9} \div \frac{9x^2 + 63x}{y^2 - 9}$

19. $\frac{4a^2 - 12a - 40}{a^2 + 5a + 6} \cdot \frac{a^2 + 2a - 3}{9a^2 - 24a + 15}$

20. $\frac{a^2 - b^2}{ab^2} \div \frac{a^2b}{a + b}$

OBJECTIVE:

To solve $ax^2 + bx + c = 0$ where $\sqrt{b^2 - 4ac} \in W$ by factoring.

You already know how to solve quadratic equations by using the quadratic formula, $x = \dfrac{-b \pm \sqrt{b^2 - 4ac}}{2a}$.

EXAMPLES

Going through these examples carefully should be an adequate review of the quadratic formula. However, a few more examples may be required for slow students.

1. Solve $2x^2 + x - 15 = 0$.

$$a = 2, \ b = 1, \ c = -15$$
$$b^2 - 4ac = 1^2 - 4 \cdot 2 \cdot (-15) = 1 + 120 = 121$$
$$x = \frac{-1 \pm \sqrt{121}}{4}$$
$$x = \frac{-1 \pm 11}{4}$$
$$x = \frac{-12}{4} \text{ or } \frac{10}{4}$$

The solution set is $\left\{ -3, \dfrac{5}{2} \right\}$.

2. Solve $2x^2 + 5x + 1 = 0$.

$$a = 2, \ b = 5, \ c = 1$$
$$b^2 - 4ac = 5^2 - 4 \cdot 2 \cdot 1 = 25 - 8 = 17$$
$$x = \frac{-5 \pm \sqrt{17}}{4}$$
$$x \doteq \frac{-5 \pm 4.12}{4}$$
$$x \doteq \frac{-5 + 4.12}{4} \quad \text{or} \quad \frac{-5 - 4.12}{4}$$
$$x \doteq -.22 \text{ or } -2.28$$

Accurate to two decimal places, the solution set is $\{ -.22, -2.28 \}$.

3. Solve $2x^2 + 2x + 5 = 0$.

$$a = 2, \ b = 2, \ c = 5$$
$$b^2 - 4ac = 2^2 - 4 \cdot 2 \cdot 5 = 4 - 40 = -36$$

Since $b^2 - 4ac$ is negative, there are no real number solutions. The solution set is $\varnothing$.

Notice in Example **1** that the discriminant is a perfect square. This means that $2x^2 + x - 15$ can be factored. Rewrite the equation in factored form.

$$2x^2 + x - 15 = 0 \Leftrightarrow (2x - 5)(x + 3) = 0$$

Stress this fact. → If a product of two numbers is 0, then one or the other of these numbers must be 0. In mathematics the word *or* is used in an inclusive sense. That is, if a product of two numbers is 0, then one or the other or both of these numbers must be 0.

EXAMPLE

Provide discussion time for this example. The reasoning involving *or* may evade slow students at first.

If $(2x - 5)(x + 3) = 0$, then either $2x - 5 = 0$ or $x + 3 = 0$. This means that $x = \dfrac{5}{2}$ or $x = -3$.

$$2x - 5 = 0 \Leftrightarrow 2x = 5 \qquad or \qquad x + 3 = 0 \Leftrightarrow x = -3$$
$$\Leftrightarrow x = \dfrac{5}{2}$$

Check for $x = \dfrac{5}{2}$.

$$(2x - 5)(x + 3) = 0$$
$$\left(2 \cdot \dfrac{5}{2} - 5\right)\left(\dfrac{5}{2} + 3\right) \stackrel{?}{=} 0$$
$$(5 - 5)\left(\dfrac{5}{2} + 3\right) \stackrel{?}{=} 0$$
$$0 \cdot \left(\dfrac{5}{2} + 3\right) \stackrel{?}{=} 0$$
$$0 = 0$$

Check for $x = -3$.

$$(2x - 5)(x + 3) = 0$$
$$(2 \cdot (-3) - 5)(-3 + 3) \stackrel{?}{=} 0$$
$$(-6 - 5)(-3 + 3) \stackrel{?}{=} 0$$
$$(-11) \cdot 0 \stackrel{?}{=} 0$$
$$0 = 0$$

The solution set, $\left\{\dfrac{5}{2}, -3\right\}$, is the same whether the equation is solved by factoring or by the quadratic formula.

EXAMPLES

1. Solve $4x^2 - 24x + 35 = 0$ by factoring.

$$4x^2 - 24x + 35 = 0 \Leftrightarrow (2x - 5)(2x - 7) = 0$$
$$2x - 5 = 0 \Leftrightarrow 2x = 5 \qquad or \qquad 2x - 7 = 0 \Leftrightarrow 2x = 7$$
$$\Leftrightarrow x = \dfrac{5}{2} \qquad\qquad\qquad \Leftrightarrow x = \dfrac{7}{2}$$

The solution set is $\left\{\dfrac{5}{2}, \dfrac{7}{2}\right\}$.

Using the quadratic formula, the same solution set is obtained.

$$x = \dfrac{-b \pm \sqrt{b^2 - 4ac}}{2a}$$
$$x = \dfrac{24 \pm \sqrt{(-24)^2 - 4 \cdot 4 \cdot 35}}{2 \cdot 4}$$

$$= \frac{24 \pm \sqrt{16}}{8}$$

$$= \frac{24 \pm 4}{8}$$

$$= \frac{20}{8} \text{ or } \frac{28}{8}$$

$$x = \frac{5}{2} \text{ or } \frac{7}{2}$$

The solution set is $\left\{\frac{5}{2}, \frac{7}{2}\right\}$.

In this example you see that when $b^2 - 4ac$ is a perfect square, the equation may be solved by factoring *or* by using the quadratic formula.

2. The quadratic equation $2x^2 + 5x + 1 = 0$ has $b^2 - 4ac = 17$. Since 17 is not a perfect square, the factoring method cannot be used to solve this equation. The quadratic formula should be used to find the solutions.

3. The quadratic equation $2x^2 + 2x + 5 = 0$ has $b^2 - 4ac = -36$. Since this is a negative number, there are no real number solutions.

EXERCISES

1. $x = 2, 5$ **2.** $x = 8, -7$
3. $x = -5$ **4.** $x = 4, -4$
5. $x = 3, -8$ **6.** $x = \frac{1}{2}, -10$
7. $x = \frac{5}{2}$ **8.** $x = -\frac{5}{2}, 3$

9. $x = \frac{4}{3}, -\frac{5}{2}$ **10.** $x = \frac{1}{4}, 6$

11. $x = 7, 9$ **12.** $x = \frac{7}{2}, -1$

13. $x = -\frac{7}{2}, 1$ **14.** $x = -\frac{9}{2}, -\frac{1}{2}$

15. $x = \frac{3}{2}$ **16.** $x = \frac{3}{4}, 3$

17. ϕ **18.** $x = \frac{-1 \pm \sqrt{13}}{2}$

Solve each equation by factoring.

1. $x^2 - 7x + 10 = 0$
2. $x^2 - x - 56 = 0$
3. $x^2 + 10x + 25 = 0$
4. $x^2 - 16 = 0$
5. $x^2 + 5x - 24 = 0$
6. $2x^2 + 19x - 10 = 0$
7. $4x^2 = 20x - 25$
8. $15 + x = 2x^2$
9. $6x^2 + 7x - 20 = 0$
10. $4x^2 = 25x - 6$

Solve each equation by factoring and then by the quadratic formula.

11. $x^2 - 16x + 63 = 0$
12. $2x^2 - 5x - 7 = 0$
13. $2x^2 + 5x - 7 = 0$
14. $4x^2 + 20x + 9 = 0$
15. $4x^2 - 12x + 9 = 0$
16. $4x^2 - 15x + 9 = 0$

Calculate $b^2 - 4ac$ for each equation.
a. If $b^2 - 4ac$ is a perfect square, solve the equation by factoring.
b. If $b^2 - 4ac$ is nonnegative but not a perfect square, solve the equation by the quadratic formula.
c. If $b^2 - 4ac$ is negative, write $\varnothing$ as the solution set.
17. $x^2 - x + 3 = 0$
18. $x^2 + x - 3 = 0$

19. $x^2 + 2x - 3 = 0$ **20.** $x^2 + 3x + 2 = 0$

21. $x^2 + 3x - 2 = 0$ **22.** $6x^2 + 7x + 2 = 0$

23. $6x^2 + 2x + 7 = 0$ **24.** $6x^2 + 2x + 1 = 0$

25. $6x^2 + 2x - 1 = 0$ **26.** $9x^2 - 82x + 1 = 0$

27. In the same coordinate plane, graph $y = x - 1$ and $y = x - 3$.

  a. At what point does $y = x - 1$ cross the x-axis?

  b. At what point does $y = x - 3$ cross the x-axis?

  c. In the same coordinate plane as Parts **a** and **b,** graph $y = (x - 1)(x - 3) = x^2 - 4x + 3$.

  d. At what points does $y = x^2 - 4x + 3$ cross the x-axis?

28. Factor $4x^2 - 4x - 15$ into $(px + m)(qx + n)$.

  a. In the same coordinate plane, graph $y = 4x^2 - 4x - 15$, $y = px + m$ and $y = qx + n$.

  b. What value of x makes $px + m = 0$?

  c. What value of x makes $qx + n = 0$?

  d. What values of x make $4x^2 - 4x - 15 = 0$?

Write a quadratic equation with integer coefficients which has the given solution set.

Sample Write a quadratic equation with $\left\{\dfrac{1}{3}, -\dfrac{3}{4}\right\}$ as a solution set.

$$x = \frac{1}{3} \Leftrightarrow \quad 3x = 1 \quad \text{or} \quad x = -\frac{3}{4} \Leftrightarrow \quad 4x = -3$$

$$\Leftrightarrow 3x - 1 = 0 \qquad\qquad \Leftrightarrow 4x + 3 = 0$$

$$(3x - 1)(4x + 3) = 0 \Leftrightarrow 12x^2 + 5x - 3 = 0$$

Check to see that this equation has the stated solutions.

29. $\{1, 4\}$ **30.** $\{-2, 3\}$ **31.** $\left\{\dfrac{1}{3}, \dfrac{1}{4}\right\}$

32. $\left\{-\dfrac{2}{5}, \dfrac{2}{5}\right\}$ **33.** $\left\{\dfrac{2}{5}\right\}$ **34.** $\{3\}$

35. $\varnothing$ **36.** $\{\sqrt{2}, -\sqrt{2}\}$

Solve each problem.

Sample The area of the floor of a rectangular workshop is 144 m². The length is 10 m more than the width. Find the length and width of the workshop.

Let ℓ m represent the length. Then $(\ell - 10)$ m represents the width.

37. 8m by 15m
38. 6 and 13, −13 and −6
39. −14 and −12, 12 and 14
40. 1 **41.** $\frac{3}{2}$ or $\frac{2}{3}$
42. $N = 20$ **43.** $t = \frac{8}{5}, 8$
First time is the stone going up.; Second time is the stone coming back down.
44. $t = 1, 2$

$$\ell(\ell - 10) = 144 \Leftrightarrow \ell^2 - 10\ell - 144 = 0$$
$$\Leftrightarrow (\ell + 8)(\ell - 18) = 0$$
$$\text{Since } \ell > 0, \ \ell + 8 \neq 0$$
$$\ell - 18 = 0 \Leftrightarrow \ell = 18$$

Thus, the length is 18 m and the width is $(18 - 10)$ m, or 8 m.

37. The area of a rectangular floor is 120 m². The length is 7 m more than the width. Find the length and width.

38. Two numbers differ by 7. Their product is 78. What are the two numbers?

39. Two numbers differ by 2. Their product is 168. What are the two numbers?

40. The sum of a number and its reciprocal is 2. Find the number.

41. The sum of a number and its reciprocal is $\frac{13}{6}$. Find the number.

42. The sum S of the first n natural numbers is given by the formula $S = \frac{1}{2} n(n + 1)$. How many consecutive natural numbers, starting at 1, must be added together to give 210?

43. A stone is thrown vertically upward at 48 m/s. Its height h meters after t seconds is given approximately by the formula, $h = 48t - 5t^2$. Use this formula to find the number of seconds it takes for the stone to be 64 m high. Explain your answer.

44. A stone is projected vertically upward at 14.7 m/s. Its height, h meters after t seconds, is given approximately by the formula $h = 14.7t - 4.9t^2$. Use this formula to find the number of seconds it takes for the stone to be 9.8 meters high.

Excursions in Mathematics: Writing Quadratic Equations

Suppose that r_1 and r_2 are the solutions of a quadratic equation. In the previous exercises, you wrote a quadratic equation when the solutions were given. Use r_1 and r_2 to write a quadratic equation.

$$x = r_1 \Leftrightarrow x - r_1 = 0 \quad \text{or} \quad x = r_2 \Leftrightarrow x - r_2 = 0$$
$$\Leftrightarrow (x - r_1)(x - r_2) = 0$$
$$\Leftrightarrow x^2 - r_1 x - r_2 x + r_1 r_2 = 0$$
$$\Leftrightarrow x^2 - (r_1 + r_2)x + r_1 r_2 = 0$$

A general quadratic equation may be written as $ax^2 + bx + c = 0$, $a \neq 0$. Multiply both sides of this equation by $\frac{1}{a}$.

$$\frac{1}{a}(ax^2 + bx + c) = 0 \cdot \frac{1}{a} \Leftrightarrow x^2 + \frac{b}{a}x + \frac{c}{a} = 0$$

Compare the two ways of writing a general quadratic equation.

$$x^2 - (r_1 + r_2)x + r_1 r_2 = 0$$

$$x^2 + \frac{b}{a}x + \frac{c}{a} = 0$$

The relationship between the solutions, or *roots*, r_1 and r_2 and the coefficients a, b, and c of the general quadratic equation now can be seen.

$$\frac{b}{a} = -(r_1 + r_2) \Leftrightarrow -\frac{b}{a} = r_1 + r_2$$

$$\frac{c}{a} = r_1 r_2$$

That is, the sum of the roots of any quadratic equation equals $-\frac{b}{a}$ and the product of the roots equals $\frac{c}{a}$. How might this be used to write quadratic equations when the roots are given?

EXAMPLES

1. Write the quadratic equation which has the roots $r_1 = -4$ and $r_2 = -2$.

$$r_1 + r_2 = -4 + -2 = -6$$
$$r_1 r_2 = -4 \cdot -2 = 8$$

The equation is $x^2 + 6x + 8 = 0$.

2. Write the quadratic equation which has the roots $r_1 = \frac{1}{4}$ and $r_2 = \frac{3}{2}$.

$$r_1 + r_2 = \frac{1}{4} + \frac{3}{2} = \frac{7}{4}$$

$$r_1 r_2 = \frac{1}{4} \cdot \frac{3}{2} = \frac{3}{8}$$

$$x^2 - \frac{7}{4}x + \frac{3}{8} = 0 \Leftrightarrow 8x^2 - 14x + 3 = 0$$

EXERCISES

1. $x^2 + 3x + 2 = 0$
2. $x^2 + 2x - 15 = 0$
3. $x^2 - 9 = 0$
4. $4x^2 + 4x - 3 = 0$

Write a quadratic equation which has each pair of roots as solutions.

1. $r_1 = -1, r_2 = -2$

2. $r_1 = 3, r_2 = -5$

3. $r_1 = -3, r_2 = 3$

4. $r_1 = \frac{1}{2}, r_2 = -\frac{3}{2}$

5. $2x^2 - 11x + 15 = 0$
6. $x^2 - 3 = 0$
7. $x^2 - 23x + 120 = 0$
8. $8x^2 + 34x + 15 = 0$
9. $3x^2 - 10x - 8 = 0$
10. $32x^2 - 18x + 1 = 0$

5. $r_1 = \dfrac{5}{2}, r_2 = 3$

6. $r_1 = \sqrt{3}, r_2 = -\sqrt{3}$

7. $r_1 = 8, r_2 = 15$

8. $r_1 = -\dfrac{1}{2}, r_2 = -\dfrac{15}{4}$

9. $r_1 = 4, r_2 = -\dfrac{2}{3}$

10. $r_1 = \dfrac{1}{2}, r_2 = \dfrac{1}{16}$

Chapter Summary

1. To factor a number or expression means to write the number or expression as a product.
2. A prime number is a whole number which cannot be factored as a product of two numbers between 1 and itself.
3. Fractions may be reduced by factoring both numerator and denominator and then dividing by any common terms.
4. Two integers which have only 1 or -1 as common factors are relatively prime.
5. A polynomial which cannot be factored into polynomials of lower degree is called irreducible. An irreducible polynomial which has relatively prime integers as coefficients is called prime.
6. A polynomial is completely factored when it is written as a product of primes.
7. If $ax^2 + bx + c = (px + m)(qx + n)$, then $a = pq$, $b = pn + qm$, and $c = mn$.
8. If $a, b, c \in Z$, then $ax^2 + bx + c$ can be factored into $(px + m)(qx + n)$ where p, q, m and $n \in Z$ if $b^2 - 4ac$ is a perfect square.
9. Factoring may be used to solve a quadratic equation when $b^2 - 4ac$ is a perfect square.
10. A quadratic equation may be found when only its solutions are known.

REVIEW EXERCISES 14-1

Write each expression in factored form.

1. 240   **2.** $4an + 2n^2$ **3.** $a^2x - ax^2$

4. $3xy - 9y^2$ **5.** $2\pi R + 2\pi r$ **6.** $6anx - 3abn$

14-2

1. $2^4 \cdot 3 \cdot 5$ **2.** $2n(z^2 + n)$
3. $ax(a - x)$ **4.** $3y(x - 3y)$
5. $2\pi(R + r)$ **6.** $3u(2x - b)$
7. $\dfrac{3}{8}$ **8.** $\dfrac{x^2}{a}$ **9.** $\dfrac{7a}{8}$ **10.** $\dfrac{1}{1 + y}$
11. $\dfrac{x - 1}{x + n}$ **12.** $\dfrac{x + 2}{x - 2}$

Write each fraction in lowest terms. Assume that all denominators are nonzero.

7. $\dfrac{12}{32}$ **8.** $\dfrac{ax^3}{a^2x}$ **9.** $\dfrac{49ax}{56a^2x}$

10. $\dfrac{x}{x + xy}$ **11.** $\dfrac{nx - n}{n^2 + nx}$ **12.** $\dfrac{x^2 + 4x + 4}{x^2 - 4}$

14-3

Make the coefficients of each quadratic expression relatively prime integers by factoring out a rational number.

13. $9a^2 - 36y^2$ **14.** $3b^2 + 18b - 27$

15. $4c^2 - 28c - 100$ **16.** $\dfrac{1}{5}x^2 + \dfrac{3}{5}x + 6$

17. $\dfrac{1}{8}y^2 - \dfrac{1}{4}y + \dfrac{3}{16}$ **18.** $\dfrac{1}{3}x^2 + \dfrac{1}{9}xy + 4y^2$

13. $9\,(a^2 - 4y^2)$
14. $3\,(b^2 + 6b - 9)$
15. $4\,(c^2 - 7c + 25)$
16. $\dfrac{1}{5}(x^2 + 3x + 30)$
17. $\dfrac{1}{16}(2y^2 - 4y + 3)$
18. $\dfrac{1}{9}(3x^2 + xy + 36y^2)$

14-4

Factor each polynomial completely.

19. $p^2 + 4p - 5$ **20.** $b^2x^2 - 4b$

21. $a^2bx^2 + 2a^2bx - 3a^2b$ **22.** $\dfrac{y^2}{3} + 2y + 3$

19. $(p + 5)(p - 1)$
20. $b(bx^2 - 4)$
21. $a^2b\,(x + 3)(x - 1)$
22. $\dfrac{1}{3}(y + 3)^2$

14-5

Write the value for b which makes each sentence true.

23. $2r^2 - 9rs - 5s^2 = (2r + s)(r - b)$
24. $2r^2 + 9rs - 5s^2 = (2r - b)(r + 5s)$
25. $12 - 11p + 2p^2 = (4 - p)(3 - b)$
26. $2p^2 + 11p + 12 = (2p + 3)(p + b)$

23. $b = 5s$ **24.** $b = s$
25. $b = 2p$ **26.** $b = 4$ **27.** NF

14-6

Use the discriminant to decide if each quadratic expression can be factored over Q. Factor any quadratic for which $b^2 - 4ac$ is a perfect square.

27. $x^2 + x + 2$ **28.** $a^2 + 15a + 26$
29. $4xy + 4y^2 + x^2$ **30.** $2 - 2x - 3x^2$
31. $4p^2 + 16p + 15$ **32.** $2x - 1 - x^2$
33. $5p^2 - 14pq + 3q^2$ **34.** $4 - 9a + 2a^2$
35. $6x^2 + 13x + 5$ **36.** $4x^2 - xy - 3y^2$
37. $6x^2 + 13x + 7$ **38.** $6x^2 + 13x - 6$
39. $9a^2 - 3ab - b^2$ **40.** $6x^2 + 24x + 25$

28. $(a + 2)(a + 13)$
29. $(x + 2y)^2$ **30.** NF
31. $(2p + 5)(2p + 3)$
32. $(-x + 1)(x - 1)$
33. NF **34.** $(2a - 1)(a - 4)$
35. $(2x + 1)(3x + 5)$
36. $(4x + 3y)(x - y)$
37. $(6x + 7)(x + 1)$
38. NF **39.** NF **40.** NF **41.** $\dfrac{1}{7}$

14-7

Reduce each fraction. Factor both numerator and denominator and divide by any common terms. Assume that all denominators are nonzero.

41. $\dfrac{x + y}{7x + 7y}$ **42.** $\dfrac{4a^2 - 8ab}{a - 2b}$

43. $\dfrac{x^2 - 7x - 18}{2x + 4}$ **44.** $\dfrac{x^2 - y^2}{6x^2 - 5xy - y^2}$

45. $\dfrac{a^2 + 2ab + b^2}{(a + b)^2}$ **46.** $\dfrac{m^2 - \ell m}{\ell^2 - m^2}$

42. $4a$ **43.** $\dfrac{x - 9}{2}$
44. $\dfrac{x + y}{6x + y}$ **45.** 1 **46.** $\dfrac{-m}{(\ell + m)}$

Find the solution set for each quadratic equation. Use $b^2 - 4ac$ to determine if the quadratic expression is factorable. If it is not factorable, solve by using the quadratic formula. Approximate your answers to 3 significant digits.

47. $x^2 - 3x + 2 = 0$ **48.** $b^2 - 7b - 18 = 0$

49. $q^2 + 7q + 3 = 0$ **50.** $2x^2 = x + 1$

51. $3v^2 - 10v + 3 = 0$ **52.** $2a^2 + 5a - 3 = 0$

53. $y^2 + 3y - 8 = 0$ **54.** $15 - 2y - y^2 = 0$

55. $4x^2 - 7x + 12 = 0$ **56.** $9d^2 + 24d + 16 = 0$

57. $4x^2 + 13x + 2 = 0$

58. The sum S of the first n natural numbers is given by the formula $S = \frac{1}{2} n(n + 1)$. How many consecutive natural numbers, starting at 1, must be added to give 66?

59. Suppose a baseball is thrown. Its height h meters above the ground after traveling x meters horizontally is given approximately by the formula $h = 10x - 0.5x^2$.

   a. Find the height of the baseball at a horizontal distance of 20 m.

   b. At what distances horizontally is its height 18 m?

   c. How far is the ball from the thrower when it hits the ground?

   d. How far has the ball traveled horizontally when it reaches its greatest height? (Hint: Sketch the graph.)

60. The sum S of the first n even numbers is given by the formula $S = n(n + 1)$. How many consecutive even numbers, starting at 2, add up to 156?

61. The hypotenuse of a right triangle is 50 cm long. The longer of the other two sides exceeds the shorter by 10 cm. Find the lengths of these two sides. Calculate the area of the triangle.

62. A triangle has a perimeter of 56 cm and a hypotenuse 25 cm long. Calculate the lengths of its other sides.

47. $\{1, 2\}$ **48.** $\{9, -2\}$
49. $\{-0.459, -6.54\}$ **50.** ϕ
51. $\frac{1}{3}$ 3 **52.** $\frac{1}{2}$ -3
53. $\{1.70, -4.70\}$ **54.** $\{-5, 3\}$
55. ϕ **56.** $\frac{-4}{3}$
57. $\{-.162, -3.09\}$
58. $N = 11$ **59. a.** $h = 0$ m
b. 18 m and 2 m **c.** 20 m **d.** 10 m
60. $N = 12$ **61.** 30 cm, 40 cm
62. 7 cm, 24 cm

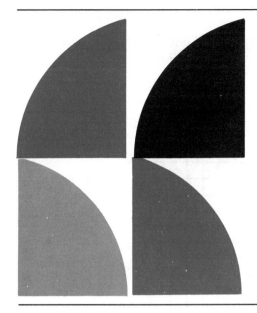

CHAPTER 15

quadratic inequations

15-1
Quadratic
Inequations

OBJECTIVE:

To solve a quadratic inequation by inspecting the graph of its corresponding quadratic function.

A *quadratic inequation* is an inequation which may be written in one of the following forms where $a \neq 0$.

$$ax^2 + bx + c < 0$$
$$ax^2 + bx + c > 0$$
$$ax^2 + bx + c \leq 0$$
$$ax^2 + bx + c \geq 0$$
$$ax^2 + bx + c \neq 0$$

Let x be a variable on R. To solve a quadratic inequation means to find all values of x which make the sentence true.

EXAMPLES

Remind students that this is the same technique used early in Chapter 13.

1. Solve $x^2 + 2x - 3 < 0$ by drawing and inspecting a graph. The problem may be restated in the following way. For which values of x is the graph of $f(x) = x^2 + 2x - 3$ *below* the x-axis?

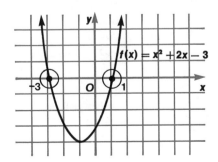

As you can see in the graph, $f(x) < 0$ if x is between -3 and 1. The solution set is $\{x \mid -3 < x < 1, x \in R\}$.

2. Solve $x^2 - 4 \geq 0$ by drawing and inspecting a graph. The problem may be restated in the following way. For which values of x is the graph of $f(x) = x^2 - 4$ *on* or *above* the x-axis?

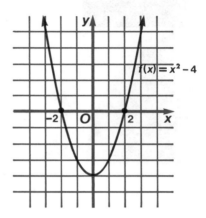

As you can see in the graph, $f(x) \geq 0$ if $x \leq -2$ or $x \geq 2$. The solution set is $\{x \mid x \leq -2, x \in R\} \cup \{x \mid x \geq 2, x \in R\}$.

In general, you will not be asked to solve quadratic inequations of the form $ax^2 + bx + c \neq 0$. In this instance, the solution set is R except for any solutions of $ax^2 + bx + c = 0$.

EXERCISES

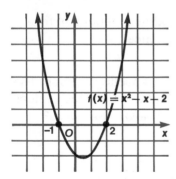

1. b 2. d 3. e 4. a 5. c
6. $\{x \mid -7 < x < 3, x \in R\}$
7. $\{x \mid -7 \leq x \leq 3, x \in R\}$
8. $\{x \mid x \leq -7\} \cup \{x \mid x \geq 3\}$
9. $\{x \mid x < -7\} \cup \{x \mid x > 3\}$
10. $\{x \mid x < -3\} \cup \{x \mid x > 7\}$
11. $\{x \mid x \leq -3\} \cup \{x \mid x \geq 7\}$
12. $\{x \mid -3x \leq 7\}$
13. $\{x \mid -3 < x < 7\}$

Match each solution set to a quadratic inequation. Use the graph of $f(x) = x^2 + x - 2$.

1. $x^2 + x - 2 < 0$ **a.** $\{x \mid x < -2\} \cup \{x \mid x > 1\}$
2. $x^2 + x - 2 \leq 0$ **b.** $\{x \mid -2 < x < 1\}$
3. $x^2 + x - 2 \geq 0$ **c.** $\{x \mid x \neq -2, x \neq 1\}$
4. $x^2 + x - 2 > 0$ **d.** $\{x \mid -2 \leq x \leq 1\}$
5. $x^2 + x - 2 \neq 0$ **e.** $\{x \mid x \leq -2\} \cup \{x \mid x \geq 1\}$

Graph $f(x) = x^2 + 4x - 21$. By inspecting the graph, write the solution set of each quadratic inequation.

6. $x^2 + 4x - 21 < 0$ **7.** $x^2 + 4x - 21 \leq 0$
8. $x^2 + 4x - 21 \geq 0$ **9.** $x^2 + 4x - 21 > 0$

Graph $f(x) = -x^2 - 4x + 21$. By inspecting the graph, write the solution set of each quadratic inequation.

10. $-x^2 - 4x + 21 < 0$ **11.** $-x^2 - 4x + 21 \leq 0$
12. $-x^2 - 4x + 21 \geq 0$ **13.** $-x^2 - 4x + 21 > 0$

Graph $f(x) = x^2 + 4x + 5$. By inspecting the graph, write the solution set of each quadratic inequation.

14. $x^2 + 4x + 5 < 0$ **15.** $x^2 + 4x + 5 \leq 0$

16. $x^2 + 4x + 5 \geq 0$ **17.** $x^2 + 4x + 5 > 0$

Each of the following is a graph of some quadratic function $f(x) = ax^2 + bx + c$. Use the information provided in each graph. Write the solution sets of $ax^2 + bx + c < 0$ and $ax^2 + bx + c > 0$.

18.

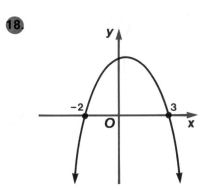

19.

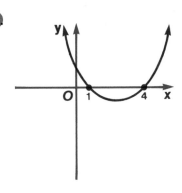

20.

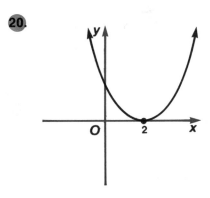

21.

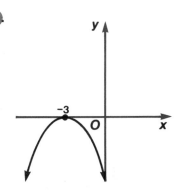

22.

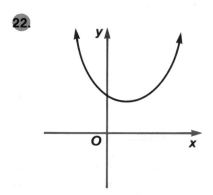

23.

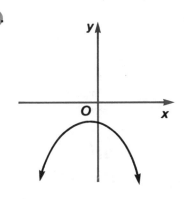

Stress that with $\leq$ and $\geq$, the
solutions to $ax^2 + bx + c = 0$
are also included.

Each of the following is a graph of some quadratic function
$f(x) = ax^2 + bx + c$. Use the information provided in each graph.
Write the solution sets of $ax^2 + bx + c \leq 0$ and $ax^2 + bx + c \geq 0$.

24.

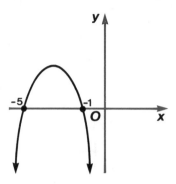

25.

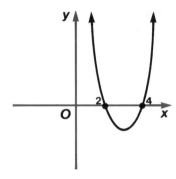

26.

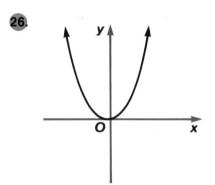

27.

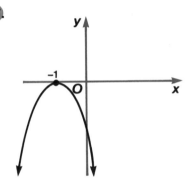

28.

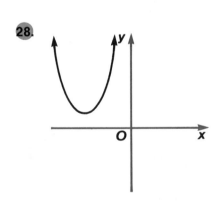

29.

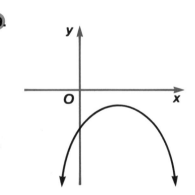

OBJECTIVE:
To name the solution set of a quadratic inequation without drawing the
graph for the corresponding quadratic function.

15-2
Solving
Quadratic
Inequations

Quadratic inequations may be written in the following forms.

$$ax^2 + bx + c > 0 \qquad ax^2 + bx + c \geq 0$$
$$ax^2 + bx + c < 0 \qquad ax^2 + bx + c \leq 0$$

If clarification is needed, refer to exercises of Section 15-1.

You may solve a quadratic inequation by using the answers of two questions.

> **a.** Does $f(x) = ax^2 + bx + c$ have a minimum or maximum point?
> **b.** Where does $f(x) = ax^2 + bx + c$ intersect the x-axis?

From your experience with quadratic functions, you may ask these questions another way.

> **a.** Is $a > 0$, or is $a < 0$?
> **b.** What is the solution set of $ax^2 + bx + c = 0$?

EXAMPLES

1. Solve $4x^2 - 9 < 0$.
   a. Since $4 > 0$, the graph of $f(x) = 4x^2 - 9$ has a minimum point.
   b. The solution set of $4x^2 - 9 = 0$ is $\left\{-\dfrac{3}{2}, \dfrac{3}{2}\right\}$.

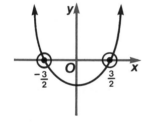

   Using this information, a partial sketch of $f(x) = 4x^2 - 9$ may be made. In your own work, you may imagine the sketch of the graph. Since the minimum point is between $-\dfrac{3}{2}$ and $\dfrac{3}{2}$, $4x^2 - 9 < 0$ between $-\dfrac{3}{2}$ and $\dfrac{3}{2}$. The solution set is $\left\{x \mid -\dfrac{3}{2} < x < \dfrac{3}{2}\right\}$.

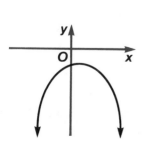

2. Solve $x^2 - 5x - 6 \geq 0$.
   a. Since $1 > 0$, the graph of $f(x) = x^2 - 5x - 6$ has a minimum point.
   b. The solution set of $x^2 - 5x - 6 = 0$ is $\{2, 3\}$.
   Since the minimum point is between 2 and 3, $x^2 - 5x - 6 \geq 0$ if $x \leq 2$ or $x \geq 3$. The solution set of $x^2 - 5x - 6 \geq 0$ is $\{x \mid x \leq 2\} \cup \{x \mid x \geq 3\}$.

3. Solve $-x^2 + x - 2 < 0$.
   a. Since $-1 < 0$, the graph of $f(x) = -x^2 + x - 2$ has a maximum point.
   b. The solution set of $-x^2 + x - 2 = 0$ is $\varnothing$.
   The graph is always below the x-axis. The solution set of $-x^2 + x - 2 < 0$ is R.

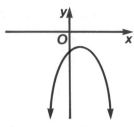

4. Solve $-2x^2 + x - 1 \geq 0$.

  a. Since $-2 < 0$, the graph of $f(x) = -2x^2 + x - 1$ has a maximum point.

  b. The solution set of $-2x^2 + x - 1 = 0$ is $\varnothing$.

The graph is never on or above the x-axis. The solution set of $-2x^2 + x - 1 \geq 0$ is $\varnothing$.

1. $\{x \mid -5 \leq x \leq 3\}$
2. $\{x \mid x \in R\}$

EXERCISES

3. $\{x \mid x = -3\}$ **4.** ϕ
5. $\{x \mid x \neq -3, x \in R\}$
6. $\{x \mid x \in R\}$
7. $\{x \mid \dfrac{-7 - \sqrt{13}}{2} < x < \dfrac{-7 + \sqrt{13}}{2}\}$
8. $\{x \mid x < \dfrac{-7 - \sqrt{13}}{2}\}$
  $\cup \{x \mid x > \dfrac{-7 + \sqrt{13}}{2}\}$
9. $\{x \mid x < -9\} \cup$
  $\{x \mid x > -1\}$
10. $\{x \mid -9 < x < -1\}$
11.-17. See section notes in T.G.

Solve each quadratic inequation.

1. $x^2 + 2x - 15 \leq 0$ **2.** $x^2 + 2x + 15 > 0$
3. $x^2 + 6x + 9 \leq 0$ **4.** $x^2 + 6x + 9 < 0$
5. $x^2 + 6x + 9 > 0$ **6.** $x^2 + 6x + 9 \geq 0$
7. $x^2 + 7x + 9 < 0$ **8.** $x^2 + 7x + 9 > 0$
9. $x^2 + 10x + 9 > 0$ **10.** $x^2 + 10x + 9 < 0$
11. $6x^2 + 7x - 5 < 0$ **12.** $-6x^2 - 7x + 5 < 0$
13. $6x^2 + 7x - 5 \geq 0$ **14.** $-6x^2 - 7x + 5 \geq 0$
15. $6x^2 + 7x + 5 > 0$ **16.** $-6x^2 - 7x - 5 > 0$

17. Graph each solution set in Exercises **1–6** on a separate number line.

15-3 *Writing Quadratic Inequations*

OBJECTIVE:

To name a quadratic inequation having a given appropriate solution set.

In Chapter 14, you studied how to write a quadratic equation with a given set as its solution set.

EXAMPLE

See T.G. on how this section may be used.

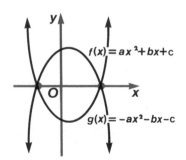

Write a quadratic equation with the solution set $\left\{-\dfrac{1}{3}, \dfrac{4}{3}\right\}$.

$$x = -\frac{1}{3} \text{ or } x = \frac{4}{3} \Leftrightarrow 3x = -1 \text{ or } 3x = 4$$

$$\Leftrightarrow 3x + 1 = 0 \text{ or } 3x - 4 = 0$$
$$\Leftrightarrow (3x + 1)(3x - 4) = 0$$
$$\Leftrightarrow 9x^2 - 9x - 4 = 0$$

The quadratic equation $9x^2 - 9x - 4 = 0$ has the solution set $\left\{-\dfrac{1}{3}, \dfrac{4}{3}\right\}$.

You also saw in Chapter 13 that $ax^2 + bx + c = 0$ and $-ax^2 - bx - c = 0$ both have the same solution set.

EXAMPLE

The solution set of $9x^2 - 9x - 4 = 0$ is $\left\{-\dfrac{1}{3}, \dfrac{4}{3}\right\}$. This set is also the solution set of $-9x^2 + 9x + 4 = 0$.

$$\text{Check: } -9x^2 + 9x + 4 = -9\left(-\frac{1}{3}\right)^2 + 9\left(-\frac{1}{3}\right) + 4$$
$$= -1 - 3 + 4 = 0$$
$$-9x^2 + 9x + 4 = -9\left(\frac{4}{3}\right)^2 + 9\left(\frac{4}{3}\right) + 4$$
$$= -16 + 12 + 4 = 0$$

It also is possible to write a quadratic inequation if given a solution set.

EXAMPLES

1. Find values for a, b, and c such that $ax^2 + bx + c \leq 0$ if the solution set of the inequation is $\{x \mid x \leq -1\} \cup \{x \mid x \geq 3\}$.

Find a quadratic equation which has the solution set $\{-1, 3\}$.

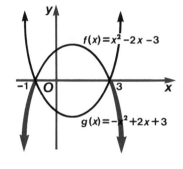

$$x = -1 \quad \text{or} \quad x = 3$$
$$\Leftrightarrow x + 1 = 0 \quad \text{or} \quad x - 3 = 0$$
$$\Leftrightarrow (x + 1)(x - 3) = 0$$
$$\Leftrightarrow x^2 - 2x - 3 = 0$$

Of course, $-x^2 + 2x + 3 = 0$ is the other quadratic equation with the same solution set.

By inspecting the graphs, you can see that $-x^2 + 2x + 3 \leq 0$ has a solution set $\{x \mid x \leq -1\} \cup \{x \mid x \geq 3\}$. Therefore, $a = -1$, $b = 2$, and $c = 3$ are the desired values.

2. Find values of a, b, and c such that $ax^2 + bx + c > 0$ if the solution set of the inequation is $\left\{x \mid -\dfrac{1}{2} < x < 4\right\}$.

Find a quadratic equation which has the solution set $\left\{-\dfrac{1}{2}, 4\right\}$.

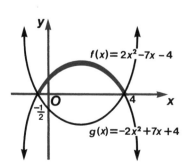

$$x = -\frac{1}{2} \quad \text{or} \quad x = 4$$
$$\Leftrightarrow 2x + 1 = 0 \quad \text{or} \quad x - 4 = 0$$
$$\Leftrightarrow (2x + 1)(x - 4) = 0$$
$$\Leftrightarrow 2x^2 - 7x - 4 = 0$$

Of course, $-2x^2 + 7x + 4 = 0$ is the other quadratic equation with this solution set.

Since you are trying to find a, b, and c such that $ax^2 + bx + c > 0$

439

between $-\frac{1}{2}$ and 4, a *maximum* point should occur between $-\frac{1}{2}$ and 4. Since $a < 0$ in $f(x) = -2x^2 + 7x + 4$, there is a maximum point in the desired region. Therefore, if $a = -2$, $b = 7$, and $c = 4$, then $ax^2 + bx + c > 0$ for $\left\{x \mid -\frac{1}{2} < x < 4\right\}$.

EXERCISES

Write two quadratic *equations* which have the indicated solution set.

1. $\{-2, 4\}$

2. $\left\{-\frac{1}{2}, -\frac{1}{5}\right\}$

3. $\left\{\frac{5}{3}, \frac{7}{3}\right\}$

4. $\{2\}$

5. $\left\{\frac{2}{5}\right\}$

6. $\varnothing$

Find values for a, b, and c such that each quadratic *inequation* has the indicated solution set.

Inequation	Solution Set
7. $ax^2 + bx + c \leq 0$	$\{x \mid -2 \leq x \leq 4\}$
8. $ax^2 + bx + c > 0$	$\left\{x \mid -\frac{1}{5} < x < -\frac{1}{2}\right\}$
9. $ax^2 + bx + c \geq 0$	$\left\{x \mid x \leq \frac{5}{3}\right\} \cup \left\{x \mid x \geq \frac{7}{3}\right\}$
10. $ax^2 + bx + c > 0$	$\{x \mid x < 2\} \cup \{x \mid x > 2\}$
11. $ax^2 + bx + c \geq 0$	$\left\{\frac{2}{5}\right\}$
12. $ax^2 + bx + c > 0$	R
13. $ax^2 + bx + c < 0$	$\{x \mid -4 < x < 4\}$
14. $ax^2 + bx + c > 0$	$\{x \mid x < -3\} \cup \{x \mid x > 3\}$
15. $ax^2 + bx + c \leq 0$	$\{x \mid 0 \leq x \leq 5\}$
16. $ax^2 + bx + c \geq 0$	$\left\{\frac{1}{3}\right\}$
17. $ax^2 + bx + c < 0$	$\varnothing$
18. $ax^2 + bx + c \geq 0$	$\{x \mid -\sqrt{3} \leq x \leq \sqrt{3}\}$
19. $ax^2 + bx + c > 0$	$\left\{x \mid x < -\frac{5}{4}\right\} \cup \{x \mid x > 6\}$
20. $ax^2 + bx + c \leq 0$	$\{x \mid -2\sqrt{5} \leq x \leq 1\}$
21. $ax^2 + bx + c \geq 0$	$\left\{x \mid 0 \leq x \leq \frac{\sqrt{5}}{4}\right\}$

OBJECTIVE:

15-4

To solve a quadratic inequation for which $\sqrt{b^2 - 4ac} \in W$ by using factoring procedures.

Factoring Quadratic Inequations

You have been solving quadratic inequations by drawing and inspecting graphs. However, if the quadratic expression in an inequation is factorable, then you may solve the quadratic inequation without drawing graphs.

EXAMPLES

1. Solve $x^2 + x - 12 < 0$.

$$x^2 + x - 12 < 0 \Leftrightarrow (x + 4)(x - 3) < 0$$

If the product of two numbers is negative, then one must be positive and the other must be negative.

$$(x + 4)(x - 3) < 0$$

$(x + 4) < 0$ and $(x - 3) > 0$	OR	$(x + 4) > 0$ and $(x - 3) < 0$
$x < -4$ and $x > 3$	OR	$x > -4$ and $x < 3$
Impossible		$-4 < x < 3$

It is impossible for a number to be both less than -4 and greater than 3. So the solution set must be $\{x \mid -4 < x < 3\}$.

2. Solve $x^2 + x - 12 > 0$.

$$x^2 + x - 12 > 0 \Leftrightarrow (x + 4)(x - 3) > 0$$

If a product of two numbers is positive, then both must be positive or both must be negative.

$$(x + 4)(x - 3) > 0$$

$x + 4 > 0$ and $x - 3 > 0$	OR	$x + 4 < 0$ and $x - 3 < 0$
$x > -4$ and $x > 3$	OR	$x < -4$ and $x < 3$
$x > 3$	OR	$x < -4$

In the first possibility, if $x > -4$ *and* $x > 3$, then x always must be greater than 3 to satisfy both conditions. In other words, saying $x > -4$ and $x > 3$ is the same as saying $x > 3$. In the same way, saying $x < -4$ and $x < 3$ is the same as saying $x < -4$.

Therefore, the solution set of $x^2 + x - 12 > 0$ is $\{x \mid x < -4\} \cup \{x \mid x > 3\}$.

Provide adequate time for discussing statements of the form (P and Q) OR (S and T). By using capital letters, OR serves as punctuation. The meaning is the same if the parentheses are omitted.

EXERCISES

Solve each quadratic inequation by factoring.

1. $x^2 - 4 < 0$

2. $x^2 - x - 56 < 0$

3. $x^2 - 16 \geq 0$

4. $x^2 + x - 6 > 0$

5. $25 - x^2 \leq 0$

6. $2x^2 + x > 0$

1. $\{x \mid -2 < x < 2\}$ 2. $\{x \mid -7 < x < 8\}$ 3. $\{x \mid x \geq 4\} \cup \{x \mid x \leq -4\}$ 4. $\{x \mid x > 2\} \cup \{x \mid x < -3\}$ 5. $\{x \mid x \geq 5\} \cup \{x \mid x \leq -5\}$ 6. $\{x \mid x > 0\} \cup \{x \mid x < -\frac{1}{2}\}$

441

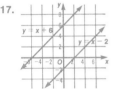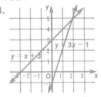
7. $x^2 - 2x < 0$

8. $9x^2 - 12x + 4 < 0$

9. $4x^2 - 2x - 6 > 0$

10. $-4x^2 + 2x + 6 > 0$

Solve each quadratic inequation by writing an equivalent inequation which you can factor.

11. $x^2 \geq 24 - 2x$

12. $5x - 6 < x^2$

13. $4x^2 + 12x < 7$

14. $4x(x - 4) \geq 7$

15. $4(2x - 1) \leq x(x + 4)$

16. $6x^2(x + 1) > 6x^3 - x + 1$

17. Graph $y = x - 2$ and $y = x + 6$ in the same coordinate plane.
   a. State the values of x for which the graphs of $y = x - 2$ and $y = x + 6$ are both above the x-axis.
   b. State the values of x for which the graphs of $y = x - 2$ and $y = x + 6$ are both below the x-axis.
   c. Is the union of the sets in Parts a and b the solution set of $x^2 + 4x - 12 > 0$?

18. Graph $y = x + 3$ and $y = 3x - 1$ in the same coordinate plane.
   a. State the values of x for which one of the lines is above the x-axis while the other line is below the x-axis.
   b. Is the set of points in Part a the solution set of $3x^2 + 8x - 3 < 0$?

19. When a projectile is x feet from a gun muzzle measured horizontally, its height above the gun muzzle is given by $h(x) = \frac{1}{1000}(1600x - x^2) + 10$. At which distances is a projectile more than 290 feet above the gun muzzle?

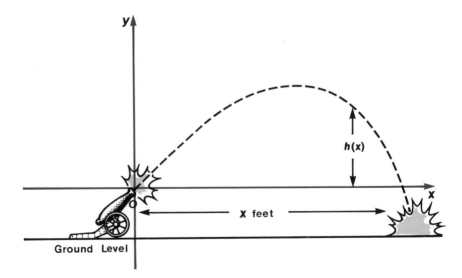

h(x)

X feet

Ground Level

MATHEMATICS AND HISTORY

NUMBER AND RELIGION

How do you feel about beans? The mathematician Pythagoras, who lived about 530 B.C. and is usually remembered for his theorem about right triangles, founded a religious society whose members believed that to eat beans was a sin. Strange as it may seem, this religious brotherhood gave focus to mathematics.

When Pythagoras said, "All things are number," he made mathematics a fundamental part of the religion of the brotherhood. This brotherhood's passionate belief established a tradition of caring about mathematics and reasoning which has endured to this day.

Pythagoras gave numbers special meanings. Six was called a *perfect number* because it equals the sum of its divisors (excluding 6 itself): $6 = 1 + 2 + 3$. Can you find another perfect number?

Eight was called a *deficient number* because the sum of its divisors (excluding 8 itself) is less than 8: $1 + 2 + 4 < 8$. Can you see why numbers such as 12 were called *abundant numbers?* The numbers 220 and 224 were called *friendly numbers*. Can you find a special relationship between these numbers? The number 16 was special because it was the first square of the first square.

A modern Pythagorean would be pleased to be named Alan. As *N* is the fourteenth letter, *A* is the first, and *L* the twelfth, Alan corresponds to $1 + 12 + 1 + 14 = 28$, a perfect number.

Pythagoreans believed that all mathematics came from the whole numbers. When they discovered that the relationship between the side and diagonal of a square required irrational numbers, they kept it a secret. It is said that they went so far as to drown a person who told the secret.

As silly as Pythagorean numerology may seem today, it played an important role historically as it started a tradition of people feeling strongly about reason and mathematics for their own sake.

15-5

Systems of Equations

In Chapter 10 you studied linear equations and systems of linear equations. You learned that solving a system of equations means finding the set of points their graphs have in common.

EXAMPLE

Use the graphing method to solve $y = 2x - 4$ and $y = x + 1$.

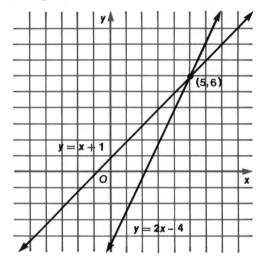

By inspecting the graph, you can see that (5, 6) is the point of intersection. The solution set is $\{(5, 6)\}$.

You also may find the solution set by setting the two expressions for y equal to each other and solving for x.

EXAMPLE

The example on this page reviews earlier work in the book.

Solve $y = 2x - 4$ and $y = x + 1$.

Assume (x, y) is a point on the graphs of both equations. Then, the following equivalence must be true. It is simply a way of saying $y = y$.

$$2x - 4 = x + 1 \Leftrightarrow 2x - x = 1 + 4$$
$$\Leftrightarrow \qquad x = 5$$

The value of y may be found by substituting the value of x, 5, into one of the equations.

$$y = 2x - 4$$
$$y = 2 \cdot 5 - 4$$
$$y = 6$$

The solution set is $\{(5, 6)\}$.

It is possible to solve systems of quadratic equations of the form $y = ax^2 + bx + c$, and $y = dx^2 + ex + f$. The same methods used to solve systems of linear equations may be used to solve systems of quadratic equations.

EXAMPLE

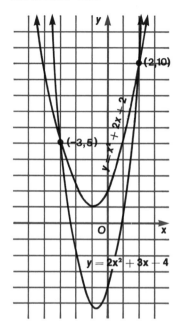

Solve $y = 2x^2 + 3x - 4$ and $y = x^2 + 2x + 2$.
You may draw and inspect a graph to arrive at the solution set.

You also may set the two expressions for y equal to each other and solve for x.

$$y = 2x^2 + 3x - 4 \qquad y = x^2 + 2x + 2$$
$$2x^2 + 3x - 4 = x^2 + 2x + 2 \Leftrightarrow 2x^2 - x^2 + 3x - 2x - 4 - 2 = 0$$
$$\Leftrightarrow \qquad\qquad x^2 + x - 6 = 0$$
$$\Leftrightarrow \qquad\qquad (x + 3)(x - 2) = 0$$
$$\Leftrightarrow \qquad\qquad x = -3 \text{ or } x = 2$$

You now know the values of x at which $y = 2x^2 + 3x - 4$ and $y = x^2 + 2x + 2$ intersect. To find the values of y at which $y = 2x^2 + 3x - 4$ and $y = x^2 + 2x + 2$ intersect, substitute the values of x into the equations and solve for y.

Let $x = -3$.

$y = 2x^2 + 3x - 4$	$y = x^2 + 2x + 2$
$y = 2(-3)^2 + 3(-3) - 4$	$y = (-3)^2 + 2(-3) + 2$
$y = 5$	$y = 5$

The point $(-3, 5)$ is an intersection point.

Let $x = 2$.

$y = 2x^2 + 3x - 4$	$y = x^2 + 2x + 2$
$y = 2(2)^2 + 3 \cdot 2 - 4$	$y = 2^2 + 2 \cdot 2 + 2$
$y = 10$	$y = 10$

The point $(2, 10)$ is an intersection point. The solution set of $y = 2x^2 + 3x - 4$ and $y = x^2 + 2x + 2$ is $\{(2, 10), (-3, 5)\}$.

You also can solve a system of equations involving a quadratic equation and a linear equation. The same method of solution may be used. That is, set the two expressions for y equal to each other and solve for x.

The method in this section uses the following first step:
$y = f(x)$ and $y = g(x)$
$\Rightarrow f(x) = g(x)$. It may help some students to see the step written this way.

445

EXAMPLE

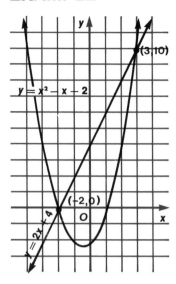

Solve $y = 2x + 4$ and $y = x^2 + x - 2$.

$$y = x^2 + x - 2 \qquad y = 2x + 4$$
$$x^2 + x - 2 = 2x + 4 \Leftrightarrow \qquad x^2 - x - 6 = 0$$
$$\Leftrightarrow (x - 3)(x + 2) = 0$$
$$\Leftrightarrow \qquad x = 3 \text{ or } x = -2$$

Let $x = 3$. $\qquad y = 2x + 4 \qquad\qquad y = x^2 + x - 2$
$\qquad\qquad\qquad y = 2 \cdot 3 + 4 \qquad\quad y = 3^2 + 3 - 2$
$\qquad\qquad\qquad y = 10 \qquad\qquad\quad y = 10$

One point of intersection is (3, 10).

Let $x = -2$. $\qquad y = 2x + 4 \qquad\qquad y = x^2 + x - 2$
$\qquad\qquad\qquad y = 2(-2) + 4 \qquad y = (-2)^2 + (-2) - 2$
$\qquad\qquad\qquad y = 0 \qquad\qquad\qquad y = 0$

Another point of intersection is $(-2, 0)$.
The solution set of the system $y = 2x + 4$, $y = x^2 + x - 2$ is $\{(-2, 0), (3, 10)\}$.

EXERCISES

Exercises 1-5 may be used in class as examples for discussion prior to making an assignment from Exercises 6-24.

1. 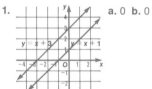 a. 0 b. 0

2. 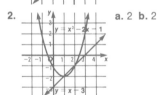 a. 2 b. 2

3. 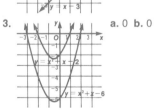 a. 0 b. 0

4.- 7. See section notes in T.G.

1. Graph $y = x + 1$ and $y = x + 3$ in the same coordinate plane.
   a. How many points do the two lines have in common?
   b. How many solutions are there for $x + 1 = x + 3$?
2. Graph $y = x^2 - 2x - 1$ and $y = x - 3$ in the same coordinate plane.
   a. How many points do the two graphs have in common?
   b. How many solutions are there for $x^2 - 2x - 1 = x - 3$?
3. Graph $y = x^2 + x - 6$ and $y = x^2 + x - 2$ in the same coordinate plane.
   a. How many points do the two graphs have in common?
   b. How many solutions are there for $x^2 + x - 6 = x^2 + x - 2$?
4. Graph $y = x^2 + x - 6$ and $y = 2x^2 + 4x - 6$ in the same coordinate plane.
   a. How many points do the two graphs have in common?
   b. How many solutions are there for $x^2 + x - 6 = 2x^2 + 4x - 6$?
5. Graph $y = x^2 - 2x + 3$ and $y = 2x - 1$ in the same coordinate plane.
   a. How many points do the two graphs have in common?
   b. How many solutions are there for $x^2 - 2x + 3 = 2x - 1$?

Solve each system of equations.
6. $y = x^2$, $y = 3x + 2$
7. $y = x^2$, $y = 4x - 4$

8. $x = 0, y = 7$ **9.** φ

10. $x = -\frac{2}{3}, y = 3; x = \frac{5}{2}, y = \frac{25}{2}$

11. $x = -\frac{2}{3}, y = \frac{13}{9}; x = \frac{5}{2}, y = 7$

12. $x = \frac{7}{3}, y = \frac{142}{9}$ **13.** $x =$

$\sqrt{2}, y = 0; x = -\sqrt{2}, y = 0$

14. $x = -5, y = 4; x = 3, y = 20$

15. $x = 4, y = \frac{13}{2}; x = -4,$

$y = -\frac{3}{2}$ **16.** φ **17.** $\{(x, y) \mid y =$

$(x + 1)^2, x \in R\}$ **18.** $x = \frac{\sqrt{5}}{5},$

$y = 10 + \frac{3\sqrt{5}}{5}; x = -\frac{\sqrt{5}}{5}, y =$

$10\frac{-3\sqrt{5}}{5}$ **19.** $\{(x, y) \mid y = 16x^2 +$

$8x + 3, x \in R\}$ **20.** 30 yd by

30 yd **21.** $x = 1100$

Exercise 17 requires dividing
both sides of the equation by
$(x + 1)$. Ask students which
value for x is denied by
the divisor.

It may be best to allow slow
students and poor readers to
work with more able students
on these word problems.

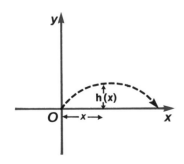

8. $y = 2x + 7, y = 3x + 7$

9. $y = 2x^2 + 2x - 5, y = x^2 + x - 10$

10. $y = 6x^2 - 8x - 5, y = 3x + 5$

11. $y = 4x^2 - 10x - 7, y = -2x^2 + x + 3$

12. $y = x^2 + 4x + 1, y = x^2 + x + 8$

13. $y = x^2 - 2, y = 2 - x^2$

Solve each system of equations. First find equivalent equations of the form $y = mx + c$ or $y = ax^2 + bx + c$.

14. $y + 1 = x(x + 4)$ $\qquad \dfrac{y + 16}{2} = x(x + 3)$

15. $y - x = \dfrac{x^2}{4} - \dfrac{3}{2}$ $\qquad y - x = \dfrac{5}{2}$

16. $\dfrac{y}{3} - 1 = x(x + 1)$ $\qquad y - x(x + 1) = 1$

17. $y - 1 = x(x + 2)$ $\qquad y(x + 1) = (x + 1)^3$

18. $5x^2 + 1 = \dfrac{y - 3x}{5}$ $\qquad x(5x + 1) = \dfrac{y - 7}{3}$

19. $\dfrac{y - 3}{8} = x(2x + 1)$ $\qquad y = 16x^2 + 8x + 3$

20. A carpet company uses a formula to calculate the amount to charge a customer. To cover a rectangular room with medium quality carpeting, the following formula is used. The cost, C, is in dollars.

$C = 3 \cdot$ (square yards of floor) $+ 1 \cdot$ (yards of perimeter) $+ 60$

An exhibit hall spends 24 dollars for each yard of perimeter to carpet a very large square room. How large is the room? Hint: Let x be the length of the square room. Write two equations for the cost of the carpeting and then solve the system. If there are two answers, choose the reasonable answer.

21. The height above the ground for a projectile is given by $h(x) = \dfrac{1}{1000}(1600x - x^2)$ where x is the distance along the ground away from the muzzle.

At what point on the ground is the height of the projectile twice the horizontal distance from the muzzle? That is, when is $2x$ equal to $h(x)$?

The focal point of a parabola is a point on the axis of symmetry.

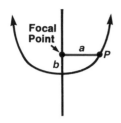

Focal Point

a

b

P

Its distance to the maximum or minimum point is half of the distance to the parabola along a line perpendicular to the axis.

In other words, the ratio of *a* to *b* in the diagram is 2 to 1. Use this information for Exercises 22–24.

22. State the coordinates of the focal point for $y = x^2$ by first finding the coordinates of point *P* in the figure. Hint: If you have difficulty, graph the equation and write a second equation which gives the ratio between *x* and *y* for the coordinates of point *P*.

23. State the coordinates of the focal point for $y = \frac{1}{4}x^2$ by first finding the coordinates of point *P* in the figure.

24. State the coordinates of the focal point for $y = 4x^2$ by first finding the coordinates of point *P* in the figure.

Chapter Summary

1. A quadratic inequation is an inequation which may be written in one of the following forms where $a \neq 0$.

$$ax^2 + bx + c < 0 \qquad ax^2 + bx + c > 0 \qquad ax^2 + bx + c \neq 0$$
$$ax^2 + bx + c \leq 0 \qquad ax^2 + bx + c \geq 0$$

2. Quadratic inequations may be solved by using a graphing method. The answers to the following questions are used to construct a partial sketch of the graph of the corresponding quadratic function $f(x) = ax^2 + bx + c$.
   a. Is $a > 0$, or is $a < 0$?
   b. What is the solution set of $ax^2 + bx + c = 0$?
   Look at the graph to determine the solution set of the quadratic equation.

3. Given a solution set, it is possible to write a quadratic inequation which has the original set as its own solution set.

4. Assume that the quadratic expression in a quadratic inequation is factorable. Then the quadratic inequation may be solved through factoring and an analysis of possible solutions.

5. Systems of equations may involve quadratic or linear equations of the forms $y = ax^2 + bx + c$ or $y = mx + c$. These systems may be solved by first setting equal the two expressions for *y*. Then the resulting equation is solved for *x*. A *y*-coordinate of any solution may be found by substituting a solution for *x* into one of the original equations.

Match each quadratic inequation with its solution set. Sketch an appropriate graph if necessary.

1. d 2. b 3. a 4. e 5. c 6. b
7. e 8. a 9. d 10. c 11. $\{x \mid -1 < x < -\frac{1}{2}\}$ 12. $\{x \mid x \geq 5\} \cup \{x \mid x \leq -1\}$ 13. $\{x \mid -3 \leq x \leq 3\}$ 14. ϕ 15. $\{x \mid x = 1\}$
16. $\{x \mid -\frac{4}{3} < x < \frac{4}{3}\}$

17. $\{x \mid x \geq 4\} \cup \{x \mid x \leq 3\}$
18. $\{x \mid \frac{5 - \sqrt{46}}{3} < x < \frac{5 + \sqrt{46}}{3}\}$

19. $\{x \mid x \geq 1\} \cup \{x \mid x \leq -2\}$

1. $x^2 - 5x + 4 < 0$
2. $x^2 - 5x + 4 \geq 0$
3. $x^2 - 5x + 4 \leq 0$
4. $x^2 - 5x + 4 > 0$
5. $x^2 - 5x + 4 \neq 0$

a. $\{x \mid 1 \leq x \leq 4\}$
b. $\{x \mid x \leq 1\} \cup \{x \mid x \geq 4\}$
c. $\{x \mid x \neq 1, x \neq 4\}$
d. $\{x \mid 1 < x < 4\}$
e. $\{x \mid x < 1\} \cup \{x \mid x > 4\}$

6. $8 - 2x - x^2 > 0$
7. $x^2 - 2x - 8 < 0$
8. $x^2 - 2x - 8 \geq 0$
9. $8 - 2x - x^2 \leq 0$
10. $8 - 2x - x^2 \geq 0$

a. $\{x \mid x \leq -2\} \cup \{x \mid x \geq 4\}$
b. $\{x \mid -4 < x < 2\}$
c. $\{x \mid -4 \leq x \leq 2\}$
d. $\{x \mid x \leq -4\} \cup \{x \mid x \geq 2\}$
e. $\{x \mid -2 < x < 4\}$

15-2

20. $\{x \mid -3 \leq x \leq 12\}$ 21. $\{x \mid \frac{3 - \sqrt{41}}{4} \leq x \leq \frac{3 + \sqrt{41}}{4}\}$ 22. $\{x \mid \frac{5 - \sqrt{10}}{3} \leq x \leq \frac{5 + \sqrt{10}}{3}\}$ 23. $-x^2 - 2x + 3 \geq 0$ 24. $4x^2 + 4x - 3 > 0$

Solve each quadratic inequation by finding where the corresponding function crosses the x-axis. Also find if it has a maximum or minimum point. Find equivalent equations if necessary.

11. $-1 - 3x - 2x^2 > 0$
12. $x^2 - 4x - 5 \geq 0$
13. $x^2 \leq 9$
14. $x^2 - 11x + 31 \leq 0$
15. $3(x^2 - 2x) + 3 \leq 0$
16. $9x^2 - 16 < 0$
17. $x^2 + 12 - 7x \geq 0$
18. $-3x^2 + 10x + 7 > 0$
19. $3x^2 - x + 2 \geq 2x^2 - 2x + 4$ 20. $x(x - 9) - 36 \leq 0$
21. $2x^2 - 3x - 4 \leq 0$
22. $3x^2 \leq 10x - 5$

15-3

25. $x^2 + 5x + 4 < 0$ 26. $-3x^2 + 14x - 8 \geq 0$ 27. $-7x^2 - 46x - 24 \leq 0$ 28. $-x^2 + 12 > 0$
29. Answers will vary.
30. $12x^2 - 11x - 36 \geq 0$
31. $-x^2 + 3\sqrt{3}x \leq 0$
32. Answers will vary.

Find values of a, b, and c such that the indicated inequation has the given solution set.

Inequation	Solution Set
23. $ax^2 + bx + c \geq 0$	$\{x \mid -3 \leq x \leq 1\}$
24. $ax^2 + bx + c > 0$	$\{x \mid x < \frac{-3}{2}\} \cup \{x \mid x > \frac{1}{2}\}$
25. $ax^2 + bx + c < 0$	$\{x \mid -4 < x < -1\}$
26. $ax^2 + bx + c \geq 0$	$\{x \mid \frac{2}{3} \leq x \leq 4\}$
27. $ax^2 + bx + c \leq 0$	$\{x \mid x \leq -6\} \cup \{x \mid x \geq \frac{-4}{7}\}$
28. $ax^2 + bx + c > 0$	$\{x \mid -2\sqrt{3} < x < 2\sqrt{3}\}$
29. $ax^2 + bx + c \leq 0$	$\emptyset$
30. $ax^2 + bx + c \geq 0$	$\{x \mid x \leq -\frac{4}{3}\} \cup \{x \mid x \geq \frac{9}{4}\}$
31. $ax^2 + bx + c \leq 0$	$\{x \mid x \leq 0\} \cup \{x \mid x \geq 3\sqrt{3}\}$
32. $ax^2 + bx + c > 0$	$\mathbb{R}$

Solve each inequation by factoring.

33. $3x^2 + 19x < 14$　　　　**34.** $-2x \geq -x^2 + 15$

35. $(x - 3)(x + 2) \leq 14$　　**36.** $5x^2 + 15x > 0$

37. $30 \leq x^2 + 7x$　　　　　**38.** $-x^2 - 8 > 6x$

39. $4x^2 + 36 \geq 24x$　　　　**40.** $4x^2 + 12x + 9 < 0$

15-5

Solve each system of equations.

41. $y = 3x + 4$ *and* $y = x^2 - 2x - 26$

42. $y = 3x^2 - 5x + 6$ *and* $y = x^2 + 6x - 9$

43. $y = -x^2 + 6x + 9$ *and* $y = 3 - 4x - x^2$

44. $y = x^2 + x + 1$ *and* $y = 2 + x + 2x^2$

45. $y = 3x^2$ and $y = 2x + 1$

46. $y = 5x^2 - 3x + 8$ *and* $y = 3x^2 + 5x - 12$

47. $y = x^2 + 7x + 12$ *and* $y = x + 3$

48. $y = 2x^2 + 3x + 5$ *and* $y = \dfrac{1}{10}x - \dfrac{1}{10}$

33. $\{x \mid -7 < x < \frac{2}{3}\}$

34. $\{x \mid x \geq 5\} \cup \{x \mid x \leq -3\}$

35. $\{x \mid -4 \leq x \leq 5\}$

36. $\{x \mid x > 0\} \cup \{x \mid x < -3\}$

37. $\{x \mid x > 3\} \cup \{x \mid x < -10\}$

38. $\{x \mid x > -2\} \cup \{x \mid x < -4\}$ **39.** R **40.** φ

41. $x = 7, y = 25; x = -3$ $y = -5$ **42.** $x = \frac{5}{2}, y = \frac{49}{4}$; $x = 3, y = 18$ **43.** $x = -\frac{3}{5}$, $y = \frac{126}{25}$ **44.** φ **45.** $x = -\frac{1}{3}$, $y = \frac{1}{3}$; $x = 1, y = 3$ **46.** φ

47. $x = -3, y = 0$ **48.** φ

CHAPTER 16

multiplying and dividing polynomials

16-1

OBJECTIVE:
To multiply two polynomials using the vertical form algorithm.

Multiplying Polynomials

In Chapter 12, you learned how to find the expansion of two polynomial factors. In that chapter you used the Distributive Property to find expansions.

EXAMPLE

Expand $(x^2 + 3x + 5)(2x - 6)$.

$$
\begin{aligned}
(x^2 + 3x + 5)(2x - 6) &= (x^2 + 3x + 5)(2x) + (x^2 + 3x + 5)(-6) \\
&= x^2 \cdot 2x + 3x \cdot 2x + 5 \cdot 2x \\
&\qquad + x^2 \cdot (-6) + 3x \cdot (-6) + 5(-6) \\
&= 2x^3 + 6x^2 + 10x - 6x^2 - 18x - 30 \\
&= 2x^3 - 8x - 30
\end{aligned}
$$

This section is primarily review, except that analogies to whole number arithmetic are stressed.

There is another form to write the expansion of two polynomial factors. This other form makes the mental computation and simplification of terms easier. It is similar to the way you multiply two whole numbers in arithmetic.

For example, multiplying 379 by 84 requires six multiplications: $4 \cdot 9, \ 4 \cdot 70, \ 4 \cdot 300, \ 80 \cdot 9, \ 80 \cdot 70, \ 80 \cdot 300$.

$$
\begin{array}{r}
3\,7\,9 \\
\times\ 8\,4 \\
\hline
\end{array}
$$

Using the usual method you must be careful to keep units in the units column, tens in the tens column, and so on.

Repeated comparisons to whole number arithmetic are made to prepare students for Section 16-3.

CORRECT	INCORRECT
3 7 9	3 7 9
$\times$ 8 4	$\times$ 8 4
1 5 1 6 $= 379 \cdot 4$	1 5 1 6
3 0 3 2 $= 379 \cdot 80$	3 0 3 2
3 1 8 3 6 $= 379 \cdot 84$	4 5 4 8

Using a form such as that used in arithmetic, you may find the expansion of $(x^2 + 3x + 5)(2x - 6)$. Notice, however, that no terms need to be "carried" to the next column.

$$
\begin{array}{r}
x^2 + 3x + 5 \\
2x - 6 \\
\hline
\end{array}
$$

$$-6x^2 - 18x - 30 = (x^2 + 3x + 5)(-6)$$
$$+2x^3 + 6x^2 + 10x = (x^2 + 3x + 5)(2x)$$
$$\overline{2x^3 - 8x - 30} = (x^2 + 3x + 5)(2x - 6)$$

In arithmetic, you must watch the place value of each column. A similar concern occurs in the multiplication of polynomials. You should keep monomials with identical variable parts in the same column. This makes adding the partial products easier.

CORRECT	INCORRECT
$2x^2 + 3xy + y^2$	$2x^2 + 3xy + y^2$
$2x - 2y$	$2x - 2y$
$-4x^2y - 6xy^2 - 2y^3$	$-4x^2y - 6xy^2 - 2y^3$
$+4x^3 + 6x^2y + 2xy^2$	$+4x^3 + 6x^2y + 2xy^2$
$4x^3 + 2x^2y - 4xy^2 - 2y^3$	? ? ?

EXERCISES

Find each product.

1. $x + 3$
$x - 2$

2. $2x - 3y$
$2x + 3y$

3. $2x + 3y$
$2x + 3y$

4. $5a - b$
$5a - b$

5. $x^2 + x + 1$
$x + 1$

6. $x^2 + x + 1$
$x - 1$

7. $x^4 + x^3 + x^2 + x + 1$
$x - 1$

8. $x^2 + 2x + 1$
$x + 1$

9. $x^2 - 2x + 1$
$x - 1$

10. $a^3b + a^2b^2 + ab^3$
$a + b$

Able students may need only a
minimal assignment for
review purposes.

11. $x^2 + 2x + 1$
$\underline{x^2 + 2x + 1}$

12. $x^2 + 2x + 1$
$\underline{x^2 - 2x + 1}$

13. $3x^2 + 5xy + 6y^2$
$\underline{2x^2y + 2xy^2}$

14. $x + y + z$
$\underline{a + b}$

15. $3 + 5y + y^2$
$\underline{2 + y}$

16. $xy + 2xy^3$
$\underline{xy^2 - 2xy^4}$

17. $a^4 + 2a^2b^2 + b^4$
$\underline{a^2 + b^2}$

18. $x^3 + x^2 + x + 1$
$\underline{x^3 - x^2 + x - 1}$

19. $x^3 + x^2 + x + 1$
$\underline{x^2 - 1}$

20. $3a^3 + 2a + 1$
$\underline{a^2 + 5}$

16-2
Order of Terms

OBJECTIVE:

To arrange the terms of a
polynomial in ascending or
descending order relative to the
variable specified.

In writing polynomials, it often is helpful to write the terms so that powers of a variable are in **ascending** or **descending order.** For example, in $3x^5 + 2x^3 + 5x^2 + 3$, the powers of x are in descending order: 5, 3, 2, 0. That is, the powers of x become smaller as you read left-to-right.

EXAMPLE

Rewrite $15z^3 + 13z + 8z^4 + 16$ so that the powers of z are in ascending order.

$$15z^3 + 13z + 8z^4 + 16 = 16 + 13z + 15z^3 + 8z^4$$

3	1	4	0	0	1	3	4

Unordered powers of z | Powers of z in ascending order

Stress this. →

There are difficulties, of course, if there is more than one variable in a polynomial. In such cases, you should arrange one of the variables in ascending or descending order.

EXAMPLE

Rewrite $7xy^2 - 13x^3y^4 - 8x + 16xy^5$ so that the powers of y are in descending order.

$$7xy^2 - 13x^3y^4 - 8x + 16xy^5 = 16xy^5 - 13x^3y^4 - 7xy^2 - 8x$$

2	4	0	5	5	4	2	0

Unordered powers of y | Powers of y in descending order

If, however, you are interested in the variable x, the polynomial could be written in the following form.

$$7xy^2 - 13x^3y^4 - 8x + 16xy^5 = -13x^3y^4 + (16y^5 + 7y^2 - 8)x$$

1	3	1	1	3	1
	Unordered powers of x			Powers of x in descending order	

Writing polynomials so that the powers of a variable are in ascending or descending order often makes the multiplication of polynomials easier.

Remember that in arithmetic, the place value system for whole numbers uses descending order.

EXAMPLE

Rewrite 36,872 in an expanded form to show the descending order of the powers of 10.

$$36{,}872 = 3 \cdot 10^4 + 6 \cdot 10^3 + 8 \cdot 10^2 + 7 \cdot 10 + 2$$

4   3   2   1   0
Descending powers of 10

If $t = 10$, then the following is true.

$$36{,}872 = 3t^4 + 6t^3 + 8t^2 + 7t + 2$$

4   3   2   1   0
Descending powers of t

EXERCISES

1. $x^5 + x^3 + x^2 + 1$ **2.** $3x^2y + 6xy + 5y^2$ **3.** $2ax^3 - 3bx^2 - 5cx$ **4.** $x^3y^2z + x^2y^2z^2 + xy^2z^3$ **5.** $-3x^4 + x^2y^2 + 2xyz^2 - 16$ **6.** $1 + w + w^2 + w^3$ **7.** $-x^4 + xw - xw^2z - w^3z^2$ **8.** $5s^2t^2u^2v^2 + 16stuvw$ **9.** $1 + x^3 - x^2w + xw^2 + w^3$ **10.** $1 - 5s^4w + s^3w^2 - s^3w^3$ **11.** $x^4z + x^3y^2 + x^2yz + xy$ **12.** $8p^2q^2 + 27pq - p + 1$

Arrange the terms of each polynomial so that the powers of x are in descending order.

1. $1 + x^3 + x^5 + x^2$

2. $6xy + 5y^2 + 3x^2y$

3. $-3bx^2 - 5cx + 2ax^3$

4. $xy^2z^3 + x^3y^2z + x^2y^2z^2$

5. $2xyz^2 - 3x^4 - 16 + (xy)^2$

Arrange the terms of each polynomial so that the powers of w are in ascending order.

6. $1 + w^2 + w^3 + w$

7. $xw - w^3z^2 - xw^2z - x^4$

8. $16stuvw + 5s^2t^2u^2v^2$

9. $x^3 + x^2w + xw^2 + w^3 + 1$

10. $1 + s^3w^2 - (sw)^3 - 5s^4w$

Arrange the terms of each polynomial so that the powers of the variable occurring most often are in descending order.

11. $xy + x^3y^2 + x^2yz + x^4z$

12. $27pq + 8p^2q^2 - p + 1$

13. $st^3 + s^2t^2 + s^3t + 5s^4$
14. $3x^3y^3 + x^5y^5 + 5x^2y^2 + 7$
15. $x^2 + 2xy + y^2$

Arrange the terms of each polynomial so that the powers of the variable occurring most often are in ascending order.
16. $xy + x^3y^2 + x^2yz + x^4z$
17. $27pq + 8p^2q^2 - p + 1$
18. $st^3 + s^2t^2 + s^3t + 5s^4$
19. $3x^3y^3 + x^5y^5 + 5x^2y^2 + 7$
20. $x^2 + 2xy + y^2$

Expand each product two ways.
  a. As written
  b. By first arranging the powers of x in descending order in each polynomial

21. $\quad x + 3$
$\quad\underline{-2 + x}$

22. $x - y$
$\underline{y + x}$

23. $1 + x^2 + x$
$\quad\quad\underline{x + 1}$

24. $1 + x^2 + x$
$\quad\quad\underline{x - 1}$

25. $3xy + x^2 + y^2$
$\quad\underline{y^2 - x^2 - 2xy}$

26. $1 + x + x^2 + x^3$
$\quad\quad\quad\quad\underline{1 - x}$

Expand each product two ways.
  a. As written
  b. By first arranging the terms in each polynomial so that the powers of x are in ascending order

27. $\quad x + 5$
$\quad\underline{-4 + x}$

28. $2x - 2y$
$\underline{2y + 2x}$

29. $1 + x^4 + x^2$
$\quad\quad\underline{x^2 + 1}$

30. $1 + x^2 + x$
$\quad\quad\underline{x - 1}$

31. $2xy + x^2 + y^2$
$\quad\underline{y^2 - x^2 - 3xy}$

32. $x^3 + x^2 + x + 1$
$\quad\quad\quad\underline{x - 1}$

33. In which problems of Exercises **21–32** does writing polynomial factors in some order help make the multiplication easier?
34. Suppose you want a product of two polynomials to have the

35. In descending order

powers of the variable in ascending order. In what order should the powers of the polynomial factors be written before multiplying?

35. Suppose you want a product of two polynomials to have the powers of the variable in descending order. In what order should the powers of the polynomial factors be written before multiplying?

16-3
Dividing Polynomials

OBJECTIVE:

To find the quotient of two polynomials by the "long division" algorithm.

This rather elaborate treatment assumes that in some classes the chapter will be assigned only to more able students, working much on their own. If so, poor readers should be free to consult with other students.

You have seen that multiplication of polynomials is similar to the multiplication of whole numbers. In this section, you will see that you may divide polynomials much as you divide whole numbers.

Before studying the division of polynomials, review the method used in whole number division. Study the solution of the problem $24073 \div 63 = ?$ closely.

Step 1 Find the first digit of the quotient, 3. Multiply this partial quotient by the divisor and subtract from the dividend.

$$
\begin{array}{r}
3 \\
63\overline{)24073} \\
-18900 \quad 300 \cdot 63 \\
\hline
5173
\end{array}
$$

Step 2 Find the next digit of the quotient, 8. Multiply this partial quotient by the divisor and subtract from the first difference.

$$
\begin{array}{r}
38 \\
63\overline{)24073} \\
-18900 \quad 300 \cdot 63 \\
\hline
5173 \\
-5040 \quad 80 \cdot 63 \\
\hline
133
\end{array}
$$

Step 3 Find the next digit of the quotient, 2. Multiply this partial quotient by the divisor and subtract from the second difference.

$$
\begin{array}{r}
382 \\
63\overline{)24073} \\
-18900 \quad 300 \cdot 63 \\
\hline
5173 \\
-5040 \quad 80 \cdot 63 \\
\hline
133 \\
-126 \quad 2 \cdot 63 \\
\hline
7
\end{array}
$$

Step 4 The last difference is less than
the divisor. Complete the quotient by adding

$$\frac{\text{the last difference}}{\text{divisor}}$$

to the quotient.

$$
\begin{array}{r}
382\frac{7}{63} \\
63\overline{)24073} \\
-18900 \\
\hline
5173 \\
-5040 \\
\hline
133 \\
-126 \\
\hline
7
\end{array}
$$

$$24073 \div 63 = 382\frac{7}{63}$$

$$= 382\frac{1}{9}$$

The method you will use in the division of polynomials is similar to the method used to divide whole numbers. For example, $(x^3 + 6x^2 + 14x + 21) \div (x + 3)$ may be written in the long-division form. Assume that the divisor does not equal 0.

$$x + 3\overline{)x^3 + 6x^2 + 14x + 21}$$

Powers of x: 1   0 | 3   2   1   0

           Divisor | Dividend

Notice that each polynomial is written with the powers of x in descending order. This arrangement copies the place-value system of whole numbers which places the powers of 10 in descending order.

In whole number division, you find the quotient of two whole numbers digit by digit. In a similar way, the quotient of two polynomials is found term by term.

To obtain the first term of the quotient in the example, divide x into x^3. That is, divide the term in the divisor with the highest degree, x, into the term in the dividend with the highest degree, x^3. $x^3 \div x = x^2$.

$$
\begin{array}{r}
x^2 \\
x + 3\overline{)x^3 + 6x^2 + 14x + 21}
\end{array}
$$

The divisor is multiplied by x^2 and the result subtracted from the dividend. It is important to remember that $-(x^3 + 3x^2) = -x^3 - 3x^2$.

$$
\begin{array}{r}
x^2 \\
x + 3\overline{)\ x^3 + 6x^2 + 14x + 21} \\
-(x^3 + 3x^2) \\
\hline
3x^2 + 14x + 21
\end{array}
\qquad x^2(x + 3)
$$

Again, a division is performed to obtain the next term of the quotient. $3x^2 \div x = 3x$.

$$
\begin{array}{r}
x^2 \\
x + 3\overline{)\ x^3 + 6x^2 + 14x + 21} \\
-(x^3 + 3x^2) \\
\hline
3x^2 + 14x + 21
\end{array}
\qquad x^2(x + 3)
$$

The divisor is multiplied by $3x$ and the result subtracted from the previous remainder, $3x^2 + 14x + 21$.

$$
\begin{array}{r}
x^2 + 3x \\
x + 3\overline{)\ x^3 + 6x^2 + 14x + 21} \\
-(x^3 + 3x^2) \\
\hline
3x^2 + 14x + 21 \\
-(3x^2 + 9x) \\
\hline
5x + 21
\end{array}
\qquad
\begin{array}{l}
\\
x^2(x + 3) \\
\\
3x(x + 3)
\end{array}
$$

Notice that throughout the problem, terms with identical variable parts are kept in the same column. The next term of the quotient is found by dividing x into $5x$.

$$
\begin{array}{r}
x^2 + 3x \\
x + 3\overline{)\ x^3 + 6x^2 + 14x + 21} \\
-(x^3 + 3x^2) \\
\hline
3x^2 + 14x + 21 \\
-(3x^2 + 9x) \\
\hline
5x + 21
\end{array}
\qquad
\begin{array}{l}
\\
x^2(x + 3) \\
\\
3x(x + 3)
\end{array}
$$

The divisor is multiplied by 5, and the result is subtracted from the previous remainder, $5x + 21$.

$$\begin{array}{r}
x^2 + 3x + 5 \\
x + 3 \overline{) x^3 + 6x^2 + 14x + 21} \\
\underline{-(x^3 + 3x^2)} \\
3x^2 + 14x + 21 \\
\underline{-(3x^2 + 9x)} \\
5x + 21 \\
\underline{-(5x + 15)} \\
6
\end{array}$$

$x^2(x + 3)$

$3x(x + 3)$

$5(x + 3)$

Stress this, as suggested on page 457.

Since the degree of the remainder, 6, is less than the degree of the divisor, the process stops. All that remains is to express the remainder in fractional form. Notice that the condition $x \neq -3$ must be stated to ensure a nonzero denominator.

$$\begin{array}{r}
x^2 + 3x + 5 + \dfrac{6}{x + 3}, x \neq -3 \\
x + 3 \overline{) x^3 + 6x^2 + 14x + 21} \\
\underline{-(x^3 + 3x^2)} \\
3x^2 + 14x + 21 \\
\underline{-(3x^2 + 9x)} \\
5x + 21 \\
\underline{-(5x + 15)} \\
6
\end{array}$$

Just as in whole number division, an expression has been found such that the quotient times the divisor equals the dividend.

Students should be encouraged to check this.

$$\left(x^2 + 3x + 5 + \frac{6}{x + 3}\right)(x + 3) = x^3 + 6x^2 + 14x + 21$$

When dividing with whole numbers, time and effort are saved by not recording digits until you are ready to use them in computation.

$$\begin{array}{r}
162\dfrac{19}{37} \\
37\overline{)6013} \\
\underline{-3700} \\
2313 \\
\underline{-2220} \\
93 \\
\underline{-74} \\
19
\end{array}
\qquad
\begin{array}{r}
162\dfrac{19}{37} \\
37\overline{)6013} \\
\underline{37} \\
231 \\
\underline{222} \\
93 \\
\underline{74} \\
19
\end{array}$$

More time is saved by not recording monomials until you are ready to use them in computation.

EXAMPLE

This shortcut is analogous to that of the usual algorithm for whole numbers.

Divide $3x^3 + 4x^2y - 3xy^2 + 2y^3$ by $x + 2y$.

$$
\begin{array}{r}
3x^2 \;-\; 2xy \;+\; y^2 \\
x + 2y \overline{)\; 3x^3 + 4x^2y - 3xy^2 + 2y^3} \\
-(3x^3 + 6x^2y) \\
\overline{ -2x^2y - 3xy^2 } \\
-(-2x^2y - 4xy^2) \\
\overline{ xy^2 + 2y^3} \\
-(xy^2 + 2y^3) \\
\overline{ 0}
\end{array}
$$

Since the remainder is zero in the example, the divisor is a **factor** of the dividend. You may write the dividend as a product of polynomial factors.

$$3x^3 + 4x^2y - 3xy^2 + 2y^3 = (3x^2 - 2xy + y^2)(x + 2y)$$

EXERCISES

1. a. $(2x^3)\ (2x^2 + 3)$ **b.** $(-3x^2)$ $(2x^2 + 3)$ **c.** $(5)\ (2x^2 + 3)$
2. a. $(2x^2)\ (2x^3 - 3x^2 + 5)$
b. $(3)\ (2x^3 - 3x^2 + 5)$
3. a. $2x^2 + x - 5$ **b.** Yes
c. The multiplication was performed incorrectly.

Write the multiplication needed to obtain the product indicated by each arrow.

$$
\begin{array}{r}
2x^3 - 3x^2 + 15 \\
2x^2 + 3 \overline{)\; 4x^5 - 6x^4 + 6x^3 + x^2 + 15} \\
-(4x^5 + 6x^3) \quad \leftarrow \textbf{a.} \\
\overline{ -6x^4 + x^2 } \\
-(-6x^4 - 9x^2) \quad \leftarrow \textbf{b.} \\
\overline{ 10x^2 + 15} \\
-(10x^2 + 15) \quad \leftarrow \textbf{c.} \\
\overline{ 0}
\end{array}
$$

1. (shown above)

$$
\begin{array}{r}
2x^2 + 3 \\
2x^3 - 3x^2 + 5 \overline{)\; 4x^5 - 6x^4 + 6x^3 + x^2 + 15} \\
-(4x^5 - 6x^4 + 10x^2) \quad \leftarrow \textbf{a.} \\
\overline{ 6x^3 - 9x^2 + 15} \\
-(6x^3 - 9x^2 + 15) \quad \leftarrow \textbf{b.} \\
\overline{ 0}
\end{array}
$$

2. (shown above)

3. a. Multiply $(2x^2 + x - 5)$ by $(x^2 - 3x + 6)$. Then divide the product by $(x^2 - 3x + 6)$.

4. $x + 2$ **5.** $x + 5 + \dfrac{2}{x - 2}$
6. $x^2 - 2xy + y^2$ **7.** $x + y$
8. $2x + 3 + \dfrac{x + 1}{x^2 + 5x + 1}$
9. $3a + 5b + \dfrac{b^2}{a - 2b}$ **10.** $a - b$
11. $x^2 + 2xw + w^2$ **12.** $x + 2y$
13. $3x + 5$ **14.** $a^2b + ab + b$
15. $x^4 + x^3 + x^2 + x + 1$
16. $x^3 + x^2 + x + 1$

b. Can division be used in *all* cases to check multiplication of polynomials?

c. What does it mean if in a check you obtain a nonzero remainder?

Perform each division and check your work.

$$
\begin{array}{r}
2x^2 + 1 + \dfrac{5x^2 + 4}{3x^4 + 2x^2 + 1}
\end{array}
$$

$$\textbf{Sample}\quad 3x^4 + 2x^2 + 1 \overline{\smash{)}\, 6x^6 + 7x^4 + 9x^2 + 5}$$
$$
\begin{array}{r}
-(6x^6 + 4x^4 + 2x^2) \\ \hline
3x^4 + 7x^2 + 5 \\
-(3x^4 + 2x^2 + 1) \\ \hline
5x^2 + 4
\end{array}
$$

Check:

$$
\begin{array}{r}
3x^4 + 2x^2 + 1 \\
2x^2 + 1 \\ \hline
3x^4 + 2x^2 + 1 \\
6x^6 + 4x^4 + 2x^2 \\ \hline
6x^6 + 7x^4 + 4x^2 + 1 \\
+ (5x^2 + 4) \\ \hline
6x^6 + 7x^4 + 9x^2 + 5
\end{array}
$$

Divisor
times the partial quotient,

plus the remainder,
equals the dividend.

4. $x - 5 \overline{\smash{)}\, x^2 - 3x - 10}$

5. $x - 2 \overline{\smash{)}\, x^2 + 3x - 8}$

6. $x - y \overline{\smash{)}\, x^3 - 3x^2y + 3xy^2 - y^3}$

7. $x^2 + 2xy + y^2 \overline{\smash{)}\, x^3 + 3x^2y + 3xy^2 + y^3}$

8. $x^2 + 5x + 1 \overline{\smash{)}\, 2x^3 + 13x^2 + 18x + 4}$

9. $a - 2b \overline{\smash{)}\, 3a^2 - ab - 9b^2}$

Divide. First arrange the terms of each polynomial so that the powers of one variable are in descending order.

10. $(a^2 - b^2) \div (b + a)$

11. $(3xw^2 + w^3 + x^3 + 3x^2w) \div (w + x)$

12. $(x^3 + 4y^3 + x^2y) \div (2y^2 + x^2 - xy)$

13. $(8xz + 5z + 3x^2z) \div (z + xz)$

14. $(2a^3b - 3b - ab - a^2b) \div (2a - 3)$

15. Divide $(x^5 - 1)$ by $(x - 1)$. Hint: To keep like terms in their proper columns, remember that $x^5 - 1 = x^5 + 0x^4 + 0x^3 + 0x^2 + 0x - 1$.

16. Divide $(x^4 - 1)$ by $(x - 1)$.

For Exercise 15, ask if the division is analogous to $1 \overline{\smash{)}\, 100001}$.

State whether or not the first polynomial in each pair is a factor of the second.

17. $x - 1, x^3 + 2x^2 + 2x - 5$

18. $x - 1, x^2 + 2x - 2$

19. $x - 3, 17x^2 - 31x - 60$

20. $x - 3, x^3 - 4x^2 + 2x + 8$

21. $x + 2, x^3 + 5x^2 + x - 10$

22. $x + 2, 5x^2 - 3x - 6$

23. $2x^2 + x + 1, 4x^3 + 8x^2 + 7x + 1$

24. $2x^2 + x + 1, 6x^3 + 3x^2 + 3x$

Exercises 25 and 26 anticipate Section 16-4.

25. Let $p(x)$ represent the second polynomial in each pair in Exercises **17–22**. If $x - c$, the first polynomial, is a factor of $p(x)$, what seems to be a true statement about $p(c)$?

26. If $x - c$ is a factor of $p(x)$ in Exercises **17–22,** is there a relationship between each c and the constant term in each second polynomial? If there is a relationship, what is it?

16-4
Finding Factors

OBJECTIVE:

To factor $p(x)$ as $(x - c) \cdot g(x)$ if $p(c) = 0$.

In the last set of exercises, you were asked to investigate the following statement.

If $x - c$ is a factor of a polynomial $p(x)$, then $p(c) = 0$.

This is a true statement. The converse of this statement also is true and is a great aid in factoring polynomials.

If $p(x) = 0$ is a polynomial equation and $p(c) = 0$, then $x - c$ is a factor of $p(x)$.

EXAMPLE

Factor $x^3 - 6x^2 - x + 30$.

First, find a value c such that $p(c) = 0$. Unfortunately, trial and error methods must be used at this time.

Value for c	$c^3 - 6c^2 - c + 30$	Value for $p(c)$
0	$0^3 - 6 \cdot 0^2 - 0 + 30$	30
1	$1^3 - 6 \cdot 1^2 - 1 + 30$	24
2	$2^3 - 6 \cdot 2^2 - 2 + 30$	12
3	$3^3 - 6 \cdot 3^2 - 3 + 30$	0

Stress again the analogy with whole numbers. With whole numbers also, a zero remainder means the divisor is a factor of the dividend.

This shows that $x - 3$ should be a factor of $x^3 - 6x^2 - x + 30$. Check this by division.

$$
\begin{array}{r}
x^2 - 3x - 10 \\
x - 3 \overline{)\, x^3 - 6x^2 - x + 30} \\
-(x^3 - 3x^2) \\
\hline
-3x^2 - x \\
-(-3x^2 + 9x) \\
\hline
-10x + 30 \\
-(-10x + 30) \\
\hline
0
\end{array}
$$

This shows that $x - 3$ is a factor of $x^3 - 6x^2 - x + 30$. All that remains is to factor the quadratic expression.

Divide by $x - 3$. $\qquad x^3 - 6x^2 - x + 30 = (x - 3)(x^2 - 3x - 10)$
Factor the quadratic expression. $\qquad\qquad\qquad = (x - 3)(x - 5)(x + 2)$

Guessing to find a value of c such that $p(c) = 0$ can take a lot of time. However, the process is made easier if you remember the following fact.

If $c \in \mathbf{Z}$, $p(x)$ is a polynomial, and $p(c) = 0$, then c is a factor of the constant term of $p(x)$.

EXAMPLE

This statement limits the amount of guessing and testing required to factor a polynomial.

Solve $x^3 - 3x^2 - 4x + 12 = 0$ by factoring. The factors of 12 are 1, 2, 3, 4, 6, and 12. If $p(x) \neq 0$ for any of these replacements, remember to try their additive inverses.

Value of c	$c^3 - 3c^2 - 4c + 12$	$p(c)$
1	$1^3 - 3 \cdot 1^2 - 4 \cdot 1 + 12$	6
2	$2^3 - 3 \cdot 2^2 - 4 \cdot 2 + 12$	0

$$
\begin{array}{r}
x^2 - x - 6 \\
x - 2 \overline{)\, x^3 - 3x^2 - 4x + 12} \\
-(x^3 - 2x^2) \\
\hline
- x^2 - 4x \\
-(- x^2 + 2x) \\
\hline
-6x + 12 \\
-(-6x + 12) \\
\hline
0
\end{array}
$$

Divide by $x - 2$.

$$x^3 - 3x^2 - 4x + 12 = 0 \Leftrightarrow (x - 2)(x^2 - x - 6) = 0$$

Factor the quadratic expression.

$$\Leftrightarrow (x - 2)(x - 3)(x + 2) = 0$$

$$\Leftrightarrow x - 2 = 0 \text{ or } x - 3 = 0$$
$$\text{or } x + 2 = 0$$
$$\Leftrightarrow x = 2 \text{ or } x = 3 \text{ or } x = -2$$

The solution set is $\{-2, 2, 3\}$. In this case, the solutions are all integers, and they are all factors of the constant term, 12.

EXERCISES

1. $(x - 1)(x - 2)(x - 3)$
2. $(x - 2)(x + 2)(x - 3)$
3. $(x - 3)(2x - 3)(x + 2)$
4. $(x - 4)^3$ 5. $(x - 1)(2x + 3)$ $(2x - 1)$ 6. $(x - 1)(x^2 + 4)$ $(x - 2)(x + 2)$ 7. $x = 1, 2, 5$
8. $x = 1, 2$ 9. $x = 1$ 10. ϕ
11. $x = 1$ 12. $x = 2$ 13. $\{1, 2, 3\}$
14. $\{x \mid 1 < x < 2\} \cup \{x \mid x > 3\}$
15. $\{x \mid x < 1\} \cup \{x \mid 2 < x < 3\}$ 16. $p(x) \neq 0$ and the values are either positive or negative, but not both.
17. $f(x) = 0$, Yes

For Exercises 7–12, remind students that $a \cdot b \cdot \ldots \cdot c = 0$ $\Leftrightarrow a = 0$ or $b = 0$ or...$c = 0$.

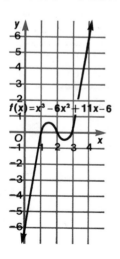

Each polynomial has as a factor $x - 1$, $x - 2$, $x - 3$, or $x - 4$. Factor each expression completely.

1. $x^3 - 6x^2 + 11x - 6$
2. $x^3 - 3x^2 - 4x + 12$
3. $2x^3 - 5x^2 - 9x + 18$
4. $x^3 - 12x^2 + 48x - 64$
5. $4x^3 - 7x + 3$
6. $x^5 - x^4 - 16x + 16$

Solve each polynomial equation where x is a variable on the set of integers.

7. $x^3 - 8x^2 + 17x - 10 = 0$
8. $x^3 - 4x^2 + 5x - 2 = 0$
9. $x^3 - 3x^2 + 3x - 1 = 0$
10. $6x^3 - 17x^2 + 4x - 12 = 0$
11. $x^3 - x^2 + x - 1 = 0$
12. $x^3 - x^2 - x - 2 = 0$

Use the graph for Exercises **13–17**.

13. State the solution set for $x^3 - 6x^2 + 11x - 6 = 0$.
14. State the solution set for $x^3 - 6x^2 + 11x - 6 > 0$.
15. State the solution set for $x^3 - 6x^2 + 11x - 6 < 0$.
16. Assume you know two consecutive solutions of a polynomial equation $p(x) = 0$. Two solutions are consecutive if there are no other solutions between them. What can you say about the value of $p(x)$ between those two solutions?
17. Assume you know that $f(a)$ is positive and $f(b)$ is negative. As a model use $f(1.5)$ and $f(2.5)$ in the graph. What do you think must happen to $f(x)$ between $f(a)$ and $f(b)$? Can it happen more than once in the interval?

Solve each polynomial equation.

18. $2x + 8 = 0$

19. $x - 4 = 0$

20. $2x^2 + 4x + 4 = 0$

21. $x^2 + 6x + 9 = 0$

22. $x^2 - x - 20 = 0$

23. $x^3 - 8 = 0$

24. $x^3 + 2x^2 - 15x - 36 = 0$

25. $x^3 - x^2 - 22x + 40 = 0$

26. Using the results of Exercises **18** and **19,** how many solutions do you think a polynomial of degree 1 may have at most?

27. Using the results of Exercises **20–22,** how many solutions do you think a polynomial of degree 2 may have at most?

28. Using the results of Exercises **23–25,** how many solutions do you think a polynomial of degree 3 may have at most?

29. How many solutions do you think a polynomial of degree 4 may have at most? Can it have fewer?

30. The sides of a rectangular solid measure $x - 1$, $x - 3$, and $x + 2$ feet. The volume of the solid is 18 cubic feet. Find the value of x. Hint: Write a polynomial of degree 3 and solve it by factoring.

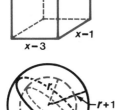

31. A ball is blown up to have a radius of r feet. Later it is blown up so that its radius is increased by 1 foot. Its final volume is $\dfrac{256\pi}{3}$ cubic feet. What was the original radius r? The volume of a sphere is given by the formula $V = \dfrac{4}{3}\pi r^3$.

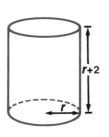

32. The height of a cylinder is two meters longer than its radius. The volume of the cylinder is $\dfrac{66}{7}$ m³. What is the radius of the cylinder? The volume of a cylinder is given by $V = \pi r^2 h$. Let $\pi = \dfrac{22}{7}$.

Excursions in Mathematics:
Solving Cubic Equations with Formulas

Thus far in this text, you have seen formulas that may be used to solve polynomial equations of degrees 1 and 2.

Degree	Equation	Formula for Solutions
1	$mx + b = 0$	$x = \dfrac{-b}{m}$
2	$ax^2 + bx + c = 0$	$x = \dfrac{-b \pm \sqrt{b^2 - 4ac}}{2a}$

The formula used to solve a polynomial of degree 3 is a bit more complicated, but it does exist.

Consider a cubic equation $y^3 + py^2 + qy + r = 0$. If you let $y = x - \dfrac{p}{3}$, the equation becomes $x^3 + ax + b = 0$. In this equation, a and b have the following values.

$$a = \frac{1}{3}(3q - p^2) \quad \text{and} \quad b = \frac{1}{27}(2p^3 - 9pq + 27r)$$

Let A and B have the following values.

$$A = \sqrt[3]{-\frac{b}{2} + \sqrt{\frac{b^2}{4} + \frac{a^3}{27}}} \qquad B = \sqrt[3]{-\frac{b}{a} - \sqrt{\frac{b^2}{4} + \frac{a^3}{27}}}$$

Then the values of x are given by the following formulas.

$$x = A + B$$

$$x = -\frac{A + B}{2} + \frac{A - B}{2}\sqrt{-3}$$

$$x = -\frac{A + B}{2} - \frac{A - B}{2}\sqrt{-3}$$

EXERCISES

1. Use the previous formulas to solve each equation.
  a. $y^3 - 8 = 0$
  b. $y^3 - 6y^2 + 11y - 6 = 0$
  c. $y^3 - 6y^2 + 12y - 8 = 0$
  d. $y^3 + y^2 + y + 1 = 0$

2. Write two of the cubic solution formulas in terms of a and b.

3. Letting $a = \dfrac{1}{3}(3q - p^2)$ and $b = \dfrac{1}{27}(2p^3 - 9pq + 27r)$, rewrite one of your answers in Exercise **2** in terms of p, q, and r.

The other formulas are variations on the preceding.

4. A formula exists to solve a fourth degree equation in terms of its coefficients. No formulas exist for the solution of equations of higher degree.

4. Try to find the formulas used to solve polynomial equations of degrees 4, 5, and 6. Use reference books, not computation.

Chapter Summary

1. Two polynomials may be multiplied in a method similar to that used in the multiplication of whole numbers.
2. The powers of a variable in a polynomial are in descending order if they become smaller as the polynomial is read left-to-right.
3. The powers of a variable in a polynomial are in ascending order if they become larger as the polynomial is read left-to-right.
4. One polynomial may be divided into another using a method similar to that used in the division of whole numbers.
5. If the remainder of a polynomial division problem is zero, then the divisor is a factor of the dividend.
6. If $x - c$ is a factor of a polynomial $p(x)$, then $p(c) = 0$.
7. If $p(x) = 0$ is a polynomial equation and $p(c) = 0$, then $x - c$ is a factor of $p(x)$.
8. If $p(x) = 0$ is a polynomial equation and $p(c) = 0$, then c is a factor of the constant term in $p(x)$.

REVIEW EXERCISES 16-1, 16-2

1. $x^2 + 4x - 45$
2. $y^2 - 4y - 45$ 3. $x^3 - y^3$
4. $-p^3q + 2p^2q + p^2q^2 + 3pq - 3pq^2$ 5. $3x^4y + 5x^3y^2 - 6x^2y^3 - 4xy^4$ 6. $2m^4 - 17m^3 + 26m^2 + 16m - 15$
7. $x^4 - 9x^3 - 3x^2 + 36x - 4$
8. $a^4 - 3a^3b + 4a^2b^2 + 3ab^3 - 5b^4$ 9. $x^5 - 6x^3 + 6x^2 + 8x - 24$ 10. $x^5 + x^4y^2 + x^3y + x^2y^3 - x^3y^2 - x^2y^4 - xy^3 - y^5$
11. $- 2x^3 + 4x^2y - 5x^2 + 12x + 10xy + 30$
12. $x^6 + x^5 - 3x^4 - 4x^3 - x^2 + 2x + 6$
13. $2x^3y^5 - 6x^3y^3 + 12x^2y^2 - 2xy^3 + 6xy - 4x^2y^4$
14. $-2x^5 - 13x^4 + 9x^3 + 52x^2 + 8x - 24$
15. $x + 3$ 16. $y^2 - 3$
17. $3x^2 + 9x + 8$
18. $3x - 5y + \dfrac{10y^2}{x - 3y}$

Find each product. If necessary, arrange the polynomials so that the powers of one variable are in descending order.

1. $(x - 5)(x + 9)$
2. $(y - 9)(y + 5)$
3. $(x - y)(x^2 + xy + y^2)$
4. $(3p - p^2)(pq + q - q^2)$
5. $(xy^2 + x^2y)(3x^2 + 2xy - 4y^2)$
6. $(m^3 - 2m + 3 - 6m^2)(2m - 5)$
7. $(x + 2)(x - 2)(x^2 - 9x + 1)$
8. $(a^2 - b^2)(a^2 - 3ab + 5b^2)$
9. $(x^3 - 2x + 6)(x^2 - 4)$
10. $(x + y^2)(x^2 - y^2)(x^2 + y)$
11. $(5 + 2x)(6 - x^2 + 2xy)$
12. $(x^2 - x^3 + 2)(3 - 2x^2 + x - x^3)$
13. $(6x - 2y^2x)(y + 2xy^2 - x^2y^3)$
14. $(x + 6 - 2x^2)(7x^2 + 2x - 4 + x^3)$

Divide.

15. $(x^2 + 5x + 6) \div (x + 2)$
16. $(y^4 - 5y^2 + 6) \div (y^2 - 2)$
17. $(3x^3 - 24 + 19x) \div (x - 3)$
18. $(3x^2 - 14xy + 25y^2) \div (x - 3y)$

19. $x - 1 + \dfrac{3}{x - 3}$

20. $x^2 + 4x + 4 + \dfrac{11}{x - 2}$

21. $3x^2 + 2x + 5$

22. $x^2 - x + 9 + \dfrac{13}{2x - 3}$

23. $x + 5$ **24.** $x^2 - 2x + 3$

25. $3x^2 - 5x + 2$

26. $x^2 + 2x - 1$

19. $(x^2 - 4x + 6) \div (x - 3)$

20. $(x^3 + 3 - 4x + 2x^2) \div (x - 2)$

21. $(3x^3 + 11x + 11x^2 + 15) \div (x + 3)$

22. $(2x^3 - 5x^2 + 21x - 14) \div (2x - 3)$

23. $(3x^2 + 14x - 5) \div (3x - 1)$

24. $(x^4 - 4x^3 - 12x + 10x^2 + 9) \div (x^2 - 2x + 3)$

25. $(6x^3 + 19x - 19x^2 - 6) \div (2x - 3)$

26. $(x^4 + 4x^3 - 4x + 1 + 2x^2) \div (2x - 1 + x^2)$

16-3   Is the first polynomial a factor of the second?

27. Yes **28.** No **29.** No
30. Yes **31.** No **32.** No

27. $x + 8, x^2 + 7x - 8$

28. $m - 2, m^3 - 7$

29. $x - 2, x^4 + 4x - 2x^2 + x^3 - 10$

30. $x - 4, x^3 - x^2 - 13x + 4$

31. $2y + 3, 6y^3 + 2y^2 + y - 9$

32. $3x - 2, 9x^3 - 5x - 4x^2 + 8$

16-4   Solve each equation by factoring.

33. $x = 1, -1, 2$

34. ϕ **35.** $x = 2, -2$

36. $x = 5, -4, -3$

37. $x = 0, \dfrac{3}{2}, -5$

38. $x = 1, -1, -5$

39. $x = 4, 5, -10$

40. $x = -1$

33. $x^3 - 2x^2 - x + 2 = 0$ **34.** $x^3 + 4x^2 + x + 6 = 0$

35. $x^3 + 2x^2 - 4x - 8 = 0$ **36.** $x^3 + 2x^2 - 23x - 60 = 0$

37. $2x^3 + 7x^2 - 15x = 0$ **38.** $x^3 + 5x^2 - x - 5 = 0$

39. $x^3 + x^2 - 70x + 200 = 0$ **40.** $x^3 + 3x^2 + 3x + 1 = 0$

CHAPTER 17

algebraic fractions

To find the simplified form of a rational expression and list restrictions on the variables.

17-1
Rational Expressions

A fraction which has polynomials as the numerator and as the denominator is called a **rational expression**.

EXAMPLES

This section offers a substantial review of earlier work.

1. The expression $\dfrac{3}{a^2 - b^2}$ is a rational expression.

2. The expression $\dfrac{x + 2y}{x^2 + 4xy + 4y^2}$ is a rational expression.

As you know, a rational expression is said to be in **simplest form** when the numerator and denominator have no common factor. You reduce fractions by first factoring numerator and denominator into primes. Then the numerator and denominator are divided by any common factors.

EXAMPLES

1. Reduce $\dfrac{32x^2y}{24xy^3}$.

$$\frac{32x^2y}{24xy^3} = \frac{2^5x^2y}{2^3 \cdot 3xy^3} = \frac{2^2x}{3y^2} = \frac{4x}{3y^2} \qquad \text{when } x, y \neq 0$$

2. Write $\dfrac{4x^3 - 4x^2 - 24x}{6x^3y - 36x^2y + 54xy}$ in simplest form.

$$\frac{4x^3 - 4x^2 - 24x}{6x^3y - 36x^2y + 54xy} = \frac{4x(x^2 - x - 6)}{6xy(x^2 - 6x + 9)}$$

$$= \frac{2^2x(x + 2)(x - 3)}{2 \cdot 3xy(x - 3)^2}$$

$$= \frac{2(x + 2)}{3y(x - 3)}$$

$$= \frac{2x + 4}{3xy - 9y} \qquad \text{when } x \neq 0, 3; \ y \neq 0$$

EXERCISES

1. $\frac{s}{30}$ $(2s^2 + 3s + 5)$

2. $5s^3w \ (w - 1)^2$

3. $.01xy(x + 30) \ (x + 40)$

4. $xy^2 \ (8x^4 - 81y^4)$

5. $\frac{wp}{10}$ $(4w^2 - 19w + 10)$

6. $(ab + cd) \ (ab - cd)$

7. $(ax + 3by)^2$ 8. $(x - 2)$ $(x + 2) \ (x^2 + 4) \ (y - z) \ (y + z)$

9. $(x - 1) \ (x + 1)^2$

10. $2(7x - 2y) \ (x - 5y)$

11. $\frac{1}{b}$ $(a + 2b)$ 12. $\frac{x - 1}{x}$

13. $\frac{3}{4x}$ 14. $\frac{x + y}{2x + y}$ 15. $\frac{b + c}{b - c}$

16. $\frac{(a - b) \ (a + b)}{a^2 + b^2}$

Factor each polynomial as a product of primes. Remember to look for a common term and to make numerical coefficients relatively prime.

Sample $\quad \frac{1}{3}x^3y^2z^2 - \frac{1}{3}x^2y^2z^2 - 4xy^2z^2$

Make coefficients relatively prime. $\quad = \frac{1}{3}(x^3y^2z^2 - x^2y^2z^2 - 12xy^2z^2)$

Remove the common term. $\quad = \frac{1}{3}xy^2z^2 \ (x^2 - x - 12)$

Factor the polynomial. $\quad = \frac{1}{3}xy^2z^2 \ (x - 4)(x + 3)$

1. $\frac{s^3}{15} + \frac{s^2}{10} + \frac{s}{6}$

2. $5s^3w^3 - 10s^3w^2 + 5s^3w$

3. $.01x^3y + .7x^2y + 12xy$

4. $8x^5y^2 - 81xy^6$

5. $\frac{2w^3p}{5} - \frac{19w^2p}{10} + wp$

6. $a^2b^2 - c^2d^2$

7. $a^2x^2 + 6abxy + 9b^2y^2$

8. $x^4y^2 - x^4z^2 - 16y^2 + 16z^2$

9. $x^3 + x^2 - x - 1$

10. $14x^2 - 74xy + 20y^2$

Reduce each rational expression to simplest form.

11. $\frac{a^2c - 4b^2c}{abc - 2b^2c}$

12. $\frac{x^4 - 1}{x^4 + x^3 + x^2 + x}$

13. $\frac{3x^3 + 3x^2 + 3x}{4x^4 + 4x^3 + 4x^2}$

14. $\frac{2x^2 + 3xy + y^2}{4x^2 + 4xy + y^2}$

Students may need coaching on factoring in Exercise 15.

15. $\frac{ab^2 + abc + bc + c^2}{ab^2 - abc + bc - c^2}$

16. $\frac{(a^2 - 2ab + b^2)(a^2 + 2ab + b^2)}{a^4 - b^4}$

17. $\frac{x}{x + 1}$ 18. 1 19. $\frac{a + 2b}{a}$

20. a. $x = 3, 2$ b. $x = 3$

c. $x = 3, 2$ 21. $x = 6, -4$

22. $x = 2, -2$, 23. $x = -\frac{3}{2}, \frac{3}{2}$

24. $x = 1, -1$ 25. $x = 0, 3$

26. 0, 3

27. Answers will vary.

Remind students that when a polynomial has 4 unlike terms, they should suspect $(a + b)$ $(c + d)$ as the factored form.

Some students may be thoroughly familiar with Exercise 27. If so, use the exercise for discussion.

17. $\dfrac{x^3 - 2x^2 + x}{x^3 - x^2 - x + 1}$

18. $\dfrac{x^4 - 13x^2 + 36}{(x^2 + x - 6)(x^2 - x - 6)}$

19. $\dfrac{a^2c + a^2d - 4b^2c - 4b^2d}{a^2c + a^2d - 2abc - 2abd}$

20. a. For which real number values of x is the denominator of the following fraction zero?

$$\frac{(x + 3)(x - 2)}{(x - 3)(x - 2)}$$

b. For which real number values of x is the denominator of the reduced form of Part **a** zero?

c. For which real number values of x is the following sentence meaningless?

$$\frac{(x + 3)(x - 2)}{(x - 3)(x - 2)} = \frac{x + 3}{x - 3}$$

Factor each denominator into primes. Then tell with which real number values x cannot be replaced.

21. $\dfrac{a^2x^2 + ax + 1}{x^2 - 2x - 24}$ **22.** $\dfrac{3}{x^2 - 4}$ **23.** $\dfrac{7x + 5}{4x^2 - 9}$

24. $\dfrac{17}{x^4 - 1}$ **25.** $\dfrac{x^2 + x - 12}{x^2 - 3x}$

26. Name real number values for x for which the following statement is not true. $\dfrac{(x + 4)(x - 3)}{x(x - 3)} = \dfrac{x + 4}{x}$

27. Several errors in reducing rational expressions are shown. For each expression, substitute 1 for x to see that the error makes a false statement.

a. $\dfrac{3x + 6}{4x + 4} = \dfrac{3(\cancel{x} + 2)}{4(\cancel{x} + 1)} = \dfrac{3 \cdot 2}{4 \cdot 1} = \dfrac{6}{4} = \dfrac{3}{.2}$

b. $\dfrac{x^2 + 2\cancel{x} + 1}{2\cancel{x} + 1} = \dfrac{x^2 + 1}{1} = x^2 + 1$

c. $\dfrac{x^2 + x + 3}{3x + 9} = \dfrac{x^2 + \cancel{x + 3}}{3(\cancel{x + 3})} = \dfrac{x^2}{3}$

28. a. Not permissible
b. Not permissible
c. Permissible d. Permissible
29. Answers will vary.

28. Discuss with classmates which of the following are permissible when reducing fractions.
  a. Add the same number to numerator and denominator.
  b. Subtract the same number from numerator and denominator.
  c. Multiply numerator and denominator by the same nonzero number.
  d. Divide numerator and denominator by the same nonzero number.

Encourage testing each case by using specific real numbers.

29. Discuss with classmates the errors made in Exercise 27.

OBJECTIVE:

17-2

Multiplying and Dividing

To find the product or quotient of two rational expressions and express the answer in simplest form, listing all restrictions.

When multiplying or dividing rational numbers, first factor numerator and denominator into primes. When you do this, reducing the fraction is much easier.

EXAMPLES

This section provides a review of earlier material.

1. $\dfrac{12}{16} \cdot \dfrac{6}{9} = \dfrac{2^2 \cdot 3}{2^4} \cdot \dfrac{2 \cdot 3}{3^2}$

$= \dfrac{2^3 \cdot 3^2}{2^4 \cdot 3^2}$

$= \dfrac{1}{2}$

2. $\dfrac{15}{24} \div \dfrac{25}{20} = \dfrac{15}{24} \cdot \dfrac{20}{25}$

$= \dfrac{3 \cdot 5}{3 \cdot 2^3} \cdot \dfrac{2^2 \cdot 5}{5^2}$

$= \dfrac{3 \cdot 2^2 \cdot 5^2}{3 \cdot 2^3 \cdot 5^2}$

$= \dfrac{1}{2}$

This same procedure may be used to multiply and divide algebraic expressions.

EXAMPLES

1. $\dfrac{x^2 + 4x + 4}{2x^2 + x - 6} \cdot \dfrac{4x^2 - 9}{3x^2 + x - 10}$

$= \dfrac{(x + 2)^2}{(2x - 3)(x + 2)} \cdot \dfrac{(2x - 3)(2x + 3)}{(x + 2)(3x - 5)}$

$= \dfrac{(2x + 3)(x + 2)^2(2x - 3)}{(3x - 5)(x + 2)^2(2x - 3)}$

$$= \frac{2x + 3}{3x - 5} \quad \text{when } x \neq -2, \frac{3}{2}, \frac{5}{3}$$

2. $\dfrac{4x^3 - 9x}{2x^2 - 7x + 6} \div \dfrac{6x^2 + 3x - 9}{4x - 8}$

$$= \frac{4x^3 - 9x}{2x^2 - 7x + 6} \cdot \frac{4x - 8}{6x^2 + 3x - 9}$$

$$= \frac{x(2x - 3)(2x + 3)}{(2x - 3)(x - 2)} \cdot \frac{2^2(x - 2)}{3(2x + 3)(x - 1)}$$

$$= \frac{2^2 x(2x - 3)(2x + 3)(x - 2)}{3(x - 1)(2x - 3)(2x + 3)(x - 2)}$$

$$= \frac{2^2 x}{3(x - 1)}$$

$$= \frac{4x}{3x - 3} \quad \text{when } x \neq 2, \frac{3}{2}, 1, -\frac{3}{2}$$

Remember that it is necessary to restrict the values of x so that the denominators of the fractions will be nonzero.

EXERCISES

1. 1 **2.** 1, $x \neq -4, -3, -2, -1$
3. $\frac{7}{18}$ **4.** $\frac{x(x - 4)}{x + 3}$, $x \neq -4, -3,$
$-2, -1, 0, 4$ **5.** $\frac{(x + 3)(x - 1)}{x}$,
$x \neq -1, 0, 3$ **6.** $\frac{1}{4}$, $w \neq -\frac{1}{3}, 0, 1$
7. $\frac{s - 1}{s(x + 1)}$, $s \neq 0, 1$; $x \neq -1$
8. $\frac{p - 11}{p - 2}$, $p \neq -2, 2$
9. $\frac{w}{(w - s)(w - 1)}$, $w \neq s, -s,$
$1, -1, 2$ **10.** $\frac{4(x - 5)}{3(3x - 5)}$, $x \neq \frac{5}{3},$
$-2, -3, 1$ **11.** $\frac{2a}{a - b}$,
$a \neq b, 0, -b$ **12.** $\frac{(a + b)^2}{a - b}$,
$a \neq b, -b$ **13.** $\frac{m^2 + n^2}{a}$, $a \neq 0,$
$m \neq n, -n$ **14.** $\frac{4x^2}{m + n}$,
$m \neq n, -n$ **15.** $\frac{3(a - 4)}{2(4a + 1)}$,
$a \neq -\frac{1}{4}, -2, -4, \frac{2}{3}$

Perform each multiplication or division. Write the product or quotient in simplest form. List any necessary restrictions when a variable appears in a denominator.

1. $\dfrac{6}{9} \cdot \dfrac{12}{8}$

2. $\dfrac{x^2 + 3x + 2}{x^2 + 5x + 4} \cdot \dfrac{x^2 + 7x + 12}{x^2 + 5x + 6}$

3. $\dfrac{28}{9} \div \dfrac{24}{3}$

4. $\dfrac{x^2 + 3x + 2}{x^2 + 5x + 4} \div \dfrac{x^2 + 5x + 6}{x^3 - 16x}$

5. $\dfrac{x^2 - 9}{x^2 + x} \cdot \dfrac{x^2 - 1}{x - 3}$

6. $\dfrac{3w^2 + w}{2w - 2} \div \dfrac{2w + 6w^2}{w - 1}$

7. $\dfrac{(s - 1)^3}{s(x + 1)^2} \cdot \dfrac{x + 1}{(s - 1)^2}$

8. $\dfrac{p^2 - 121}{p^2 - 4} = \dfrac{p + 11}{p + 2}$

9. $\dfrac{w^2 - w - 2}{w^2 - s^2} \cdot \dfrac{w(w + s)}{(w^2 - 1)(w - 2)}$

10. $\dfrac{4x^2 - 12x - 40}{x^2 + 5x + 6} \div \dfrac{9x^2 - 24x + 15}{x^2 + 2x - 3}$

11. $\dfrac{8a^2}{a^2 - b^2} \cdot \dfrac{a + b}{4a}$

12. $\dfrac{(a + b)^2}{(a - b)^2} \cdot \dfrac{a^2 - b^2}{a + b}$

13. $\dfrac{m^2 - n^2}{am + an} \cdot \dfrac{m^2 + n^2}{m - n}$

14. $(mx - nx) \div \dfrac{m^2 - n^2}{4x}$

15. $\dfrac{3a^2 - 6a - 24}{a^2 + 6a + 8} \cdot \dfrac{3a^2 + 10a - 8}{24a^2 - 10a - 4}$

16. $\dfrac{2x}{y} \div \dfrac{x^2 - xy}{10} \cdot \dfrac{3(x^2 - y^2)}{5}$

17. $\dfrac{r^2 - 12r + 35}{r^2 + 3r + 2} \div \dfrac{r^2 - 1}{r^2 - 3r - 10}$

18. $\dfrac{a^2 - 4b^2}{9x^2} \cdot \dfrac{a^2 + 2ab}{(a - 2b)^2} \cdot \dfrac{27x^3(a - 2b)}{a^2}$

19. $\dfrac{x^2 - 3x + 2}{p + q} \cdot \dfrac{p^2x - q^2x}{x^2 - 4} \cdot \dfrac{x + 2}{(p - q)x^3}$

20. $\dfrac{x^2 - 1}{x^2 - 3x - 10} \div \dfrac{x^2 - 12x + 35}{x^2 + 3x + 2}$

17-3

Adding and Subtracting

When adding or subtracting rational numbers, the first step is to find the least common denominator, **LCD.** One method of finding the LCD is to factor the denominator of the fractions into primes. Then each factor is used as a factor of the LCD as many times as it appears in the denominator which has it as a factor the most times.

EXAMPLE

$\dfrac{7}{12} + \dfrac{9}{20} = \dfrac{7}{2^2 \cdot 3} + \dfrac{9}{2^2 \cdot 5}$

$\left. \begin{array}{l} 12 = 2^2 \cdot 3 \\ 20 = 2^2 \cdot 5 \end{array} \right\}$ LCD $= 2^2 \cdot 3 \cdot 5$

$= \dfrac{7 \cdot 5}{2^2 \cdot 3 \cdot 5} + \dfrac{9 \cdot 3}{2^2 \cdot 3 \cdot 5}$

$= \dfrac{7 \cdot 5 + 9 \cdot 3}{2^2 \cdot 3 \cdot 5}$

$= \dfrac{35 + 27}{2^2 \cdot 3 \cdot 5}$

$= \dfrac{62}{2^2 \cdot 3 \cdot 5}$

$= \dfrac{31}{2 \cdot 3 \cdot 5}$

$= \dfrac{31}{30}$

Algebraic fractions are added and subtracted in this same way.

EXAMPLES

1. $\dfrac{x}{x^2 + 2x + 1} + \dfrac{1}{x^2 - 1}$

$= \dfrac{x}{(x + 1)^2} + \dfrac{1}{(x + 1)(x - 1)}$

$$\left.\begin{array}{l} x^2 + 2x + 1 = (x + 1)^2 \\ x^2 - 1 = (x + 1)(x - 1) \end{array}\right\} \text{LCD} = (x + 1)^2(x - 1)$$

$$= \frac{x(x - 1)}{(x + 1)^2(x - 1)} + \frac{1(x + 1)}{(x + 1)^2(x - 1)}$$

$$= \frac{x(x - 1) + (x + 1)}{(x + 1)^2(x - 1)}$$

$$= \frac{x^2 - x + x + 1}{(x + 1)^2(x - 1)}$$

$$= \frac{x^2 + 1}{(x + 1)^2(x - 1)}$$

$$= \frac{x^2 + 1}{x^3 + x^2 - x - 1} \qquad \text{when } x \neq 1, -1$$

Since $x^2 + 1$ is prime, the fraction is in lowest terms after the numerator is simplified.

2. $\dfrac{x - 3}{x + 3} - \dfrac{-12x}{x^2 - 9} = \dfrac{x - 3}{x + 3} - \dfrac{-12x}{(x + 3)(x - 3)}$

$$\left.\begin{array}{l} x + 3 = (x + 3) \\ x^2 - 9 = (x + 3)(x - 3) \end{array}\right\} \text{LCD} = (x + 3)(x - 3)$$

$$= \frac{(x - 3)(x - 3)}{(x + 3)(x - 3)} - \frac{-12x}{(x + 3)(x - 3)}$$

$$= \frac{(x - 3)(x - 3) + 12x}{(x + 3)(x - 3)}$$

$$= \frac{x^2 - 6x + 9 + 12x}{(x + 3)(x - 3)}$$

$$= \frac{x^2 + 6x + 9}{(x + 3)(x - 3)}$$

$$= \frac{(x + 3)(x + 3)}{(x + 3)(x - 3)}$$

$$= \frac{x + 3}{x - 3} \qquad \text{when } x \neq 3, -3$$

EXERCISES

Write the LCD for each group of denominators.

1. 21, 49

2. xy, y^2

3. $x^2 + 3x + 2, x^2 + 4x + 4$

4. 3, 6, 30

5. a, ab, abc

6. $w, w^2 + 3w, w^3 - 9w$

7. 3, 5, 7

8. x, y, z

9. $x - 2, x^2 + x + 1, x^2 + 1$

10. 6, 10, 14

11. ab, ac, ad

12. $x^2 - 2x, 5x - 10, x^2 - 4$

Perform each addition or subtraction.

13. $\dfrac{1}{3} + \dfrac{1}{7}$

14. $\dfrac{1}{x} + \dfrac{1}{y}$

15. $\dfrac{a}{b} + \dfrac{a}{2b}$

16. $\dfrac{2}{x + 1} + \dfrac{2}{x^2 + 2x + 1}$

17. $\dfrac{1}{x + 1} - \dfrac{1}{x - 1}$

18. $\dfrac{1}{x^2 + 1} - \dfrac{1}{2x^2 + 2}$

19. $\dfrac{x}{x^2 - 1} - \dfrac{2 - x}{1 - x}$

20. $\dfrac{4x - 7}{7x^2} - \dfrac{7x - 3}{9x} + \dfrac{3x - 2}{3x^2}$

21. $\dfrac{y}{y^2 - 16} - \dfrac{1}{1 - y} - \dfrac{3}{1 + y}$

22. $\dfrac{2}{a} + \dfrac{1}{a + 1} - \dfrac{3}{a^2 + 2a + 1}$

13. $\dfrac{10}{21}$ 14. $\dfrac{x + y}{xy}$ 15. $\dfrac{3a}{2b}$

16. $\dfrac{2x + 4}{x^2 + 2x + 1}$ 17. $\dfrac{-2}{x^2 - 1}$

18. $\dfrac{1}{2(x^2 + 1)}$ 19. $\dfrac{(2 - x)}{x - 1}$

20. $\dfrac{-49x^2 + 120\,x - 105}{63x^2}$

21. $\dfrac{-y^3 + 4y^2 + 31y - 64}{(y^2 - 16)\,(y^2 - 1)}$

22. $\dfrac{(3a + 2)\,x^2 + (6a + 4)\,x + (2 - 3a^2)}{(a)\,(a + 1)\,(x + 1)^2}$

17-4
False Solutions

OBJECTIVE:

To name possible impostor solutions introduced when multiplying both sides of an equation by a polynomial.

Ask which values are not allowed in using the symbol ⇔ the first time.

Study the following method for solving the equation. Notice that rational expressions appear on both sides of the equal sign.

Solve $\dfrac{x + 6}{x + 1} = \dfrac{6x - 4}{x^2 - 1}$ if $x \ne 1, -1$.

$\text{LCD} = (x + 1)(x - 1)$

$$\dfrac{x + 6}{x + 1} = \dfrac{6x - 4}{(x - 1)(x + 1)}$$

Multiply both sides by LCD. $\Leftrightarrow (x + 6)(x - 1) = 6x - 4$

Expand. $\Leftrightarrow x^2 + 5x - 6 \quad = 6x - 4$

Subtract $6x - 4$ from both sides. $\Leftrightarrow x^2 - x - 2 \quad = 0$

$\Leftrightarrow (x - 2)(x + 1) = 0$

$\Leftrightarrow x = 2 \text{ or } x = -1$

Now check the two solutions in the original equation.

Check $x = 2$:

$$\dfrac{x + 6}{x + 1} = \dfrac{6x - 4}{x^2 - 1}$$

$$\dfrac{2 + 6}{2 + 1} \overset{?}{=} \dfrac{6 \cdot 2 - 4}{2^2 - 1}$$

$$\dfrac{8}{3} \overset{?}{=} \dfrac{12 - 4}{4 - 1}$$

$$\dfrac{8}{3} = \dfrac{8}{3}$$

Check $x = -1$:

$$\dfrac{x + 6}{x + 1} = \dfrac{6x - 4}{x^2 - 1}$$

$$\dfrac{-1 + 6}{-1 + 1} \overset{?}{=} \dfrac{6 \cdot (-1) - 4}{(-1)^2 - 1}$$

$$\dfrac{5}{0} \overset{?}{=} \dfrac{-6 - 4}{1 - 1}$$

$$\dfrac{5}{0} \overset{?}{=} \dfrac{-10}{0}$$

When -1 is substituted for x in the original equation, a meaningless statement results. Why does this happen?

When both sides of the equation were multiplied by $(x - 1)(x + 1)$, it was possible that $(x - 1)(x + 1)$ was equal to zero. In solving an equation, you may multiply both sides by any number except zero. If $x = 1$ or if $x = -1$, then multiplying by $(x - 1)(x + 1)$ is multiplying by zero.

You know that $2 \neq 1$. If you multiply both sides of $2 \neq 1$ by 0, however, the result will be the true statement $2 \cdot 0 = 1 \cdot 0$. In general, when you multiply both sides of an equation by 0, the resulting equation may not be equivalent to the first.

When both sides of an equation are multiplied by a polynomial, some possible solutions may result which are not really solutions.

These extra possible solutions are numbers which make the multiplier equal to zero. Check all possible solutions in the original equation to spot such impostors. For $\dfrac{x + 6}{x + 1} = \dfrac{6x - 4}{x^2 - 1}$ there seemed to be two possible solutions, 2 and -1. When each possible solution was checked, only 2 proved to be a solution. So the solution set for $\dfrac{x + 6}{x + 1} = \dfrac{6x - 4}{x^2 - 1}$ is $\{2\}$.

Stress this humble example involving $2 \neq 1$. The concept is important.

EXERCISES

1. $x = 5$ 2. $x = 0$ 3. $x = 6, -3$
4. $x = 5$ 5. $x = 3$ 6. $x = 3, 5$
7. $x = 5$ 8. $x = 3, 5$ 9. ϕ

Exercises 4-8 may be used for discussion before assigning Exercises 11-17.

Solve each equation by multiplying both sides of the equation by the same expression. Be sure to check for impostors.

1. $\dfrac{x - 2}{x + 2} = \dfrac{14 - x}{x^2 - 4}$

2. $\dfrac{x - 2}{x + 2} = \dfrac{x + 2}{x - 2}$

3. $\dfrac{x - 2}{x + 2} = \dfrac{22 - x}{x^2 - 4}$

4. $1 + \dfrac{x^2 + 9}{x^2 - 9} = \dfrac{x^2 + 8x - 15}{x^2 - 9}$

5. $\dfrac{x}{x - 5} + \dfrac{x}{x + 5} = \dfrac{x^2 + 8x - 15}{x^2 - 25}$

6. $\dfrac{x}{x - 2} + \dfrac{x}{x + 2} = \dfrac{x^2 + 8x - 15}{x^2 - 4}$

7. $\dfrac{x}{x - 3} + \dfrac{x}{x + 3} = \dfrac{x^2 + 8x - 15}{x^2 - 9}$

8. $\dfrac{x}{x - 1} + \dfrac{x}{x + 1} = \dfrac{x^2 + 8x - 15}{x^2 - 1}$

9. $\dfrac{x}{x + 1} = x + 1$

10. $\dfrac{4x}{x + 1} = x + 1$

11. $\dfrac{x - 3}{x - 2} + \dfrac{x^2 - 3x + 1}{x^2 - 5x + 6} = \dfrac{x - 2}{x - 3}$

12. $\dfrac{x - 3}{x - 2} + \dfrac{x^2 - x - 3}{x^2 - 5x + 6} = \dfrac{x - 2}{x - 3}$

13. $\dfrac{x - 3}{x - 2} + \dfrac{x^2 - 8x + 20}{x^2 - 5x + 6} = \dfrac{x - 2}{x - 3}$

14. $\dfrac{x - 3}{x - 2} + \dfrac{x^2 - 3x - 1}{x^2 - 5x + 6} = \dfrac{x - 2}{x - 3}$

15. $\dfrac{1}{3} = \dfrac{x}{x^2 + 2}$

16. Look closely at the possible solutions and at the true solutions for Exercises **11–14**.
   a. Do impostors always make the LCD $= 0$?
   b. If none of the possible solutions made the LCD $= 0$, would you expect to find any impostors?

17. In Exercise **15**, LCD $= x^2 + 2$.
   a. How many real number values for x make $x^2 + 2 = 0$ a true sentence?
   b. Is there any reason to check for impostors when the LCD has no replacements for x which give zero?

Suppose that each of the following expressions is the LCD for solving an equation such as in Exercises **1–15**. For each, name the set of real numbers which might be impostors when solving the equation.

18. $x^2 - 1$ 19. $x^2 + x + 1$ 20. $x^2 - 2x + 1$
21. $x^2 + x - 6$ 22. $x^3 + x^2 - 6x$ 23. $x^3 + x^2 + 6x$

17-5
Hidden
Solutions

Study the following method for solving the equation $(x - 2)(x^2 - 6) = x^2 - 2x$.

$$(x - 2)(x^2 - 6) = x^2 - 2x$$

Factor.

Divide both sides by $(x - 2)$.

$\Leftrightarrow (x - 2)(x^2 - 6) = x(x - 2)$
$\Leftrightarrow x^2 - 6 = x$
$\Leftrightarrow x^2 - x - 6 = 0$
$\Leftrightarrow (x - 3)(x + 2) = 0$
$\Leftrightarrow x = 3 \text{ or } x = -2$

Both of these possible solutions check in the original equation.

Check $x = -2$:

$$(x - 2)(x^2 - 6) = x^2 - 2x$$
$$(-2 - 2)((-2)^2 - 6) \stackrel{?}{=} (-2)^2 - 2(-2)$$
$$(-4)(-2) \stackrel{?}{=} 4 + 4$$
$$8 = 8$$

Check $x = 3$:

$$(x - 2)(x^2 - 6) = x^2 - 2x$$
$$(3 - 2)(3^2 - 6) \stackrel{?}{=} 3^2 - 2(3)$$
$$1 \cdot 3 \stackrel{?}{=} 9 - 6$$
$$3 = 3$$

However, there is another solution, 2.

Check $x = 2$:

$$(x - 2)(x^2 - 6) = x^2 - 2x$$
$$(2 - 2)(2^2 - 6) \stackrel{?}{=} 2^2 - 2(2)$$
$$0 \cdot (-2) \stackrel{?}{=} 4 - 4$$
$$0 = 0$$

Why was 2 not found as a solution when the equation was solved? When both sides of the equation were divided by $x - 2$, it is possible that $x - 2$ was zero. You may divide both sides of an equation by any number *except* zero. For $x = 2$, dividing both sides by $x - 2$ is the same as dividing both sides by zero.

Stress this. →
When both sides of an equation are divided by a polynomial, fewer solutions may result than there are for the original equation. If there are solutions in hiding, they will be numbers which make the divisor equal to zero. Check all such numbers in the original equation to find solutions in hiding.

The method for solving $(x - 2)(x^2 - 6) = x^2 - 2x$ resulted in two solutions, -2 and 3. However, there was a solution in hiding, namely the value for x which made $x - 2 = 0$. So the solution set for $(x - 2)(x^2 - 6) = x^2 - 2x$ is $\{-2, 2, 3\}$.

EXERCISES

Use Exercises 1-8 for work in class. They are intended to make Exercise 9 meaningful.

1. $x = 2$ 2. $x = 2, 3$ 3. $x = 4, 5$
4. $x = 1, 2, 5$ 5. $x = 3$
6. $x = -2, 2$ 7. $x = -2, 2$
8. $x = \sqrt{7}, -\sqrt{7}, 2, -2$

Solve each equation by first dividing both sides of the equation by any common factor. Be sure to check for solutions in hiding.

1. $(x - 2)(x - 5) = (x - 2)(x - 4)$
2. $2x(x - 3) = 4(x - 3)$
3. $x^2 - 5x = 4x - 20$
4. $(x - 3)(x^2 - 3x + 2) = 2x^2 - 6x + 4$
5. $x^3 + x^2 + x = 3x^2 + 3x + 3$
6. $x^4 - 5x^2 + 4 = 3x^2 - 12$
7. $x^4 - 16 = 3x^2 - 12$
8. $x^4 - 16 = 3x^2 + 12$

9. Study Exercises **1–8** to help you answer each question.
   a. If both sides of an equation are divided by $x^2 − 4$, how many solutions might be in hiding?
   b. How many real number solutions are there for $x^2 + 4 = 0$?
   c. If both sides of an equation are divided by $x^2 + 4$, how many solutions in hiding would you expect?

Suppose you divide both sides of an equation by each of the following expressions. Name the possible solutions in hiding for each.

10. $x^2 − 1$ 11. $x^2 + x + 1$ 12. $x^2 − 2x + 1$
13. $x^2 + x − 6$ 14. $x^3 + x^2 − 6x$ 15. $x^3 + x^2 + 6x$

Solve each equation by first dividing both sides of the equation by any common factor.

16. $x^2(x^2 − 3x + 2) = (3x − 2)(x^2 − 3x + 2)$
17. $x(x^2 − 3x + 2) = 2(x^2 − 3x + 2)$
18. $x(x^2 − 3x + 2) = (x^2 − 3x + 2)$
19. $x(x^2 − 3x + 2) = 4(x^2 − 3x + 2)$
20. $x^2(x^2 − 3x + 2) = 9(x^2 − 3x + 2)$

In each of Exercises **16–20,** the common factor of both sides of the equation was $x^2 − 3x + 2$.

21. In dividing both sides of an equation by $x^2 − 3x + 2$, what possible real number solutions in hiding are there?
22. Are possible solutions in hiding always in hiding? Look closely at Exercises **16–20** to decide.

17-6
Complex Fractions

OBJECTIVE:

To find the simplified form of a complex fraction.

EXAMPLES

Fractions may have numerators or denominators which are themselves fractions or which contain fractions. Such fractions are called *complex fractions.*

1. $\dfrac{\dfrac{3}{4}}{1 + \dfrac{2}{3}}$

2. $\dfrac{x + \dfrac{1}{x}}{\dfrac{x + 1}{x - 1}}$

3. $\dfrac{2}{1 + \dfrac{1}{1 + \dfrac{1}{x}}}$

A complex fraction is said to be in **simplest form** when it is re-written as a polynomial or as a quotient of two polynomials without common factors. Be careful to state which values you cannot consider for the variable.

EXAMPLES

1. $\dfrac{\dfrac{3}{4}}{1 + \dfrac{2}{3}} = \dfrac{\dfrac{3}{4}}{\dfrac{5}{3}}$

$= \dfrac{\dfrac{3}{4} \cdot \dfrac{3}{5}}{\dfrac{5}{3} \cdot \dfrac{3}{5}}$

$= \dfrac{\dfrac{9}{20}}{1}$

$= \dfrac{9}{20}$

2. $\dfrac{1 + \dfrac{1}{x}}{\dfrac{x + 1}{x - 1}} = \dfrac{\dfrac{x + 1}{x}}{\dfrac{x + 1}{x - 1}}$

Point out that *only* numerators of fractions not appearing as denominators may be ignored in listing restrictions.

$= \dfrac{\dfrac{x + 1}{x} \cdot \dfrac{x - 1}{x + 1}}{\dfrac{x + 1}{x - 1} \cdot \dfrac{x - 1}{x + 1}}$

$= \dfrac{\dfrac{(x + 1)(x - 1)}{x(x + 1)}}{1}$

$= \dfrac{(x + 1)(x - 1)}{x(x + 1)}$

$= \dfrac{x - 1}{x} \qquad \text{when } x \neq 0,\ -1,\ 1$

3.
$$\cfrac{2}{1 + \cfrac{1}{1 + \cfrac{1}{x}}} = \cfrac{2}{1 + \cfrac{1}{\cfrac{x+1}{x}}}$$

$$= \cfrac{2}{1 + \cfrac{x}{x+1}}$$

$$= \cfrac{2}{\cfrac{x+1+x}{x+1}}$$

$$= \cfrac{2}{\cfrac{2x+1}{x+1}}$$

$$= \cfrac{2}{1} \cdot \cfrac{x+1}{2x+1}$$

$$= \cfrac{2x+2}{2x+1} \qquad \text{when } x \neq 0, -\frac{1}{2}, -1$$

Mention that there is no overlap between the set of restrictions for the original expression and the final. This will be a new phenomenon to students.

Remember, you may think of $\cfrac{\cfrac{a}{b}}{\cfrac{c}{d}}$ as a division, $\dfrac{a}{b} \div \dfrac{c}{d} = \dfrac{ad}{bc}$.

EXERCISES

1. $\frac{21}{2}x$, $x \neq 0$ 2. $\frac{7}{2}$, $x \neq 0$

3. x, $x \neq 0, -1$ 4. $\frac{x}{x-1}$,

$x \neq 1, 0, -1$ 5. $\frac{x+1}{x+2}$,

$x \neq -2, -1, 1, 2$ 6. $\frac{x}{x+1}$,

$x \neq -1, 0, 2$ 7. $\frac{x-1}{x}$, $x \neq 0, 3$

8. $\frac{3w+2}{4w+2}$, $w \neq 0, -1, -\frac{1}{2}, -\frac{2}{3}$

Simplify each fraction. State the values which you cannot consider for the variable.

1. $\cfrac{\cfrac{7}{x}}{\cfrac{2}{3}}$

2. $\cfrac{\cfrac{7}{x}}{\cfrac{2}{x}}$

3. $\cfrac{1+x}{1+\cfrac{1}{x}}$

4. $\cfrac{\cfrac{x+1}{x-1}}{1+\cfrac{1}{x}}$

5. $\cfrac{\cfrac{x-1}{x-2}}{\cfrac{x^2+x-2}{x^2-x-2}}$

6. $\cfrac{1-\cfrac{2}{x}}{1-\cfrac{1}{x}-\cfrac{2}{x^2}}$

7. $\cfrac{\cfrac{1}{x}-\cfrac{4}{x^2}+\cfrac{3}{x^3}}{\cfrac{1}{x}-\cfrac{3}{x^2}}$

8. $\cfrac{1+\cfrac{1}{1+\cfrac{1}{w}}}{2+\cfrac{2}{2+\cfrac{2}{w}}}$

Solve each equation. Simplify each complex fraction first. Then find an equivalent equation to the given equation.

9. $\dfrac{1 + \dfrac{4}{x}}{x - 3} = \dfrac{8}{x^2 - 3x}$

10. $\dfrac{1 + \dfrac{4}{x}}{x - 3} = \dfrac{7}{x^2 - 3x}$

11. $\dfrac{\dfrac{1}{x} + \dfrac{1}{x^2}}{\dfrac{1}{x} + \dfrac{2}{x^2}} = -3$

12. $\dfrac{\dfrac{1}{x} + \dfrac{1}{x^2}}{\dfrac{1}{x} + \dfrac{2}{x^2}} = \dfrac{x + 1}{x + 2}$

13. $\dfrac{\dfrac{1}{x} + \dfrac{1}{x^2}}{\dfrac{1}{x} + \dfrac{2}{x^2}} = \dfrac{x + 3}{x + 2}$

14. $\dfrac{x^2 - 1}{\dfrac{1}{x} + \dfrac{1}{x^2} - \dfrac{2}{x^3}} = x^3$

Chapter Summary

1. A fraction which has a polynomial as the numerator and as the denominator is called a rational expression.
2. A rational expression is in simplest form when the numerator and denominator have no common factor.
3. Rational expressions may be added, subtracted, multiplied, and divided by methods used for rational numbers.
4. If both sides of an equation are multiplied by a polynomial that could possibly equal zero, impostor solutions may result.
5. If both sides of an equation are divided by a polynomial that could possibly equal zero, there may be solutions in hiding.
6. A complex fraction is in simplest form when it is written as a polynomial or as a quotient of two polynomials without common factors.

REVIEW EXERCISES 17-1

Express each fraction in simplest form.

1. $\dfrac{84}{198}$

2. $\dfrac{36x^2y^4}{52xy^2}$

3. $\dfrac{3a - 6b}{9ay - 18by}$

4. $\dfrac{x^2 + 4xy + 4y^2}{x^2 - 4y^2}$

5. $\dfrac{x^2 - x - 6}{x^2 + x - 12}$

6. $\dfrac{3nx^2 - 27nx + 60n}{2nx^2 - 12nx + 16n}$

17-2

Perform each operation. Express the result in simplest form.

7. $\frac{xn}{m}$ 8. $\frac{12abc^2}{5}$ 9. $\frac{35}{3y}$ 10. $\frac{3dx}{d-x}$

11. $\frac{2(m+3)(m-2)}{m+2}$

12. $\frac{2(x-2)}{x+3}$ 13. $\frac{a(a+3)}{2(a-3)}$

14. $\frac{5(a-b)}{4(a+b)}$ 15. $\frac{3}{a(m-5)}$

16. $\frac{3}{a}$ 17. $\frac{3(n-2)}{a(n+4)}$ 18. 1

7. $\dfrac{rx^2}{m} \div \dfrac{rx}{n}$

8. $\dfrac{6a^3}{25c} \cdot \dfrac{15b^2c}{2a^2} \cdot \dfrac{4c^2}{3b}$

9. $\dfrac{5y^2}{x+7} \div \dfrac{3y^3}{7x+49}$

10. $\dfrac{d^3x^2}{d^2-x^2} \div \dfrac{5d^2x}{15d+15x}$

11. $\dfrac{2m^2-18}{m+2} \cdot \dfrac{m^2-4}{m^2-m-6}$

12. $\dfrac{x^2+2x-15}{x^2+7x+10} \div \dfrac{3x^2-27}{6x^2-24}$

13. $\dfrac{a^3+3a}{(a-3)^2} \cdot \dfrac{a^2-9}{2a^2+6}$

14. $\dfrac{a^2-b^2}{4a^2} \cdot \dfrac{5a^2}{(a+b)^2}$

15. $\dfrac{n+3}{n^2-25} \cdot \dfrac{3n+15}{an+3a}$

16. $\dfrac{n^2-4}{n^2-n-6} \cdot \dfrac{3n-9}{an-2a}$

17. $\dfrac{n^2-4}{ax-ay} \div \dfrac{n^2+6n+8}{3x-3y}$

18. $\dfrac{4x^2-4x-3}{4x^2-1} \div \dfrac{4x^2-9}{4x^2+4x-3}$

17-3

Perform each operation. Express the result in simplest form.

19. $\frac{1}{4x^2}$ 20. $\frac{7}{2x+4y}$

21. $\frac{-x^2+8x+5xy-15y}{x^2-25y^2}$

22. $\frac{2a^2+3a+1}{2(a^2-9)}$ 23. $\frac{4a+b}{3(a^2-4b^2)}$

24. $\frac{5y+3xy}{x-2}$ 25. $\frac{x^2+2x+8}{x^2-4}$

26. $\frac{-2(y^2-2y-1)}{(y-1)^2(y+1)}$

27. $\frac{2a^2+5a+8}{a(a+2)}$

28. $\frac{-3x+13}{(x-5)(x+5)(x-2)}$

19. $\dfrac{2}{3x^2} - \dfrac{5}{12x^2}$

20. $\dfrac{5}{x+2y} - \dfrac{3}{2x+4y}$

21. $\dfrac{5x}{x^2-25y^2} - \dfrac{x-3}{x+5y}$

22. $\dfrac{2a-1}{2a-6} - \dfrac{a-2}{a^2-9}$

23. $\dfrac{4}{3a+6b} + \dfrac{3b}{a^2-4b^2}$

24. $\dfrac{5y}{x-2} - \dfrac{3xy}{2-x}$

25. $\dfrac{x-1}{x+2} + \dfrac{x+3}{x-2} - \dfrac{x^2}{x^2-4}$

26. $\dfrac{1}{1-y} + \dfrac{y+1}{(y-1)^2} - \dfrac{2y}{y^2-1}$

27. $\dfrac{a+2}{a} + \dfrac{a}{a+2} + \dfrac{3}{a}$

28. $\dfrac{x+1}{x^2-25} - \dfrac{x-3}{x^2-7x+10}$

17-4, 17-5

Solve each equation. Be sure to check for impostor solutions and solutions in hiding.

29. x = 33 30. x = 6, -6
31. x = 2, 4 32. x = 2, -2
33. x = 3

29. $\dfrac{3}{8x} + \dfrac{4}{x} = \dfrac{x+2}{8x}$

30. $\dfrac{x-2}{x+2} + \dfrac{x+2}{x-2} = \dfrac{5}{2}$

31. $x^2 - 5x + 6 = x - 2$

32. $3x(x+2) = 6(x+2)$

33. $x^3 + 6x = 3x^2 + 18$

17-6

Simplify each fraction. State the values that you cannot consider for the variable.

34. $\frac{4x^2}{x-4}$, $x \neq 4, 0$

35. $\frac{2x}{4x^2+1}$, $x \neq \frac{1}{4}$

36. $\frac{2(y-2)}{4y+3}$, $y \neq -\frac{3}{4}, 0$

37. $\frac{3-4x}{9+4x}$, $x \neq -\frac{9}{4}, 0$

38. $\frac{b}{c}$, $c \neq 0$, $b \neq 0$, $ab \neq 2dc$

34. $\dfrac{4x}{1-\dfrac{4}{x}}$

35. $\dfrac{1}{2x+\dfrac{1}{2x}}$

36. $\dfrac{1-\dfrac{2}{y}}{2+\dfrac{3}{2y}}$

37. $\dfrac{\dfrac{1}{4x}-\dfrac{1}{3}}{\dfrac{3}{4x}+\dfrac{1}{3}}$

38. $\dfrac{\dfrac{ab}{c}-2d}{a-\dfrac{2cd}{b}}$

CHAPTER 18

trigonometry

18-1 Geometric Concepts

OBJECTIVE:

To identify corresponding equal parts and corresponding parts related by the same ratio of two similar polygons in the same relative position.

When the word *line* is used in everyday conversation, it may mean one of several things. It may mean a *straight line segment* which has two endpoints. Or, it may refer to a *ray* which has one endpoint. Or, it may describe a complete *straight line* which has no endpoints. Special notation is used to indicate if you are to consider a line segment, a ray, or a line.

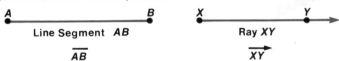

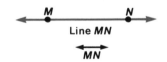

The purpose here is to establish meaning for terms at an intuitive level.

A similar problem occurs when the word *angle* is used in everyday conversation. In mathematics, however, an angle may be defined as follows. An *angle* is formed when two rays have a common endpoint. The common endpoint is the *vertex* of the angle. Each ray is a *side* of the angle.

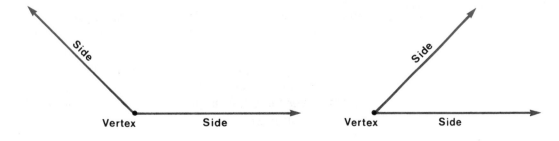

In most daily applications, people work with angles formed by two line segments with a common endpoint. In such cases, you may imagine that each line segment is part of an undrawn ray.

One reason for insisting that an angle be formed by two rays concerns the measurement of angles. When you discuss the size of an angle, you should not consider the lengths of the sides.

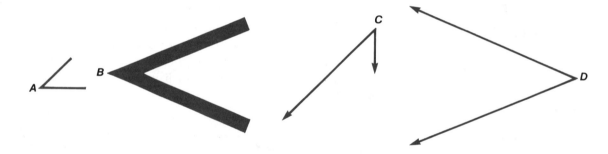

For example, look at the sides of angles *A*, *B*, *C*, and *D*. All four angles are the same size. This is true even if their sides as drawn make them look different. When two angles are the same size, you may say they are ***congruent.***

To name an angle, the symbol ∠ is used. The phrase ∠*A* is read "angle *A*." It refers to an angle whose vertex is point *A*. In polygons, three letters may be used to name an angle. Angle *A* in the following triangle also may be named ∠*CAB* or ∠*BAC*. Notice the name of the vertex always appears in the center position.

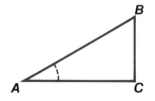

To show that two angles are congruent, or have the same size, the symbol ≅ is used. The sentence ∠*A* ≅ ∠*B* is read "angle A is congruent to angle B." To see if two angles are congruent, make a copy of one angle on tracing paper. Then see if the copy fits exactly over the other angle. If the angles fit over each other, then they are congruent.

EXERCISES

It is suggested these exercises
be used for discussion or
group work. They provide an
overview of sections yet to come.

1. Consider the following two figures as photographs of the same polygon. One is an enlargement of the other. The labels were added after the picture was taken and enlarged.

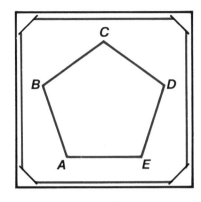 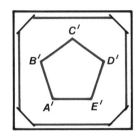

a. Do you think $\angle CDE$ is the same size as $\angle C'D'E'$?

b. Do you think side $\overline{AB}$ is the same size as side $\overline{A'B'}$?

c. Do you think the ratio $\dfrac{\text{length of } \overline{AB}}{\text{length of } \overline{CD}}$ is the same as $\dfrac{\text{length } \overline{A'B'}}{\text{length } \overline{C'D'}}$?

d. Do you think $\dfrac{\text{length of } \overline{AB}}{\text{length of } \overline{A'B'}} = \dfrac{\text{length of } \overline{CD}}{\text{length of } \overline{C'D'}}$?

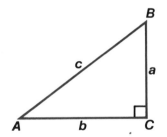

In the right triangle, a is the length of side $\overline{CB}$, b is the length of side $\overline{AC}$, and c is the length of side $\overline{AB}$. Use this triangle for Exercises **2–5**.

2. Assume that you have a photographic enlargement of the triangle. State which of the following properties would not change through enlargement.

a. $a \div c$	**b.** Size of $\angle A$	**c.** ac
d. Size of $\angle B$	**e.** $c \div b$	**f.** b
g. $\sqrt{a^2 + b^2}$	**h.** $a \div \sqrt{a^2 + b^2}$	

3. If $c = 5$ and $b = 4$, what does a equal?

4. Assume that $c = 5$ and $b = 4$. Assume that an enlargement is made such that b becomes 12. What does a become in the enlargement?

5. In the figure $\angle A' \cong \angle A$ of the previous triangle. In the previous triangle, $b = 4$ and $c = 5$. Find the height of the television tower.

The two arcs in the figure are parts of circles whose centers are at O. Length of arc $\overset{\frown}{AB}$ refers to the distance between points A and B *along* the arc. In Exercises **6–14,** state whether each statement is true (T) or false (F).

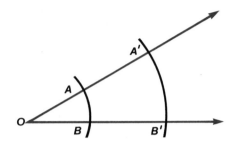

6. length of $\overline{OB}$ = length of $\overline{OA}$

7. length of arc $\overset{\frown}{AB}$ = length of arc $\overset{\frown}{A'B'}$

8. length of $\overline{OA'}$ = length of $\overline{OB'}$

9. $\dfrac{\text{length of } \overline{OB}}{\text{length of } \overline{OB'}} = \dfrac{\text{length of } \overline{OA}}{\text{length of } \overline{OA'}}$

10. $\dfrac{\text{length of } \overline{OB}}{\text{length of } \overline{OB'}} = \dfrac{\text{length of arc } \overset{\frown}{AB}}{\text{length of arc } \overset{\frown}{A'B'}}$

11. $\dfrac{\text{length of } \overline{OB}}{\text{length of } \overline{BB'}} = \dfrac{\text{length of arc } \overset{\frown}{AB}}{\text{length of arc } \overset{\frown}{A'B'}}$

12. $\dfrac{\text{length of arc } \overset{\frown}{AB}}{\text{length of } \overline{OB}} = \dfrac{\text{length of } \overline{A'B'}}{\text{length of } \overline{OB'}}$

13. $\dfrac{\text{length of } \overline{OA}}{\text{length of } \overline{AA'}} = \dfrac{\text{length of } \overline{OB}}{\text{length of } \overline{BB'}}$

14. $\angle B'OA' \cong \angle BOA$

15. Is it possible to change the size of angles in a polygon by photographically enlarging or reducing the polygon?

16. Imagine that x is the ratio of the lengths of two sides of a polygon. Is it possible to change the value of x by photographically enlarging or reducing the polygon?

In the following figure, line segments $\overline{AB}$, $\overline{CD}$, $\overline{EF}$, and $\overline{GH}$ lie on parallel lines.

Replace the variables P and Q in each sentence with names of

17.-19. Answers will vary.

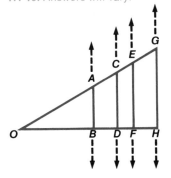

line segments which will make the sentence true. Several solutions for each sentence are possible.

17. $\dfrac{\text{length of } \overline{EF}}{\text{length of } \overline{OE}} = \dfrac{\text{length of } P}{\text{length of } Q}$

18. $\dfrac{\text{length of } \overline{OD}}{\text{length of } \overline{OC}} = \dfrac{\text{length of } P}{\text{length of } Q}$

19. $\dfrac{\text{length of } \overline{GH}}{\text{length of } \overline{OH}} = \dfrac{\text{length of } P}{\text{length of } Q}$

18-2
Similarity

OBJECTIVE:

To identify corresponding sides and angles of two similar polygons in different positions.

The following polygons are related in a special way. One way to describe the relationship is to say that one polygon is a photographic enlargement of the other.

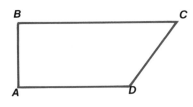

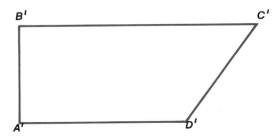

This statement summarizes for students the key idea in Section 18-1.

As you may have discovered in previous exercises, if a polygon is enlarged or reduced, the size of the angles remains the same. In these polygons, ***corresponding angles*** are congruent: $\angle A \cong \angle A'$, $\angle B \cong \angle B'$, $\angle C \cong \angle C'$, and $\angle D \cong \angle D'$. You also may have discovered that the lengths of ***corresponding sides*** are in the same ratio.

$$\frac{\text{length of } \overline{AB}}{\text{length of } \overline{A'B'}} = \frac{\text{length of } \overline{BC}}{\text{length of } \overline{B'C'}} = \frac{\text{length of } \overline{CD}}{\text{length of } \overline{C'D'}} = \frac{\text{length of } \overline{DA}}{\text{length of } \overline{D'A'}}$$

Assume you are looking at two polygons such that corresponding angles are congruent and the lengths of corresponding sides are in the same ratio. In mathematics, the two polygons are said to be ***similar.*** In the previous example, polygon *ABCD* is similar to polygon *A'B'C'D'*.

Remember that two polygons do not have to be positioned the same way to be similar. For example, if you compare corresponding angles and compute the ratios of the lengths of corresponding sides, you can show that the following polygons are similar.

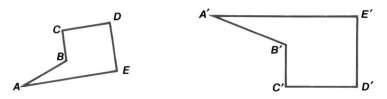

You also may think of similarity in the following way. If you can flip, rotate, or reduce one polygon so that it is congruent to the other, then the two polygons are similar.

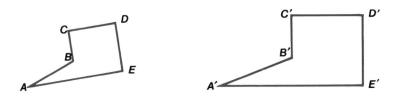

Polygons are being thought of here as things that can be manipulated.

Step 1. Flip polygon A'B'C'D'E' over.

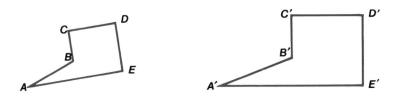

It is strongly suggested that concern with whether lines really can be moved about physically be delayed until geometry is studied.

Step 2. Rotate polygon A'B'C'D'E' so that ∠A' points in the same direction as ∠A.

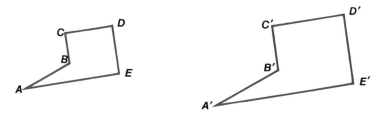

Step 3. Now reduce polygon A'B'C'D'E'. It will be identical in every measurement to polygon ABCDE.

As another example, no correct comparison of angles or computation of ratios will show these polygons to be similar.

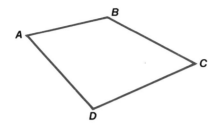

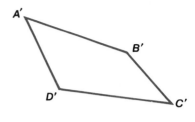

No amount of flipping, rotating, or reducing will show them to be similar either.

EXERCISES

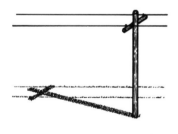

1. Consider two four-sided polygons each drawn using the same four angles. Is it possible for them to be nonsimilar? Draw an example to show your answer.

2. If two triangles are drawn using the same three angles, must the triangles be similar?

3. Imagine that you are given four line segments of different lengths. Using those four line segments in each polygon, can you construct two polygons which are not similar? Draw an example to show your answer.

4. Imagine that you are given three line segments of different lengths. Using those three line segments in each triangle, can you construct two triangles which are not similar? Draw an example to show your answer.

5. A telephone pole is standing on level ground. Without leaving the ground or moving the pole, how can you find the height of the pole? Hint: How would a meter stick placed on the ground on a sunny day help?

6. These two triangles are right triangles.

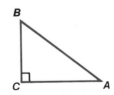

You are allowed to measure or compare one thing on each triangle. It must be a corresponding item on each triangle. Using the information gained from the measurement or comparison, state whether or not the triangles are similar. What is the one thing you might measure or compare to make your decision with certainty? Hint: See Exercise 2 of this section.

18-3
Using Similarity

EXAMPLES

Much of trigonometry is based on the fact that corresponding sides of similar figures are in the same ratio. Using this fact and your knowledge of ratios and proportion, you can solve many application problems.

1. Rita is looking at a surveyor's map of a plot of land she wishes to buy. On the map, the side facing the street, $\overline{AB}$, measures 50 mm. Side $\overline{BC}$ measures 60 mm on the map. She remembers seeing a sign that says the lot has a 400-ft frontage. How deep is the plot of land?

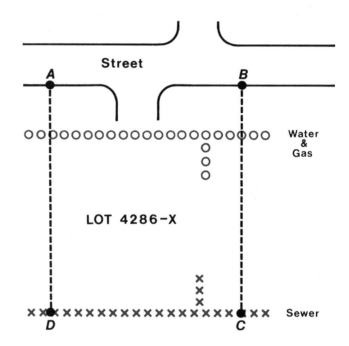

The ratio $\dfrac{\overline{BC}}{\overline{AB}}$ on the drawing is $\dfrac{60}{50} = \dfrac{6}{5}$. Since the scale drawing and the actual lot are similar figures, the corresponding sides of the actual lot must be in the same ratio. If x represents the length of $\overline{BC}$ in the actual lot, then $\dfrac{x}{400} = \dfrac{6}{5}$. This means $x = 480$, and the lot is 480 ft deep.

2. Firefighters are using a long ladder to rescue a dog from an apartment-building ledge. A reporter wants to know how high

up is the ledge. The reporter notices that the sixth rung of the ladder is five feet from the ground. The rungs of the ladder are 1 foot apart. The reporter learns from a firefighter that the ladder is 50 feet long. How high up is the dog on the ledge?

Relate this example to Exercise 5 on page 491. Suggest that it is often necessary to *impose* triangles on drawings of real life situations.

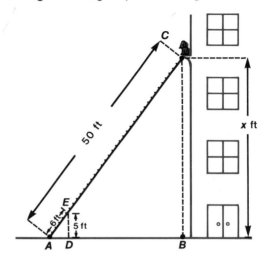

As you can see, triangle *ABC* is similar to triangle *ADE*. The ratio of the lengths of sides $\overline{DE}$ and $\overline{AE}$ is $\frac{5}{6}$. Since the triangles are similar, the ratio of the lengths of sides $\overline{BC}$ and $\overline{AC}$, $\frac{x}{50}$, should equal $\frac{5}{6}$.

$$\frac{5}{6} = \frac{x}{50} \Leftrightarrow x = 41\frac{2}{3}$$

The dog on the ledge is $41\frac{2}{3}$ feet from the ground.

EXERCISES

The following three polygons are similar to each other.

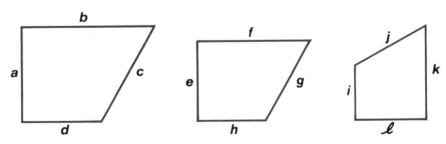

Each small letter represents the length of a side. Find one

solution for each equation where x is a variable on $\{a, b, c, d, e, f, g, h, i, j, k, l\}$.

1. $\dfrac{a}{e} = \dfrac{x}{f}$

2. $\dfrac{a}{b} = \dfrac{x}{f}$

3. $\dfrac{a}{b} = \dfrac{x}{k}$

4. $\dfrac{a}{l} = \dfrac{x}{k}$

5. $\dfrac{e}{g} = \dfrac{a}{x}$

6. $\dfrac{e}{g} = \dfrac{l}{x}$

7. $\dfrac{f}{k} = \dfrac{h}{x}$

8. $x = \dfrac{af}{e}$

9. $ag = cx$

10. $dk = bx$

The following three triangles are similar to each other.

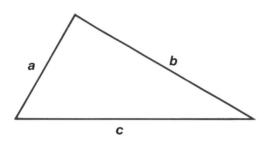 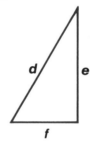 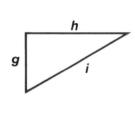

Each small letter represents the length of a side. Find one solution for each equation if x is a variable on $\{a, b, c, d, e, f, g, h, i\}$.

11. $\dfrac{a}{c} = \dfrac{x}{i}$

12. $\dfrac{a}{g} = \dfrac{c}{x}$

13. $\dfrac{d}{c} = \dfrac{f}{x}$

14. $x = \dfrac{ah}{b}$

15. $\dfrac{dx}{c} = f$

16. $\dfrac{g}{h} = \dfrac{f}{x}$

Exercises **17–20** refer to the triangles of Exercises **11–16**.

17. If $a = 6$, $c = 12$, and $g = 3$, what is i?

18. If $g = 3$, $h = 4$, and $a = 4\frac{1}{2}$, what is b?

19. If $d = 20$, $e = 15$, and $i = 4$, what is h?

20. Which of these conditions allow you to find a value for a?
   a. You know values for c, g, and i.
   b. You know values for b, g, and i.
   c. You know values for b, e, and f.
   d. You know values for b, e, and d.

21. In a picture, the width of a barn measures $1\frac{1}{2}$ inches. The height measures $1\frac{3}{4}$ inches. If the barn is actually 30 feet wide, how high is the barn?

22. 9 ft **23.** 9 cm **24.** 55 cm
25. 15 cm **26. a.** 16 cm **b.** 1:4

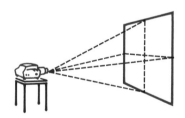

22. The high end of a conveyor is 15 feet above the ground. The conveyor is 27 feet long. The conveyor is to keep the same angle with the ground, but it is to be lengthened. After it is lengthened, the high end is to be 20 feet above the ground. By how many feet should the conveyor be lengthened?

23. An aircraft has a length of 24 m and a wingspan of 32 m. A scale model is to be made with a wingspan of 12 cm. Calculate the length of the model.

24. The figure shows the image of a slide measuring 34 mm wide and 22 mm high. If the picture on the screen is 85 cm wide, what is the height of the picture?

25. A church 25 m high and 20 m wide appears on a television screen. If the screen image is 12 cm wide, what is its height?

26. a. A photograph 8 cm high and 6 cm wide is enlarged to give a print 12 cm wide. What is the height of the print?

   b. Calculate the ratio of the area of the photograph to the area of the print.

18-4
Measuring Angles

Until now, you have compared the size of angles by making a copy of one angle and placing it over others. A method is needed to measure angles directly.

Line segments are measured by comparison to standard line segments, such as the inch or meter. In a similar way, angles may be measured by comparison to a standard angle. One standard unit of angle measure is the degree. A ***degree*** is an angle such that if its vertex is the center of a circle, there is $\frac{1}{360}$ of the circumference of the circle between the sides.

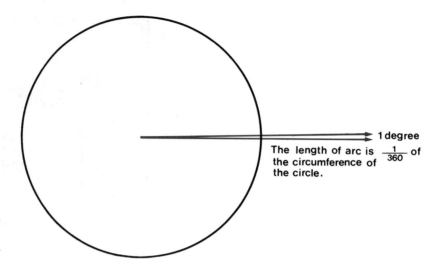

1 degree

The length of arc is $\frac{1}{360}$ of the circumference of the circle.

Remind students that the *degree* is inherited from the past, as are the inch, foot, millimeter, etc.

A tool to measure angles may be constructed by dividing the circumference of a circle into 360 equally long parts. Each division is the length of arc that would lie between the sides of a one degree angle.

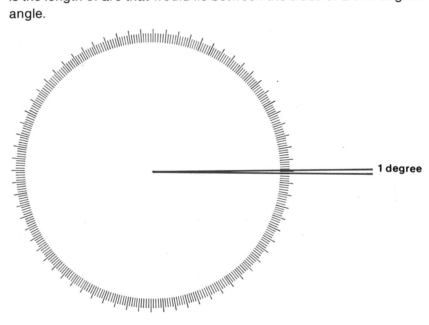

1 degree

This type of tool is called a ***circular protractor.*** To measure an angle requires that the center of the protractor be placed on the vertex of the angle. Then the number of divisions between the sides of the angle are counted. This number is the measure of the angle in degrees.

EXAMPLE

What is the measure of ∠B?

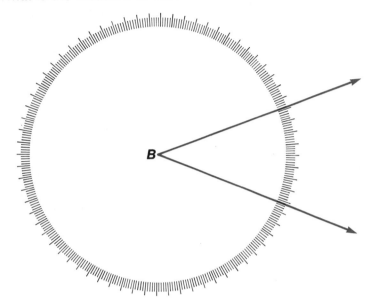

Discourage students from writing ∠B = 42°; insist that they write m∠B = 42°.

By counting the number of divisions between the sides, the measure of ∠B is 42 degrees.

The symbol ° stands for the word *degrees*. The letter *m* stands for the phrase *the measure of*. The sentence $m\angle B = 42°$ is read "the measure of angle B is 42 degrees."

Probably the protractor you have used most appears to be one-half of the circular protractor. The divisions usually are numbered to simplify the counting of degrees.

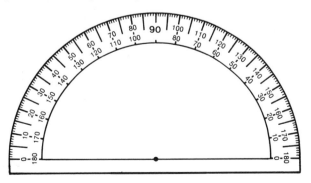

To measure an angle, follow these steps.

1. Place the marked center of the protractor on the vertex of the angle.
2. Arrange the protractor so that one side of the angle passes through a zero mark.
3. The number of the mark which the other side passes through is the measure of the angle in degrees.

EXAMPLE

What is the measure of $\angle C$?

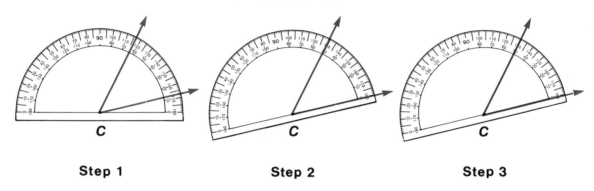

Step 1   **Step 2**   **Step 3**

Notice that the side of $\angle C$ passes through a mark labeled with two numbers. Since in Step **2** the zero is on the inner scale, the number on the inner scale is used. Therefore, $m\angle C = 50°$.

EXERCISES

You will need a protractor and ruler for these exercises.

1. Draw three different triangles using a straightedge. Draw them fairly large. Using a protractor, measure each angle. Add together the measures of angles for each triangle. Do you see a pattern? If so, what is it?

2. Very carefully, draw a right triangle as follows. Using the protractor, draw a 33° angle.

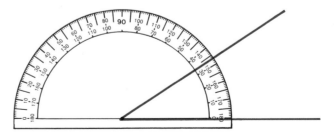

Using the protractor, draw a 90° angle, *a right angle,* on one of the segments used to make the 33° angle.

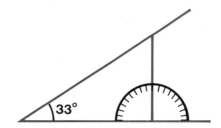

33°

Because one of the angles is a 90° angle, this triangle is a **right triangle.** Mark the length of the side opposite the 33° angle *a*. Mark the length of the side opposite the 90° angle *c*. Mark the length of the remaining side *b*.

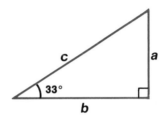

c   *a*

33°

b

a. Carefully measure *a* and *c*. Compute the ratio $\frac{a}{c}$ as a decimal. Find 33° in the left column of the table on page 519. Is the first decimal number given to the right of 33° close to your value of $\frac{a}{c}$?

b. Carefully measure *b* and *c*. Compute the ratio $\frac{b}{c}$ as a decimal. Turn to the table on page 519 and find 33°. Is the second decimal number to the right of 33° close to your value of $\frac{b}{c}$?

c. Compute the ratio $\frac{a}{b}$ as a decimal. Is the third decimal number to the right of 33° close to your value of $\frac{a}{b}$?

3. Using the protractor, draw a large right triangle. Mark the length of the side opposite the smallest angle with *a*. Mark the length of the longest side of the triangle with *c*. Mark the length of the remaining side with *b*.

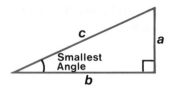

c

a

Smallest Angle

b

4. 90° **5.** 90° **6.** 70° **7.** 60°
8. 30° **9.** 7 **10.** 40 ft **11.** 6000 ft

a. Measure the smallest angle to the nearest degree. Turn to the table on page 519. Find the line with that degree measure in the left column.

b. Record the three decimal numbers in the table to the right of your angle measure.

c. Compute the ratios $\frac{a}{c}$, $\frac{b}{c}$, and $\frac{a}{b}$ by measuring sides of your triangle and then dividing. Are your values close to the three values you recorded from the table?

The pattern you found in Exercise **1** is true. The sum of the angles of a triangle is 180°. For Exercises **4–9,** imagine a triangle with corners A, B, and C.

4. If $m\angle A = 30°$ and $m\angle B = 60°$, what is $m\angle C$?
5. If $m\angle A = 45°$ and $m\angle B = 45°$, what is $m\angle C$?
6. If $m\angle A = 90°$ and $m\angle C = 20°$, what is $m\angle B$?
7. How large is $\angle A$ if $m\angle A = m\angle B = m\angle C$?
8. What is $m\angle A$ if $m\angle B$ is twice $m\angle A$ and $m\angle C$ is three times $m\angle A$?
9. Which of the triangles in Exercises **4–8** are *not* right triangles?

Accept trial and error behavior by students for Exercise 8.

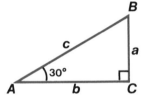

B

c

a

30°

A   b   C

If the smallest angle of a right triangle measures 30°, then $\frac{a}{c} = \frac{1}{2}$.

? ft

30°

20 ft

10. The pitch on a roof is 30°. If the high edge of the roof is 20 feet above the low edge, how long is the roof?

11. An airplane is flying 3000 feet above a flat area. The pilot notices an object on the ground ahead. The angle of depression is 30°. How far from the airplane is the object?

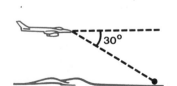

30°

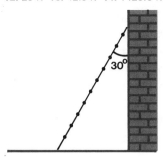

12. A 40-foot ladder forms a 30° angle with the side of a building. How far is the base of the ladder from the building?

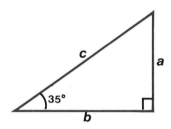

If the smallest angle of a right triangle is 35°, then $\frac{a}{b} \doteq .7$.

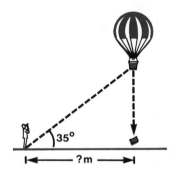

13. A conveyor forms an angle of 35° with the ground. It is being used to drop sand on a pile. The top end of the conveyor is 30 feet above the ground. How far is the center of the sandpile from the base of the conveyor?

14. From where an observer stands, the angle of elevation to a balloon is 35°. The balloon is 1000 meters above the ground. The balloonist drops a sandbag. At what distance from the observer will the sandbag hit the earth?

18-5
Trigonometric
Ratios

OBJECTIVE:

To "solve" the right triangle given enough measurements for describing the right triangle.

Triangle ABC is a right triangle. Since $m\angle A + m\angle B + m\angle C$ must equal 180°, and $m\angle C = 90°$, $m\angle A + m\angle B$ must equal 90°.

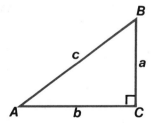

For example, if $m\angle A = 37°$, then $m\angle B = (90° - 37°) = 53°$. Remember that if two triangles have congruent corresponding angles, the triangles are similar. This idea may be extended further for the case of right triangles. If two right triangles have one pair of corresponding angles congruent, other than the right angle, then the triangles are similar.

Stress this emphatically. →

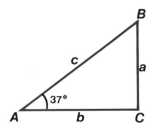

For example, this statement means that all right triangles with a 37° angle are similar to each other. If someone computed the values of the ratios $\frac{a}{b}$, $\frac{b}{c}$, and $\frac{a}{c}$ for one right triangle with a 37° angle, these values would apply to all right triangles with a 37° angle. The values of these ratios appear in a table on page 519. The entry for 37° appears as follows.

$$37° \qquad .6018 \qquad .7986 \qquad .7536$$

Because these values are constant for any right triangle with a given angle, they have special names.

$$\frac{a}{c} = \text{the \textbf{sine} of the measure of angle } A$$

$$\text{the sine of } 37° \doteq .6018$$

$$\frac{b}{c} = \text{the \textbf{cosine} of the measure of angle } A$$

$$\text{the cosine of } 37° \doteq .7986$$

$$\frac{a}{b} = \text{the \textbf{tangent} of the measure of angle } A$$

$$\text{the tangent of } 37° \doteq .7536$$

In general, you may determine approximate values of the sine, cosine, and tangent for the measure of an angle Q as follows.

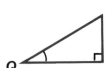

Stress the fact that sine, cosine, and tangent may be found by construction and measurement.

1. Construct any right triangle which contains $\angle Q$.
2. Name the longest side **hypotenuse.** The other side forming angle Q is labeled **adjacent side.** The remaining side is labeled the **opposite side.**

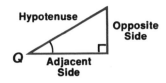

$$\text{The sine of } m \angle Q = \sin Q = \frac{\text{length of opposite side}}{\text{length of hypotenuse}}$$

$$\text{The cosine of } m \angle Q = \cos Q = \frac{\text{length of adjacent side}}{\text{length of hypotenuse}}$$

$$\text{The tangent of } m \angle Q = \tan Q = \frac{\text{length of opposite side}}{\text{length of adjacent side}}$$

Always remember that **sin** Q, **cos** Q, and **tan** Q are abbreviations. When you read "sin Q" in this text for example, you should say "the sine of the measure of angle Q." On the other hand, 37° is a measure of an angle so "sin 37°" may be read as "the sine of 37 degrees."

The table on page 519 gives the values of the sine, cosine, and tangent of angles with measures from 0° to 90°. The values in the table are accurate to four digits only. The values appear in columns labeled sin, cos, and tan.

EXERCISES

Read the value for each trigonometric ratio from the table on page 519.

1. .3584 **2.** 1.0000 **3.** .7880
4. .5000 **5.** .5000 **6.** .2588
7. .2588 **8.** .0175 **9.** 57.2900
10. .7071 **11.** .7071 **12.** .8660
13. 45° **14.** 45° **15.** 35° **16.** 20°
17. 70° **18.** 45° **19.** 22° **20.** 31°
21. 89° **22.** 45° **23.** a **24.** c
25. a **26.** b

1. sin 21°   **2.** tan 45°   **3.** cos 38°
4. sin 30°   **5.** cos 60°   **6.** sin 15°
7. cos 75°   **8.** tan 1°   **9.** tan 89°
10. cos 45°   **11.** sin 45°   **12.** cos 30°

Write a value for $m \angle Q$ to make each sentence true. $m \angle Q \in \{0°, 1°, 2°, \ldots, 90°\}$. Use the table on page 519.

13. $\sin Q \doteq .7071$ **14.** $\cos Q \doteq .7071$ **15.** $\tan Q \doteq .7002$

16. $\sin Q \doteq .3420$ **17.** $\cos Q \doteq .3420$ **18.** $\tan Q \doteq 1.0000$

19. $\tan Q \doteq \frac{101}{250}$ **20.** $\sin Q \doteq \frac{103}{200}$ **21.** $50 < \tan Q < 100$

22. $\cos Q \doteq \sin Q$

Replace each x to make the sentence true. $x \in \{a, b, c\}$ where a, b, and c represent the lengths of the sides of the triangle.

23. $\sin Q = \frac{x}{c}$ **24.** $\cos Q = \frac{b}{x}$

25. $\tan (90 - m \angle Q)° = \frac{b}{x}$ **26.** $\sin (90 - m \angle Q)° = \frac{x}{c}$

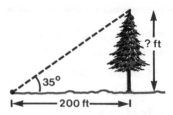

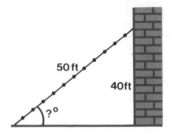

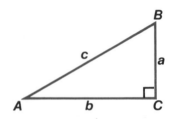

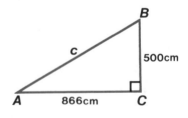

27. $\cos (90 - m \angle Q)° = \dfrac{x}{c}$

28. $x \cdot \sin Q = a$

29. $c \cdot \cos Q = x$

30. $c \cdot \sin (90 - m \angle Q)° = x$

31. $x \cdot \tan (90 - m \angle Q)° = b$

32. $\sqrt{a^2 + b^2} = x$

33. At 200 feet away from the base of a tree, the angle of elevation to the top of the tree is 35°. To the nearest foot, what is the height of the tree?

34. The top of a 50-foot ladder touches a building at 40 feet above the ground. To the nearest degree, what is the angle formed by the ladder and the ground?

In the following exercises, you are given certain information about this triangle.

Using the given information, state which trigonometric ratio you would use to find the desired item.

Sample Items Known   Item Sought
   a, b $m \angle A$

Since $\tan A = \dfrac{a}{b}$, the *tangent* should be used.

27. a 28. c 29. b 30. b 31. a
32. c 33. 140 ft 34. 53° 35. sine
36. tangent 37. tangent
38. tangent 39. cosine 40. sine
41. a. 1000 cm b. 30° c. 60°
42. a. 456 b. 596 c. 50°

Items Known	*Item Sought*
35. a, c	$m \angle A$
36. $a, m \angle A$	b
37. $a, m \angle B$	b
38. a, b	$m \angle B$
39. b, c	$m \angle A$
40. $c, m \angle B$	b

41. The two line segments forming the right angle of a right triangle measure 866 cm and 500 cm.
   a. How long is side c to the nearest centimeter?
   b. What is $m \angle A$?
   c. What is $m \angle B$?

42. The side between $\angle A$ and $\angle C$ measures 383 cm. $m \angle A = 40°$
   a. How long is side a to the nearest centimeter?
   b. How long is side c to the nearest centimeter?
   c. What is $m \angle B$?

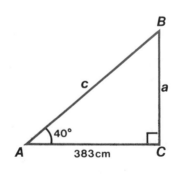

18-6
Angles in
Standard Position

Until now, sine, cosine, and tangent have been discussed in terms of right triangles. They also may be discussed in terms of angles located in a coordinate plane. The positive x-axis always will be used as one of the two rays forming the angle. The point (0, 0) always will be used as the vertex.

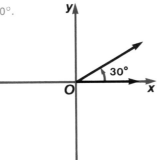
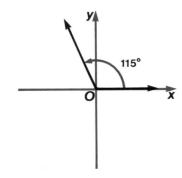

The positive x-axis is called the **initial side** of the angle. The other ray forming the angle is called the **terminal side.** Angles in this position are said to be in **standard position.** Angles are measured by moving *counterclockwise* from the initial side to the terminal side.

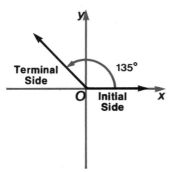
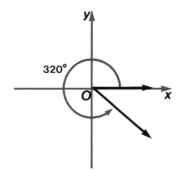

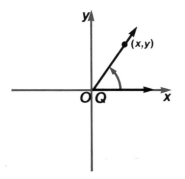

The sine, cosine, and tangent of the measure of an angle Q may be defined as follows. First, locate any point on the terminal side, say (x, y).

Then the sine, cosine, and tangent for the measure of an angle Q are defined as follows.

$$\textbf{sin } \textbf{\textit{Q}} = \frac{\textit{y}}{\sqrt{\textit{x}^2 + \textit{y}^2}}$$

$$\textbf{cos } \textbf{\textit{Q}} = \frac{\textit{x}}{\sqrt{\textit{x}^2 + \textit{y}^2}}$$

$$\textbf{tan } \textbf{\textit{Q}} = \frac{\textit{y}}{\textit{x}}$$

It is still important to remember that sin Q, cos Q, and tan Q are abbreviations. For example, when you read "tan Q" in this text, you should say "the tangent of the *measure* of angle Q."

EXAMPLES

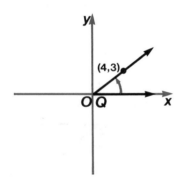

1. Find the values of the sine, cosine, and tangent of the measure of an angle whose terminal side passes through (4, 3). Use the table on page 519 to find the measure of the angle to the nearest degree.

$$\sin Q = \frac{y}{\sqrt{x^2 + y^2}} \qquad \cos Q = \frac{x}{\sqrt{x^2 + y^2}} \qquad \tan Q = \frac{y}{x}$$

$$\sin Q = \frac{3}{5} \qquad\qquad \cos Q = \frac{4}{5} \qquad\qquad \tan Q = \frac{3}{4}$$

$$\sin Q = .6000 \qquad\qquad \cos Q = .8000 \qquad\qquad \tan Q = .7500$$

From the table $m \angle Q \doteq 37°$, to the nearest degree.

2. Find the values of the sine, cosine, and tangent of the measure of an angle whose terminal side passes through (−5, 2).

$$\sin Q = \frac{y}{\sqrt{x^2 + y^2}} \qquad \cos Q = \frac{x}{\sqrt{x^2 + y^2}} \qquad \tan Q = \frac{y}{x}$$

$$\sin Q = \frac{2}{\sqrt{29}} \qquad\quad \cos Q \doteq \frac{-5}{5.3852} \qquad\quad \tan Q = \frac{2}{-5}$$

$$\sin Q \doteq \frac{2}{5.3852}$$

$$\sin Q \doteq .3714 \qquad\qquad \cos Q \doteq -.9285 \qquad\qquad \tan Q = -.4000$$

18-7
Extending the Table

OBJECTIVE:
To name the sine, cosine, and tangent by using tables ending with 90° of an ∠ A such that $0° \leq m \angle A \leq 360°$.

The table on page 519 gives values of the sine, cosine, and tangent for angles with measures from 0° to 90°. This table also can be used to find the values of the sine, cosine, and tangent for angles with measures from 0° to 360°. There are four cases to consider for the measure of an angle A.

$$\textbf{I} \quad 0° \leq m \angle A \leq 90°$$
$$\textbf{II} \quad 90° < m \angle A \leq 180°$$
$$\textbf{III} \quad 180° < m \angle A \leq 270°$$
$$\textbf{IV} \quad 270° < m \angle A \leq 360°$$

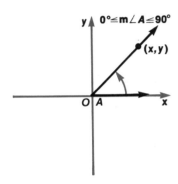

Case I

For Case **I,** the values for the sine, cosine, and tangent of the measure of angle A, $0° \leq m \angle A \leq 90°$, may be read directly from the table.

Case II

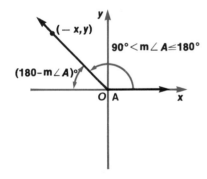

Using the formula:

$$\sin A = \frac{y}{\sqrt{(-x)^2 + y^2}} = \frac{y}{\sqrt{x^2 + y^2}}$$

$$\cos A = \frac{-x}{\sqrt{(-x)^2 + y^2}} = -\left(\frac{x}{\sqrt{x^2 + y^2}}\right)$$

$$\tan A = \frac{-x}{y} = -\left(\frac{x}{y}\right)$$

Using the lengths of the sides of a right triangle:

$$\sin (180 - m \angle A)° = \frac{y}{\sqrt{x^2 + y^2}}$$

$$\cos (180 - m \angle A)° = \frac{x}{\sqrt{x^2 + y^2}}$$

$$\tan (180 - m \angle A)° = \frac{x}{y}$$

The values of $\sin(180 - m\angle A)°$, $\cos(180 - m\angle A)°$, and $\tan(180 - m\angle A)°$ may be read from the table. These values and the fact that $\sin A = \sin(180 - m\angle A)°$, $\cos A = -\cos(180 - m\angle A)°$, and $\tan A = -\tan(180 - m\angle A)°$ in Quadrant II allow the use of the table to find the values of the sine, cosine, and tangent of the measures of angles in Quadrant II.

Do not require students to memorize the table on this page. Rather, allow them to use it while completing the exercises.

Case **III**

Again, the formulas for $\sin A$, $\cos A$, and $\tan A$ may be calculated. Also, the values of $\sin(m\angle A - 180)°$, $\cos(m\angle A - 180)°$, and $\tan(m\angle A - 180)°$ may be found using the following right triangle.

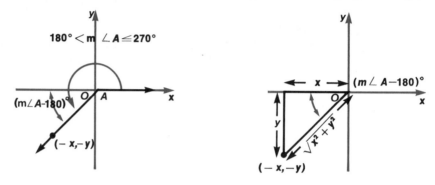

The results are that $\sin A = -\sin(m\angle A - 180)°$, $\cos A = -\cos(m\angle A - 180)°$, and $\tan A = \tan(m\angle A - 180)°$. The values of $\sin(m\angle A - 180)°$, $\cos(m\angle A - 180)°$, and $\tan(m\angle A - 180)°$ may be read from the table.

Case **IV**

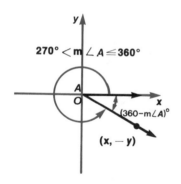

For Case **IV**, $\sin A = -\sin(360 - m\angle A)°$, $\cos A = \cos(360 - m\angle A)°$, and $\tan A = -\tan(360 - m\angle A)°$. The values of $\sin(360 - m\angle A)°$, $\cos(360 - m\angle A)°$, and $\tan(360 - m\angle A)°$ may be read from the table.

This table is a summary of the four cases.

$m\angle A$	To find sin A with the table, find:	To find cos A with the table, find:	To find tan A with the table, find:
$0° \leq m\angle A \leq 90°$	$\sin A$	$\cos A$	$\tan A$
$90° < m\angle A \leq 180°$	$\sin(180 - m\angle A)°$	$-\cos(180 - m\angle A)°$	$-\tan(180 - m\angle A)°$
$180° < m\angle A \leq 270°$	$-\sin(m\angle A - 180)°$	$-\cos(m\angle A - 180)°$	$\tan(m\angle A - 180)°$
$270° < m\angle A \leq 360°$	$-\sin(360 - m\angle A)°$	$\cos(360 - m\angle A)°$	$-\tan(360 - m\angle A)°$

EXAMPLES

1. Find cos 300°.

$$\cos 300° = \cos (360 - 300)° \quad \text{by Case IV}$$
$$= \cos 60°$$
$$\doteq .5000$$

2. Find sin 220°.

$$\sin 220° = -\sin (220 - 180)° \quad \text{by Case III}$$
$$= -\sin 40°$$
$$\doteq -.6428$$

Encourage use of the table on the preceding page.

3. Find two values of $m\angle Q$, $0° \leq m\angle Q \leq 360°$, for which $\sin Q \doteq .7660$.

a. From the table $.7660 \doteq \sin 50°$.

b. Since .7660 is positive, and the sine is positive in Cases I and II, the following sentences may be used.

$$\text{Case I} \quad \sin Q \doteq .7660 \doteq \sin 50°$$

Therefore, $m\angle Q \doteq 50°$.

$$\text{Case II} \quad \sin Q \doteq .7660 \doteq \sin (180 - 50)°$$

Therefore, $m\angle Q \doteq 130°$.
The two values are 50° and 130°.

4. Find two values of $m\angle Q$, $0° \leq m\angle Q \leq 360°$, for which $\tan Q \doteq -1.4281$.

a. From the table, $1.4281 \doteq \tan 55°$.

b. Since -1.4281 is negative, and the tangent is negative in Cases II and IV, the following sentences may be used.

$$\text{Case II} \quad -\tan 55° \doteq -1.4281 \doteq \tan (180 - m\angle Q)°$$

Therefore, $55° = (180 - m\angle Q)°$
$$m\angle Q = 125°$$

$$\text{Case IV} \quad -\tan 55° \doteq -1.4281 \doteq -\tan (360 - m\angle Q)°$$

Therefore, $55° = (360 - m\angle Q)°$
$$m\angle Q = 305°$$
The two solutions are 125° and 305°.

EXERCISES

1. .9848 2. −1.7321 3. −.9397
4. .3640 5. −.9962 6. −.0872
7. 2.9042 8. .9994 9. −1.0000
10. .9986 11. −0.0872 12. .9945

Use the table on page 519 to find a value for each expression.

1. sin 100°   **2.** tan 300°   **3.** cos 200°

4. tan 20°   **5.** cos 175°   **6.** sin 355°

7. tan 251°   **8.** sin 88°   **9.** tan 135°

10. cos 357°   **11.** sin 185°   **12.** cos 6°

For each sentence, find a value for $m \angle Q$ between 90° and 180° which makes the statement true.

13. sin $Q \doteq .2756$ **14.** tan $Q \doteq -.7002$

15. cos $Q \doteq -.9781$ **16.** tan $Q \doteq -11.4301$

17. sin $Q \doteq .9455$ **18.** cos $Q \doteq -.5150$

For each sentence, find a value for $m \angle Q$ between 180° and 270° which makes the statement true.

19. tan $Q \doteq 3.7321$ **20.** cos $Q \doteq -.9848$

21. tan $Q \doteq .0875$ **22.** sin $Q \doteq -.7071$

23. cos $Q \doteq -.3420$ **24.** sin $Q \doteq -.7660$

For each sentence, find a value for $m \angle Q$ between 270° and 360° which makes the statement true.

25. cos $Q \doteq .8387$ **26.** tan $Q \doteq -.3249$

27. sin $Q \doteq -.9659$ **28.** sin $Q \doteq -.4540$

29. cos $Q \doteq .4226$ **30.** tan $Q \doteq -1.1106$

For each sentence, find *two* values for $m \angle Q$ between 0° and 360° which make the statement true.

31. sin $Q \doteq .5000$ **32.** cos $Q \doteq .8391$

33. tan $Q \doteq .3640$ **34.** sin $Q \doteq -.5000$

35. cos $Q \doteq -.8391$ **36.** tan $Q \doteq -.3640$

37. sin $Q \doteq -.9272$ **38.** cos $Q \doteq -.2079$

39. tan $Q \doteq -19.0811$ **40.** The value of tan Q is ∞.

41. On graph paper, draw an *x*-axis and a *y*-axis as shown in the following figure.

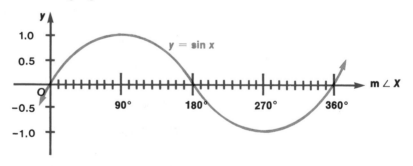

Graph $y = \sin x°$ by first copying and completing the following table.

$m \angle x$	0°	30°	45°	60°	90°	120°	135°	150°	180°	210°	225°	240°	270°	300°	315°	330°	360°
y	?	?	?	?	?	?	?	?	?	?	?	?	?	?	?	?	?

42. and **43.**
See section notes in T.G.

42. Draw another coordinate plane as in Exercise **41.** Graph $y = \cos x°$.

43. Draw another coordinate plane as in Exercise **41.** Graph $y = \tan x°$. Omit the two points at $x = 90$ and $x = 270$.

Chapter Summary

1. An angle is formed when two rays have a common endpoint. The common endpoint is the vertex of the angle. Each ray is a side of the angle.

2. Two angles are congruent if they are the same size.

3. If two polygons have congruent corresponding angles and lengths of corresponding sides are in the same ratio, then the two polygons are similar.

4. The size of angles may be measured in degrees. A degree is an angle such that if its vertex is the center of a circle, there is $\dfrac{1}{360}$ of the circumference of the circle between the sides.

5. Notation:

   $\angle$ means *angle*
   $\cong$ means *is congruent to*
   $m\angle$ means *the measure of angle*
   $°$ means *degrees*

6. the sine of the measure of angle A

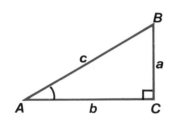

$$= \sin A = \frac{a}{c} = \frac{\text{length of opposite side}}{\text{length of hypotenuse}}$$

   the cosine of the measure of angle A

$$= \cos A = \frac{b}{c} = \frac{\text{length of adjacent side}}{\text{length of hypotenuse}}$$

   the tangent of the measure of angle A

$$= \tan A = \frac{a}{b} = \frac{\text{length of opposite side}}{\text{length of adjacent side}}$$

7. An angle is in standard position in a coordinate plane if the vertex of the angle is the origin and one side of the angle is the x-axis. The x-axis is the initial side. The other side is the

terminal side. Angles in standard position are measured by moving counterclockwise from the initial side to the terminal side.

8. For an angle Q in standard position with its terminal side passing through point (x, y), the following statements are true.

$$\sin Q = \frac{y}{\sqrt{x^2 + y^2}}$$

$$\cos Q = \frac{x}{\sqrt{x^2 + y^2}}$$

$$\tan Q = \frac{y}{x}$$

9.

$m \angle A$	To find sin A with the table, find:	To find cos A with the table, find:	To find tan A with the table, find:
$0° \leq m \angle A \leq 90°$	sin A	cos A	tan A
$90° < m \angle A \leq 180°$	$\sin(180 - m \angle A)°$	$-\cos(180 - m \angle A)°$	$-\tan(180 - m \angle A)°$
$180° < m \angle A \leq 270°$	$-\sin(m \angle A - 180)°$	$-\cos(m \angle A - 180)°$	$\tan(m \angle A - 180)°$
$270° < m \angle A \leq 360°$	$-\sin(360 - m \angle A)°$	$\cos(360 - m \angle A)°$	$-\tan(360 - m \angle A)°$

REVIEW EXERCISES 18-2

By measuring angles and computing ratios of lengths of corresponding sides, show whether each pair of polygons is similar.

1. Similar 2. Not similar

1.

2.

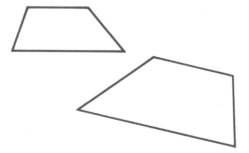

3.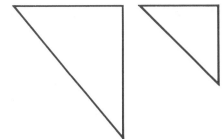

4.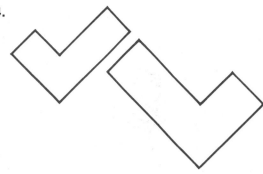

Right triangle *ABC* is similar to triangle *A'B'C'*. In Exercises **5–12**, state whether each sentence is true (T) or false (F).

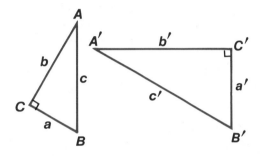

5. $\dfrac{a}{b} = \dfrac{a'}{b'}$ **6.** $\angle A' \cong \angle B'$ **7.** $\dfrac{a'}{b} = \dfrac{a}{b'}$

8. $\dfrac{(c')^2}{(c)^2} = \dfrac{(a')^2}{(a)^2} + \dfrac{(b')^2}{(b)^2}$ **9.** $\dfrac{(c')^2}{c^2} = \dfrac{(a')^2 + (b')^2}{(a)^2 + (b)^2}$

10. $m\angle B' \cong m\angle B$ **11.** $m\angle A = \dfrac{a}{b}$ **12.** $ab'cc' = a'c'bc$

18-3   Triangles *DEF* and *RST* are similar. State a value for *x* which will make each sentence true. $x \in \{d, e, f, r, s, t\}$

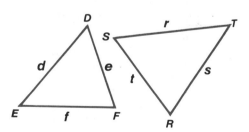

13. $\dfrac{d}{e} = \dfrac{x}{s}$ **14.** $fx = se$ **15.** $\dfrac{t}{e} = \dfrac{s}{x}$ **16.** $fr = dx$

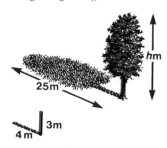

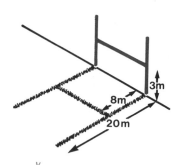

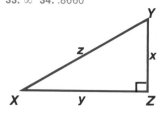

17. Which, if any, of the following could be regarded as the same shape as a soccer field measuring 100 meters by 60 meters?
  a. A square 8 cm by 8 cm
  b. A rectangle 5 mm by 3 mm
  c. A parallelogram with sides of 10 cm and 6 cm and one angle of 85°

18. Which, if any, of the following could be regarded as the same shape as a boxing ring 5-m square?
  a. A square carpet measuring 6 m by 6 m
  b. A page of your textbook
  c. A square field of side 280 m
  d. The smallest square on a sheet of graph paper

19. The tree in the figure casts a shadow 25 m long. A vertical post 3 m high casts a shadow 4 m long. Calculate the height of the tree to the nearest meter.

20. Each post of this rugby goal casts a shadow 20 m long. The part of the post below the crossbar is 3 m high and casts a shadow 8 m long. Calculate the height of the post.

18-5

Using right triangle *XYZ*, state the ratio of the lengths of sides which equals the given expression.

21. cos *Y*   **22.** sin *X*   **23.** tan *X*
24. cos *X*   **25.** (sin *Y*)²   **26.** (tan *Y*)²

27. (sin *x*)² + (cos *x*)² Hint: Remember $x^2 + y^2 = z^2$.
28. Using right triangle *XYZ*, show that (sin *X*) ÷ (cos *X*) = tan *X*.

Write the value of each expression from the table on page 519.
29. tan 45°   **30.** cos 30°   **31.** sin 18°
32. cos 72°   **33.** tan 90°   **34.** sin 60°

In the following exercises, you are given information about a right triangle *ABC*. Use this information to find the value of the desired item. If the measure of an angle is sought, state your answer to the nearest degree. If the measure of a side is sought, state your answer accurate to one decimal place. The following triangle only shows the placement of the labels. It is not in scale to any of the exercises.

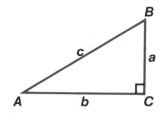

Values Known	Value Sought
35. $a = 4$; $c = 12$	$m \angle A = $ ___?___
36. $a = 6.5$; $m \angle A = 30°$	$b = $ ___?___
37. $a = 1\frac{1}{2}$; $m \angle B = 37°$	$b = $ ___?___
38. $a = 5$; $b = 12$	$m \angle B = $ ___?___
39. $b = 12$; $c = 13$	$m \angle A = $ ___?___
40. $c = 9.2$; $m \angle B = 55°$	$b = $ ___?___

35. 19° **36.** 11.3 **37.** 1.1 **38.** 67°
39. 23° **40.** 7.5 **41.** 3628 m
42. 40.3 m **43.** 47.5 km
44. 2nd and 4th; 1st and 2nd;
2nd and 3rd **45.** .2126 **46.** .7071
47. .7071 **48.** −1.0000
49. −0.0698 **50.** −28.6363
51. −.8910 **52.** −5.1446
53. −.8090

41. An observer stands on a hill 1000 m above a rocket-launching site. The angle of depression is 16°. What is x, the distance from the observer to the rocket?

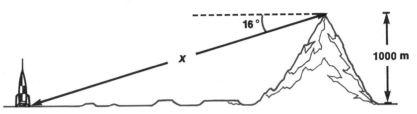

42. A hiker walks a path on a hillside that climbs at an angle of 8° for 100 m. Then the path climbs at an angle of 5° for 300 m. In those 400 m, how far has the hiker ascended? Hint: Find the total height from *two* triangles.

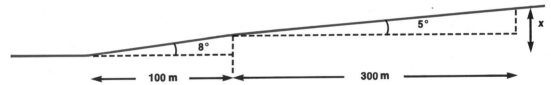

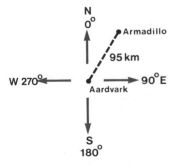

43. A pilot is scheduled to fly from Aardvark to Armadillo on a heading of 30°. The distance between the cities is 95 km. How far *east* of Aardvark is Armadillo?

18-6

44. In which quadrants is the tangent negative? In which quadrants is the sine positive? In which quadrants is the cosine negative?

18-7

Use the table on page 519 to find values for each expression.

45. tan 192°   **46.** cos 315°   **47.** sin 135°
48. cos 180°   **49.** sin 356°   **50.** tan 272°
51. sin 243°   **52.** tan 101°   **53.** cos 216°

For each sentence, find *two* values for $m \angle Q$ between 0° and 360° which make the sentence true.

54. cos Q = .8480   **55.** sin Q = −.7986   **56.** tan Q = 3.7321

57. sin Q = −.9903   **58.** tan Q = −.3640   **59.** cos Q = .7660

60. cos Q = −.2756   **61.** tan Q = 1.1918   **62.** sin Q = .2419

Excursions in Mathematics: Another Way to Measure Angles

You have learned to measure angles in degrees using a circular protractor.

Rather than counting degrees, you could measure the length of arc between the sides of the angle. Of course, the circle should be the same size for each measurement or else you would not have a standard unit of measurement. For convenience, make the radius equal to 1 unit and measure angles in the standard position.

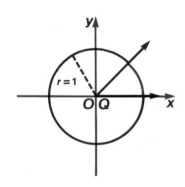

The length of the circumference of the circle is $C = 2\pi r = 2\pi \cdot 1 = 2\pi$. The angle pictured has one eighth of the length of the circumference between its sides. $m \angle Q = \frac{1}{8} \cdot 2\pi = \frac{\pi}{4} \doteq .7854$ radians.

The new unit of measure is called **radians.** There are 2π radians in 360°. One radian is approximately 57°.

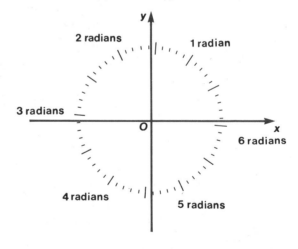

EXERCISES

Make a copy of the circle whose circumference is divided into radians and tenths of radians. Construct an angle for each measure.

1. 1.0 radian   **2.** 2.35 radians   **3.** 1.55 radians

4. 4.7 radians   **5.** $\frac{\pi}{4}$ radians   **6.** π radians

7. State the measure of each angle in Exercises **1–6** to the nearest degree.

8. By reading other books, find out the relationship between the radius of the circle and the length of arc in one radian.

TABLE OF TRIGONOMETRIC RATIOS

Angle	sin	cos	tan	Angle	sin	cos	tan
0°	.0000	1.0000	.0000	45°	.7071	.7071	1.0000
1°	.0175	.9998	.0175	46°	.7193	.6947	1.0355
2°	.0349	.9994	.0349	47°	.7314	.6820	1.0724
3°	.0523	.9986	.0524	48°	.7431	.6691	1.1106
4°	.0698	.9976	.0699	49°	.7547	.6561	1.1504
5°	.0872	.9962	.0875	50°	.7660	.6428	1.1918
6°	.1045	.9945	.1051	51°	.7771	.6293	1.2349
7°	.1219	.9925	.1228	52°	.7880	.6157	1.2799
8°	.1392	.9903	.1405	53°	.7986	.6018	1.3270
9°	.1564	.9877	.1584	54°	.8090	.5878	1.3764
10°	.1736	.9848	.1763	55°	.8192	.5736	1.4281
11°	.1908	.9816	.1944	56°	.8290	.5592	1.4826
12°	.2079	.9781	.2126	57°	.8387	.5446	1.5399
13°	.2250	.9744	.2309	58°	.8480	.5299	1.6003
14°	.2419	.9703	.2493	59°	.8572	.5150	1.6643
15°	.2588	.9659	.2679	60°	.8660	.5000	1.7321
16°	.2756	.9613	.2867	61°	.8746	.4848	1.8040
17°	.2924	.9563	.3057	62°	.8829	.4695	1.8807
18°	.3090	.9511	.3249	63°	.8910	.4540	1.9626
19°	.3256	.9455	.3443	64°	.8988	.4384	2.0503
20°	.3420	.9397	.3640	65°	.9063	.4226	2.1445
21°	.3584	.9336	.3839	66°	.9135	.4067	2.2460
22°	.3746	.9272	.4040	67°	.9205	.3907	2.3559
23°	.3907	.9205	.4245	68°	.9272	.3746	2.4751
24°	.4067	.9135	.4452	69°	.9336	.3584	2 6051
25°	.4226	.9063	.4663	70°	.9397	.3420	2.7475
26°	.4384	.8988	.4877	71°	.9455	.3256	2.9042
27°	.4540	.8910	.5095	72°	.9511	.3090	3.0777
28°	.4695	.8829	.5317	73°	.9563	.2924	3.2709
29°	.4848	.8746	.5543	74°	.9613	.2756	3.4874
30°	.5000	.8660	.5774	75°	.9659	.2588	3.7321
31°	.5150	.8572	.6009	76°	.9703	.2419	4.0108
32°	.5299	.8480	.6249	77°	.9744	.2250	4.3315
33°	.5446	.8387	.6494	78°	.9781	.2079	4.7046
34°	.5592	.8290	.6745	79°	.9816	.1908	5.1446
35°	.5736	.8192	.7002	80°	.9848	.1736	5.6713
36°	.5878	.8090	.7265	81°	.9877	.1564	6.3138
37°	.6018	.7986	.7536	82°	.9903	.1392	7.1154
38°	.6157	.7880	.7813	83°	.9925	.1219	8.1443
39°	.6293	.7771	.8098	84°	.9945	.1045	9.5144
40°	.6428	.7660	.8391	85°	.9962	.0872	11.4301
41°	.6561	.7547	.8693	86°	.9976	.0698	14.3007
42°	.6691	.7431	.9004	87°	.9986	.0523	19.0811
43°	.6820	.7314	.9325	88°	.9994	.0349	28.6363
44°	.6947	.7193	.9657	89°	.9998	.0175	57.2900
45°	.7071	.7071	1.0000	90°	1.0000	.0000	∞

TABLE OF SQUARES

Squares from 1 to 10										
	0	1	2	3	4	5	6	7	8	9
1.0	1.00	1.02	1.04	1.06	1.08	1.10	1.12	1.14	1.17	1.19
1.1	1.21	1.23	1.25	1.28	1.30	1.32	1.35	1.37	1.39	1.42
1.2	1.44	1.46	1.49	1.51	1.54	1.56	1.59	1.61	1.64	1.66
1.3	1.69	1.72	1.74	1.77	1.80	1.82	1.85	1.88	1.90	1.93
1.4	1.96	1.99	2.02	2.04	2.07	2.10	2.13	2.16	2.19	2.22
1.5	2.25	2.28	2.31	2.34	2.37	2.40	2.43	2.46	2.50	2.53
1.6	2.56	2.59	2.62	2.66	2.69	2.72	2.76	2.79	2.82	2.86
1.7	2.89	2.92	2.96	2.99	3.03	3.06	3.10	3.13	3.17	3.20
1.8	3.24	3.28	3.31	3.35	3.39	3.42	3.46	3.50	3.53	3.57
1.9	3.61	3.65	3.69	3.72	3.76	3.80	3.84	3.88	3.92	3.96
2.0	4.00	4.04	4.08	4.12	4.16	4.20	4.24	4.28	4.33	4.37
2.1	4.41	4.45	4.49	4.54	4.58	4.62	4.67	4.71	4.75	4.80
2.2	4.84	4.88	4.93	4.97	5.02	5.06	5.11	5.15	5.20	5.24
2.3	5.29	5.34	5.38	5.43	5.48	5.52	5.57	5.62	5.66	5.71
2.4	5.76	5.81	5.86	5.90	5.95	6.00	6.05	6.10	6.15	6.20
2.5	6.25	6.30	6.35	6.40	6.45	6.50	6.55	6.60	6.66	6.71
2.6	6.76	6.81	6.86	6.92	6.97	7.02	7.08	7.13	7.18	7.24
2.7	7.29	7.34	7.40	7.45	7.51	7.56	7.62	7.67	7.73	7.78
2.8	7.84	7.90	7.95	8.01	8.07	8.12	8.18	8.24	8.29	8.35
2.9	8.41	8.47	8.53	8.58	8.64	8.70	8.76	8.82	8.88	8.94
3.0	9.00	9.06	9.12	9.18	9.24	9.30	9.36	9.42	9.49	9.55
3.1	9.61	9.67	9.73	9.80	9.86	9.92	9.99	10.05	10.11	10.18
3.2	10.24	10.30	10.37	10.43	10.50	10.56	10.63	10.69	10.76	10.82
3.3	10.89	10.96	11.02	11.09	11.16	11.22	11.29	11.36	11.42	11.49
3.4	11.56	11.63	11.70	11.76	11.83	11.90	11.97	12.04	12.11	12.18
3.5	12.25	12.32	12.39	12.46	12.53	12.60	12.67	12.74	12.82	12.89
3.6	12.96	13.03	13.10	13.18	13.25	13.32	13.40	13.47	13.54	13.62
3.7	13.69	13.76	13.84	13.91	13.99	14.06	14.14	14.21	14.29	14.36
3.8	14.44	14.52	14.59	14.67	14.75	14.82	14.90	14.98	15.05	15.13
3.9	15.21	15.29	15.37	15.44	15.52	15.60	15.68	15.76	15.84	15.92
4.0	16.00	16.08	16.16	16.24	16.32	16.40	16.48	16.56	16.65	16.73
4.1	16.81	16.89	16.97	17.06	17.14	17.22	17.31	17.39	17.47	17.56
4.2	17.64	17.72	17.81	17.89	17.98	18.06	18.15	18.23	18.32	18.40
4.3	18.49	18.58	18.66	18.75	18.84	18.92	19.01	19.10	19.18	19.27
4.4	19.36	19.45	19.54	19.62	19.71	19.80	19.89	19.98	20.07	20.16
4.5	20.25	20.34	20.43	20.52	20.61	20.70	20.79	20.88	20.98	21.07
4.6	21.16	21.25	21.34	21.44	21.53	21.62	21.72	21.81	21.90	22.00
4.7	22.09	22.18	22.28	22.37	22.47	22.56	22.66	22.75	22.85	22.94
4.8	23.04	23.14	23.23	23.33	23.43	23.52	23.62	23.72	23.81	23.91
4.9	24.01	24.11	24.21	24.30	24.40	24.50	24.60	24.70	24.80	24.90
5.0	25.00	25.10	25.20	25.30	25.40	25.50	25.60	25.70	25.81	25.91
5.1	26.01	26.11	26.21	26.32	26.42	26.52	26.63	26.73	26.83	26.94
5.2	27.04	27.14	27.25	27.35	27.46	27.56	27.67	27.77	27.88	27.98
5.3	28.09	28.20	28.30	28.41	28.52	28.62	28.73	28.84	28.94	29.05
5.4	29.16	29.27	29.38	29.48	29.59	29.70	29.81	29.92	30.03	30.14

TABLE OF SQUARES

					Squares from 1 to 10					
	0	1	2	3	4	5	6	7	8	9
5.5	30.25	30.36	30.47	30.58	30.69	30.80	30.91	31.02	31.14	31.25
5.6	31.36	31.47	31.58	31.70	31.81	31.92	32.04	32.15	32.26	32.38
5.7	32.49	32.60	32.72	32.83	32.95	33.06	33.18	33.29	33.41	33.52
5.8	33.64	33.76	33.87	33.99	34.11	34.22	34.34	34.46	34.57	34.69
5.9	34.81	34.93	35.05	35.16	35.28	35.40	35.52	35.64	35.76	35.88
6.0	36.00	36.12	36.24	36.36	36.48	36.60	36.72	36.84	36.97	37.09
6.1	37.21	37.33	37.45	37.58	37.70	37.82	37.95	38.07	38.19	38.32
6.2	38.44	38.56	38.69	38.81	38.94	39.06	39.19	39.31	39.44	39.56
6.3	39.69	39.82	39.94	40.07	40.20	40.32	40.45	40.58	40.70	40.83
6.4	40.96	41.09	41.22	41.34	41.47	41.60	41.73	41.86	41.99	42.12
6.5	42.25	42.38	42.51	42.64	42.77	42.90	43.03	43.16	43.30	43.43
6.6	43.56	43.69	43.82	43.96	44.09	44.22	44.36	44.49	44.62	44.76
6.7	44.89	45.02	45.16	45.29	45.43	45.56	45.70	45.83	45.97	46.10
6.8	46.24	46.38	46.51	46.65	46.79	46.92	47.06	47.20	47.33	47.47
6.9	47.61	47.75	47.89	48.02	48.16	48.30	48.44	48.58	48.72	48.86
7.0	49.00	49.14	49.28	49.42	49.56	49.70	49.84	49.98	50.13	50.27
7.1	50.41	50.55	50.69	50.84	50.98	51.12	51.27	51.41	51.55	51.70
7.2	51.84	51.98	52.13	52.27	52.42	52.56	52.71	52.85	53.00	53.14
7.3	53.29	53.44	53.58	53.73	53.88	54.02	54.17	54.32	54.46	54.61
7.4	54.76	54.91	55.06	55.20	55.35	55.50	55.65	55.80	55.95	56.10
7.5	56.25	56.40	56.55	56.70	56.85	57.00	57.15	57.30	57.46	57.61
7.6	57.76	57.91	58.06	58.22	58.37	58.52	58.68	58.83	58.98	59.14
7.7	59.29	59.44	59.60	59.75	59.91	60.06	60.22	60.37	60.53	60.68
7.8	60.84	61.00	61.15	61.31	61.47	61.62	61.78	61.94	62.09	62.25
7.9	62.41	62.57	62.73	62.88	63.04	63.20	63.36	63.52	63.68	63.84
8.0	64.00	64.16	64.32	64.48	64.64	64.80	64.96	65.12	65.29	65.45
8.1	65.61	65.77	65.93	66.10	66.26	66.42	66.59	66.75	66.91	67.08
8.2	67.24	67.40	67.57	67.73	67.90	68.06	68.23	68.39	68.56	68.72
8.3	68.89	69.06	69.22	69.39	69.56	69.72	69.89	70.06	70.22	70.39
8.4	70.56	70.73	70.90	71.06	71.23	71.40	71.57	71.74	71.91	72.08
8.5	72.25	72.42	72.59	72.76	72.93	73.10	73.27	73.44	73.62	73.79
8.6	73.96	74.13	74.30	74.48	74.65	74.82	75.00	75.17	75.34	75.52
8.7	75.69	75.86	76.04	76.21	76.39	76.56	76.74	76.91	77.09	77.26
8.8	77.44	77.62	77.79	77.97	78.15	78.32	78.50	78.68	78.85	79.03
8.9	79.21	79.39	79.57	79.74	79.92	80.10	80.28	80.46	80.64	80.82
9.0	81.00	81.18	81.36	81.54	81.72	81.90	82.08	82.26	82.45	82.63
9.1	82.81	82.99	83.17	83.36	83.54	83.72	83.91	84.09	84.27	84.46
9.2	84.64	84.82	85.01	85.19	85.38	85.56	85.75	85.93	86.12	86.30
9.3	86.49	86.68	86.86	87.05	87.24	87.42	87.61	87.80	87.98	88.17
9.4	88.36	88.55	88.74	88.92	89.11	89.30	89.49	89.68	89.87	90.06
9.5	90.25	90.44	90.63	90.82	91.01	91.20	91.39	91.58	91.78	91.97
9.6	92.16	92.35	92.54	92.74	92.93	93.12	93.32	93.51	93.70	93.90
9.7	94.09	94.28	94.48	94.67	94.87	95.06	95.26	95.45	95.65	95.84
9.8	96.04	96.24	96.43	96.63	96.83	97.02	97.22	97.42	97.61	97.81
9.9	98.01	98.21	98.41	98.60	98.80	99.00	99.20	99.40	99.60	99.80

TABLE OF SQUARE ROOTS

	0	1	2	3	4	5	6	7	8	9
					Square roots from 1 to 10					
1.0	1.00	1.00	1.01	1.01	1.02	1.02	1.03	1.03	1.04	1.04
1.1	1.05	1.05	1.06	1.06	1.07	1.07	1.08	1.08	1.09	1.09
1.2	1.10	1.10	1.10	1.11	1.11	1.12	1.12	1.13	1.13	1.14
1.3	1.14	1.14	1.15	1.15	1.16	1.16	1.17	1.17	1.17	1.18
1.4	1.18	1.19	1.19	1.20	1.20	1.20	1.21	1.21	1.22	1.22
1.5	1.22	1.23	1.23	1.24	1.24	1.24	1.25	1.25	1.26	1.26
1.6	1.26	1.27	1.27	1.28	1.28	1.28	1.29	1.29	1.30	1.30
1.7	1.30	1.31	1.31	1.32	1.32	1.32	1.33	1.33	1.33	1.34
1.8	1.34	1.35	1.35	1.35	1.36	1.36	1.36	1.37	1.37	1.37
1.9	1.38	1.38	1.39	1.39	1.39	1.40	1.40	1.40	1.41	1.41
2.0	1.41	1.42	1.42	1.42	1.43	1.43	1.44	1.44	1.44	1.45
2.1	1.45	1.45	1.46	1.46	1.46	1.47	1.47	1.47	1.48	1.48
2.2	1.48	1.49	1.49	1.49	1.50	1.50	1.50	1.51	1.51	1.51
2.3	1.52	1.52	1.52	1.53	1.53	1.53	1.54	1.54	1.54	1.55
2.4	1.55	1.55	1.56	1.56	1.56	1.57	1.57	1.57	1.57	1.58
2.5	1.58	1.58	1.59	1.59	1.59	1.60	1.60	1.60	1.61	1.61
2.6	1.61	1.62	1.62	1.62	1.62	1.63	1.63	1.63	1.64	1.64
2.7	1.64	1.65	1.65	1.65	1.66	1.66	1.66	1.66	1.67	1.67
2.8	1.67	1.68	1.68	1.68	1.69	1.69	1.69	1.69	1.70	1.70
2.9	1.70	1.71	1.71	1.71	1.71	1.72	1.72	1.72	1.73	1.73
3.0	1.73	1.73	1.74	1.74	1.74	1.75	1.75	1.75	1.75	1.76
3.1	1.76	1.76	1.77	1.77	1.77	1.77	1.78	1.78	1.78	1.79
3.2	1.79	1.79	1.79	1.80	1.80	1.80	1.81	1.81	1.81	1.81
3.3	1.82	1.82	1.82	1.82	1.83	1.83	1.83	1.84	1.84	1.84
3.4	1.84	1.85	1.85	1.85	1.85	1.86	1.86	1.86	1.87	1.87
3.5	1.87	1.87	1.88	1.88	1.88	1.88	1.89	1.89	1.89	1.89
3.6	1.90	1.90	1.90	1.91	1.91	1.91	1.91	1.92	1.92	1.92
3.7	1.92	1.93	1.93	1.93	1.93	1.94	1.94	1.94	1.94	1.95
3.8	1.95	1.95	1.95	1.96	1.96	1.96	1.96	1.97	1.97	1.97
3.9	1.97	1.98	1.98	1.98	1.98	1.99	1.99	1.99	1.99	2.00
4.0	2.00	2.00	2.00	2.01	2.01	2.01	2.01	2.02	2.02	2.02
4.1	2.02	2.03	2.03	2.03	2.03	2.04	2.04	2.04	2.04	2.05
4.2	2.05	2.05	2.05	2.06	2.06	2.06	2.06	2.07	2.07	2.07
4.3	2.07	2.08	2.08	2.08	2.08	2.09	2.09	2.09	2.09	2.10
4.4	2.10	2.10	2.10	2.10	2.11	2.11	2.11	2.11	2.12	2.12
4.5	2.12	2.12	2.13	2.13	2.13	2.13	2.14	2.14	2.14	2.14
4.6	2.14	2.15	2.15	2.15	2.15	2.16	2.16	2.16	2.16	2.17
4.7	2.17	2.17	2.17	2.17	2.18	2.18	2.18	2.18	2.19	2.19
4.8	2.19	2.19	2.20	2.20	2.20	2.20	2.20	2.21	2.21	2.21
4.9	2.21	2.22	2.22	2.22	2.22	2.22	2.23	2.23	2.23	2.23
5.0	2.24	2.24	2.24	2.24	2.24	2.25	2.25	2.25	2.25	2.26
5.1	2.26	2.26	2.26	2.26	2.27	2.27	2.27	2.27	2.28	2.28
5.2	2.28	2.28	2.28	2.29	2.29	2.29	2.29	2.30	2.30	2.30
5.3	2.30	2.30	2.31	2.31	2.31	2.31	2.32	2.32	2.32	2.32
5.4	2.32	2.33	2.33	2.33	2.33	2.33	2.34	2.34	2.34	2.34

TABLE OF SQUARE ROOTS

Square roots from 1 to 10										
	0	1	2	3	4	5	6	7	8	9
5.5	2.35	2.35	2.35	2.35	2.35	2.36	2.36	2.36	2.36	2.36
5.6	2.37	2.37	2.37	2.37	2.37	2.38	2.38	2.38	2.38	2.39
5.7	2.39	2.39	2.39	2.39	2.40	2.40	2.40	2.40	2.40	2.41
5.8	2.41	2.41	2.41	2.41	2.42	2.42	2.42	2.42	2.42	2.43
5.9	2.43	2.43	2.43	2.44	2.44	2.44	2.44	2.44	2.45	2.45
6.0	2.45	2.45	2.45	2.46	2.46	2.46	2.46	2.46	2.47	2.47
6.1	2.47	2.47	2.47	2.48	2.48	2.48	2.48	2.48	2.49	2.49
6.2	2.49	2.49	2.49	2.50	2.50	2.50	2.50	2.50	2.51	2.51
6.3	2.51	2.51	2.51	2.52	2.52	2.52	2.52	2.52	2.53	2.53
6.4	2.53	2.53	2.53	2.54	2.54	2.54	2.54	2.54	2.55	2.55
6.5	2.55	2.55	2.55	2.56	2.56	2.56	2.56	2.56	2.57	2.57
6.6	2.57	2.57	2.57	2.57	2.58	2.58	2.58	2.58	2.58	2.59
6.7	2.59	2.59	2.59	2.59	2.60	2.60	2.60	2.60	2.60	2.61
6.8	2.61	2.61	2.61	2.61	2.62	2.62	2.62	2.62	2.62	2.62
6.9	2.63	2.63	2.63	2.63	2.63	2.64	2.64	2.64	2.64	2.64
7.0	2.65	2.65	2.65	2.65	2.65	2.66	2.66	2.66	2.66	2.66
7.1	2.66	2.67	2.67	2.67	2.67	2.67	2.68	2.68	2.68	2.68
7.2	2.68	2.69	2.69	2.69	2.69	2.69	2.69	2.70	2.70	2.70
7.3	2.70	2.70	2.71	2.71	2.71	2.71	2.71	2.71	2.72	2.72
7.4	2.72	2.72	2.72	2.73	2.73	2.73	2.73	2.73	2.73	2.74
7.5	2.74	2.74	2.74	2.74	2.75	2.75	2.75	2.75	2.75	2.75
7.6	2.76	2.76	2.76	2.76	2.76	2.77	2.77	2.77	2.77	2.77
7.7	2.77	2.78	2.78	2.78	2.78	2.78	2.79	2.79	2.79	2.79
7.8	2.79	2.79	2.80	2.80	2.80	2.80	2.80	2.81	2.81	2.81
7.9	2.81	2.81	2.81	2.82	2.82	2.82	2.82	2.82	2.82	2.83
8.0	2.83	2.83	2.83	2.83	2.84	2.84	2.84	2.84	2.84	2.84
8.1	2.85	2.85	2.85	2.85	2.85	2.85	2.86	2.86	2.86	2.86
8.2	2.86	2.87	2.87	2.87	2.87	2.87	2.87	2.88	2.88	2.88
8.3	2.88	2.88	2.88	2.89	2.89	2.89	2.89	2.89	2.89	2.90
8.4	2.90	2.90	2.90	2.90	2.91	2.91	2.91	2.91	2.91	2.91
8.5	2.92	2.92	2.92	2.92	2.92	2.92	2.93	2.93	2.93	2.93
8.6	2.93	2.93	2.94	2.94	2.94	2.94	2.94	2.94	2.95	2.95
8.7	2.95	2.95	2.95	2.95	2.96	2.96	2.96	2.96	2.96	2.96
8.8	2.97	2.97	2.97	2.97	2.97	2.97	2.98	2.98	2.98	2.98
8.9	2.98	2.98	2.99	2.99	2.99	2.99	2.99	2.99	3.00	3.00
9.0	3.00	3.00	3.00	3.00	3.01	3.01	3.01	3.01	3.01	3.01
9.1	3.02	3.02	3.02	3.02	3.02	3.02	3.03	3.03	3.03	3.03
9.2	3.03	3.03	3.04	3.04	3.04	3.04	3.04	3.04	3.05	3.05
9.3	3.05	3.05	3.05	3.05	3.06	3.06	3.06	3.06	3.06	3.06
9.4	3.07	3.07	3.07	3.07	3.07	3.07	3.08	3.08	3.08	3.08
9.5	3.08	3.08	3.09	3.09	3.09	3.09	3.09	3.09	3.10	3.10
9.6	3.10	3.10	3.10	3.10	3.10	3.11	3.11	3.11	3.11	3.11
9.7	3.11	3.12	3.12	3.12	3.12	3.12	3.12	3.13	3.13	3.13
9.8	3.13	3.13	3.13	3.14	3.14	3.14	3.14	3.14	3.14	3.14
9.9	3.15	3.15	3.15	3.15	3.15	3.15	3.16	3.16	3.16	3.16

TABLE OF SQUARE ROOTS

	.0	.1	.2	.3	.4	.5	.6	.7	.8	.9
					Square roots from 10 to 100					
10	3.16	3.18	3.19	3.21	3.22	3.24	3.26	3.27	3.29	3.30
11	3.32	3.33	3.35	3.36	3.38	3.39	3.41	3.42	3.44	3.45
12	3.46	3.48	3.49	3.51	3.52	3.54	3.55	3.56	3.58	3.59
13	3.61	3.62	3.63	3.65	3.66	3.67	3.69	3.70	3.71	3.73
14	3.74	3.75	3.77	3.78	3.79	3.81	3.82	3.83	3.85	3.86
15	3.87	3.89	3.90	3.91	3.92	3.94	3.95	3.96	3.97	3.99
16	4.00	4.01	4.02	4.04	4.05	4.06	4.07	4.09	4.10	4.11
17	4.12	4.14	4.15	4.16	4.17	4.18	4.20	4.21	4.22	4.23
18	4.24	4.25	4.27	4.28	4.29	4.30	4.31	4.32	4.34	4.35
19	4.36	4.37	4.38	4.39	4.40	4.42	4.43	4.44	4.45	4.46
20	4.47	4.48	4.49	4.51	4.52	4.53	4.54	4.55	4.56	4.57
21	4.58	4.59	4.60	4.62	4.63	4.64	4.65	4.66	4.67	4.68
22	4.69	4.70	4.71	4.72	4.73	4.74	4.75	4.76	4.77	4.79
23	4.80	4.81	4.82	4.83	4.84	4.85	4.86	4.87	4.88	4.89
24	4.90	4.91	4.92	4.93	4.94	4.95	4.96	4.97	4.98	4.99
25	5.00	5.01	5.02	5.03	5.04	5.05	5.06	5.07	5.08	5.09
26	5.10	5.11	5.12	5.13	5.14	5.15	5.16	5.17	5.18	5.19
27	5.20	5.21	5.22	5.22	5.23	5.24	5.25	5.26	5.27	5.28
28	5.29	5.30	5.31	5.32	5.33	5.34	5.35	5.36	5.37	5.38
29	5.39	5.39	5.40	5.41	5.42	5.43	5.44	5.45	5.46	5.47
30	5.48	5.49	5.50	5.50	5.51	5.52	5.53	5.54	5.55	5.56
31	5.57	5.58	5.59	5.59	5.60	5.61	5.62	5.63	5.64	5.65
32	5.66	5.67	5.67	5.68	5.69	5.70	5.71	5.72	5.73	5.74
33	5.74	5.75	5.76	5.77	5.78	5.79	5.80	5.81	5.81	5.82
34	5.83	5.84	5.85	5.86	5.87	5.87	5.88	5.89	5.90	5.91
35	5.92	5.92	5.93	5.94	5.95	5.96	5.97	5.97	5.98	5.99
36	6.00	6.01	6.02	6.02	6.03	6.04	6.05	6.06	6.07	6.07
37	6.08	6.09	6.10	6.11	6.12	6.12	6.13	6.14	6.15	6.16
38	6.16	6.17	6.18	6.19	6.20	6.20	6.21	6.22	6.23	6.24
39	6.24	6.25	6.26	6.27	6.28	6.28	6.29	6.30	6.31	6.32
40	6.32	6.33	6.34	6.35	6.36	6.36	6.37	6.38	6.39	6.40
41	6.40	6.41	6.42	6.43	6.43	6.44	6.45	6.46	6.47	6.47
42	6.48	6.49	6.50	6.50	6.51	6.52	6.53	6.53	6.54	6.55
43	6.56	6.57	6.57	6.58	6.59	6.60	6.60	6.61	6.62	6.63
44	6.63	6.64	6.65	6.66	6.66	6.67	6.68	6.69	6.69	6.70
45	6.71	6.72	6.72	6.73	6.74	6.75	6.75	6.76	6.77	6.77
46	6.78	6.79	6.80	6.80	6.81	6.82	6.83	6.83	6.84	6.85
47	6.86	6.86	6.87	6.88	6.88	6.89	6.90	6.91	6.91	6.92
48	6.93	6.94	6.94	6.95	6.96	6.96	6.97	6.98	6.99	6.99
49	7.00	7.01	7.01	7.02	7.03	7.04	7.04	7.05	7.06	7.06
50	7.07	7.08	7.09	7.09	7.10	7.11	7.11	7.12	7.13	7.13
51	7.14	7.15	7.16	7.16	7.17	7.18	7.18	7.19	7.20	7.20
52	7.21	7.22	7.22	7.23	7.24	7.25	7.25	7.26	7.27	7.27
53	7.28	7.29	7.29	7.30	7.31	7.31	7.32	7.33	7.33	7.34
54	7.35	7.36	7.36	7.37	7.38	7.38	7.39	7.40	7.40	7.41

TABLE OF SQUARE ROOTS

	.0	.1	.2	.3	.4	.5	.6	.7	.8	.9
					Square roots from 10 to 100					
55	7.42	7.42	7.42	7.44	7.44	7.45	7.46	7.46	7.47	7.48
56	7.48	7.49	7.50	7.50	7.51	7.52	7.52	7.53	7.54	7.54
57	7.55	7.56	7.56	7.57	7.58	7.58	7.59	7.60	7.60	7.61
58	7.62	7.62	7.63	7.64	7.64	7.65	7.66	7.66	7.67	7.67
59	7.68	7.69	7.69	7.70	7.71	7.71	7.72	7.73	7.73	7.74
60	7.75	7.75	7.76	7.77	7.77	7.78	7.78	7.79	7.80	7.80
61	7.81	7.82	7.82	7.83	7.84	7.84	7.85	7.85	7.86	7.87
62	7.87	7.88	7.89	7.89	7.90	7.91	7.91	7.92	7.92	7.93
63	7.94	7.94	7.95	7.96	7.96	7.97	7.97	7.98	7.99	7.99
64	8.00	8.01	8.01	8.02	8.02	8.03	8.04	8.04	8.05	8.06
65	8.06	8.07	8.07	8.08	8.09	8.09	8.10	8.11	8.11	8.12
66	8.12	8.13	8.14	8.14	8.15	8.15	8.16	8.17	8.17	8.18
67	8.19	8.19	8.20	8.20	8.21	8.22	8.22	8.23	8.23	8.24
68	8.25	8.25	8.26	8.26	8.27	8.28	8.28	8.29	8.29	8.30
69	8.31	8.31	8.32	8.32	8.33	8.34	8.34	8.35	8.35	8.36
70	8.37	8.37	8.38	8.38	8.39	8.40	8.40	8.41	8.41	8.42
71	8.43	8.43	8.44	8.44	8.45	8.46	8.46	8.47	8.47	8.48
72	8.49	8.49	8.50	8.50	8.51	8.51	8.52	8.53	8.53	8.54
73	8.54	8.55	8.56	8.56	8.57	8.57	8.58	8.58	8.59	8.60
74	8.60	8.61	8.61	8.62	8.63	8.63	8.64	8.64	8.65	8.65
75	8.66	8.67	8.67	8.68	8.68	8.69	8.69	8.70	8.71	8.71
76	8.72	8.72	8.73	8.73	8.74	8.75	8.75	8.76	8.76	8.77
77	8.77	8.78	8.79	8.79	8.80	8.80	8.81	8.81	8.82	8.83
78	8.83	8.84	8.84	8.85	8.85	8.86	8.87	8.87	8.88	8.88
79	8.89	8.89	8.90	8.91	8.91	8.92	8.92	8.93	8.93	8.94
80	8.94	8.95	8.96	8.96	8.97	8.97	8.98	8.98	8.99	8.99
81	9.00	9.01	9.01	9.02	9.02	9.03	9.03	9.04	9.04	9.05
82	9.06	9.06	9.07	9.07	9.08	9.08	9.09	9.09	9.10	9.10
83	9.11	9.12	9.12	9.13	9.13	9.14	9.14	9.15	9.15	9.16
84	9.17	9.17	9.18	9.18	9.19	9.19	9.20	9.20	9.21	9.21
85	9.22	9.22	9.23	9.24	9.24	9.25	9.25	9.26	9.26	9.27
86	9.27	9.28	9.28	9.29	9.30	9.30	9.31	9.31	9.32	9.32
87	9.33	9.33	9.34	9.34	9.35	9.35	9.36	9.36	9.37	9.38
88	9.38	9.39	9.39	9.40	9.40	9.41	9.41	9.42	9.42	9.43
89	9.43	9.44	9.44	9.45	9.46	9.46	9.47	9.47	9.48	9.48
90	9.49	9.49	9.50	9.50	9.51	9.51	9.52	9.52	9.53	9.53
91	9.54	9.54	9.55	9.56	9.56	9.57	9.57	9.58	9.58	9.59
92	9.59	9.60	9.60	9.61	9.61	9.62	9.62	9.63	9.63	9.64
93	9.64	9.65	9.65	9.66	9.66	9.67	9.67	9.68	9.69	9.69
94	9.70	9.70	9.71	9.71	9.72	9.72	9.73	9.73	9.74	9.74
95	9.75	9.75	9.76	9.76	9.77	9.77	9.78	9.78	9.79	9.79
96	9.80	9.80	9.81	9.81	9.82	9.82	9.83	9.83	9.84	9.84
97	9.85	9.85	9.86	9.86	9.87	9.87	9.88	9.88	9.89	9.89
98	9.90	9.90	9.91	9.91	9.92	9.92	9.93	9.93	9.94	9.94
99	9.95	9.95	9.96	9.96	9.97	9.97	9.98	9.98	9.99	9.99

INDEX

Origin of Cartesian plane, 70

Parabola, 372
  axis of symmetry, 374
  focal point, 406
  maximum point, 373–374
  minimum point, 373
  rotated on its axis of
    symmetry, 405
Parabolic reflector, 405
Parentheses, use of, 28, 36–37,
  49–50, 70
Perfect square, 421
Pi, 179
Plane, *see* Cartesian plane
Points
  corresponding to irrational
    numbers on number line, 13
  image of, 124
  on number line, 10–11
  ordered pairs associated with,
    70–71
  in the plane, coordinates of,
    70–71, 123
Polygons, similar, 489–490
Polynomial equations, 462
Polynomials
  addition, 352
  ascending order of terms,
    453–454
  binomial, 354–355
  completely factored, 415
  degree of, 354–355
  descending order of terms,
    453–454
  division, 456–460
  expansion of factors, 357
  factoring, 408, 412–413,
    415–416, 422–423, 462–464
  monomial, 354
  multiplication, 356–359,
    451–452
  prime, 415–416
  simplest form of, 353, 355
  subtraction, 352
  trinomial, 354–355, 396
Positive integral exponents,
  49–50
Powers
  ascending order, 453
  base, 50

descending order, 453
  exponent, 49–50
  positive integral, 49–50
Prime expressions, 164
Prime factors, 407–408
Prime numbers, 163–164, 408
Prime polynomials, 415–416
Principal square root, 319–321
Problem solving
  equations in, 66, 207–208
  formulas in, 87
  open sentences in, 66
  systems of equations, 311–313
Properties
  associative property of
    addition, 30, 31
  associative property of
    multiplication, 30, 31, 80
  closure, 35
  commutative property of
    addition, 30, 31
  commutative property of
    multiplication, 30, 31, 80
  distributive property of
    multiplication over addition,
    31
  division property of square
    roots, 324
  generalized distributive
    property for real numbers,
    47
  multiplication property of
    square roots, 324
  of order, 95, 125
  rearrangement property for
    addition and subtraction,
    46–47
Proportions
  direct, 262–263, 267, 271,
    276–277
  extremes of, 263
  inverse, 270–272
  means of, 263
  solving, 492–493
  terms of, 263
Protractor, circular, 496
Punctuation in mathematics,
  35–36
Pythagoras, 335, 443
Pythagorean theorem, 334
  formulas derived from, 338